About Pearson

Pearson is the world's learning company, with presence across 70 countries worldwide. Our unique insights and world-class expertise comes from a long history of working closely with renowned teachers, authors and thought leaders, as a result of which, we have emerged as the preferred choice for millions of teachers and learners across the world.

We believe learning opens up opportunities, creates fulfilling careers and hence better lives. We hence collaborate with the best of minds to deliver you class-leading products, spread across the Higher Education and Test Preparation spectrum.

Superior learning experience and improved outcomes are at the heart of everything we do. This product is the result of one such effort.

Your feedback plays a critical role in the evolution of our products and you can contact us - reachus@pearson.com. *We look forward to it.*

CLASS

9

Trishna's

PEARSON IIT FOUNDATION

Chemistry

Thirteenth Edition

2025

Pearson

Photo Credits

Chapter 1 Opener: Fouad A / Saad / Shutterstock
Chapter 2 Opener: ggw / Shutterstock
Chapter 3 Opener: Fouad A. Saad / Shutterstock
Chapter 4 Opener: MrJafari / Shutterstock
Chapter 5 Opener: Fouad A. Saad / Shutterstock
Chapter 6 Opener: magnetix / Shutterstock
Chapter 7 Opener: Wichy / Shutterstock
Chapter 8 Opener: elenathewise / 123RF
Chapter 9 Opener: Alexander Gold / Shutterstock

ISBN 978-93-6159-190-7

First Impression

Published by Pearson India Education Services Pvt. Ltd, CIN: U72200TN2005PTC057128.

Head Office: 1st Floor, Berger Tower, Plot No. C-001A/2, Sector 16B, Noida - 201 301, Uttar Pradesh, India.

Registered Office: Featherlite, 'The Address' 5th Floor, Survey No 203/10B, 200 Ft MMRD Road, Zamin Pallavaram, Chennai - 600044

Phone: 044-66540100

Website: in.pearson.com, Email: companysecretary.india@pearson.com

Compositor: Saksham Printographics, Delhi
Printer in India at Rajkamal Electric Press, Kundli, Haryana-131 028.

Brief Contents

Contents

Preface

"If you have a great ambition, take as big a step as possible in the direction of fulfilling it. The step may only be a tiny one, but trust that it may be the largest one possible for now".

Mildred McAfee

The *Pearson IIT Foundation* Series has been created keeping in mind the learner's ambition to excel in a competitive examination like IIT-JEE. The series can be used in addition to the books being studied in school to attain that extra edge required to strengthen the concepts and prepare well for future endeavours.

Why Start Early with Pearson IIT Foundation

Classes VI to X are the base years of a learner's academic life. In these years learner explore their interests and determine the goals they wish to attain. *Pearson IIT Foundation* series is filled with interactive learning that not only nurtures a learner's interest in science and mathematics but also strengthens their concepts.

The series uses real-life examples and application-based problems to teach theoretical concepts. The objective of this series is to help learners cultivate an analytical mind.

Most of the lessons to be learnt are introduced to the learners in the books for class VI. As they get promoted to higher classes, new topics are added to these lessons. This additive method helps the learners' span their learning over four standards, from VI-X. Thus, learners are not overwhelmed by the introduction of completely new lessons every time they are promoted to a new class.

While their learning is being spanned across five years, so is their ability to resolve doubts for further conceptual clarity. For instance, they can use concepts learnt in class VI to solve questions in class VII. If, in case, they get stuck while answering a question, the learners can infer for themselves that they might be lacking in conceptual clarity. They can then approach their teachers, requesting them to explain the concept once again. This helps the learner to clarify their concepts while revising the lessons previously learnt.

Since classes VI-X are deemed to be a student's formative years, we, at Pearson, aim to provide a foundation level course which serves more than just a standard curriculum.

Here is how it makes a difference to a learner's overall learning...

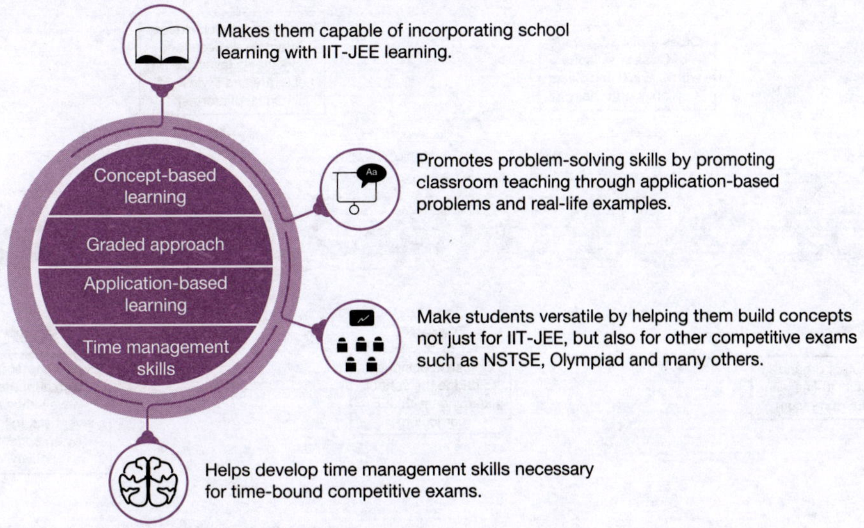

Other Uses of the Series

Instead of limiting themselves to IIT-JEE, a learner can also use this series to prepare for several other competitive examinations such as NSTSE, National and International Olympiads, NEET, BITSAT, etc. This series offers a level of concept learning that empowers learners to handle the challenging nature of questions posed in these examinations. Moreover, this will also allow the learners to have an early insight into their key strengths as well as improvement areas and help them work on themselves.

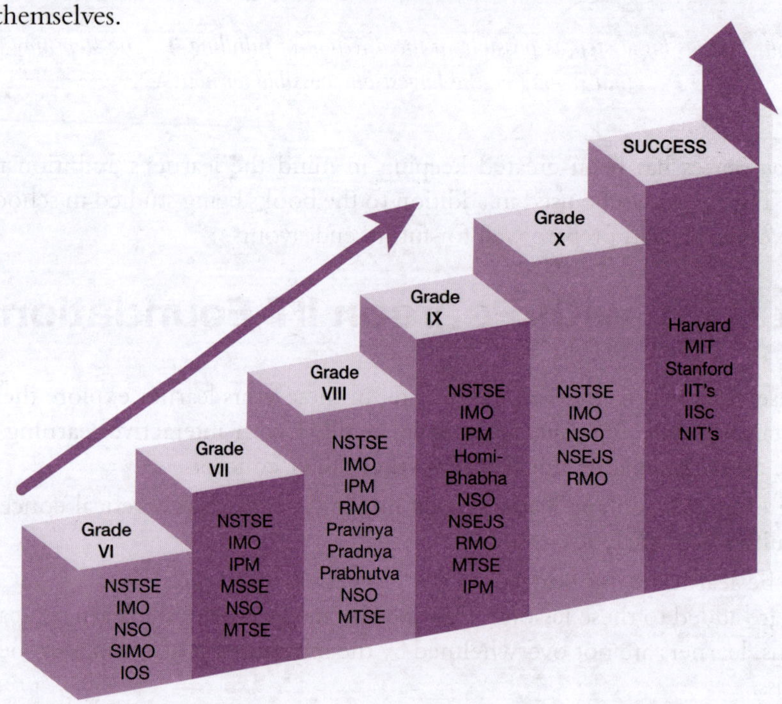

[IMO: International Mathematics Olympiad; NSO: National Science Olympiad, IOS: International Olympiad of Science, NSTSE: National Level Science Talent Search Examination, MTSE: Maharashtra Talent Search Examination, RMO: Regional Mathematical Olympiad, PPP: Pravinya Pradnya Prabhutva, NSEJS: National Standard Examination in Junior Science, IIT: Indian Institute of Technology, IISc: Indian Institute of Science, NIT: National Institute of Technology.]

Highlights of the Series

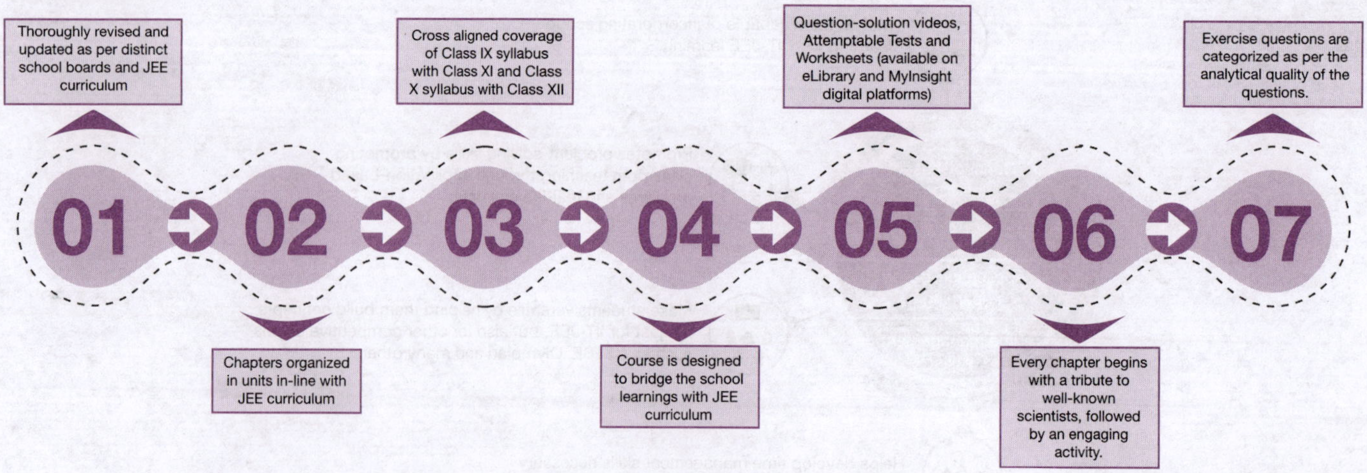

Pearson IIT Foundation series provides a perfect blend of learning through theory and practice questions with a fusion of school and JEE curriculum. It is imperative to note that this series would be as profound as you want it to be. Therefore, to get maximum benefit from this book, we recommend following the given study plan.

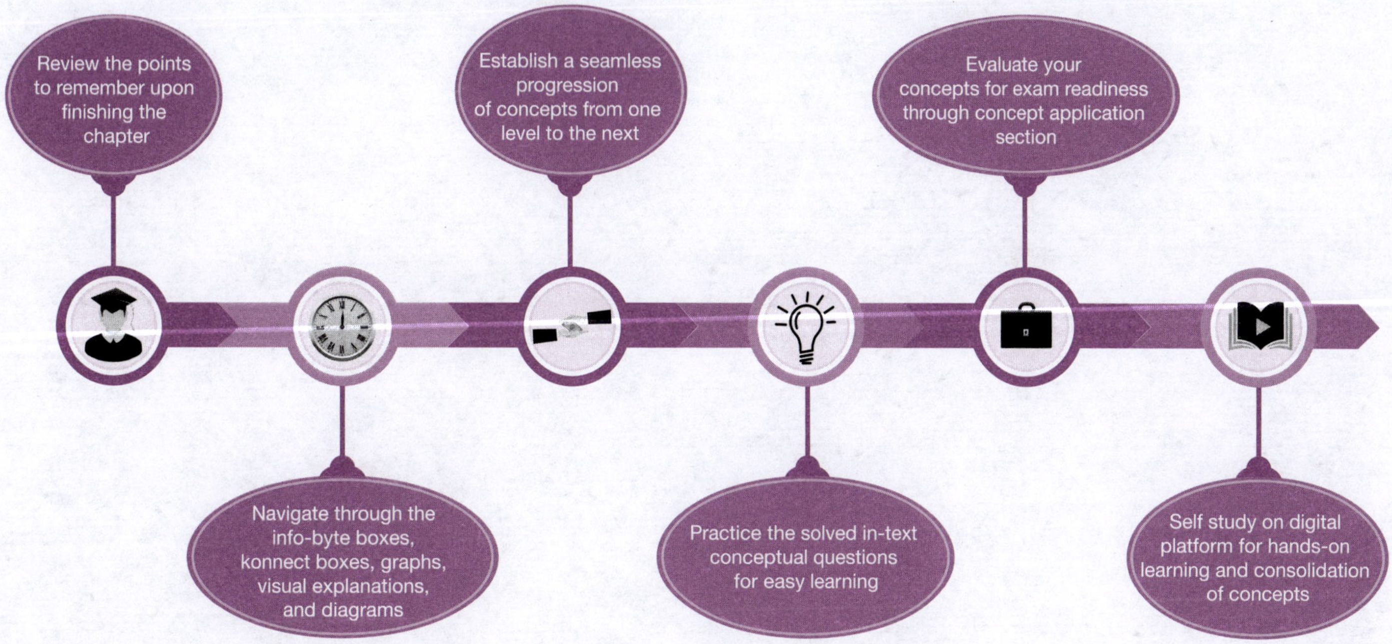

To provide a graded learning approach, the exercise part of each chapter is categorized by using four icons for question tagging. The question categorization helps the learners assess their own problem-solving and analytical skills and motivates them to improve to reach their objectives.

The following icons are used to categorize the questions with specific meanings:

Real-life Situations Questions: 

Analytical Questions: 

Conceptual Questions: 

Value-based Questions: 

With this refined and well-tuned course from Pearson, students will become more confident when they enter the competitive world for actual IIT-JEE preparation. The effort put in today will transform into a valuable asset, contributing to success in future competitive examinations.

Chapter Insights

Remember

Before beginning this chapter, you should be able to:

- understand basic concepts of kinetic molecular theory.

Remember section will help them to memorize and review the previous learning on a particular topic

Key points will help the students to identify the essential points in a chapter

Key Ideas

After completing this chapter, you should be able to:

- make the comparison between different states of matter in correlation with kinetic molecular theory.

Scientific Crypt

A Tribute to Democritus (460 BC–370 BC)

Democritus, an ancient Greek philosopher born in Abdera in the north of Greece, was the most productive and influential of Presocratic philosophers. He was also a student of Leucippus and they together formulated an atomic theory which is regarded as the culmination of early Greek thoughts. This atomic theory had no experimental proof and the ideas were simply hypothetical.

According to this hypothesis, matter is composed of indivisible atoms with different shapes and sizes having a lot of empty spaces between them and these are always in motion. Their speculations regarding atoms charted the path to 19th century scientists for the understanding of atomic structure.

Though his speculative ideas regarding atoms are very primitive and have little significance in modern science, his atomic theory remains as one of the most amazing intellectual accomplishments of ancient times.

Later, through new theories, experiments, discoveries and inventions, Lavoisier, John Dalton and Robert Brown proposed and postulated the more systematic atomic theory and kinetic aspects of matter which paved the way to the modern atomic structure.

FUN TIME

CROSSWORD

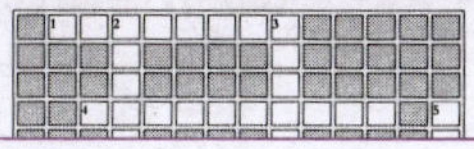

Scientific Crypt provides information about well-known scientists related to the chapter. The engaging activity is also given in the form of a crossword to keep the learners interested.

INTRODUCTION

The branch of science, chemistry deals with the study of matter in different perceptions. The important aspects of study of matter pertains to the various physical states in which matter exists and the structure and molecular composition of matter. In addition to these two areas, study of matter is also significant with reference to the type of transformations matter undergoes under various conditions. Kinetic Molecular Theory can be used to explain both Charles' and Boyle's Laws. Charles's Law states that the volume of a given amount of

Introduction section helps to lay the foundation of the following chapter and leads the way for further learning

Concepts are explained in a well-structured and lucid manner

Kinetic Molecular Theory of Matter

Matter basically exists in three states: solids, liquids, and gases. Irrespective of the state of matter, the basic units of matter are only molecules. The three states of matter differ with respect to the pattern of molecular arrangement which brings about a change in physical behavior of the substances in their respective states. The various characteristics of matter which determine the physical behavior are envisaged in the kinetic molecular theory of matter. Kinetic molecular theory states that molecules have an energy of motion (kinetic energy) that depends on temperature.

Postulates of kinetic molecular theory of matter are as follows:

1. Matter is composed of small, tiny particles called **molecules**.
2. The empty spaces existing between the molecules are called **intermolecular spaces.**

Konnect boxes are some add-on information of related topic

Konnect

The energy needed to melt one gram of ice without changing its temperature is called the heat of fusion. Remarkably, it's 80 times the energy required to raise the temperature of the same amount of water by 1°C.

Info Bytes!

The state of matter can change under different conditions. For example, the weighty gold jewellery you wear is solid, but at 1064°C, gold turns into a liquid.

Info bytes are interesting trivia and facts that engage young minds and keep the grey cells ticking!

EXAMPLE 1.1 Why do liquids have a fixed volume but not a fixed shape, while gases have neither volume nor a fixed shape? Relate your answer with the movement of a molecule.

SOLUTION

In liquids, molecules are closely packed but have enough energy to slide over each other. Because of this, they occupy a volume, but their shape is determined by the container they are placed in. Hence, they do not possess a fixed shape have a fixed volume. The sliding movement of molecules allows liquids to flow and take the shape of the container.

In gases, molecules are much more widely spaced and have higher energy. They move freely and randomly in all directions. E of this high energy and random motion, gases expand to fill any container they are in, giving them no definite shape or volu

Thus, the difference in molecular movement in liquids and gases results in their distinct characteristics of volume and s

EXAMPLE 1.2 Arrange different states of matter in the increasing order of their densities with appr reason.

SOLUTION

In solids, the molecules are tightly packed. Hence, the number of molecules per unit volume is more and density is the h In gases, the molecules are very loosely packed and the density is the least. Molecules of liquids are loosely pack intermolecular space is much less than that in gas. Hence, their densities are generally less than solids, but more than

Examples are given in the form of in-text exercises to reinforce the concepts learnt

Illustrative examples solved in a logical and step-wise manner

POINTS TO REMEMBER

- ✔ Kinetic-molecular theory states that molecules have an energy of motion (kinetic energy) that dependson temperature.
- ✔ The matter around us can be classified into three different states: solids, liquids, and gases.
- ✔ Melting is carried out by supplying heat energy to the solid substance and freezing is carried out by extracting heat energy from the liquid substance.
- ✔ The amount of heat energy required to convert 1 kg of a solid into a liquid at atmospheric
- ✔ Paper Chromatography is based on difference in adsorption of constituents by a surface of an appropriate adsorbent material or solid medium (stationary phase). The rate of adsorption of a particular constituent depends upon its solubility in the solvent (moving phase).
- ✔ A chemical reaction takes place only when the two reactants come in contact with each other.
- ✔ Certain chemical reactions take place with the

Points to remember summarises the concepts and topics presented in each chapter

PRACTICE QUESTIONS CLASSROOM WING

Very Short Answer Type Questions

Directions for questions from 1 to 11:
Fill in the blanks.

1. An increase in pressure increases the melting point. This statement is true for _______.
2. Silver is a substance which expands on melting, so, its melting point _____ when pressure is raised.
3. The atomicity of the element phosphorus is _____.

13. Can the mixture of Iron + sand be separated by the process of magnetic separation?
14. Which among the following: Ammonium chloride, Naphthalene, Sodium chloride and Sulphur, disappears with time without heating?
15. Which among the following: Bromine, Air, Oxygen and Copper possesses maximum intermolecular force of attraction?

...guish between filtration and centrifugation.

Short Answer Type Questions

25. A gas cannot be liquefied below its critical ter... ture. True or false?
26. Is 'water in capillary tube', an example of ad... force being predominant over cohesive force?
27. Pressure cooker reduces the cooking time. Why...

Essay Answer Type Questions

37. The various steps involved in the process of condensation are given below. Arrange them in a proper sequence.
   (A) Further extraction of heat results in a decrease in the potential energy of molecules, whereas kinetic energy remains constant.

Different typologies of questions have been included in the *Classroom Wing* which help students to develop the problem-solving skill

Competition Wing has been integrated chapter-wise in the exercise part to prepare students for various competitive examinations.

Graded as per complexity: Level 1; Level 2; and Level 3

PRACTICE QUESTIONS COMPETITION WING

Level 1: Apply your Concepts

Direction for questions from 1 to 10:
State whether the following statements are true or false.

1. In solids, molecules possess very high kinetic energy.
2. Addition of impurities to the solids decreases the melt...
3. ...

$2KX + Br_2 \rightarrow 2KBr + X_2$
then KX is ___________.

17. In two closed containers, substances A and B are present. After sometime, the lid of the container containing substance A alone got off with a lot of pressure. ...because substance A is _______.

...water is poured on a flask containing very hot...

Level 2: Review your Concepts

51. Cotton clothes are preferred in summer. Why?
52. Give an example of gaseous mixtures which can b... separated by fractional evaporation
53. (a) Why molten silver cannot be used to make shar... castings?
   (b) A magician took a cylinder with open sides whic...

Level 3 : Assess Your Concepts

73. When glass of water is freezed, formation of ice starts from the top layer but melting of ice starts from the bottom. Justify.
74. Solids generally undergo melting on heating. But only certain specific solids like naphthalene camphor undergo sublimation. Give a reason.
75. Fractional distillation of ethyl alcohol–water mixture gives a mixture of 95.6% ethyl alcohol and 4.4% water. Further separation can be brought...

Level 2: Review Your Concepts

86. Arrange the elements 'A', 'B', 'C' and 'D' in the ascending order of the number of valence electrons.
   (A) A is the noble gas with the least number of shells.
   (B) The number of electrons in B is 4 times that in A.
   (C) C has 7 electrons more than that in B.
   (D) D has 4 electrons less than that in C.
87. In a canal ray experiment, different gases were found to produce canal rays with the same specific charge. Explain.
88. When canal rays experiment is conducted with hydrogen gas, scientists were found to give particles with different $\frac{e}{m}$ values. Justify.
89. Energy of the electron in the atom is negative. Explain.
   [**Hint**: Energy of a free electron is taken as zero.]
90. If the energy released when an electron jumped from ...

Compare the kinetic energy of electrons in those orbits.

92. If the energy difference between the orbits when an electron in H atom gets excited to higher energy orbit from its ground state is 12.1 eV/atom, calculate the frequency of radiation emitted (1 eV = 1.602×10^{-19}J) when elec...
93. Is the en... same for...
94. Though... atom, th... of lines...
95. What is... orbit, if... twice th...
96. A partic... If the di...

127. How did Sommerfeld explain the fine structure of hydrogen spectrum?
128. Electrons occupy the degenerate orbitals with parallel spins. How can you justify this statement with respect to stability?
129. (a) 'p-' orbital has a nodal plane while 's-' orbital has a nodal region. Elaborate with the help of a diagram.
   (b) An electron in hydrogen atom has an angular momentum 3.16×10^{-34} kg m²/s. It jumps to another orbit in which its velocity is 3.64×10^7 cm s^{-1}.

The icons are used for categorisation of the questions in Classroom Wing and Competition Wing

PRACTICE QUESTIONS JEE-NEET SPECIAL WING

Multiple-Answer Type Questions

Directions for Questions number 1 to 5:

Select one or more correct alternative(s) from the given choices.

1. A picture of an activity is given below. It represents a particular phenomenon. In the choices, some applications are given. Observe the picture and identify the applications of the phenomena represented in the figure.

Metal	Description
A	No reaction with dilute acids
B	Displaces A and D
C	Displaces B
D	Can displace A and not C

A	B	C	D
Fe	Ni	Cu	Ag

Comprehension-Based Questions

Directions for questions 6 to 11:

Read the following passage and answer the que[stions] given below.

Some information is given in the table regardi[ng] hypothetical gases A, B, C, D, E. Usually, the subs[tances]

Match The Column

16. The elements and their corresponding values of EA in terms of 'x' are given in column I and column II. Match the entries in column I with those in column II.

Element		EA value
(a) T-nitrogen	(i)	50x

JEE-NEET Special Wing is curated specifically for targeted preparation of JEE and NEET examinations.

Hints and Explanations

Classroom Wing

Very Short Answer Type Questions

1. The melting points of silver and gold, which expand on melting, increase with the increase in pressure on them.
2. increases
3. 4
4. centrifugation
5. decreases
6. cohesive forces

20. Diffusion
21. Separation technique, based on difference in adsorption and solubility in the solvent.
22. Sodium on exposure to water or even moisture reacts to give sodium hydroxide and hydrogen, and hence, sodium catches fire. Due to this reason, sodium is stored in kerosene.
23. positive
24. Conversion of solid to gas. *Examples:* Camphor, naphthalene, ammonium chloride, iodine, etc.

Hints and Explanation for key questions of classroom wing, competition wing and JEE-NEET special wing along with highlights on the common mistakes that students usually make in the examinations

Competition Wing

Level 1: Apply your Concepts

1. False, in solids, molecules possess a very low kinetic energy
2. True. Addition of impurities to the solids decreases the melting point of solids.
11. Gas molecules show maximum fluidity because they have high kinetic energy and very less intermolecular forces of attraction.
12. In the mixture of NaCl and NH_4Cl, NH_4Cl sublimes on heating. Therefore, this mixture can be separated by the process of sublimation.
13. Solid carbon dioxide undergoes sublimation due to the high kinetic energy of surface molecules.
20. (i) → (D); (ii) → (A); (iii) → (E); (iv) → (F)
21. Rate of evaporation is directly proportional to wind speed and inversely proportional to humidity.

    Hence, the correct option is (c).
22. In a compound, only one type of molecule is present and it is uniformly distributed.

    Hence, the correct option is (a).
37. (2) Paper chromatography is used for the separation

    (3) paper and solvent are taken as stationary and mobile phases, respectively.

    (4) A narrow strip of paper with a line drawn is cut and a mixture of red and blue ink with the help of capillary is placed on the line marked on the paper.

    (5) The paper is suspended in the closed jar with the help of hook.

    (1) The blue and red inks are separated on the paper by adsorption technique.

    Hence, the correct answer is (c).
38. Bromine is a liquid. The molecules of liquid possess vibratory, rotatory, and translatory motions in all directions except in upward direction.

    Hence, the correct answer is (a).
39. Pressure decreases with increase in altitude, and hence, boiling point decreases. Since Darjeeling is at higher attitude, water boils below 373 K, i.e., below 100°C.

    Hence, the correct answer is (c).

JEE-NEET Special Wing

Multiple-Answer Type Questions

1. The given picture represents the phenomenon of regelation. The applications of the phenomena include melting of glaciers to form rivers and keeping dead bodies on the ice block.

   Hence, choice (a) and choice (c) follow.

2. **Sample X:**

   Mass of water = 500 g

   Heat required to reach 100°C (B.Pt) from 30°C = 500 × 70 = 35000 Cal = 35 kcal

   Heat required to convert boiled water to steam at 100°C = 500 × 540 = 270000 cal = 270 Kcal = 1130 kJ

   Total heat required = 305 kcal

   Sample Y:

   Heat withdrawn from water to reach 0°C = 500 × 30 = 15000 cal = 15 kcal = 62.7 kJ

D- Making of coffee decoction involves solvent extraction wherein the soluble component goes into hot water while the insoluble components are left behind in the filter.

Hence, choice (c) and choice (d) follow.

5. The solids which are associated with the property of contraction on melting undergo expansion on solidification. Hence, they are suitable for making perfect moulds or sharp castings. In case of these solids, the melting point decreases with increase in pressure. Ice is an example of such solid. X and Y are suitable for making moulds and hence belong to this category. Cast iron also comes into this category as it is widely used for making moulds. But pure copper shows the opposite tendency and hence is not suitable for making moulds.

   Hence, choice (b) and choice (d) follow.

Comprehension-Based Questions

WORKSHEET

CHAPTER 1: MOLE CONCEPT, STOICHIOMETRY AND BEHAVIOR OF GASES

DW

Direction for questions from 1 to 5:
Select the correct alternative from the following option.

1. A rubber balloon which is permeable to all the isotopes of hydrogen is filled with pure tritium. It is placed in a closed box containing pure hydrogen under similar conditions of temperature and pressure. Identify the correct observation regarding the balloon.
   (a) The balloon first expands and then contracts.
   (b) The balloon first contracts first and then expand.
   (c) The balloon expands.

Directions of questions from 6 to 10:
State whether the following statements are true or false.

6. 80 g of SO_3 corresponds to 1 mole.
7. Real gases behave ideally at high pressure and low temperature.
8. Reaction between an acid and a base form salt and water.
9. Equal volumes of all gases possess unequal number of moles at constant temperature and pressure.

DW: Downloadable worksheets supplementing textual exercises for hand-on learning

AI Assessments

Which of the following is the cheapest natural fiber available in the market?

- ○ Wool
- ○ Silk
- ◉ Jute
- ○ Rayon

Question 1 of 4

Next

AT

AT: Attemptable Tests for assessing understanding of concepts and getting a clear picture of your exam readiness

51. Na_2CO_3 is dissolved in water at 25°C. Which of the following is/are correct regarding the given statement?

(a) In this solution anionic hydrolysis take place.

(b) The concentration of H^+ ion in the given solution is less than 10^{-7} mole/L

Video icon: Audio and visual learning to difficult questions for effective learning and retention

Unit I

Physical Chemistry

In this Unit

- ✶ **Chapter 1** Nature of Matter
- ✶ **Chapter 2** Basic Concepts of Chemistry
- ✶ **Chapter 3** Mole Concept, Stoichiometry, and Behavior of Gases
- ✶ **Chapter 4** Atomic Structure
- ✶ **Chapter 5** Chemical Kinetics and Equilibrium

CHAPTER 1

Nature of Matter

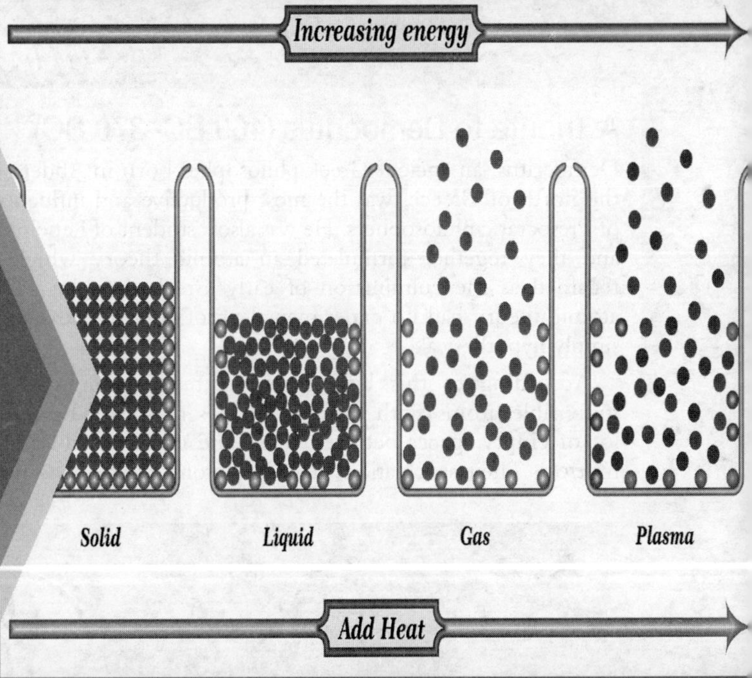

Remember

Before beginning this chapter, you should be able to:

- understand basic concepts of kinetic molecular theory.
- comprehend classification of matter and different states of matter.

Key Ideas

After completing this chapter, you should be able to:

- make the comparison between different states of matter in correlation with kinetic molecular theory.
- explain the interconversion of different states of matter and correlate it to day-to-day activities and natural phenomena.
- describe the characteristics of elements, compounds, homogeneous, and heterogeneous mixtures.
- illustrate the different separation methods for different types of mixtures.

Scientific Crypt

A Tribute to Democritus (460 BC–370 BC)

Democritus, an ancient Greek philosopher born in Abdera in the north of Greece, was the most productive and influential of Presocratic philosophers. He was also a student of Leucippus and they together formulated an atomic theory which is regarded as the culmination of early Greek thoughts. This atomic theory had no experimental proof and the ideas were simply hypothetical.

According to this hypothesis, matter is composed of indivisible atoms with different shapes and sizes having a lot of empty spaces between them and these are always in motion. Their speculations regarding atoms charted the path to 19th century scientists for the understanding of atomic structure.

Though his speculative ideas regarding atoms are very primitive and have little significance in modern science, his atomic theory remains as one of the most amazing intellectual accomplishments of ancient times.

Later, through new theories, experiments, discoveries and inventions, Lavoisier, John Dalton and Robert Brown proposed and postulated the more systematic atomic theory and kinetic aspects of matter which paved the way to the modern atomic structure.

FUN TIME

CROSSWORD

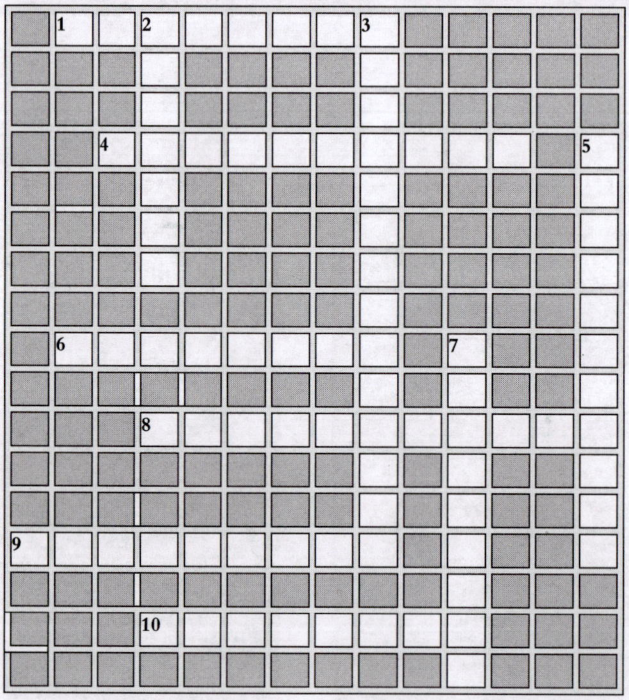

Across

1. Separation process employed for the mixture of iron powder and sand
4. Elements possess both metallic and non-metallic properties
6. The process of conversion of liquid state to solid state
8. The solids having a regular arrangement of constituents in three-dimensional space
9. The number of atoms present in the molecules of an element
10. Force of attraction between dissimilar molecules

Down

2. The state of matter having the highest compressibility
3. Method used to separate drugs from blood
5. Type of mixture in which constituent particles are distributed uniformly
7. Basic units of matter

INTRODUCTION

The branch of science, chemistry deals with the study of matter in different perceptions. The important aspects of study of matter pertains to the various physical states in which matter exists and the structure and molecular composition of matter. In addition to these two areas, study of matter is also significant with reference to the type of transformations matter undergoes under various conditions. Kinetic Molecular Theory can be used to explain both Charles' and Boyle's Laws. Charles's Law states that the volume of a given amount of gas is directly proportional to its absolute temperature, provided its pressure remains constant. Simply, it means that for a gas at constant pressure, as the temperature goes up, the volume goes up (and vice versa). Boyle's law states that the pressure and volume of a given amount of gas are inversely proportional at constant temperature. The average kinetic energy of a collection of gas particles is directly proportional to absolute temperature only.

Kinetic Molecular Theory of Matter

Matter basically exists in three states: solids, liquids, and gases. Irrespective of the state of matter, the basic units of matter are only molecules. The three states of matter differ with respect to the pattern of molecular arrangement which brings about a change in physical behavior of the substances in their respective states. The various characteristics of matter which determine the physical behavior are envisaged in the kinetic molecular theory of matter. Kinetic molecular theory states that molecules have an energy of motion (kinetic energy) that depends on temperature.

Info Bytes!

The Kinetic Molecular Theory isn't just limited to explaining gases. It also provides fundamental insights into the behaviour of liquids and solids. Imagine, that every little thing around you is constantly moving.

Postulates of kinetic molecular theory of matter are as follows:

1. Matter is composed of small, tiny particles called **molecules**.
2. The empty spaces existing between the molecules are called **intermolecular spaces.**
3. Molecules have forces of attraction between them known as **intermolecular forces of attraction.** The force of attraction between similar molecules is called **cohesive force** and that between dissimilar molecules is called **adhesive force**.
4. The molecules possess kinetic energy due to their ceaseless motion.

Different States of Matter and Their Properties

The matter around us can be classified into three different states—solids, liquids, and gases. The following table provides a comparison of the three states of matter.

Table 1.1 Different states of matter and their properties

Properties	Solids	Liquids	Gases
Mass	Definite mass	Definite mass	Definite mass
Volume	Definite volume	Definite volume	No definite volume
Shape	Definite shape	No definite shape, take the shape of the container	No definite shape
Density	High density	Lesser density than solids	Least density
Compressibility	Incompressible	Slightly compressible	Highly compressible
Rigidity	Rigid (cannot flow)	Fluid (can flow)	Fluid (can flow)

(Continued.)

Table 1.1 Continued

Properties	Solids	Liquids	Gases
Free surfaces	Any number of free surfaces	One free surface, i.e., only the upper surface	No free surfaces
Thermal expansion	Very low	Higher than solids	Much greater than both solids and liquids
Diffusion	Do not diffuse	Some liquids can diffuse spontaneously into another (e.g., water and alcohol), but others do not diffuse (e.g., oil and water)	Diffuse spontaneously and rapidly

A comparative study of molecular arrangements in solids, liquids, and gases, based on the kinetic molecular theory, is provided in the following table:

Table 1.2 Comparative study of three states of matter

Properties	Solids	Liquids	Gases
Comparative study of three states of matter	Closely packed	Loosely packed	Very loosely packed
Intermolecular space	Very less	More than those in solids	Most intermolecular space
Intermolecular force of attraction	Strong intermolecular force of attraction	Moderate force of attraction, less than that in solids	Negligible intermolecular force of attraction
Molecular movement	Possess only vibratory motion, but the mean position is fixed	Possess translatory and rotatory motions in addition to vibratory motion in one motion	Possess translatory, rotatory, and vibratory motions in all directions
Kinetic energy	Very low kinetic energy	High kinetic energy, more than that of solids	Highest kinetic energy

EXAMPLE 1.1 Why do liquids have a fixed volume but not a fixed shape, while gases have neither a fixed volume nor a fixed shape? Relate your answer with the movement of a molecule.

SOLUTION

In liquids, molecules are closely packed but have enough energy to slide over each other. Because of this, they occupy a definite volume, but their shape is determined by the container they are placed in. Hence, they do not possess a fixed shape but do have a fixed volume. The sliding movement of molecules allows liquids to flow and take the shape of the container.

In gases, molecules are much more widely spaced and have higher energy. They move freely and randomly in all directions. Because of this high energy and random motion, gases expand to fill any container they are in, giving them no definite shape or volume.

Thus, the difference in molecular movement in liquids and gases results in their distinct characteristics of volume and shape.

EXAMPLE 1.2 Arrange different states of matter in the increasing order of their densities with appropriate reason.

SOLUTION

In solids, the molecules are tightly packed. Hence, the number of molecules per unit volume is more and density is the highest. In gases, the molecules are very loosely packed and the density is the least. Molecules of liquids are loosely packed, but intermolecular space is much less than that in gas. Hence, their densities are generally less than solids, but more than gases.

Interconversion of States of Matter

Since the physical behavior of matter in various states depends upon the molecular arrangement which can be changed by changing the conditions of temperature and pressure, therefore, matter can be converted from one state to another under suitable conditions. This is also termed as **phase transition.**

Info Bytes!

The state of matter can change under different conditions. For example, the weighty gold jewellery you wear is solid, but at 1064°C, gold turns into a liquid.

Interconversion Between Solid and Liquid States

The process of conversion of a solid state to a liquid state is called **melting** or **fusion** and the opposite process from the liquid to the solid state is called **freezing**. Melting is carried out by supplying heat energy to the solid substance and freezing is carried out by extracting heat energy from the liquid substance.

Melting

When the substance in the solid state is subjected to heating, the molecules absorb heat energy which increases the kinetic energy of molecules. This results in an increase of the kinetic energy of the molecules which in turn leads to increase in temperature; however, further supply of heat energy does not increase the kinetic energy of molecules. Instead, the heat energy is stored in the form of potential energy. With increase in the potential energy, the intermolecular forces of attraction decrease which results in increase in intermolecular spaces. The molecular arrangement of the solid changes to that of the liquid. The temperature at which the solid gets converted to the liquid state at the atmospheric pressure is called **melting point** of that solid.

Although each substance has a specific value of melting point under normal atmospheric conditions, certain factors affect the melting point of the solids.

Factors Affecting the Melting Point

1. **Effect of Pressure:** The effect of pressure on the melting point of the solids depends upon the nature of the solid.
   - For solids which expand on melting, increase in pressure increases the melting point. This is because increase in pressure opposes expansion.

   Examples: Paraffin wax, silver, gold, copper, etc.

   - For solids which contract on melting, increase in pressure decreases the melting point. This is because increase in pressure favors contraction.

   Examples: Ice, cast iron, brass, etc.

2. **Effect of Addition of Impurities:** Addition of impurities to a solid decreases the melting point of the solid thereby allowing the substance to melt at a lower temperature.

   Example: Rose's metal—an alloy of tin, lead, and bismuth.

   Melting point of Rose's metal → 94.5°C

   Melting point of Pb → 327°C

   Melting point of Sn → 231.9°C

   Melting point of Bi → 271°C

Konnect

The energy needed to melt one gram of ice without changing its temperature is called the heat of fusion. Remarkably, it's 80 times the energy required to raise the temperature of the same amount of water by 1°C.

Freezing

The process of conversion from a liquid state to a solid state is called freezing. It is the opposite process of melting. This is carried out by extracting heat from the liquid.

When a substance in the liquid state is subjected to cooling, heat is extracted from the liquid. Then kinetic energy of molecules decreases which results in a decrease in temperature. On reaching a certain temperature, further extraction of heat from the liquid results in decrease in potential energy instead of decrease in kinetic energy. Decrease in potential energy leads to increase in intermolecular forces of attraction, and hence, decrease in intermolecular spaces. Hence, the molecular arrangement of the liquid changes to that of solid. The temperature at which the liquid converts into the solid at the atmospheric pressure is called **freezing point** of the liquid.

Konnect

The freezing point of the liquid is equal to the melting point of the solid for the same substance.

The factors that affect the melting point of a substance also affect the freezing point. For example, addition of impurities to the solids decreases the melting point of the solid and at the same time decreases the freezing point of the liquid to the same extent. The above principle can be used in the preparation of freezing mixtures. A mixture of three parts of ice and one part of common salt is called freezing mixture which is used to produce a lower temperature of −21°C. Freezing mixtures are used for preservation of food items especially perishables such as fish and meat.

Interconversion Between the Liquid and Gaseous States

Vaporization

The process of conversion of the liquid state to the gaseous state is called **vaporization.** When the liquid is subjected to heating, kinetic energy of molecules increases which results in increase in temperature. At a particular temperature, there is no further increase in the kinetic energy of molecules. The heat energy supplied increases the potential energy of the molecules. As a result, the intermolecular forces of attraction decrease. The molecules move apart and the substance passes from liquid to gaseous state. This process is called **boiling** and the temperature at which the conversion of the liquid to the vapour state takes place at normal atmospheric pressure is called **boiling point.**

Info Bytes!

Boiling is a bulk phenomenon, not just surface-based. This means even water from the bottom of a pot can vaporize.

Factors Affecting the Boiling Point

Although every liquid is characterized by a specific value for the boiling point, it depends on some factors as discussed below:

1. **Effect of Pressure:** The boiling point of a liquid increases with increase in external pressure. This is the reason why water boils at a lower temperature than 100°C at higher altitudes.

   This principle is responsible for the working of a pressure cooker.

   In the pressure cooker, water is subjected to heating in a closed vessel in confined space. The steam generated in fixed volume increases the pressure beyond the normal atmospheric pressure.

   Since the external pressure is more, the boiling point of water rises beyond 100°C. The temperature of cooking medium is greater than the normal boiling point, therefore food gets cooked at a faster rate, and saves time and fuel.

2. **Effect of Impurities:** When solid substances are dissolved in a liquid, the boiling point of the liquid increases beyond the normal boiling point. For example, when common salt is dissolved in water, the solution boils at a temperature greater than 100°C.

Evaporation

Conversion of liquid to gaseous states can also be brought about even without supplying heat energy to the liquid. In the liquid, the surface molecules possess higher kinetic energies than the molecules in the bulk of the liquid. Due to this reason, the molecules break away from the forces of attraction of the other molecules and go into a vapour state. This process of conversion of the liquid into the vapour takes place at a temperature below the boiling point and is called **evaporation.**

In contrast to boiling, evaporation is considered as a surface phenomenon since it is confined to only surface molecules. It is also a slow process taking place over a period of time at any temperature, whereas boiling takes place rapidly at a specific temperature. Vaporization is a common term applicable for both evaporation and boiling.

Factors Affecting Evaporation

1. **Surface Area:** Increase in surface area increases the rate of evaporation.
2. **Temperature:** Increase in temperature increases the rate of evaporation.
3. **Humidity:** The amount of water vapour which the atmospheric air holds decreases the rate of evaporation.
4. **Wind Speed:** Increase in wind speed increases the rate of evaporation.

Table 1.3 Critical temperatures of common gases

Gases	Critical temperatures
CO_2	31.1°C
NH_3	132°C
O_2	−118°C
N_2	−147°C
H_2	−165°C
He	−240°C
SO_2	20°C

Condensation

The conversion of a gaseous substance into a liquid state is called **condensation.** This can be carried out by cooling the gas below a particular temperature.

When heat is extracted from the gas, the kinetic energy of molecules decreases, and hence, temperature falls. When sufficiently low temperature is reached, further extraction of heat from the gas does not reduce the kinetic energy. This in turn results in an increase in intermolecular forces of attraction bringing the molecules closer. At this point, the gas passes into the liquid state.

The conversion of the gaseous to the liquid state can also be brought about by the application of pressure. The gases have to be cooled below a certain temperature and then subjected to application of high pressure. This entire process is called **liquefaction.** Every gas requires a certain minimum temperature for passing into the liquid state. That means, above that minimum temperature, application of any amount of pressure cannot bring about the transformation from the gaseous to the liquid state. This temperature above which a gas cannot be liquefied, irrespective of how much high pressure is applied, is called **critical temperature.** Every gas is associated with a specific critical temperature.

Effects of Condensation on Climate

The formation of dew, fog, and clouds is the application of condensation.

When the temperature is high, water in water bodies evaporates and during day time. This process goes on continuously and the air does not become saturated with water vapour. When the temperature falls during night time, the air becomes saturated with water vapour. The temperature at which the atmospheric air becomes saturated with water vapour is called **dew point.** On further lowering of temperature, some of the water vapour condenses and the water droplets condense as dew. If the condensation of water vapour takes place on floating dust particles, it results in the formation of fog or mist. In the upper part of the atmosphere, the condensed water droplets appear as clouds.

Apart from these interconversions, the conversion of the solid to the gaseous state is also possible in some cases. This process of conversion of the solid into the vapour state directly without passing through the intermittent liquid state is called **sublimation.** The vapours when condensed give back the solids. Such solids formed from the vapour are called **sublimates.** Only some solids undergo sublimation.

Examples: Camphor, naphthalene, ammonium chloride, iodine, etc.

Latent Heat

The change of state of a substance is invariably associated with absorption or liberation of heat. However, the change is not associated with a change in temperature of the substance in any process. It is considered that the heat energy gets hidden into the substances involved in the process and is called **latent heat.**

For example, when ice melts, the temperature of ice remains constant only at the melting point until the entire process is completed. The entire heat absorbed during the process is utilized to carry out the change. Therefore, the amount of heat energy required to convert 1 kg of a solid into a liquid at atmospheric pressure at its melting point is known as the **latent heat of fusion.** For ice, it is equal to 80 cal/g/°C.

Example: When water is subjected to boiling, the temperature of water remains constant at the boiling point until all the water is converted to steam. The heat energy supplied during the process is stored in the steam and is called **latent heat of vaporization.** For steam, this equals 540 cal/g/°C.

Applications of Latent Heat

The liquid molecules absorb energy from the surroundings and overcome the forces of attraction thereby going into a vapour state. Since surroundings lose energy, they become cold. This principle is used in various activities of daily living as listed below:

1. Cool sensation produced when alcohol is poured on palm.
2. Cotton clothes producing cooling effect during summer.
3. Formation of water droplets on the outer surface of glass containing ice-cold water.
4. Cooling of water in earthen pots during summer.

Konnect

When water evaporates from your skin, it uses your body heat, making you feel cooler. This principle is the essence of sweating – nature's own air conditioner.

EXAMPLE 1.3 Why does food cook faster at higher altitudes in a pressure cooker than in an open pot?

SOLUTION

At higher altitudes, the atmospheric pressure is less than that at sea level. Due to this reduced pressure, the boiling point of water also drops and is below 100°C. This means in an open pot, water boils at a temperature lower than 100°C. As a result, cooking in an open pot at higher altitudes is slower since the cooking temperature is reduced.

However, when we use a pressure cooker at higher altitudes, the inside pressure is increased due to the steam trapped inside. This increases the boiling point of water inside the pressure cooker, making it closer to or even higher than 100°C. Thus, in a pressure cooker, food gets cooked at a relatively higher temperature than in an open pot, making the cooking process faster. This is why a pressure cooker is especially advantageous at higher altitudes where the atmospheric pressure is lower.

EXAMPLE 1.4 When two pieces of ice are pressed together, they form a single lump. Explain.

SOLUTION

When two pieces of ice are pressed together, they form a single lump. This principle is known as regelation. When two ice cubes are pressed together, the ice at the interface melts due to the application of pressure and when the pressure is released, it solidifies again thereby joining the two ice cubes.

EXAMPLE 1.5 Why does the temperature remain constant when a solid changes to its liquid state at its melting point?

SOLUTION

When a solid changes to its liquid state at its melting point, the temperature remains constant because the energy supplied is utilized in breaking the intermolecular forces of attraction in the solid, which results in a change of state from solid to liquid. During this phase transition, the kinetic energy of the particles remains unchanged, and thus the temperature does not rise. Instead, the added energy goes into changing the potential energy of the substance by overcoming the forces holding the solid together. Hence, throughout the melting process, the temperature remains constant at the melting point until the entire solid has melted.

EXAMPLE 1.6 The critical temperatures of gases A, B, C, and D are –118°C, –240°C, 132°C, and 20°C, respectively. Arrange them in the decreasing order of intermolecular force of attraction.

SOLUTION

The higher the critical temperature. more is the intermolecular force of attraction and they can be liquefied easily. Decreasing order of intermolecular force of attraction is C > D > A > B.

EXAMPLE 1.7 What happens when water is kept in a plastic bottle wrapped with a wet towel?

SOLUTION

During the evaporation of water from the wet towel, heat is absorbed from the bottle and its content. Due to this, the water present in the bottle becomes cool.

EXAMPLE 1.8 Why are cotton clothes preferred in summer?

SOLUTION

People wear cotton clothes to keep themselves cool in summer. Cotton fabric absorbs sweat more due to greater adhesive forces between cotton and water, and allows the sweat to be evaporated at a faster rate. The sweat absorbs heat energy from the body and gets evaporated, thus keeping the body cool.

EXAMPLE 1.9 Discuss the change in energy and arrangement of molecules on increasing the temperature of ice from –5°C to 10°C at 1 atm pressure.

SOLUTION

When ice is heated at −5°C, its temperature increases upto 0°C , i.e., the kinetic energy of the molecules increases. At 0°C, the ice starts melting. During this process, the energy supplied is utilized to increase the potential energy of the molecules keeping kinetic energy constant, and the arrangement of molecules changes. Once the process ends, the heat supplied is again used to increase the temperature of water by increasing the kinetic energy. However, from 0°C to 4°C, the molecules of water come closer, and above 4°C, the molecules move farther away.

Classification of Matter on the Basis of Chemical Composition

The basic units of matter in any state are considered as molecules as far as the physical behavior of matter in different states and their interconversion under different conditions are concerned. This is because a **molecule** is considered as the smallest particle of matter which has an independent existence. However, when focus is laid on the chemical behavior of matter, the classification of matter with respect to molecular composition becomes inevitable. This is because a molecule is broken down into smaller particles called **atoms** which take part in chemical reactions.

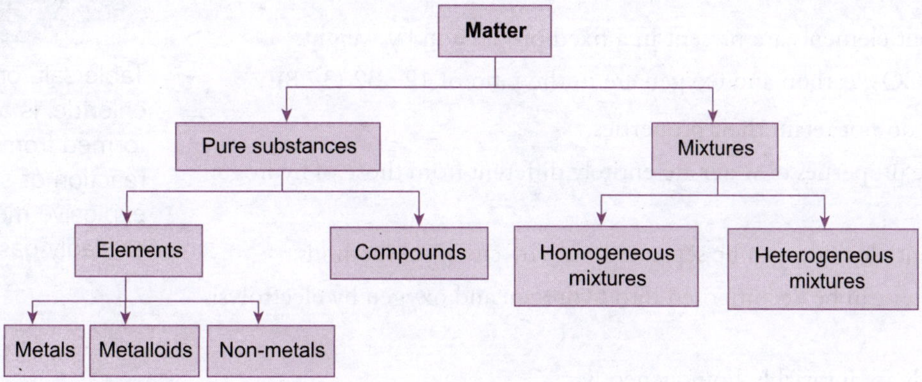

Figure 1.1 Classification of matter

A **pure substance** is the one which is made up of molecules containing same kind of atoms. For example, in case of pure water, all the molecules are made up of two hydrogen atoms and one oxygen atom.

In case of a pure substance, the molecule may contain similar atoms or dissimilar atoms. The first category of pure substances in which a molecule is made up of atoms of the same kind are called **elements.** For example, in hydrogen gas, a molecule of hydrogen is made up of two hydrogen atoms. The second category of substances is called **compounds.** A molecule of carbon dioxide is made up of one carbon atom and two oxygen atoms.

A **mixture** is such a substance which contains two or more kinds of molecules. For example, common salt solution contains molecules of NaCl and molecules of water. A mixture may include constituents as elements, an element and a compound, or only compounds.

Depending on the distribution of the different kinds of molecules within the mixture, the mixture is classified into two types: homogeneous and heterogeneous. A **homogeneous mixture** has uniform distribution of the different types of molecules in the mixture. A **heterogeneous mixture** has non-uniform distribution of the different types of molecules. For example, aqueous solution of glucose is a homogeneous mixture, whereas muddy water is a heterogeneous mixture.

Characteristics of Elements

1. Based on their nature, elements are classified as metals, non-metals, and metalloids.

   Examples: Na, Mg, Al, Cu, etc., are metals.

   H_2, O_2, He, S, etc., are non-metals.

   As, Sb, Se, Te, Ge are metalloids.

2. Elements can also be classified on the basis of their atomicity. The number of atoms present in the molecule of an element is called **atomicity.**

   (a) Monoatomic Elements: The molecule of the element is made up of only one atom. All metals, noble gases, and some non-metals are monoatomic.

   Examples: Ag, Al, Au

   He, Ne

   B, C

   (b) Diatomic Elements: The molecule of the element is made up of two atoms. Only some gaseous non-metals are diatomic.

   Examples: H_2, O_2, N_2

   (c) Polyatomic Elements: The molecule of the element is made up of more than two atoms. Very few elements are polyatomic.

   Examples: O_3, P_4, S_8

Info Bytes!

Gold, a treasured element, remains non-reactive and doesn't tarnish, making it ideal for crafting jewellery that lasts for generations

Characteristics of Compounds

1. The constituent elements are present in a fixed proportion by weight.

   Example: In CO_2, carbon and oxygen are in the ratio of 12 : 32 (3 : 8)

2. The elements do not retain their properties.

   Example: The properties of water are entirely different from those of hydrogen and oxygen.

3. The constituent elements can be separated only by chemical methods.

   Example: Water can be decomposed into hydrogen and oxygen by electrolysis method.

4. All compounds are invariably homogeneous.

5. The formation of a compound is generally associated with significant energy changes.

   $C + O_2 \rightarrow CO_2 - 94$ kcal

Konnect

Table salt, or sodium chloride, is a compound formed from the violent reaction of sodium, an explosive metal, and chlorine, a deadly gas.

Characteristics of a Mixture

1. The constituents may be present in any proportion.
2. The constituents retain their individual properties.

   Example: Aqueous solution of sugar.

3. Separation of constituents is carried out by physical methods.
4. A mixture can be either heterogeneous or homogeneous.
5. Formation of a mixture does not involve significant energy change.

Info Bytes!

Air, something we breathe every moment, is not a compound but a mixture of several gases including nitrogen, oxygen, and small amounts of others like carbon dioxide.

Table 1.4 Examples of different types of mixtures

Types of mixture	Homogeneous	Heterogeneous
Solid–solid	Stainless steel, brass, and bronze	Iron and sulphur
Solid–liquid	NaCl in water and iodine in CCl_4	Sulphur in water
Liquid–liquid	Alcohol and water, and benzene and toluene	Oil and water
Liquid–gas	Liquor ammonia and soda water	–
Gas–gas	Air	–
Solid–gas	–	Hydrogen gas adsorbed on Pd

EXAMPLE 1.10 'All pure metals are elements, but all elements are not pure metals.' Explain.

SOLUTION

Pure metals consist of atoms of only one kind and are hence considered elements because elements are substances that cannot be broken down into simpler substances by chemical means. However, not all elements are metals. The periodic table consists of metals, non-metals, and metalloids. While metals are good conductors of electricity and heat and are malleable and ductile, non-metals possess the opposite properties. Metalloids have properties that are intermediate between metals and non-metals. Therefore, while all pure metals are elements, all elements do not qualify as pure metals due to their varied properties.

EXAMPLE 1.11 Water is a compound. Explain.

SOLUTION

Water is made up of hydrogen and oxygen which are present in fixed proportion, and the properties of water are entirely different from its constituents. hence, it is a compound.

Separation of a Mixture

Most of the substances available in nature are not pure substances and are actually a mixture. The useful component present in the mixture can be obtained only by separating the individual components of the mixture by following a suitable method. The method of separation used depends upon the nature of components in the mixture.

Table 1.5 Types of separation methods of a solid–solid mixture

Methods	Properties	Description with examples
Solvent extraction	Solubility of one component in a solvent	A mixture of sulphur and sand. Sulphur is soluble in CS_2 and sand is insoluble
Magnetic separation	Magnetic property of one component	Mixture of iron ore and sand. Iron ore is attracted by magnet and sand is left behind
Gravity method	Difference in densities of components	Mixture of sand and chalk powder. Sand being heavier than chalk powder sinks in water, whereas chalk powder floats on water
Sublimation	Ability of one component to sublime	Mixture of iodine and sand. On heating, iodine sublimes leaving behind sand. The vapours on cooling give solid iodine
Fractional crystallization	Difference in solubility of the components in the same solvent	Mixture of KNO_3 and NaCl. KNO_3 being more soluble than NaCl, when the aqueous solution of this mixture is subjected to heating, the more soluble KNO_3 escapes along with water vapour and less soluble NaCl is left behind and crystallizes

Table 1.6 Types of separation method af a solid–liquid mixture

Methods	Properties	Description with examples
Sedimentation and decantation	High density of an insoluble solid component	Mixture of sand and water. Sand being heavier, settles at the bottom and liquid is slowly transferred into another container
Filtration	Size of the particles of an insoluble solid component	Mixture of $BaSO_4$ and H_2O. On passing through filter paper, water passes through and $BaSO_4$ remains on the filter paper
Evaporation	The ability of a solid to remain undecomposed when a solution is heated up to the boiling point of the liquid component	Mixture of sugar and water. Water evaporates on heating leaving behind crystals of sugar
Distillation	Heating the solution to the boiling point of the liquid component followed by condensation of the vapours	Mixture of NaCl and water. Water evaporates and condenses back to water, and NaCl is left behind in the distillation flask
Centrifugation	Size of density of solid particles in comparison to the size of liquid particles	Milk contains solid fat particles in water. Size of solid particles is less, and hence, they pass through the filter paper. When this is subjected to centrifugation, heavier fat particles settle down at the bottom leaving behind lighter water on the top

Table 1.7 Types of separation methods of a liquid–liquid mixture

Methods	Properties	Description with examples
Separating funnel	Difference in densities of the two liquid components	Kerosene oil and water are immiscible liquids. When the mixture is taken in the separating funnel, the lighter liquid (kerosene) forms top layer and the heavier liquid (water) settles down
Fractional distillation	Difference in boiling points of the liquids	Distillation carried out by including a fractionating column. E.g., ethyl alcohol + water Ethyl alcohol has a lower boiling point than water, and hence vaporizes. On passing through fractionating column, the vapours condense to give alcohol in a receiver. Water is left behind in the distillation flask

Table 1.8 Types of separation methods af a gas–gas mixture

Methods	Properties	Description with examples
Diffusion	Difference in densities of component gases	The gas with lower molecular weight diffuses faster than the gas with higher molecular weight E.g., H_2 and CH_4, and He and SO_2
Dissolution in suitable solvents	Difference in solubility of component gases in a given solvent	A mixture of CO_2 and CO. CO_2 is soluble in KOH leaving behind CO In a mixture of NH_3 and N_2, NH_3 is soluble in water and N_2 is insoluble
Preferential liquefaction	Difference in liquefaction of component gases under pressure	In a mixture of NH_3 and H_2, ammonia gets liquefied under high pressure and hydrogen gas is left behind.
Fractional evaporation	Difference in boiling points of the component gases	When air is liquefied, the major components of air, N_2, and O_2 can be separated by subjecting the liquid to evaporation. N_2 has a lower boiling point, and hence boils off, whereas O_2 has a higher boiling point and remains behind

Table 1.9 Types of separation methods of a liquid–gas mixture

Methods	Properties	Description with examples
Heating	Decrease in solubility of a gas with increase in temperature	When a solution containing a gas is subjected to slight heating below the boiling point of the liquid, the gas escapes out leaving behind the liquid component E.g., Separation of dissolved O_2 by heating water
Lowering the pressure	Difference in solubility of a gas in the liquid at different pressures	When a soda water bottle is opened, the pressure inside the bottle decreases. CO_2 gas fizzes out of the bottle

Paper Chromatography

Apart from all different methods of separation of types of a mixture, there is a special technique for separation and identification of the constituents in the mixture.

Principle: Based on difference in adsorption of constituents by a surface of an appropriate adsorbent material or solid medium (stationary phase). The rate of adsorption of a particular constituent depends upon its solubility in the solvent (moving phase).

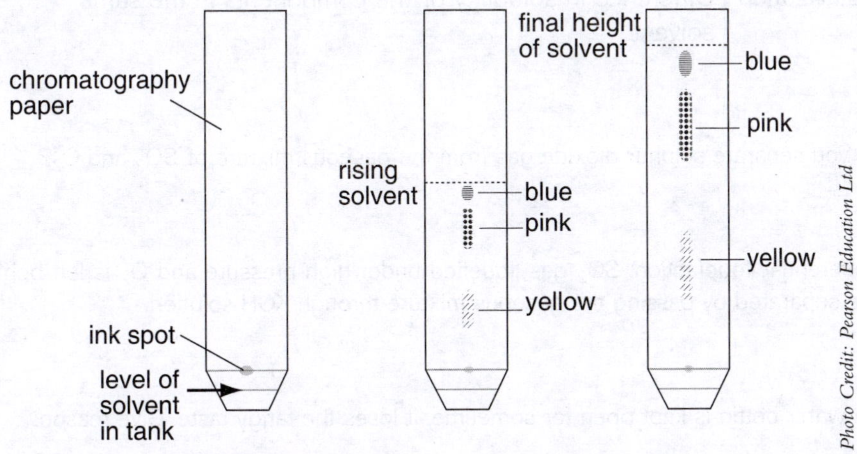

Figure 1.2 Paper chromatography of ink

> **Konnect**
>
> Paper Chromatography is like a race where each component in a mixture travel at a different speed, helping scientists identify and separate them.

Example: Separation of a colored constituent in a mixture of ink by paper chromatography.

Process: A filter paper is taken that generally absorbs water. It acts as a **stationary phase**. The mixture containing different constituents is taken on the filter paper which is then dipped in another solvent called **moving phase**. If the constituent has more affinity for the adsorbent material, it moves slowly on the filter paper. If the constituent has more affinity for the solvent acting as a moving phase, it moves rapidly on the filter paper. Therefore, depending on the relative affinities of the various constituents with the stationary and moving phases, spots or lines appear on the filter paper at different positions.

Example: Separation of colored constituents in a mixture of ink.

EXAMPLE 1.12 How is carbon dioxide separated from exhaled air?

SOLUTION

Exhaled air contains a higher concentration of carbon dioxide compared to inhaled air. Carbon dioxide can be separated from exhaled air using a solution of sodium hydroxide or calcium hydroxide (lime water). When exhaled air is passed through these solutions, carbon dioxide reacts with the solution to form a respective carbonate, leaving other components of the air unreacted. This method is particularly useful in demonstrating the presence of carbon dioxide in exhaled air, as carbon dioxide turns lime water milky due to the formation of calcium carbonate.

EXAMPLE 1.13 Suggest a method of separation for a mixture of sodium chloride and ammonium chloride. Explain the process.

SOLUTION

Mixture of NaCl and NH_4Cl can be separated by sublimation.

Process: NH_4Cl and NaCl mixture is taken in a porcelain dish.

It is covered by an inverted funnel. The opening of the stem of the funnel is closed by a cotton plug. The outside of the funnel is kept cool by wrapping with wet blotting paper.

On heating the porcelain dish, ammonium chloride changes into vapour state, which on coming in contact with the inner wall of the cooled funnel condenses into the original solid and gets collected there.

EXAMPLE 1.14 Mention the separation method and property exploited in the separation of the following solid-solid mixtures.

(a) S + sand **(b)** I_2 + sand **(c)** KNO_3 + NaCl

SOLUTION

(a)	**S + sand**	Solvent extraction	Solubility of one component in a given solvent
(b)	**I_2 + sand**	Sublimation	Ability of one component to sublime.
(c)	**KNO_3 + NaCl**	Fractional crystallization	Difference in solubility of the components in the same solvent.

EXAMPLE 1.15 How will you separate sulphur dioxide gas from the gaseous mixture of SO_2 and O_2?

SOLUTION

SO_2 gas from O_2 can be separated by preferential liquefaction. SO_2 gas liquefied under high pressure and O_2 is left behind. Since SO_2 is acidic in nature, it can also be separated by passing the gaseous mixture through KOH solution.

EXAMPLE 1.16 When soda water bottle is kept open for sometime, it loses the tangy taste. Give reason.

SOLUTION

At high pressure, more amount of CO_2 is dissolved in water. When the bottle is opened, excess amount of CO_2 comes out as solubility of gas decreases with decrease in pressure, and hence, the soda water loses its tangy taste.

Chemical Changes and Chemical Reactions

Matter has an inherent tendency to undergo transformation under suitable conditions. The transformations are basically of two types. Firstly, the changes which do not involve any change in molecular composition of the substance. They are termed as **physical changes.** Secondly, the changes which involve changes in molecular composition of the substance. These are termed as **chemical changes.**

Conditions Required for Chemical Changes

1. **Physical Contact between Reactants**: A chemical reaction takes place only when the two reactants come in contact with each other. For example, sodium on exposure to water or even moisture reacts to give sodium hydroxide and hydrogen, and hence, sodium catches fire. Due to this reason, only sodium is stored in kerosene.

2. **Heat**: Generally, chemical reaction involves absorption or release of heat energy. Based on the heat changes, the reactions are classified as exothermic and endothermic reactions. The change in energy is represented as ΔH.

Many compounds decompose on absorption of heat. These are **endothermic reactions** and their ΔH is positive.

Examples: $KNO_3 \xrightarrow{\Delta} KNO_2 + O_2$; $\Delta H = 244.7$ kJ

$CaCO_3 \xrightarrow{\Delta} CaO + CO_2$; $\Delta H = 178$ kJ

Certain chemical reactions, such as combustion, are associated with release of heat energy. These are **exothermic reactions** and their ΔH is negative.

Example: $CH_4 + 2O_2 \xrightarrow{\Delta} CO_2 + 2H_2O$; $\Delta H = -890.4$ kJ

3. **Light**: Certain chemical reactions take place with the help of light energy. These are called **photochemical reactions.**

Example: $H_2 + Cl_2 \xrightarrow{\text{light}} 2HCl$

$6CO_2 + 6H_2O \xrightarrow{\text{sunlight}} C_6H_{12}O_6$ (photosynthesis)

Some chemical reactions are also associated with release of light energy.

Example: $Mg + O \rightarrow 2MgO + \text{Light}$

4. **Pressure**: There are some chemical reactions which require high-pressure conditions for the reaction to take place at a reasonable rate:

Example: $2SO + O_2 \xrightarrow{V_2O_5} 2SO_2$ (Manufacture of H_2SO_4 by Contact process)

$Pb + S \rightarrow PbS$

5. **Catalyst**: A **Catalyst** is a substance that alters the rate of a chemical reaction. Generally, a catalyst speeds up a chemical reaction. They are termed as positive catalysts in contrast to the negative catalysts which deteriorate the rate of a chemical reaction.

Example: $N_2 + 3H_2 \xrightarrow[450°C;\ 200\ atm]{Fe} 2NH_3$

Acetanilide acts as a negative catalyst for the decomposition of H_2O_2, and hence, acts as a stabilizer for the solution of H_2O_2.

Example: $H_2O_2 \rightarrow H_2O + O_2$

Since there are vast numbers of chemical reactions, the study of these reactions becomes easier and convenient by classifying them into various types.

Info Bytes!

For the manufacture of ammonia by Haber process, iron acts as a positive catalyst.

Table 1.10 Chemical reactions and their examples

Types of chemical reactions	Features	Examples
Chemical combination	Combination of two or more substances	$N_2 + O_2 \rightarrow 2NO$ (synthesis) and $2CO + O_2 \rightarrow 2CO_2$ (compound–element) $NH_3 + H_2O \rightarrow NH_4OH$ (compound–compound)
Chemical decomposition	Splitting of a compound into two or more simpler substances	$2NaNO_3 \xrightarrow{\Delta} 2NaNO_2 + O_2$ (thermal decomposition) $2HgO \xrightarrow{\Delta} 2Hg + O_2$ $2HOC \xrightarrow{light} 2HCl + O_2$ (photolytic decomposition) $2H_2O \xrightarrow{electric} 2H_2 + O_2$ (electrolyte decomposition)
Double decomposition	The radicals of the reactants are interchanged. A double decomposition reaction between an acid and a base is called neutralization reaction Precipitation reactions also are double decomposition reactions	$Na_2SO_4 + Zn(NO_3)_2 \rightarrow 2NaNO_3 + ZnSO_4$ $2KOH + H_2SO_4 \rightarrow K_2SO_4 + 2H_2O$ $CaBr_2 + K_2SO_4 \rightarrow CaSO_4 + 2KBr$
Displacement	A less reactive element is displaced by a more reactive element	$Zn + CuSO_4 \rightarrow ZnSO_4 + Cu$ $2KCl + F_2 \rightarrow 2KF + Cl_2$

Since the displacement reaction depends upon the relative reactivities of various metals, they are arranged in a decreasing order of reactivity.

Displacement Reaction

In a displacement reaction, the more reactive element displaces the less reactive element from its compound.

Representation: $AB + C \rightarrow CB + A$

$XY + Z \rightarrow XZ + Y$

The ability of an element to displace another element is known by its relative position in the reactivity series.

Metal Reactivity Series

Potassium	K	(Most reactive metal)
Sodium	Na	
Calcium	Ca	
Magnesium	Mg	
Aluminium	Al	Reactivity decreases
Zinc	Zn	
Iron	Fe	
Nickel	Ni	
Tin	Sn	
Lead	Pb	
Hydrogen	H	
Copper	Cu	
Mercury	Hg	
Silver	Ag	
Gold	Au	
Platinum	Pt	(Least reactive metal)

Info Bytes!

In a displacement reaction, a more reactive element can 'push out' or displace a less reactive element from a compound

The more reactive metal displaces the less reactive metal from its compound.

Example: $Fe + CuSO_4 \longrightarrow FeSO_4 + Cu$

(Blue) (Light Green)

(copper sulphate) (ferrous sulphate)

As iron is more reactive than copper, it displaces copper from copper sulphate solution, thereby forming ferrous sulphate.

Similarly, halogens also can be arranged in the order of reactivities which represents their relative abilities for displacement from the respective compounds.

Halogen Reactivity Series

F_2 (Most reactive halogen)

Cl_2

Br_2

I_2 (Least reactive halogen)

Reactivity decreases ↓

The more reactive halogen displaces the less reactive halogen from its compound.

Example: $2NaBr + Cl_2 \rightarrow 2NaCl + Br_2$

Exothermic and Endothermic Reactions

During a chemical reaction, some of the bonds of the molecules of reactants break and some new bonds are formed thereby forming molecules of products. Breaking of bonds requires absorption of energy whereas formation of new bonds is associated with the release of energy. The absorption and the release of energy are generally in the form of heat.

If the release of energy during the formation of bonds of the products is more than the energy required for breaking the bonds of the reactants, the reaction is called **exothermic reaction.**

Examples of Exothermic Reactions: Combustion reactions, displacement reactions, and the reaction between an acid and a base are generally exothermic reactions.

If the absorption of energy during the breaking of bonds of the reactants is more than the energy released during the formation of the bonds of the products, the reaction is called **endothermic reaction.**

Examples of Endothermic Reactions: The formation of nitric oxide from nitrogen and oxygen. The decomposition of calcium carbonate. The formation carbon monoxide due to the reaction between red hot coke and carbon dioxide.

Info Bytes!

Those instant 'hot packs' and 'cold packs' used for injuries work based on exothermic and endothermic reactions. The pack gets hot or cold due to the release or absorption of energy.

POINTS TO REMEMBER

- ✔ Kinetic-molecular theory states that molecules have an energy of motion (kinetic energy) that dependson temperature.
- ✔ The matter around us can be classified into three different states: solids, liquids, and gases.
- ✔ Melting is carried out by supplying heat energy to the solid substance and freezing is carried out by extracting heat energy from the liquid substance.
- ✔ The amount of heat energy required to convert 1 kg of a solid into a liquid at atmospheric pressure at its melting point is known as the latent heat of fusion.
- ✔ The heat energy supplied during the process is stored in the steamand is called latent heat of vaporization.
- ✔ A molecule is considered as the smallest particle of matter which has an independent existence.
- ✔ A molecule is broken down into smaller particles called atoms which take part in chemical reactions.
- ✔ A pure substance is the one which is made up of molecules containing same kind of atoms.
- ✔ A homogeneous mixture has uniform distribution of the different types of molecules in the mixture. A heterogeneous mixture has non-uniform distribution of the different types of molecules.
- ✔ Paper Chromatography is based on difference in adsorption of constituents by a surface of an appropriate adsorbent material or solid medium (stationary phase). The rate of adsorption of a particular constituent depends upon its solubility in the solvent (moving phase).
- ✔ A chemical reaction takes place only when the two reactants come in contact with each other.
- ✔ Certain chemical reactions take place with the help of light energy. These are called photo chemical reactions.
- ✔ A catalyst is a substance which alters the rate of a chemical reaction.
- ✔ In a displacement reaction, the more reactive element displaces the less reactive element from its compound.
- ✔ If the release of energy during the formation of bonds of the products is more than the energy required for breaking the bonds of the reactants, the reaction is called exothermic reaction.
- ✔ If the absorption of energy during the breaking of bonds of the reactants is more than the energy released during the formation of the bonds of the products, the reaction is called endothermic reaction.

PRACTICE QUESTIONS CLASSROOM WING

Very Short Answer Type Questions

Directions for questions from 1 to 11:
Fill in the blanks.

1. An increase in pressure increases the melting point. This statement is true for _____.
2. Silver is a substance which expands on melting, so, its melting point _____ when pressure is raised.
3. The atomicity of the element phosphorus is _____.
4. _____ is the method of separating heavier fat particles of milk from lighter particles of water.
5. Solubility of a gas in a liquid _____ with rise of temperature.
6. The forces of attraction existing between similar molecules are _____.
7. The formation of phosphorus pentachloride from phosphorus trichloride and chlorine gas is a _____ type of combination reaction.
8. The addition of MnO_2 to $KClO_3$ decreases the temperature at which $KClO_3$ decomposes because MnO_2 added acts as a _____ catalyst.
9. A mixture of NH_3 and H_2 can be separated by applying pressure, because of their high difference in _____.
10. A compound is always _____.
11. The temperature above which no amount of pressure can cause a gas to liquefy is _____.

Directions for questions from 12 to 24:
Answer the following questions.

12. In early winter morning, exhaled air appears foggy. Is evaporation involved in this process?
13. Can the mixture of Iron + sand be separated by the process of magnetic separation?
14. Which among the following: Ammonium chloride, Naphthalene, Sodium chloride and Sulphur, disappears with time without heating?
15. Which among the following: Bromine, Air, Oxygen and Copper possesses maximum intermolecular force of attraction?
16. Distinguish between filtration and centrifugation.
17. Give an example each for solid–liquid and solid–solid types of a homogeneous mixture.
18. A metal 'A' reacts with a metallic chloride of "B" to give metal 'B.' But metallic chloride of 'A' cannot give metal 'A' on reaction with metal 'B.' What conclusion can you draw from this?
19. Give an example for a liquid–liquid heterogeneous mixture. Suggest a method of separation for it.
20. How do you separate a mixture of the following?
    (a) CO_2 and O_2 (b) H_2 and O_2
21. What is paper chromatography?
22. Why is sodium stored in kerosene?
23. A reaction of decomposition of a compound AB is accompanied by absorption of some heat energy. What is the sign of ΔH?
24. What is sublimation? Give some examples.

Short Answer Type Questions

25. A gas cannot be liquefied below its critical temperature. True or false?
26. Is 'water in capillary tube', an example of adhesive force being predominant over cohesive force?
27. Pressure cooker reduces the cooking time. Why?
28. Distinguish between evaporation and boiling.
29. When a glass of ice cold water is taken in a glass, water drops are formed on the outer surface of the glass. Give a reason.
30. What is a double decomposition reaction? Give an example each for neutralization and precipitation reactions.

31. Why is it not possible to displace fluorine from metallic fluorides by any other halogens?

32. Explain the process of condensation with respect to kinetic molecular theory.

33. What is critical temperature? How does it affect the liquefaction of gas?

34. Why does steam cause more burns than boiling water?

35. List out the differences between physical and chemical changes.

36. What are the different types of combination reactions? Give an example of each.

Essay Answer Type Questions

37. The various steps involved in the process of condensation are given below. Arrange them in a proper sequence.

(A) Further extraction of heat results in a decrease in the potential energy of molecules, whereas kinetic energy remains constant.

(B) The gas molecules, on cooling, lose heat energy which decreases the kinetic energy as well as potential energy of the molecules.

(C) Increase in the forces of attraction results in the conversion of state.

(D) Decrease in potential energy leads to an increase in intermolecular forces of attraction.

38. Explain the factors affecting:

(a) melting point

(b) boiling point

(c) evaporation

39. Give the postulates of kinetic molecular theory of matter. Explain the process of melting on the basis of this theory.

40. (a) Explain the process of separation of different constituents in coloured ink.

(b) A solid mixture contains sand, camphor, sulphur, potassium nitrate and sodium chloride. How will you separate each constituent from the mixture?

41. Explain the following methods of separation with an example each.

(a) Fractional crystallization

(b) Sedimentation and decantation

(c) Preferential liquefaction

(d) Fractional distillation

PRACTICE QUESTIONS COMPETITION WING

Level 1: Apply your Concepts

Direction for questions from 1 to 10:
State whether the following statements are true or false.

1. In solids, molecules possess very high kinetic energy.
2. Addition of impurities to the solids decreases the melting point of solids.
3. The rate of evaporation decreases with increase in humidity.
4. During melting of a solid, there is no change in the kinetic energy of molecules.
5. The reaction of sodium chloride with bromine gas is a chemical displacement reaction.
6. The strong intermolecular forces of attraction are responsible for high rigidity of solids.
7. Burning of a piece of magnesium wire is a synthesis reaction.
8. The addition of impurities does not change the melting or boiling point of the substance.
9. A mixture of three parts of ice and one part of common salt is called freezing mixture.
10. The effect of pressure does not depend on the nature of the substance.

Direction for questions from 11 to 19:
Fill in the blanks.

11. Maximum fluidity of gases is due to ________.
12. Mixture of NaCl and NH_4Cl can be separated by _____.
13. Solid carbon dioxide undergoes sublimation due to ________.
14. A liquid wets the given surface if ________ forces are predominant over ________ forces.
15. A mixture contains nitre, common salt, and silver chloride as the components. The different separation techniques involved are __________, __________ and ________.
16. The reactions of a compound KX with fluorine, chlorine, bromine in three different reactions are given below:

    $2KX + F_2 \rightarrow 2KF + X_2$

    $2KX + Cl_2 \rightarrow 2KCl + X_2$

    $2KX + Br_2 \rightarrow 2KBr + X_2$

    then KX is __________.
17. In two closed containers, substances A and B are present. After sometime, the lid of the container containing substance A alone got off with a lot of pressure. This is because substance A is ________.
18. If cold water is poured on a flask containing very hot distilled water and water vapour. The water inside the flask started to boil below 100°C. The principle involved is _________.
19. Three solid substances x, y, and z are heated, the number of free surfaces of substances x and y decreases to zero and one, respectively. The number of free surfaces of z does not change. The substances associated with an increase in PE is/are __________.

Direction for question 20:
Match the entries in Column A with the appropriate ones in Column B.

20. Match the statements of Column A with those of Column B.

Column A	Column B
(i) Solvent extraction	(A) Difference in densities
(ii) Gravity method	(B) Size of the particles of insoluble solid
(iii) Sublimation	(C) High density of insoluble solid
(iv) Fractional crystallization	(D) Solubility of one component in a solvent
	(E) Ability of one component to sublime
	(F) Difference in solubility of the components in the same solvent at a certain temperature range

Direction for questions from 21 to 44:
For each of the questions, four choices have been provided. Select the correct alternative.

21. **Assertion (A):** Wet clothes dry faster on a windy day.
Reason (R): Rate of evaporation is proportional to humidity.
(a) Both A and R are true and R is the correct explanation of A.
(b) Both A and R are true, but R is not the correct explanation of A.
(c) A is true and R is false.
(d) A is false and R is true.

22 **Assertion (A):** Compounds are invariably homogeneous.
Reason (R): Compounds are constituted of only one kind of molecule distributed uniformly.
(a) Both A and R are true and R is the correct explanation of A.
(b) Both A and R are true, but R is not the correct explanation of A.
(c) A is true and R is false.
(d) A is false and R is true.

23. Assertion (A): Wet cloth is placed on the forehead of a person who is running a high temperature.
Reason (R): Evaporation causes cooling.
(a) Both A and R are true and R is the correct explanation of A.
(b) Both A and R are true, but R is not the correct explanation of A.
(c) A is true and R is false.
(d) A is false and R is true.

24. **Assertion (A):** All pure substances are homogeneous.
Reason (R): Pure substances are made up of only one kind of molecule and they are uniformly distributed.
(a) Both A and R are true and R is the correct explanation of A.
(b) Both A and R are true, but R is not the correct explanation of A.
(c) A is true and R is false.
(d) A is false and R is true.

25. Which is the first step for separation of Kerosene and water?
(a) The mixture is kept standstill.
(b) The liquid mixture is taken in a separating funnel.
(c) The heavier component is first collected by opening the stop lock.
(d) Clear layers of the liquids are formed and the heavier liquid that is water forms the bottom layer.

26. During the phase transition of a substance the temperature (T) versus heat energy (Q) graph is shown below. Identify the regions of the graph which show an increase in only PE.

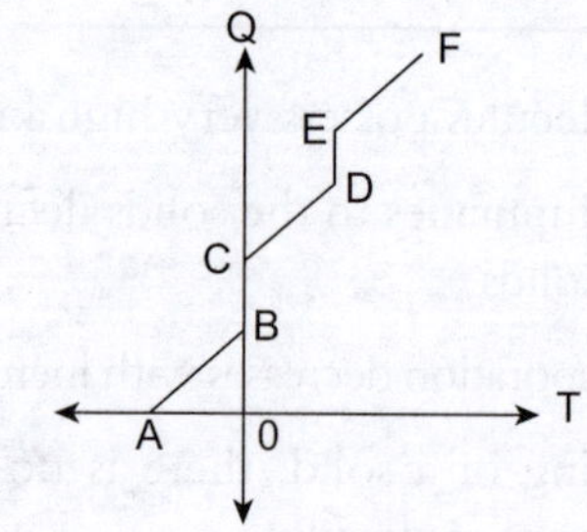

(a) AB, BC (b) BC, DE
(c) CD, EF (d) all the regions

27. A chromatogram of pure samples of food colours X, Y, and Z is given in the following illustration 1. Three samples of same food materials A, B, and C are analyzed for purity, with the help of the chromatogram in illustration 2. Identify the impure sample.

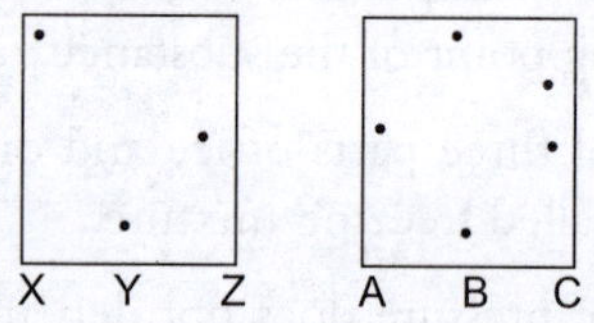

Illustration 1 Illustration 2

(a) A (b) B
(c) C (d) A and C

28. Maximum intermolecular forces of attraction exists in:
(a) bromine (b) air
(c) oxygen (d) copper

29. A gaseous mixture of A, B, and C is passed through water. The gaseous mixture B and C remains. If this gaseous mixture of B and C is subjected to sudden expansion followed by application of high pressure, B liquefies leaving behind C. Identify the set of gases.
(a) SO_3, NO_2, O_2 (b) Cl_2, SO_2, H_2
(c) CO_2, CO, N_2 (d) NH_3, N_2, H_2

30. Identify the element from the following.
(a) air (b) iodine vapour
(c) water vapour (d) amalgam

31. In which of the following cases, cooking is very slow?

(a) pressure cooker at sea level

(b) pressure cooker at higher altitude

(c) open vessel at sea level

(d) open vessel at higher altitude

32. Which of the following reactions is not a combination reaction?

(a) reaction of iodine with white phosphorus

(b) reaction of iron with sulphur

(c) addition of water to lime

(d) addition of concentrated sulphuric acid to sugar

33. A mixture of three liquids X, Y, and Z when subject to fractional distillation, the order in which the vapours condense back to liquid state in fractionating tower is Y, X, and Z. Arrange them in the correct order of vapour pressures.

(a) $Z < X < Y$ (b) $Y < X < Z$

(c) $X < Z < Y$ (d) $X < Y < Z$

34. Grease spots from garments can be separated by a method of:

(a) chromatography

(b) solvent extraction

(c) sublimation

(d) dissolution in suitable solvents

35. Which of the following involves both neutralization as well as precipitation?

(a) reaction between baking powder and H_2SO_4

(b) reaction between $BaCl_2$ and Na_2SO_4

(c) reaction between $AgNO_3$ and HCl

(d) reaction between slaked lime and H_2SO_4

36. Arrange the following changes of energy during following phase transition in a proper order.

Ice (0°C) → water (50°C) → ice (0°C)

(1) potential energy increases and kinetic energy remains constant

(2) potential energy decreases and kinetic energy remains constant

(3) potential energy increases and kinetic energy increases

(4) potential energy decreases and kinetic energy decreases

(a) 4 2 3 1 (b) 1 3 2 4

(c) 1 3 4 2 (d) 3 4 1 2

37. For the separation of red ink from blue ink a technique is used which is described below. Arrange the statements in a proper sequence.

(1) The blue and red ink form spots at certain distances on the paper.

(2) Paper chromatography is used for the separation.

(3) Paper and solvent are taken as stationary and mobile phases, respectively.

(4) A narrow strip of paper with a line drawn is cut and a mixture of red and blue ink with the help of capillary is placed on the line marked on the paper.

(5) The paper is suspended in the closed jar with the help of hook.

(a) 2 4 3 5 1 (b) 2 5 3 1 4

(c) 2 3 4 5 1 (d) 1 4 5 3 2

38. Among the following, identify the substance in which molecules possess vibratory, rotatory, and translatory motions in all directions except in one direction.

(a) bromine (b) iodine

(c) ammonia (d) silicon dioxide

39. In Darjeeling, distilled water boils at a temperature:

(a) above 373 K

(b) above 473 K

(c) below 373 K

(d) at 373 K

40. Which among the following is true?

(a) Air is a bad conductor of heat and thermal expansion of solids is more than that of gases.

(b) Air is a good conductor of heat and thermal expansion of solids is less than that of gases.

(c) Air is a bad conductor of heat and thermal expansion of solids is less than that of gases.

(d) Air is a good conductor of heat and thermal expansion of solids is more than that of gases.

41. Which of the following phenomena is based on the principle that cooling results due to evaporation?

(a) formation of water drops on the surface of cold drink bottle

(b) formation of crystals of ice on the inner surface of the lid of an ice cream box in freezer

(c) white foggy appearance on the surface of large ice blocks

(d) stretching out of tongues by dogs during summer

42. Which among the following is the false statement?

(a) Water boils below 100°C on mountain peaks.

(b) Ice undergoes sublimation on surface of moon.

(c) Ice melts above 0°C on mountain peaks.

(d) Cooking of food is faster on mountain peaks.

43. The order of vapour pressures of four solids is P << R < Q < S. Which of the following has the maximum tendency to sublime?

(a) P (b) Q

(c) R (d) S

44. Identify the methods by which the individual components of mixture containing water, potassium nitrate, sodium chloride, alcohol, and carbon tetrachloride can be separated.

(a) separating funnel, fractional distillation, fractional crystallization, distillation

(b) fractional distillation, distillation, fractional crystallization

(c) separating funnel, fractional distillation, filtration, distillation

(d) separating funnel, fractional distillation, sedimentation, and decantation

Level 2: Review your Concepts

45. Cotton clothes are preferred in summer. Why?

46. Give an example of gaseous mixtures which can be separated by fractional evaporation

47. (a) Why molten silver cannot be used to make sharp castings?

(b) A magician took a cylinder with open sides which can be closed by means of screws. He filled the cylinder with water after closing one of the ends with screw (A) and then froze the water. A coin was placed on the column of ice and the other screw (B) was fixed tightly. After sometime, the coin was found at the other end. Analyze the above observation and write the principle involved in the process.

48. A tarnished silver rod when kept in water containing magnesium bars regains its lustre. Justify.

49. In summer, Khus Khus mats are used for reducing the heating effect. Explain the principle involved in this.

50. A statue coated with chemical substance X on long exposure to polluted atmosphere becomes black. This colour can be restored by treatment with H_2O_2. Identify element X and also the types of chemical changes involved.

51. A mixture of X and Y on subjecting to paper chromatography gave the chromatogram 'A.' When the same mixture is subjected to heating, chromatogram B was obtained. What do you infer from the chromatograms?

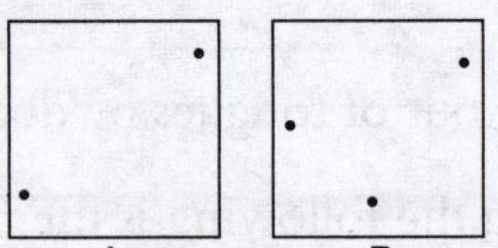

52. Why is solid $CaCl_2$ spread on roads in cold countries during winter season?

53. Explain the separation techniques involved in the separations of constituents in gunpowder. What types of reactions are involved in the explosion of gunpowder?

54. Sodium cannot be preserved in water. However, sodium amalgam can be kept in water. Justify.

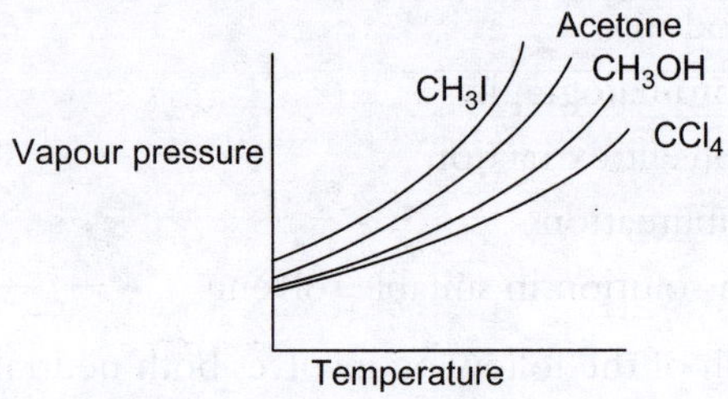

55. When a mixture of these four liquids is taken, how can they be separated? Justify.

56. (a) Explain why N_2O supports combustion more vigorously than air.

(b) Powered alumina and duralumin are taken in two test tubes A and B respectively. Concentrated hydrochloric acid is added to two test tubes. In one case a gas is evolved. Give reasons.

57. A copper rod is placed in $AgNO_3$ solution and $FeSO_4$ solution. What changes do you observe? What type of reactions takes place? Justify your observation.

58. H_2SO_4 is always diluted by adding it to water but not by adding water to it. Justify.

59. What type of reaction is involved in the usage of AgBr in photography? The positive print developed is dipped in $AuCl_3$ solution at the end to impart beautiful appearance to the photograph. Explain the reaction involved in this. Justify.

Directions for questions from 60 to 66:
Application-Based Questions

60. In a chemistry lab, Rina took some mercury and water in two test tubes separately. Then she drained off both the liquids and on observing the empty test tubes, found some difference. Can you guess what the difference is? Explain with appropriate reasons.

61. If we keep a box of ice cream in a freezer for too long, crystals of ice are formed inside the box. Give reasons.

62. Why are cotton clothes preferred in summer?

63. Small pieces of steel and some powdered rust are taken in two test tubes separately. What will you observe when concentrated hydrochloric acid is poured into both the test tubes? Justify your observation.

64. Explain how individual gases can be separated from a gaseous mixture of O_2, H_2, and CO_2.

65. The critical temperatures of CO_2 gas and N_2 gas are 31°C and −147°C, respectively. Which gas is liquefied easily and why?

66. Can water be boiled below 100°C temperature? If yes, give a reason.

Level 3 : Assess Your Concepts

67. When glass of water is freezed, formation of ice starts from the top layer but melting of ice starts from the bottom. Justify.

68. Solids generally undergo melting on heating. But only certain specific solids like naphthalene camphor undergo sublimation. Give a reason.

69. Fractional distillation of ethyl alcohol–water mixture gives a mixture of 95.6% ethyl alcohol and 4.4% water. Further separation can be brought about either by the addition of CaO or by the addition of a water-soluble salt such as potassium acetate. Justify the formation of pure ethyl alcohol in both the cases.

70. In cold countries, ethylene glycol is used in car radiators for both winter as well as summer seasons. Explain.

71. When a mixture of three miscible liquids is subjected to fractional distillation, liquid B is obtained in the receiver flask. The remaining mixture on further fractional distillation, A, is left behind in the distillation flask. On the basis of the results, comment on the critical temperatures of A, B, and C when they are in gaseous state.

Directions for questions from 72 to 77:
Application-Based Questions

72. Dicky, Micky, and Vicky had three liquids, A, B, and C, respectively. They mixed these liquids and observed that they form a homogeneous mixture. They were unable to separate the liquids and asked their teacher to separate these for them. The teacher subjected the given mixture to fractional distillation. Liquid B was obtained in the receiver flask. On further distillation, A was left behind in the distillation flask. On the basis of the results, comment on the critical temperatures of A, B, and C in their respective gaseous states.

73. Two ice blocks of 10 g each are placed in 2 L distilled water at 273 K. One of the ice blocks is made up of sea water and other one is made up of distilled water. What will you observe if the ambient temperature is also 273 K? Give reasons to support your observation.

74. Can phase transition be used to test the purity of gold?

75. The melting point of a non-sublimable solid is 100°C. What do you observe when a small piece of this solid is taken in a test tube and placed in boiling water?

76. What is the shape of the meniscus observed when water and mercury are taken in two different capillary tubes and why?

77. Chromatogram of pure samples of food colours A, B, and C is given in Fig. (1). Three samples of mixture containing the same food colours P, Q and R are subjected to chromatography and the chromatogram is shown in Fig. (2).

Determine the qualitative composition and purity of the given samples P, Q and R.

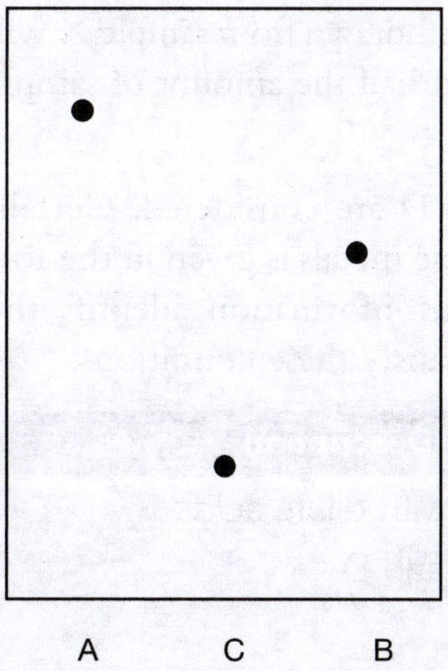

Fig (1)

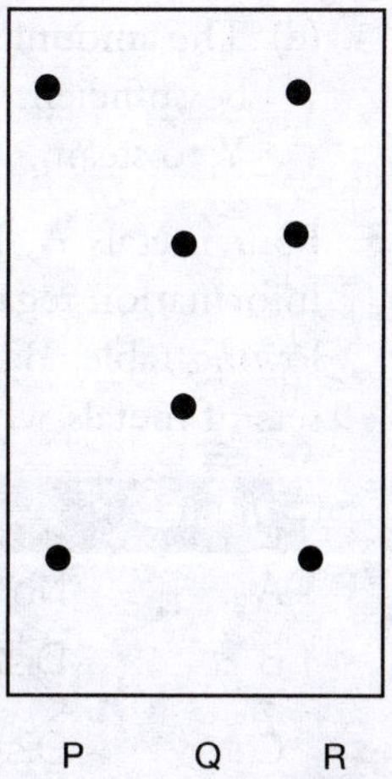

Fig (2)

AT

PRACTICE QUESTIONS JEE-NEET SPECIAL WING

Multiple-Answer Type Questions

Directions for Questions number 1 to 5:

Select one or more correct alternative(s) from the given choices.

1. A picture of an activity is given below. It represents a particular phenomenon. In the choices, some applications are given. Observe the picture and identify the applications of the phenomena represented in the figure.

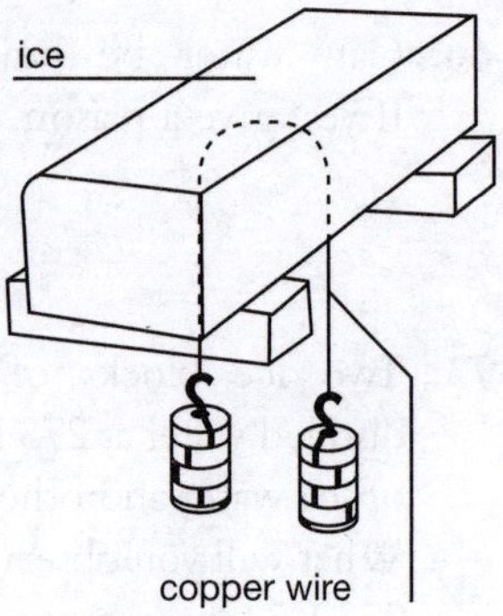

   (a) Melting of glaciers to form rivers.
   (b) Clearing of ice blocked roads by using brine solution.
   (c) Keeping dead body intact on the ice block for a short time.
   (d) Freeze drying of vegetables and fruits for preservation.

2. Two samples of water; X and Y of 500 g each are taken at 30°C and are converted to ice and steam respectively. Identify the correct statements which comply with the above activity.
   (a) 305 kcal of heat is required for the sample Y.
   (b) 55 kcal or heat is withdrawn from the sample X.
   (c) 167 kJ heat needs to be withdrawn from sample X after reaching its freezing point.
   (d) The amount of heat withdrawn from sample X will be sufficient to convert half the amount of sample Y to steam.

3. Four metals A, B, C and D are considered. Certain information regarding these metals is given in the following table. Based on this information, identify the sets of metals which can satisfy these conditions.

Metal	Description
A	No reaction with dilute acids
B	Displaces A and D
C	Displaces B
D	Can displace A and not C

	A	B	C	D
(a)	Fe	Ni	Cu	Ag
(b)	Cu	Ni	Zn	Pb
(c)	Pb	Zn	Ca	Fe
(d)	Ag	Sn	Mg	Fe

4. The figures A, B, C, D given below represent the applications of some separation methods. Corresponding principles of those separation methods are given in the options. Identify the correct options which comply with the given figures.

A

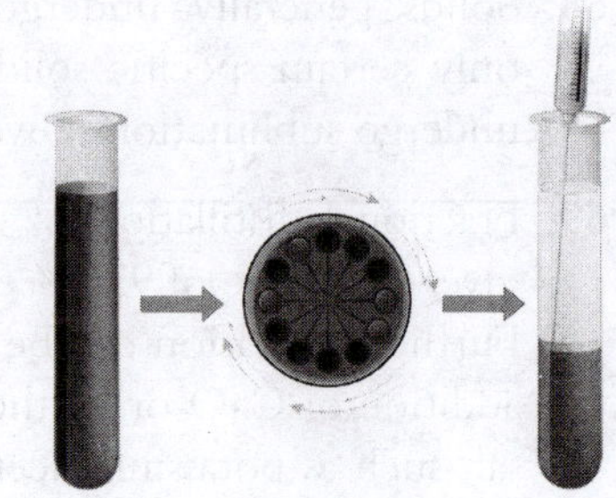

B

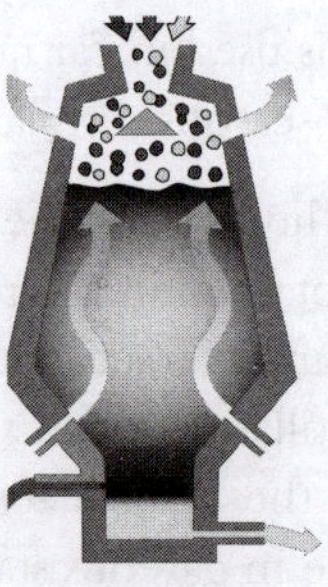

C

D

   (a) A-Solubility of a gas in liquid decreases with increase in temperature.
   (b) B-The lower density solid particles settle down when centrifugal force is applied.
   (c) C-Different components of the mixture vaporise at different temperatures.
   (d) D-The soluble component gets extracted into the solvent leaving behind the insoluble ones.

5. Two alloys X and Y with major component as copper are very much suitable for making sharp castings or perfect moulds. Identify the correct statements regarding the effect of increase in pressure on these materials.

(a) Melting points of X and Y decrease just like copper.

(b) Melting points of X and Y show the same tendency as ice.

(c) Melting point of copper shows the same tendency as cast iron.

(d) Melting points of X and Y decrease while that of copper increases

Comprehension-Based Questions

Directions for questions 6 to 11:

Read the following passage and answer the questions given below.

Some information is given in the table regarding the hypothetical gases A, B, C, D, E. Usually, the substances with stronger intermolecular forces like hydrogen bonding can coexist in liquid state and gaseous state. van der Waal's forces of attractions are the weakest intermolecular forces.

Based on the information given, answer the questions given below.

Metal	Description
Gas A	It has higher boiling point than gas B in liquid state
Gas B	Can be liquified at room temperature at high pressure
Gas C	It is called vapour
Gas D	Called permanent gas
Gas E	It has least intermolecular forces of attraction among all

6. Match the entries in column-I with those in column II

Column I (Gas)		Column II Critical temperature[0°C]	
(a)	A	(i)	-240
(b)	B	(ii)	30
(c)	C	(iii)	20
(d)	D	(iv)	-130
(e)	E	(v)	132

7. Arrange the given gases in the increasing order of intermolecular forces of attraction.

(a) C; B; D; A; E (b) A; D; C; B; E
(c) C; B; A; E; D (d) E; A; D; B; C

8. Identify the gases with minimum and maximum boiling points respectively.

(a) E; C (b) E; D
(c) C; B (d) C; E

9. Predict the gas which is likely to possess intermolecular hydrogen bonding.

(a) E (b) B
(c) A (d) C

10. Assume that all the gases are cooled to zero degree Celsius. Which gas requires maximum pressure to get liquified?

(a) A (b) B
(c) C (d) E

11. Predict the gases with only vander Waal's forces of attraction as intermolecular forces.

(a) A and B (b) A; B; C
(c) D and E (d) C; D; E

Directions for questions 12 to 16:

Read the following passage and answer the questions given below.

The metals along with hydrogen are generally arranged in the form of a metal reactivity series. Consider four metals P, Q, R and S. 'Q' can displace any metal from its aqueous solution. 'Q' along with two other metals below it react with cold water. Metals A and B are present above and below 'P' in the metal reactivity series. Metal 'B' shows the valencies of 2 and 4 which is same as the metal 'P'. Metal 'R' has no reaction with dilute acid but gets oxidised on treatment with concentrated sulphuric acid or nitric acid. Metal 'S' is a divalent metal which reacts rapidly with steam and not with water.

12. Identify the incorrect statement regarding the metals-P, A and B.

(a) All three metals can liberate hydrogen gas on reaction with dilute sulphuric acid.

(b) Metal 'B' cannot displace any other metal present above hydrogen in the series.

(c) The addition of aqueous solution of salt of B to the sulphate salt of 'Q' results the formation of white precipitate.

(d) None of these

13. A sample of sulphate salt solution of the metal 'R' is taken in two test tubes X and Y. An iron nail and a silver rod are dipped in the two solutions.

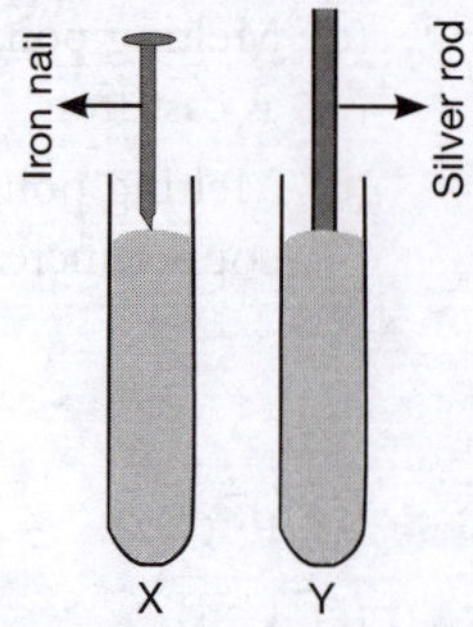

Which among the following observations would be correct after the two test tubes are kept without disturbing for few days?

(a) The solutions in both the test tubes were found to undergo change in colour.
(b) The iron nail is found to get a brown coating.
(c) Both iron nail and silver rod are found to get a brown coating.
(d) Both (a) and (b)

14. Which among the following statements complies with the nature of the metal 'S'?

(a) The metal present below 'S' shows trivalency.
(b) 'S' can displace all the transition metals from their aqueous solutions.
(c) 'S' can be reduced by alkali metals.
(d) All of these

15. Identify the characteristic(s) of the metal 'Q'?

(a) It is the strongest oxidising agent among all given ones.
(b) The bicarbonate of 'Q' on thermal decomposition produces carbon dioxide
(c) The nitrate of 'Q' on thermal decomposition produces nitrogen dioxide
(d) Both (b) and (c)

16. The probable formulae of some common compounds of the metals P, Q, R and S are given in a tabular form. Identify the correct sets among the following and choose the correct option.

	X	Y	Z
P	PO_2	PCl_3	PO_4
Q	QO	QCl_2	Q_2SO_4
R	R_2O	RCl_4	RNO_3
S	SO_2	SCl	$S(HCO_3)_2$

(a) P-X; Q-Z; R-X; S-Z
(b) P-Y; Q-X; R-X; S-Z
(c) P-X; Q-Z; R-Y; S-X
(d) P-Z; Q-X; R-Y; S-X

Directions for questions 17:

Read the following passage and answer the question given below.

Crude oil or petroleum is a thick black viscous liquid. It is a mixture of hydrocarbons. As the boiling point of hydrocarbons increases with increase in the number of carbon atoms in the chain, crude oil is subjected to fractional distillation yields various fractions. These fractions are put to different uses depending on the composition of the hydrocarbons which constitute these fractions. The process is carried out in a long vertical set up called fractionating tower. The solid residue left in the tower is known as asphalt and used for laying roads. The fuel gas which comes out of the tower contains lower hydrocarbons such as propane and butane. The most volatile liquid component separated is petrol. The next component with higher boiling point than petrol is naphtha used for making a number of chemicals. The highest boiling liquid component is fuel oil which is used as fuel in ships and factories. The component with slightly lower boiling point than this is lubricating oil. The next component to this is diesel which is to an extent used as a substitute for petrol.

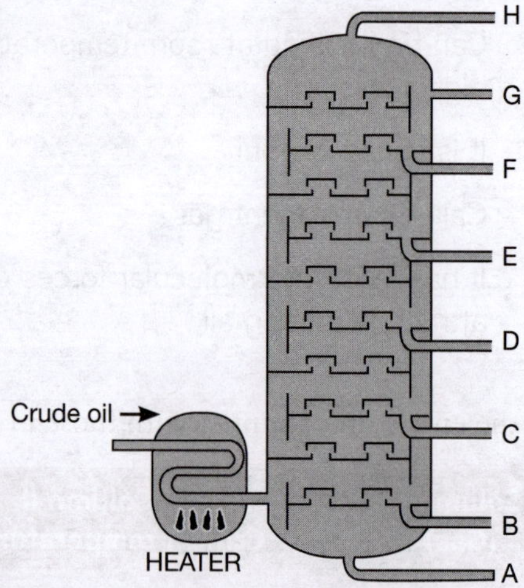

17. Match the entries in column I with those in column II.

Column I Component		Column II Name of the fraction	
(a)	E	(i)	Naphtha
(b)	H	(ii)	Residue (Bitumen)
(c)	D	(iii)	Fuel gas
(d)	A	(iv)	Lubricating oil
(e)	F	(v)	Diesel

ANSWER KEYS

Crossword

Across

1. Magnetic 4. Metalloids 6. Freezing 8. Crystalline 9. Atomicity
10. Adhesive

Down

2. Gaseous 3. Chromatography 5. Homogeneous 7. Molecules

Classroom Wing

Very Short Answer Type Questions

1. Gold and silver 2. increases 3. 4 4. centrifugation 5. decreases
6. cohesive forces 7. compound–element 8. positive 9. critical temperatures
10. homogenous 11. critical temperature

Competition Wing

Level 1: Apply your Concepts

1. False 2. True 3. True 4. True 5. False
6. True 7. True 8. False 9. True 10. False
11. High kinetic energy 12. Sublimation 13. High Kinetic energy
14. adhesive forces, cohesive forces 15. solvent extraction, filtration, fractional crystallization
16. KI 17. sublimes at normal atmospheric pressure
18. decreasing pressure decreases the boiling point 19. x, y
20. (i) → (D); (ii) → (A); (iii) → (E); (iv) → (F) 21. (c) 22. (a)
23. (a) 24. (a) 25. (b) 26. (b) 27. (c)
28. (d) 29. (d) 30. (b) 31. (d) 32. (d)
33. (c) 34. (b) 35. (d) 36. (c) 37. (c)
38. (a) 39. (c) 40. (c) 41. (d) 42. (d)
43. (d) 44. (a)

JEE-NEET Special Wing

Multiple-Answer Type Questions

1. (a; c) 2. (a; b; c) 3. (b; d) 4. (c; d) 5. (b; d)
6. (a) ↔ (iii), (b) ↔ (ii), (c) ↔ (v), (d) ↔ (iv), (e) ↔ (i) 7. (b) 8. (a)
9. (c) 10. (c) 11. (c)

Comprehension-Based Questions

12. (d) 13. (b) 14. (d) 15. (d) 16. (a)
17. (a) ↔ (v), (b) ↔ (iii), (c) ↔ (iv), (d) ↔ (ii), (e) ↔ (i)

Hints and Explanations

Classroom Wing

Very Short Answer Type Questions

1. The melting points of silver and gold, which expand on melting, increase with the increase in pressure on them.
2. increases
3. 4
4. centrifugation
5. decreases
6. cohesive forces
7. compound–element
8. positive
9. critical temperatures
10. homogenous
11. critical temperature
12. No, evaporation is not involved in this process. The appearance of fog is due to the condensation of water vapour into tiny droplets due to very low temperatures in winter mornings.
13. Yes. In a mixture of iron and sand, iron is magnetic and sand is non-magnetic in nature. Therefore, it can be separated by magnetic separation method.
14. Naphthalene undergoes sublimation at room temperature and hence, it disappears with time.
15. Copper exists in solid form and in solids molecules possess high intermolecular forces of attraction.
16. Property exploited in filtration: Size of the particles of an insoluble solid component.

    Property exploited in centrifugation: Size of density of solid particles in comparison to the size of liquid particles.
17. Solid–liquid: NaCl in water and iodine in CCl_4 Solid–solid: Stainless steel.
18. Displacement of less reactive metal by more reactive metal.
19. Oil in water, separating funnel.
20. Diffusion
21. Separation technique, based on difference in adsorption and solubility in the solvent.
22. Sodium on exposure to water or even moisture reacts to give sodium hydroxide and hydrogen, and hence, sodium catches fire. Due to this reason, sodium is stored in kerosene.
23. positive
24. Conversion of solid to gas. *Examples:* Camphor, naphthalene, ammonium chloride, iodine, etc.

Short Answer Type Questions

25. Critical temperature is the temperature above which a gas cannot be liquified, no matter what amount of high pressure is applied to it.
26. Yes, as water rises in a capillary tube due to strong adhesive forces between glass molecules and water molecules.
27. Pressure cooker reduces cooking time because pressure inside the cooker is more, so the boiling point of water increases. The temperature of the cooking medium being greater than the normal boiling point, food gets cooked at a faster rate, thus saving time and fuel.
28. Evaporation and boiling are distinguished on the basis of the following:

    (i) Rate of process.

    (ii) Surface phenomenon and bulk phenomenon.

    (iii) Temperature at which the process takes place.
29. (i) Decrease in temperature due to the cold water glass.

    (ii) Condensation of water vapour.
30. Exchange of radicals among reactants.

    Example of neutralization reaction:

    $2KOH + H_2SO_4 \rightarrow K_2SO_4 + 2H_2O$

    Example of Precipitation reaction:

    $CaBr_2 + K_2SO_4 \rightarrow CaSO_4 + 2KBr$
31. High reactivity of fluorine among halogens.

32. (i) Extraction of heat from gas.
(ii) Decrease in potential energy.
(iii) Increase in intermolecular forces of attraction.

33. (i) Minimum temperature required for liquefaction of gas.
(ii) High critical temperature and easy liquefaction of gas.

34. (i) Lower potential energy associated with molecules of boiling water.
(ii) Higher potential energy associated with molecules of steam.

35. (i) Change in molecular composition in chemical changes.
(ii) Temporary and reversible nature of physical and chemical changes.
(iii) Net gain or loss of energy in chemical change.
(iv) Vibratory motion in solids.
(v) Vibratory, translatory, and rotatory motions in gases.
(vi) Differences between liquids and gases with respect to translatory motion.

36. (i) Element–element combination reactions.
(ii) Element–compound combination reactions.
(iii) Compound–compound combination reactions.

Essay Answer Type Questions

37. On cooling, the gas molecules lose heat energy which decreases the kinetic energy as well as potential energy of the molecules.

Further extraction of heat results in a decrease in the potential energy of molecules whereas kinetic energy remains constant.

Decrease in potential energy leads to an increase in intermolecular forces of attraction.

Increase in forces of attraction results in the conversion of state.

Hence, the correct order is BADC.

38. (i) The effect of pressure on the melting point and boiling point.
(ii) Nature of solid: opposition to expansion with increase in pressure.
(iii) Decrease in melting point and increase in boiling point by addition of impurities.
(iv) Temperature.
(v) Humidity.

39. The postulates of kinetic theory of gases are the following:
(i) Gases contain large number of tiny particles known as molecules.
(ii) The force of attraction between the molecules is very low.
(iii) The intermolecular space is large.
(iv) Molecules of a gas are in a state of random motion resulting in continuous collisions among themselves and with the walls of the container, exerting pressure.
(v) The kinetic energy of molecules is proportional to the temperature. Process of melting on the basis of this theory can be explained by the following points:
(a) Supply of heat and increase in potential energy.
(b) Decrease in intermolecular forces of attraction.
(c) Conversion to liquid state.

40. (a) (i) Paper chromatography.
(ii) Stationary phase and moving phase.
(iii) Adsorption of constituents and affinity of constituents to two phases.

(b) Camphor from the mixture can be separated by sublimation. Sulphur from the remaining mixture can be separated by solvent extraction by using carbon disuphide as solvent.

Sand from the remaining mixture can be separated by solvent extraction by using water as solvent followed by filtration. From the aqueous solution of sodium nitrate and potassium nitrate, KNO_3 can be separated by fractional crystallization. Sodium nitrate can be separated by evaporation of the aqueous solution.

41. (a) To separate solid–solid mixture by fractional crystallization, solubility of both components in a solvent.
(b) Difference in solubility of two components.
(c) Liquefaction of a gas under high pressure.
(d) Difference in boiling point of two components.

Competition Wing

Level 1: Apply your Concepts

1. False, in solids, molecules possess a very low kinetic energy

2. True. Addition of impurities to the solids decreases the melting point of solids.

11. Gas molecules show maximum fluidity because they have high kinetic energy and very less intermolecular forces of attraction.

12. In the mixture of NaCl and NH_4Cl, NH_4Cl sublimes on heating. Therefore, this mixture can be separated by the process of sublimation.

13. Solid carbon dioxide undergoes sublimation due to the high kinetic energy of surface molecules.

20. (i) → (D); (ii) → (A); (iii) → (E); (iv) → (F)

21. Rate of evaporation is directly proportional to wind speed and inversely proportional to humidity.

Hence, the correct option is (c).

22. In a compound, only one type of molecule is present and it is uniformly distributed.

Hence, the correct option is (a).

23. Water present in the wet cloth undergoes evaporation which causes cooling.

Hence, the correct option is (a).

24. Pure substances are made up of only one kind of molecule.

Hence, the correct option is (a).

25. The liquid mixture is taken in a separating funnel.

The mixture is kept still.

Clear layers of the liquids are formed and the heavier liquid, that is, water forms the bottom layer.

The heavier component is collected first by opening the stop lock.

Hence, the correct option is (b).

36. (1) potential energy increases and kinetic energy remains constant

(3) potential energy increases and kinetic energy increases

(4) potential energy decreases and kinetic energy decreases

(2) potential energy decreases and kinetic energy remains constant

Hence, the correct answer is (c).

37. (2) Paper chromatography is used for the separation

(3) paper and solvent are taken as stationary and mobile phases, respectively.

(4) A narrow strip of paper with a line drawn is cut and a mixture of red and blue ink with the help of capillary is placed on the line marked on the paper.

(5) The paper is suspended in the closed jar with the help of hook.

(1) The blue and red inks are separated on the paper by adsorption technique.

Hence, the correct answer is (c).

38. Bromine is a liquid. The molecules of liquid possess vibratory, rotatory, and translatory motions in all directions except in upward direction.

Hence, the correct answer is (a).

39. Pressure decreases with increase in altitude, and hence, boiling point decreases. Since Darjeeling is at higher attitude, water boils below 373 K, i.e., below 100°C.

Hence, the correct answer is (c).

40. Conduction of heat in matter takes place via the molecules. One molecule absorbs heat and passes it to the other molecule. As in gaseous state the molecules are far away from each other, the heat cannot be transferred from molecule to molecule, and thus, there is no conduction of heat through air which is a mixture of gases.

In case of solids, the molecules are closely packed and the intermolecular forces of attraction are maximum. Therefore, on heating, the molecules cannot move freely there by showing less expansion than gases in which the forces of attraction between molecules is less, and hence, on heating KE of molecules increases, and therefore, the volume increases.

Hence, the correct answer is (c).

41. Dogs stretch out their tongues during summer because the surface area of tongue provides scope for evaporation which protects the body from overheating during summer. This is because they cannot sweat like human beings. All other phenomena are due to the condensation of water vapour due to very low temperature.

Hence, the correct answer is (d).

42. With increasing altitude, pressure decreases, and hence, boiling point of water also decreases. As a result, cooking of food is delayed on mountain peaks.

Hence, the correct answer is (d).

43. Rate of sublimation is directly proportional to vapour pressure. Hence, 'S' undergo sublimation more easily at room temperature.

Hence, the correct answer is (d).

44. Both KNO_3 and NaCl are soluble in water forming a homogeneous solution which is soluble in alcohol and forming a mixture. This mixture is insoluble in CCl_4. Hence, CCl_4 is separated by separating funnel. Alcohol is separated by fractional distillation. As KNO_3 is more soluble than NaCl in water, therefore, it is separated by fractional crystallization. NaCl from water is separated by distillation.

Hence, the correct answer is (a).

Level 2: Review your Concepts

45. Cotton clothes are preferred in summer because they absorb sweat more and allow the sweat to evaporate at a faster rate. The sweat absorbs heat energy from the body and gets evaporated, thus keeping the body cool.

46. An example of such a gaseous mixture is $O_2 + N_2$. Since N_2 and O_2 differ in boiling points in their liquid state, they can be separated by fractional evaporation.

47. (a) Molten silver contains mercury, which is a weak metal, hence it does not support to make sharp castings.

(b) When the screw is tightened, pressure is exerted on the coin. Due to this, the ice below the coin melts and the coin slides down. Then the water above the coin solidifies. Since water expands on solidification, it exerts pressure on the coin. The ice below the coin melts and this process continues till the coin is pushed to the other end. This is how the coin is found at other end A. The principle involved is regelation.

48. When the silver rod is dipped in water containing magnesium bars, the magnesium cations displace the silver anions due to their high reactivity and hence, the tarnished silver rod regains its lustre.

49. Principle involved in this is that the air going through these mats cool downs and the cools air reaches us.

50. Long exposure to atmosphere converts white lead into black PbS due to H_2S present in the atmosphere. This is why statues turn black.

$$PbO + H_2S \rightarrow PbS + H_2O$$

On treatment with H_2O_2, the black PbS gets oxidized to white $PbSO_4$ and the color is restored.

51. X and Y components of the mixtures travel at different rates and are separated at different distances on different external conditions.

52. $CaCl_2$ is spread on roads in cold countries to decrease the melting point of ice.

53. Gunpowder is a mixture of sulphur, charcoal, and potassium nitrate (nitre).

- Add water to the mixture. Potassium nitrate will dissolve in water. Filter the solution.
- Filtrate is solution of potassium nitrate and residue contains sulphur and charcoal.
- Evaporate the filtrate, water will vaporize leaving behind potassium nitrate.
- To the residue containing sulphur and charcoal, add carbon disulphide: this will dissolve sulphur.
- Filter this solution.
- The filtrate will contain sulphur dissolved in carbon disulphide and residue will be charcoal.
- Evaporate the filtrate to obtain crystals of sulphur

54. Sodium is a highly reactive metal, so it cannot be kept in water in its free state, whereas it can be kept in water because in alloys, metals lose their individual property and have all the properties of the alloy.

55. The four liquids in a mixture can be separated using different methods. These methods include filtration, evaporation, distillation, and chromatography.

56. (a) The heat from the flame causes the nitrous oxide (N_2O) to decompose into nitrogen and oxygen, which supports combustion more vigorously than air.

(b) Duralumin is an alloy, that is a mixture in which aluminium is the major component and it retains its properties in duralumin. Hence, duralumin liberates hydrogen and effervescence will be observed. However, alumina (Al_2O_3) being a compound of aluminium does not exhibit the chemical properties of aluminium.

57. When a copper rod is placed in the solution of silver nitrate, copper being a more reactive metal than silver displaces silver from its compound by forming copper

nitrate with a shiny greyish white deposit of silver on the copper rod. Whereas, in case of $FeSO_4$ solution, no reaction takes place as iron is more reactive than copper. More reactive metals displace less reactive metal from solutions.

58. Adding acid to water releases heat. As it is an exothermic process, it is avoided.

59. AgBr is exposed to form the image depending on the frequency of light which is involved. After that the AgBr forms an image on the film.

60. Water droplets are found on the inner surface of one test tube while the other test tube is completely dry. In the case of water, adhesive forces are more than cohesive forces but in case of mercury cohesive forces are more than adhesive forces. Due to stronger adhesive force, water droplets stick to the test tube.

61. Due to very low temperature in the freezer, the water vapour gets deposited as crystals of ice. Therefore, we get crystals of ice inside the box if kept in freezer for longer time.

62. People wear cotton clothes to keep themselves cool in summer. Cotton fabric absorbs sweat more due to greater adhesive forces between cotton and water and also allows the sweat to be evaporated at a faster rate. The sweat absorbs heat energy equal to the latent heat of vaporization from the body and gets evaporated, thus keeping the body cool.

63. Steel is an alloy, i.e., a mixture in which iron is the major component and it retains its property in steel. Hence, pieces of steel will liberate hydrogen and effervescence will be observed. However, rust being a compound of iron does not exhibit the chemical property of iron. Rust dissolves in hydrochloric acid due to the formation ferric chloride and no effervescence will be observed in that test tube.

64. When a mixture of O_2, H_2, and CO_2 is present, the mixture can first be passed through KOH as it will dissolve the CO_2. This CO_2 can be obtained back from KOH by adding diluted HCl. The left over mixture contains O_2 and H_2. As the molecular weight difference is high, therefore they can be separated by diffusion, where H_2 will come out first.

65. Since the critical temperature of CO_2 is high, the intermolecular forces of attraction among CO_2 molecules are more when compared with N_2. Hence, CO_2 will liquefy easily.

66. Yes, water can be boiled below its boiling point as the boiling point of the water decreases with decrease in pressure.

Level 3 : Assess Your Concepts

67. Freezing depends on the movement of water molecule since the region of molecule present at surface is in direct contact with external environment. Whereas melting depends on the factor of pressure among the solid molecules of water, since the pressure at the bottom is under greater stress than the pressure at the surface.

68. Solids like naphthalene have very high vapour pressures due to which heating leads to direct vaporization (sublimation) even before the melting point is reached.

69. Addition of a soluble salt brings about the change in the boiling point due to which different components vaporize at different temperatures.

70. Ethylene glycol, which has hydroxyl group, shows properties like elevation of boiling point, decrease in rate of evaporation, etc.

71. Fractional distillation is used to separate miscible liquid having difference in their boiling point. Liquid B has low boiling point due to which it vaporizes first and obtained in receiver. Amongst all, it has lowest boiling point so it has weaker intermolecular forces. On further heating, A remains in the distillation flask, which implies that it has highest boiling point of the three solutions and has strongest intermolecular forces. Higher the intermolecular forces, higher will be the critical temperature of the liquid.

72. Fractional distillation is employed to separate miscible liquids which have a difference in their boiling points. In this process of separation, the liquid with a low boiling point, i.e., a high vapour pressure, distils. Therefore, from the given data, it can be said that the boiling point of B is less than that of C which is less than that of A. For liquids with high boiling points, the intermolecular forces of attraction are also high, and hence, they have high critical temperatures. Therefore, the critical temperature of A is greater than that of C which is greater than that of B.

73. After some time, one ice block will disappear and the other one remains intact. The ice block which is made up of sea water melts because of lowering of melting point due to the presence of dissolved salts.

74. Yes, the melting point of pure solid is always constant. The purity of gold can be measured with the help of its melting point. However, if the gold is not pure, then it does not have a sharp melting point, because the presence of impurities reduces the melting point of the pure gold.

75. The solid remains as it is. Water boils at 100°C. Transmission of heat takes place as long as the temperature of the solid is below 0°C. As soon as the temperature of the solid reaches 100°C, transmission of heat from water to the solid stops. Hence, it does not melt.

76. Mercury shows a convex meniscus as it has higher cohesive forces than adhesive forces with glass. Water, on the other hand, shows a concave meniscus as the adhesive forces between water and glass are higher than the cohesive forces between water molecules.

77. The two spots corresponding to sample (P) in Fig. (2) indicates the presence of food colours A, C.

The three spots corresponding to sample (R) in Fig. (2) indicates the presence of A, B, C.

The spot corresponding to sample (Q) in Fig. (2) indicates the presence of sample (B).

The additional spot corresponding to (Q) in Fig. (2) indicates the presence of impurity in sample Q.

JEE-NEET Special Wing

Multiple-Answer Type Questions

1. The given picture represents the phenomenon of regelation. The applications of the phenomena include melting of glaciers to form rivers and keeping dead bodies on the ice block.

2. **Sample X:**

   Mass of water = 500 g

   Heat required to reach 100°C (B.Pt) from 30°C = 500 × 70 = 35000 Cal = 35 kcal

   Heat required to convert boiled water to steam at 100°C = 500 × 540 = 270000 cal

   = 270 Kcal = 1130 kJ

   Total heat required = 305 kcal

   Sample Y:

   Heat withdrawn from water to reach 0°C = 500 × 30 = 15000 cal = 15 kcal = 62.7 kJ

   Heat withdrawn from water during conversion to ice = 500 × 80 = 40000 cal

   = 40 kcal =167.2 kJ

   Total heat withdrawn from water = 55 kcal

   Amount of sample Y that can be converted to steam with 55 kcal = 90 g

3. A – Metal below hydrogen in metal reactivity series (Cu; Ag)

   B- More reactive than A, D and less reactive than C (Ni; Sn)

   C- More reactive than A,B (Zn; Mg)

   D- Less reactive than B, C and more reactive than A (Pb; Fe)

4. A- The gas fizzes out of the cool drink can when opened because CO_2 is present in dissolved state under high pressure and release of pressure decreases the solubility of gas.

   B- The higher density solid particles settle down when the mixture is centrifuged.

   C- Different components of the mixture vaporise at different temperatures due to their different boiling points.

   D- Making of coffee decoction involves solvent extraction wherein the soluble component goes into hot water while the insoluble components are left behind in the filter.

5. The solids which are associated with the property of contraction on melting undergo expansion on solidification. Hence, they are suitable for making perfect moulds or sharp castings. In case of these solids, the melting point decreases with increase in pressure. Ice is an example of such solid. X and Y are suitable for making moulds and hence belong to this category. Cast iron also comes into this category as it is widely used for making moulds. But pure copper shows the opposite tendency and hence is not suitable for making moulds.

Comprehension-Based Questions

Common solution From 6-11:

E and D are called permanent gases as their critical temperatures are very low and hence these gases are associated with negligible intermolecular forces of attraction. Therefore, liquefaction becomes highly difficult. Since E has least intermolecular forces of attraction, it should have least critical temperature that is -240°C. Gas D should have critical temperature of -130°C. Gas C is called vapour since its critical temperature is much higher than room temperature. That means, C should have critical temperature of 132°C. Gas B has critical temperature of 30°C while gas A has slightly lower critical temperature than B(20°C)

6.

	Column I (Gas)		Column II (Critical temperature)
(a)	A	(iii)	20
(b)	B	(ii)	30
(c)	C	(v)	132
(d)	D	(iv)	−130
(e)	E	(i)	−240

7. **Hence, choice (A), choice (D), choice (C), choice (B) and choice (E) follow.**

8. **Hence, choice (E) and choice (C) follow.**

9. **Hence, choice is (C) follow.**

10. **Hence, choice is (C) follow.**

11. **Hence, choice (D) and choice (E) follow.**

Common solutions for questions 12 to 16:

Metal indicated	Metal identified from the information
P	Tin
Q	Potassium
R	Copper
S	Magnesium
A	Nickel
B	Lead

12. All the given statements are correct.

13. The iron nail gets a brown coating as iron can displace copper from its aqueous solution. Silver rod does not undergo any change as silver cannot displace copper from its aqueous solution.

14. The metal below 'S' that is magnesium is chromium. It shows trivalency. It is more reactive than all the transition metals and hence can displace them from their solutions. Alkali metals being more reactive and electropositive than magnesium, they are stronger reducing agents. Hence, they can reduce magnesium.

15. 'Q' is potassium which is at the top of the metal reactivity series and hence is the strongest reducing agent among all the given metals. Potassium carbonate is highly thermally stable and hence cannot decompose to give carbon dioxide. Potassium nitrate on decomposition gives potassium nitrite and oxygen. Both these statements are correct, and the first statement is incorrect.

16. P-SnO_2; Q-K_2SO_4; R-Cu_2O; S-$Mg(HCO_3)_2$

17.

	Column I Component		Column II Name of the fraction
(a)	E	(v)	Diesel
(b)	H	(iii)	Fuel gas
(c)	D	(iv)	Lubricating oil
(d)	A	(ii)	Residue (Bitumen)
(e)	F	(i)	Naphtha

CHAPTER
2

Basic Concepts of Chemistry

Remember

Before beginning this chapter, you should be able to:

- recapitulate the concept of shorthand notations of an atom and a molecule, the method of writing the formula of a compound, naming of inorganic compounds
- understand the process of writing a chemical equation
- understand the law of conservation of mass, balancing a chemical equation
- understand the concept of saturated, unsaturated, and supersaturated solution

Key Ideas

After completing this chapter, you should be able to:

- write the formula and name of a compound
- calculate molecular mass and equivalent mass
- write a chemical equation and balance it
- define the laws of chemical combination
- identify the type of reaction
- calculate the solubility of a solute in a solvent
- understand the factors affecting the solubility
- understand the importance of solubility curve

Scientific Crypt

A Tribute to Jons Jacob Berzelius (1779–1848)

Jons Jacob Berzelius is considered as father of modern chemistry for his remarkable work in chemistry. Prior to Berzelius, John Dalton who did pioneering work in the field of the structure of atoms proposed a set of symbols for the elements. Since these symbols were not indicative of their names in any way, they were not of much practical use. Later, Berzelius not only suggested the modern symbols for elements but also proposed modern chemical formulae for various substances.

Berzelius was a Swedish scientist born into an educated family in 1779. He received an M.D. degree and was appointed as assistant professor in medicine and pharmacy at Stockholm. His latent interest in chemistry led him to do extensive work in the field of chemistry. He published about 250 papers in his lifetime covering almost every aspect of chemistry. In addition to symbols and formulae, his contributions also include the discovery of elements such as cerium, selenium, silicon and thorium, the introduction of certain important terms such as organic chemistry, isomerism, allotropy, catalysis, protein, polymer, halogen and electronegativity and also the invention of mercury cathode. He also provided experimental proof for the law of definite proportions. In the area of practical chemistry, he was associated with the introduction of the usage of water baths, desiccators, wash bottles, filter paper, rubber tubing and improved blowpipe technique. He passed away in 1848. Berzelius medal was established by the Royal Swedish Academy in honour of this distinguished scientist.

FUN TIME

CROSSWORD

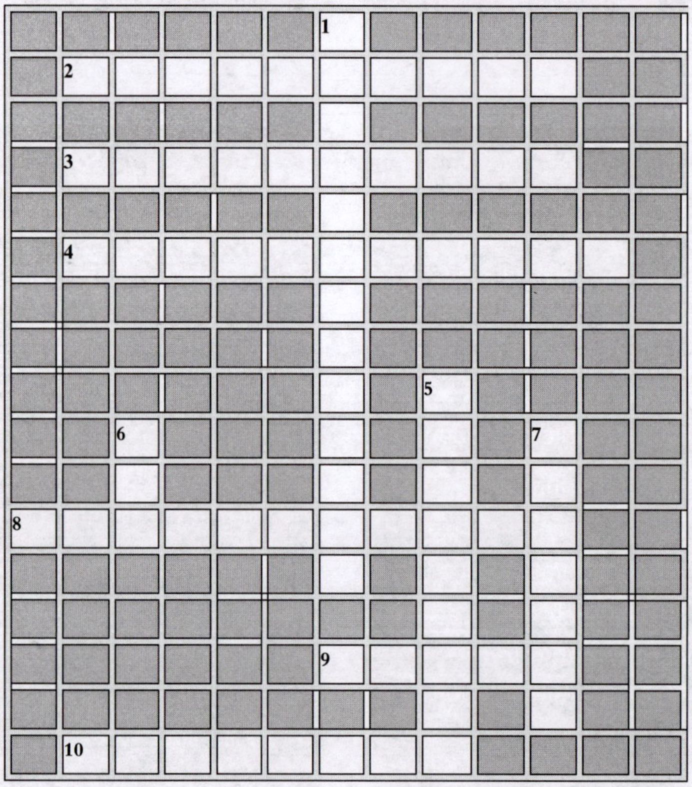

Across

2. The decomposition of a substance in the presence of light
3. Name of the oxy acid of nitrogen with one hydrogen, one nitrogen and three oxygen atoms
4. Greek name of mercury
8. The solid insoluble product formed in a double decomposition reaction
9. Name of the anion present in the rust
10. Name of the ion which contains one nitrogen and four hydrogen atoms

Down

1. The type of decomposition of alumina
5. Sodium metal is less reactive than
6. The suffix used for naming binary compounds
7. In an exothermic reaction, the energy released during the formation of a bond is _______ than the energy absorbed during the breaking of a bond.

INTRODUCTION

In our journey through the intricate world of chemistry, we come across myriad symbols, names, and equation, everything is a crucial element in decoding the mysteries of matter and its transformations. Just as a written language uses alphabets, words, and grammar to convey messages, chemistry employs its unique notation and nomenclature to represent and communicate its principles.

We'll revisit the shorthand notations for atoms and molecules, enabling efficient and universal representation.

-The process of crafting the formula of a compound and naming inorganic compounds will be explored, ensuring we can accurately identify and communicate about specific substances.

-We'll then dive into the realm of chemical equations, understanding their creation and the foundational law of conservation of mass that governs them. Balancing these equations will emphasize this law's immutable nature.

Concluding our journey, we'll distinguish between saturated, unsaturated, and supersaturated solutions, shedding light on solvents' capacities to dissolve solutes.

Language of Chemistry

Language is a mode of communication and is the key to the success of human civilization. Exchange of views and sharing of knowledge are the most important factors for any constructive activity. Chemistry is the branch of science in which we need to deal with a wide variety of substances like different elements, numerous number of compounds and mixtures.

Many studies based on these chemical substances go on all over the world. For a proper communication regarding these chemicals, a common language is necessary.

Every chemical substance has a unique composition. Each of them is known by a particular name and its name is decided following certain standard rules. Thus the study of nomenclature of elements and compounds is indispensable in the field of chemistry.

However, representing the chemicals with their name (in full form) is a cumbersome process. Hence, a standard system or protocol has been developed to abbreviate the names of the chemicals.

Chemistry is basically the study of different chemical processes that take place around us as well as the development of useful products from the existing ones. Thinkers and philosophers have observed different chemical processes, carried out a number of experiments and finally established certain fundamental principles which are the inevitable part of the study of chemistry.

Apart from these, another significant aspect of the study of chemistry is the classification of reactions. All the reactions can be categorized based on certain criteria like nature of reaction, energy changes during a chemical reaction, etc. These kinds of classifications simplify the study of wide range of chemical processes involved in the study of chemistry. Since most of the reactions take place in solution state, study of solutions is closely entangled with the study of chemical reactions.

The innumerable chemical changes occurring in nature can conveniently be represented in the form of chemical equations. For the sake of convenience and universal application, the 118 elements discovered so far have been assigned unique symbols. The molecules formed by the combination of the various elements are represented by distinct formulae. The study of symbols, formulae, and chemical equations comes under the purview of **language of chemistry.**

Representation of Chemical Changes

Every chemical change can be conveniently represented in the form of a chemical equation. This is because describing a chemical change with the names of the substances becomes cumbersome. The elements and compounds are, therefore, given shorthand notations called symbols and formulae, respectively.

Symbols are the shorthand notations representing a single atom of an element, and generally consist of a letter or combination of letters derived from the name of the element.

In 1811, Berzelius suggested a simple system of writing symbols to represent an atom of an element in the following way.

1. In most of the cases the first letter of the name of the element in capital letter is used as the symbol of the element.

Table 2.1 Name of element and their symbol

Element	Symbol
Boron	B
Carbon	C
Fluorine	F
Hydrogen	H
Iodine	I
Nitrogen	N
Oxygen	O
Phosphorus	P
Sulphur	S
Vanadium	V
Uranium	U

2. When the names of two or more elements have the same initial letter for example, carbon and calcium), another letter from the name of the element is written in small letter along with the initial letter written in capital.
3. For some elements the symbols are derived from their Latin, German, or Greek names.

Table 2.2 Name of element and their symbol

Element	Symbol
Aluminium	Al
Arsenic	As
Argon	Ar
Barium	Ba
Beryllium	Be
Bromine	Br
Bismuth	Bi
Cobalt	Co
Calcium	Ca
Cadmium	Cd
Chromium	Cr
Chlorine	Cl
Caesium	Cs
Palladium	Pd
Platinum	Pt
Selenium	Se
Silicon	Si
Strontium	Sr

Table 2.3 Name of element, their latin and their symbol

Name of the element	Traditional name	Symbol
Sodium	*Natrium (Greek)*	Na
Potassium	*Kalium*	K
Iron	*Ferrum*	Fe
Copper	*Cuprum*	Cu
Silver	*Argentum*	Ag
Gold	*Aurum*	Au
Mercury	*Hydrargyrum*	Hg
Lead	*Plumbum*	Pb
Tin	*Stannum*	Sn
Antimony	*Stibnum (Greek)*	Sb
Tungsten	*Wolfram (German)*	W

Just as an atom is represented by a symbol, a molecule of an element, or a compound is represented by means of a formula. The **formula** represents the number of atoms of each element present in the molecule.

Examples: Hydrogen – H_2
Chlorine – Cl_2
Ozone – O_3
Water – H_2O
Sulphuric acid – H_2SO_4

Info Bytes!

Representation of chemical changes is typically done using chemical equations, showing the conversion of reactants to products.

Valency

During the formation of the molecules or compounds, atoms combine in certain fixed proportions. This is due to the fact that different atoms have different combining capacities. The combining capacity of an atom is known as its **valency**.

The valency of hydrogen atom is taken as one and is selected as the standard. Valencies of the other elements are expressed in terms of hydrogen. Valency of an element can also be defined as the number of hydrogen atoms which combine with one atom of the element.

Table 2.4 Valencies of elements with respect to hydrogen in a given substance.

Molecule	Description	Valency of the element
Hydrogen chloride, HCl	One hydrogen atom combines with one chlorine atom	1 (Chlorine)
Water, H_2O	Two hydrogen atoms combine with one oxygen atom	2 (Oxygen)
Ammonia, NH_3	Three hydrogen atoms combine with one nitrogen atom	3 (Nitrogen)
Methane, CH_4	Four hydrogen atoms combine with one carbon atom	4 (Carbon)

Since most of the elements do not combine with hydrogen, the valency of the element is also defined in terms of other elements like chlorine or oxygen. This is because almost all the elements combine with chlorine or oxygen.

Valency with Respect to Chlorine: Since valency of chlorine is one, the number of chlorine atoms with which one atom of an element can combine is called its valency.

Example: NaCl ⇒ Valency of Na = 1

Valency with Respect to Oxygen: In another way, **valency** can be defined as double the number of oxygen atoms with which one atom of an element can combine since valency of oxygen is two.

Example: MgO ⇒ Valency of Mg = 2

Ions or Radicals: An atom or a group of atoms, when they either lose or gain electron(s), gets converted into ions. Ions formed by the loss of electron(s) are positively charged and are called **cations** or **positive ions.**

Example: $Na \xrightarrow{-1e^-} \underset{\text{cation}}{Na^+}$

The ions formed by the gain of electron(s) are negatively charged and are called **anions** or **negative ions**.

Example: $F \xrightarrow{-1e^-} \underset{\text{anion}}{F^-}$

Group of atoms bound together with a specific charge and behave as an ion is called a **polyatomic ion** or **radical.** These radicals retain their identity in a chemical reaction.

Examples: NH_4^+, CO_3^{-2}, SO_4^{-2}, ClO_4^- etc.

An ion or radical is classified as monovalent, divalent, trivalent, or tetravalent when the magnitude of charges over it is 1, 2, 3, or 4, respectively.

Table 2.5 A list of positive ions or radicals and their charges.

POSITIVE IONS OR RADICALS	
Ion/Radical	**Valency**
Sodium (Na^+)	Monovalent
Potassium(K^+)	Monovalent
Lithium (Li^+)	Monovalent
Ammonium (NH_4^+)	Monovalent
Hydronium (H_3O^+)	Monovalent
Hydrogen (H^+)	Monovalent
Barium (Ba^{2+})	Divalent
Calcium (Ca^{2+})	Divalent
Zinc (Zn^{2+})	Divalent
Magnesium (Mg^{2+})	Divalent
Nickel (Ni^{2+})	Divalent
Cobalt (Co^{2+})	Divalent
Aluminium (Al^{3+})	Trivalent
Chromium (Cr^{3+})	Trivalent

Some metals show **variable valency** since in these metals the electrons of penultimate shell can also participate in the bond formation.

Example: Iron loses two electrons from its valence shell to form Fe^{2+} and loses one more electron from penultimate shell to form Fe^{3+}. Thus, iron exhibits variable valency.

Naming of Metallic Ions that Exhibit Variable Valency

Some metallic elements show variable valency (more than one valency) and form positive ions with different charges. In that case, the ion with lower charge gets **'ous'** suffix and the ion with higher charge gets **'ic'** suffix or the value of charge of an ion is shown by Roman numerals (such as I, II, III, IV, etc.) in parentheses, which is followed by the name of the metal.

Table 2.6 A list of negative ions or radicals and their charges

NEGATIVE IONS OR RADICALS	
Ion/Radical	**Valency**
Hydride (H^-)	Monovalent
Hydroxide (OH^-)	Monovalent
Bisulphite or Hydrogen sulphite (HSO_3^-)	Monovalent
Bisulphate or Hydrogen sulphate (HSO_4^-)	Monovalent
Fluoride (F^-)	Monovalent
Chloride (Cl^-)	Monovalent
Bromide (Br^-)	Monovalent
Iodide (I^-)	Monovalent
Hypochlorite (ClO^-)	Monovalent
Chlorite (ClO_2^-)	Monovalent
Chlorate (ClO_3^-)	Monovalent
Perchlorate (ClO_4^-)	Monovalent
Bicarbonate or Hydrogen carbonate (HCO_3^-)	Monovalent
Dihydrogen phosphate ($H_2PO_4^-$)	Monovalent
Permanganate (MnO_4^-)	Monovalent
Nitrate (NO_3^-)	Monovalent
Nitrite (NO_2^-)	Monovalent
Chromate (CrO_4^{2-})	Divalent
Oxide (O^{2-})	Divalent
Peroxide (O_2^{2-})	Divalent
Silicate (SiO_3^{2-})	Divalent
Sulphide (S^{2-})	Divalent
Sulphite (SO_3^{2-})	Divalent
Sulphate (SO_4^{2-})	Divalent
Zincate (ZnO_2^{2-})	Divalent
Biphosphate (HPO_4^{2-})	Divalent
Carbonate (CO_3^{2-})	Divalent
Dichromate ($Cr_2O_7^{2-}$)	Divalent
Phosphate (PO_4^{3-})	Trivalent
Phosphide (P^{3-})	Trivalent
Nitride (N^{3-})	Trivalent
Carbide (C^{4-})	Tetravalent

Examples:

Element	Cation	Names
Copper	Cu^+ Cu^{2+}	Cuprous or Copper (I) Cupric or Copper (II)
Iron	Fe^{2+} Fe^{3+}	Ferrous or Iron (II) Ferric or Iron (III)
Tin	Sn^{2+} Sn^{4+}	Stannous or Tin (II) Stannic or Tin (IV)
Mercury	Hg^+ Hg^{2+}	Mercurous or Mercury (I) Mercuric or Mercury (II)
Lead	Pb^{2+} Pb^{4+}	Plumbous or Lead (II) Plumbic or Lead (IV)

Derivation of Formulae of Compounds

Two basic principles are followed in writing the formulae of the compounds. Firstly, the electropositive element or positive radical is written first followed by the electronegative element or negative radical. Secondly, the total charge on the positive radicals should be balanced by the total charge on the negative radicals, since a molecule is electrically neutral.

Example	K^+ Cl^-	Fe^{3+} O^{2-}	Si^{4+} O^{2-}	Ca^{2+} NO_3^-	Fe^{2+} O^{2-}
	1 1	3 2	4 2	2 1	
			2 1		
	1 1	2 3	1 2	1 2	2 2
Formula	KCl	Fe_2O_3	SiO_2	$Ca(NO_3)_2$	FeO

EXAMPLE 2.1

Write the formulae in the following table.

Cation	Anion	Formula of the compound
Ca^{2+}	CO_3^{2-}	?
Fe^{2+}	NO_3^-	?
Al^{3+}	O^{2-}	?
Li^+	SO_3^{2-}	?
Ba^{2+}	OH^-	?

SOLUTION

Cation	Anion	Formula of the compound
Ca^{2+}	CO_3^{2-}	$CaCO_3$
Fe^{2+}	NO_3^-	$Fe(NO_3)_2$
Al^{3+}	O^{2-}	Al_2O_3
Li^+	SO_3^{2-}	Li_2SO_3
Ba^{2+}	OH^-	$Ba(OH)_2$

Naming of Inorganic Compounds

Inorganic compounds are basically classified into three categories namely acids, bases, and salts. Naming of the respective categories follows certain rules.

1. **Naming of Acids:** Acids contain hydrogen ion (H^+) as the positive radical. Hence, the name of the acid depends on the constituent(s) of its negative radical.

Type of Acid	Type of negative radical	Suffix
Binary acid	Negative radical consists of a single non-metal *Examples:* HCl, HBr	'ic' (prefix hydro) Hydrochloric acid, hydrobromic acid
Oxyacid	Negative radical consists of a non-metal and oxygen. The name of the oxyacid depends on the percentage of the oxygen associated with a specific non-metal. • Acids with comparatively less percentage of oxygen. *Examples:* H_2SO_3, HNO_2, H_3PO_3	 'ous' sulphurous acid, nitrous acid, phosphorous acid
	• Acids with comparatively more percentage of oxygen. *Examples:* H_2SO_4, HNO_3, H_3PO_4	'ic' sulphuric acid, nitric acid phosphoric acid

If the acid contains lesser number of oxygen atoms than the corresponding 'ous' acid, 'hypo' prefix is given to the negative radical whereas 'per' prefix is given to the negative radical when the acid contains greater number of oxygen atoms than the corresponding 'ic' acid.

Examples:		
	Hypochlorous acid	$HClO$
	Chlorous acid	$HClO_2$
	Chloric acid	$HClO_3$
	Perchloric acid	$HClO_4$

If a non-metal forms only one oxyacid, it is named as 'ic' acid

Example: Carbonic acid H_2CO_3

2. **Naming of Bases:** Bases contain hydroxyl radical (OH^-) as the negative radical and a metal ion as its positive radical. While writing the name of the base, the name of the metal is written first followed by hydroxide.

Examples:		
	$Ca(OH)_2$	Calcium hydroxide
	$Mg(OH)_2$	Magnesium hydroxide
	$NaOH$	Sodium hydroxide
	$Al(OH)_3$	Aluminium hydroxide

3. **Naming of Salts:** The positive radical present in the salt comes from the corresponding base and the negative radical comes from the corresponding acid.

Name of the salt starts with the name of the metal present as positive radical which is followed by the name of the negative radical. Name of the negative radical depends on the name of the acid from which the salt is produced.

Acid from which the salt is produced	Suffix and name of the salt		
'ous' acid	'ite'		
Examples: Sulphurous acid (H_2SO_3)	$CaSO_3$	→	Calcium sulphite
Nitrous acid (HNO_2)	$Zn(NO_2)_2$	→	Zinc nitrite
'ic' acid	'ate'		
Examples: Sulphuric acid (H_2SO_4)	$ZnSO_4$	→	Zinc sulphate
Nitric acid (HNO_3)	$NaNO_3$	→	Sodium nitrate
Phosphoric acid (H_3PO_4)	$AlPO_4$	→	Aluminium phosphate

If NH_4^+ is present as positive radical in the base or in the salt, ammonium is written in place of the name of the metal.

Example: Ammonium hydroxide (base) → NH_4OH
Ammonium phosphate (salt) → $(NH_4)_3PO_4$

EXAMPLE 2.2

A salt is formed due to the reaction between an oxy acid containing sulphur and a base containing a divalent metal of atomic mass y. The number of oxygen atoms in one molecule of the acid is one less than the corresponding 'ic' acid. Calculate the molecular mass of the salt.

SOLUTION

Let the metal be N.

The acid is sulphurous acid (H_2SO_3).

Therefore, the formula of the salt is $N_2(SO_3)_2$ and its molecular weight is 2y + 32 + 48 = 80 + 2y.

EXAMPLE 2.3

The formula of a metal sulphide is M_2S_3. Identify formulae of the

(a) metal hydroxide
(b) metal carbonate
(c) metal sulphate

SOLUTION

Since the formula of the metal sulphide is M_2S_3, the metal ion is M^{3+}.

(a) Formula of metal hydroxide is $M^{3+}(OH)^- \Rightarrow M(OH)_3$
(b) Formula of metal carbonate is $M^{3+}CO_3^{2-} \Rightarrow M_2(CO_3)_3$
(c) Formula of metal sulphate is $M^{3+}SO_4^{2-} \Rightarrow M_2(SO_4)_3$

EXAMPLE 2.4

Metal M forms two oxides A and B in which the ratios of number of oxygen atoms to the total number of atoms present in the molecule are 3 : 5 and 1 : 2, respectively. Determine the formulae of A and B.

SOLUTION

Metal ions present in A and B are $M^{a+}$and M^{b+}respectively,

∴ Formula of A is $M^{a+}O^{2-} \Rightarrow M_2O_a$

$$\therefore \text{Ratio} = \frac{a}{2+a} = \frac{3}{5}$$

$\Rightarrow 5a = 6 + 3a \Rightarrow 2a = 6 \Rightarrow a = 3$

∴ metal oxide A is $M^{3+}O^{2-} \Rightarrow M_2O_3$

Formula of B is $M^{b+}, O^{2-} \Rightarrow M_2O_b$

$\therefore$ Ratio $= \dfrac{b}{2+b} = \dfrac{1}{2}$

$\Rightarrow 2b = 2 + b \Rightarrow b = 2$

$\therefore$ metal oxide B is $M^{2+}, O^{2-} \Rightarrow MO$

Atomic Mass

At first, relative atomic mass of an element was determined by taking hydrogen as the standard. In hydrogen scale, relative atomic mass is defined as the number of times an atom of an element is heavier than one atom of hydrogen. Atomic mass of hydrogen is taken as one unit.

Relative Atomic Mass and Atomic Mass Unit

Subsequently, the mass of $\dfrac{1}{12}^{th}$ part of carbon –12 isotope is taken as the standard. The mass of the atoms of other elements are calculated with respect to the number of times an atom of an element is heavier than $\dfrac{1}{12}^{th}$ part of a carbon –12 isotope. This is called the **atomic mass** or **the relative atomic mass.** Since the mass of $\dfrac{1}{12}^{th}$ part of a carbon –12 isotope is called **atomic mass unit,** the relative atomic mass is expressed in amu. Nowadays, amu is named as 'dalton' or unified mass and designated as u. Value of amu is 1.624×10^{-24} g. This is also equal to the mass of one atom of hydrogen.

Gram Atomic Mass or Gram Atom

The relative atomic mass expressed in grams is called **gram atomic mass**. The amount of substance equal to gram atomic mass is called **gram atom.**

Example: Atomic mass of oxygen = 16 amu

Gram atomic mass of oxygen = 16 g

> **Konnect**
>
> The term 'Gram Atom' refers to the mass of an element that is numerically equal to its atomic mass but expressed in grams.

Molecular Mass or Relative Molecular Mass

Relative molecular mass also was first determined in hydrogen scale and later by taking carbon – 12 isotope as standard. **Molecular mass** is a number which indicates how many times, a molecule of a substance is heavier in comparison to $\dfrac{1}{12}^{th}$ part of a one carbon –12 isotope.

Gram Molecular Mass or Gram Molecule

Molecular mass expressed in grams is called **gram molecular mass.** The amount of substance equal to its gram molecular mass is called **gram molecule.**

Atomicity of an Element

The number of atoms present in the molecule of an element is called its **atomicity**. Based on the atomicity, the elements are classified into three types.

(i) Monoatomic Elements: The elements each of whose molecules contains only one atom.

Examples: Cu, Ag, and He

(ii) Diatomic Elements: The elements each of whose molecules contains two atoms.

Examples: H_2, O_2, and N_2

(iii) Polyatomic Elements: The elements each of whose molecules contain more than two atoms.

Examples: O_3, P_4, and S_8

Molecular mass of an element depends on the atomicity of the element.

Examples: (1) Atomic mass of sodium = 23 amu

Molecular mass of sodium = 23 amu

Gram molecular mass of sodium = 23 g

$\therefore$ 23 g of sodium = 1 gram atom or 1 gram molecule of sodium.

(2) Atomic mass of oxygen = 16 amu

Molecular mass of oxygen = 32 amu

Gram molecular mass of oxygen = 32 g

$\therefore$ 32 g of oxygen = 1 gram molecule of oxygen.

The molecular masses of the various compounds can be determined from their formulae by adding up the atomic masses of the constituent elements in one molecule.

Example: Calculation of molecular mass of calcium carbonate ($CaCO_3$).

Atomic mass of calcium = 40 amu

Atomic mass of carbon = 12 amu

Atomic mass of oxygen = 16 amu

$\therefore$ Molecular mass of calcium carbonate = $40 + 12 + (16 \times 3) = 100$ amu

Gram molecular mass of $CaCO_3$ = 100 g

$\therefore$ 100 g of $CaCO_3$ = 1 gram molecule of calcium carbonate.

Chemical Equations

All chemical reactions are represented by chemical equations. For example, calcium carbonate on heating produces calcium oxide and carbon dioxide.

The word equation can be written as calcium carbonate → calcium oxide + carbon dioxide.

The chemical equations are written by using symbols and formulae of the various substances involved in the reaction. The above reaction can be written as

$$CaCO_3 \rightarrow CaO + CO_2$$

Law of Conservation of Mass

All chemical reactions occurring in nature should comply with law of conservation of mass. The law states that the total mass of reactants taking part in a chemical reaction is equal to the total mass of products obtained. This law holds good only for chemical reactions and not for nuclear reactions.

For example, this law can be verified by taking any chemical reaction. The reaction of formation of white precipitate of silver chloride by the reaction of solution of silver nitrate and a solution of sodium chloride.

$$AgNO_3 + NaCl \rightarrow AgCl^{-} + NaNO_3$$

Experiment: A 'H'-shaped tube called Landolt's tube is taken. Sodium chloride solution is taken in one limb of the tube while silver nitrate solution is taken in another limb. Both the limbs are then sealed. The mass of the tube is measured, and the glass tube is inverted. The solutions in the two tubes come in contact with each other when they react to form a white precipitate of silver chloride. Now, the mass of the tube is measured again. The mass of the tube before the reaction is found to be same as the mass of the tube after the reaction.

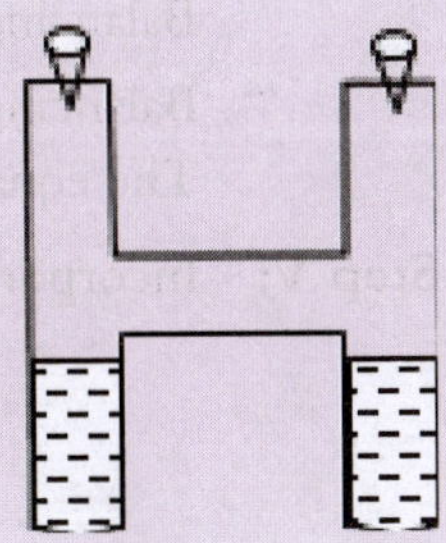

Example: Calcium carbonate decomposes to give calcium oxide and carbon dioxide. 100 g of calcium carbonate on heating produces 56 g of calcium oxide and 44 g of CO_2. The total mass of the products becomes equal to 100 g. Thus, it follows the law of conservation of mass.

Such an equation which depicts the same number of atoms of different elements on reactants and products side is called **balanced chemical equation.** Any chemical equation should be balanced with respect to the number of atoms of all the elements.

Example: $Mg + O_2 \rightarrow MgO$ is an unbalanced chemical equation. This is called **skeletal equation.**

Balancing of Chemical Equation

This is done by hit and trial method as the smallest whole number coefficient is used and its multiples are tried till the suitable number is obtained.

Step I: The number of atoms of different elements present in the reaction are counted. The number of atoms of reactants and products is written on left-hand side and right-hand side, respectively.

Step II: The balancing can be started with the compound containing maximum number of atoms or minimum number of atoms.

Step III: The various elements are balanced in the decreasing order of number of atoms in the first case and increasing order of number of atoms in the second case.

Step IV: Certain symbols will be incorporated in the balanced chemical equation in order to give additional information regarding the reaction. A two-sided arrow ($\rightleftharpoons$) indicates that the reaction is reversible. The physical states of the substances can be represented as s, l, and g in brackets for solid, liquid, and gas, respectively. The symbol (aq) represents aqueous solution.

Step V: The symbol D represents heating. Other conditions such as temperature, pressure, catalyst are written above the arrow($\rightarrow$). Upward arrow ($\uparrow$) indicates the gaseous product and downward arrow ($\downarrow$) indicates the substance in the form of precipitate.

Example: For both the methods skeleton equation is written and the number of atoms of various elements are listed.

Step I: Writing skeletal equation

$Fe_2O_3 + C \rightarrow Fe + CO$

Step II: Listing out number of atoms of various elements.

$Fe_2O_3 + C \rightarrow Fe + CO$

Reactant	Element	Product
2	Fe	1
1	C	1
3	O	1

Step III: Balancing based on maximum number of atoms

Balancing of oxygen $Fe_2O_3 + C \rightarrow Fe + 3CO$

Balancing of iron $Fe_2O_3 + C \rightarrow 2Fe + 3CO$

Balancing of carbon $Fe_2O_3 + 3C \rightarrow 2Fe + 3CO$

Or

Step IV: Balancing based on least number of atoms

Balancing of carbon $Fe_2O_3 + C \rightarrow Fe + CO$

Balancing of iron $Fe_2O_3 + C \rightarrow 2Fe + CO$

Balancing of oxygen $Fe_2O_3 + 3C \rightarrow 2Fe + 3CO$

The equation is perfectly balanced.

Step V: Incorporating physical states and reaction conditions

$$Fe_2O_3(s) + 3C(s) \xrightarrow{\Delta} 2Fe(s) + 3CO(g)$$

1. **Given the reaction:**
   a $C_2H_5OH(l)$ + b $O_2(g) \rightarrow$ c $CO_2(g)$ + d $H_2O(g)$,
   Find out a, b, c, and d, the coefficients of the reactants and the products.

   SOLUTION:
   $C_2H_5OH + 3O_2 \rightarrow 2CO_2 + 3H_2O$
   $\therefore$ a = 1, b = 3, c = 2, and d = 3.

2. **Given the reaction:**
   a $C_4H_{10}(g)$ + b $O_2(g) \rightarrow$ c $CO_2(g)$ + d $H_2O(g)$,
   Find out a, b, c, and d, the coefficients of the reactants and the products.

   SOLUTION:
   $2C_4H_{10} + 13O_2 \rightarrow 8CO_2 + 10H_2O$
   $\therefore$ a = 2, b = 13, c = 8, and d = 10.

EXAMPLE 2.5 In the reaction a $CO_2(aq)$ + b $H_2O \xrightarrow{Sunlight}$ c $C_6H_{12}O_6(aq)$ + d $O_2(aq)$.
Find out a, b, c, and d, the coefficients of the reactants and the products.

SOLUTION

$6CO_2 + 6H_2O \rightarrow C_6H_{12}O_6 + 6CO_2$

$\therefore$ a = 6, b = 6, c = 1 and d = 6

Equivalent Mass

Depending on the relative proportions of elements which can combine with or which can displace other elements, the concept of equivalent mass is developed.

The **equivalent mass** of an element is defined as the number of parts by mass of that element which can displace or combine with 1.008 parts by mass of hydrogen or 8 parts by mass of oxygen or 35.5 parts by mass of chlorine. Like molecular mass, equivalent mass has no units. Equivalent mass expressed in grams is called **gram equivalent mass.**

Relation Between Equivalent Mass and Atomic Mass

The valency of an element can be defined as the number of hydrogen atoms with which one atom of an element can combine to form a compound.

If an element 'X' having an atomic mass 'A' and a valency 'n' is considered, the formula of hydride of element is written as ^XH_n.

Atomic mass of X = A

Atomic mass of hydrogen = 1.008

'A' g of X combines with n × 1.008 g of hydrogen.

$\therefore$ 1.008 g of hydrogen combines with $\frac{A}{n}$ g

$$\therefore \text{Equivalent mass of element 'X'} = \frac{\text{Atomic mass of 'X'}}{\text{Valency}}$$

Examples: (1) For univalent elements, equivalent mass = Atomic mass
Equivalent mass of sodium = 23

Konnect

Equivalent mass is particularly useful in redox reactions, where different atoms and molecules can donate or accept varying numbers of electrons.

(2) Equivalent mass of magnesium $= \dfrac{24}{2} = 12$

The elements which show variable valency possess different equivalent masses.

Equivalent mass of copper in

cuprous oxide, $E_{Cu} = 63.5$

cupric oxide, $E_{Cu} = \dfrac{63.5}{2} = 31.75$

EXAMPLE 2.6 Molecular mass of sodium is same as its atomic mass, but, molecular mass of chlorine not same as its atomic mass. Give reason.

SOLUTION

Sodium is monoatomic element. Therefore, the atomic mass and molecular mass are equal. Chlorine is a diatomic element. Therefore, the molecular mass is double the atomic mass.

EXAMPLE 2.7 Identify unbalanced chemical equations from among the following and balance them.

(a) $6HNO_3 + S \rightarrow H_2SO_4 + 6NO_2 + 2H_2O$

(b) $K_2Cr_2O_7 + 6HCl \rightarrow 2KCl + CrCl_3 + 7H_2O + Cl_2$

(c) $2Ca_3(PO_4)_2 + 6SiO_2 + 2C \rightarrow 6CaSiO_3 + P_4 + 2CO$

(d) $2KMnO_4 + SO_2 + H_2O \rightarrow K_2SO_4 + MnSO_4 + H_2SO_4$

SOLUTION

Sodium is a monoatomic element. Therefore, the atomic mass and molecular mass are equal. Chlorine is a diatomic element. Therefore, the molecular mass is double the atomic mass.

The chemical equations b, c, d are not balanced.

(b) $K_2Cr_2O_7 + 14HCl \rightarrow 2KCl + 2CrCl_3 + 7H_2O + 3Cl_2$

(c) $2Ca_3(PO_4)_2 + 6SiO_2 + 10C \rightarrow 6CaSiO_3 + P_4 + 10CO$

(d) $2KMnO_4 + 5SO_2 + 2H_2O \rightarrow K_2SO_4 + 2MnSO_4 + 2H_2SO_4$

EXAMPLE 2.8 The halide of a divalent metal M on treatment with calcium hydroxide undergoes double displacement reaction. One of the products formed is heated to produce its corresponding oxide of molecular mass 40. Identify the element M and also give the necessary balanced chemical equations.

SOLUTION

Displacement reactions generally take place between the elements having same valency. Calcium in calcium hydroxide is divalent in nature. So, the metal is bivalent in nature.

$MX_2 + Ca(OH)_2 \rightarrow M(OH)_2 + CaX_2$

One of the products on heating gives its corresponding oxide.

$M(OH)_2 \xrightarrow{\Delta} MO + H_2O$

Given that molecular mass of oxide is 40.

$\therefore$ x + 16 = 40, x be the atomic mass of metal

$\therefore$ x = 24

$\therefore$ Metal is magnesium.

Laws of Chemical Combination and Types of Chemical Reactions

Each chemical reaction is fundamentally governed by the three laws of chemical combination.

They are law of **definite proportion, law of multiple proportion,** and **law of reciprocal proportion**.

During a chemical reaction, existing bonds break and new bonds are formed between atoms.

Law of Definite Proportions

The law of definite proportions states that a pure compound contains the various elements combined in definite proportions by weight irrespective of the method of preparation.

Example:

Carbon dioxide can be prepared by various methods such as:

1. burning of carbon
2. action of dilute acid on metal carbonate
3. heating of calcium carbonate or sodium bicarbonate

In all the above methods, the mass ratio of carbon and oxygen in carbon dioxide is 12 : 32 or 3 : 8.

EXAMPLE 2.9 1.2 g of zinc was converted into zinc oxide and 1.5 g of zinc oxide was obtained. In another experiment, 1.8 g of zinc oxide when heated with carbon gave 1.35 g of zinc. Show that these results illustrate the law of definite proportions.

SOLUTION

Experiment 1: Weight of zinc oxide = 1.5 g

Weight of zinc = 1.2 g

Weight of oxygen = 1.5 – 1.2 = 0.3 g

Ratio of the weights of zinc and oxygen = 1.2 : 0.3 = 4 : 1

Experiment 2: Weight of zinc oxide = 1.8 g

Weight of zinc = 1.35 g

Weight of oxygen = 1.8 – 1.35 = 0.45 g

Ratio of the weights of zinc and oxygen = 1.8 : 0.45 = 4 : 1

In both the experiments, the ratio of weights of zinc and oxygen is the same (4 : 1). Hence, it illustrates the law of definite proportions.

Law of Multiple Proportions

When two elements combine in different ratios to give more than one type of compound, the masses of the element that combines with a fixed weight of the other element always bear a simple integral ratio.

Example: Carbon can form carbon monoxide and carbon dioxide. The ratio of carbon and oxygen in CO and CO_2 are 12 : 16 and 12 : 32, respectively. The ratio of the weight of oxygen combining with fixed weight of carbon is 1 : 2.

Table 2.7 Oxides of Nitrogen

Name	Formula	Weight ratio of nitrogen and oxygen
Nitrous oxide	N_2O	28 : 16 = 7 : 4
Nitric oxide	NO	14 : 16 = 7 : 8
Nitrogen trioxide	N_2O_3	28 : 48 = 7 : 12
Nitrogen tetroxide	N_2O_4	28 : 64 = 7 : 16
Nitrogen pentoxide	N_2O_5	28 : 80 = 7 : 20

Konnect

The validity of the law is confined only in case of compounds in which the elements are in the same isotopic form.

EXAMPLE 2.10 Iron forms three oxides A, B, and C. The quantity of oxygen in each of the oxides A, B, and C are 28.57%, 42.85%, and 30.09%, respectively. Show that the law of multiple proportions is obeyed.

SOLUTION

As the percentage of oxygen is given, we can find the percentage of iron.

	A	B	C
Iron oxide	100.00	100.00	100.00
Oxygen	28.57	42.85	30.09
Iron	71.43	57.15	69.91

As iron forms different oxides, let us take a fixed weight of iron, say 10 g, and find out the weights of oxygen combining with 10 g iron in the three oxides.

In A, 71.43 g of iron combines with 28.57 g of oxygen.

In B, 57.15 g of iron combines with 42.84 g of oxygen.

In C, 69.91 g of iron combines with 30.09 g of oxygen.

$\Rightarrow \frac{28.57}{71.43} \times 10 : \frac{42.85}{57.15} \times 10 : \frac{30.09}{69.91} \times 10 \Rightarrow 1 : 2 : 1$ (approx) It is whole number ratio.

Law of Reciprocal Proportions

The law states that when two elements combine separately with a definite mass of another element, the ratio of the mass of the two combining elements is an integral multiple of the ratio in which they combine with each other.

Example:

In CH_4, 12 g of carbon combines with 4 g of hydrogen.

Therefore the ratio by mass of carbon to hydrogen = 12 : 4 = 3 : 1

Similarly in CO_2, the ratio by mass of carbon to oxygen = 12 : 32 = 3 : 8

Therefore, the ratio by mass of hydrogen to oxygen which combine with equal mass of carbon = 1 : 8

When hydrogen and oxygen react to form H_2O, the ratio in which they combine with each other = 2 : 16 = 1 : 8.

Types of Chemical Reactions

All the chemical reactions can be broadly classified into four types depending upon the nature of the reaction.

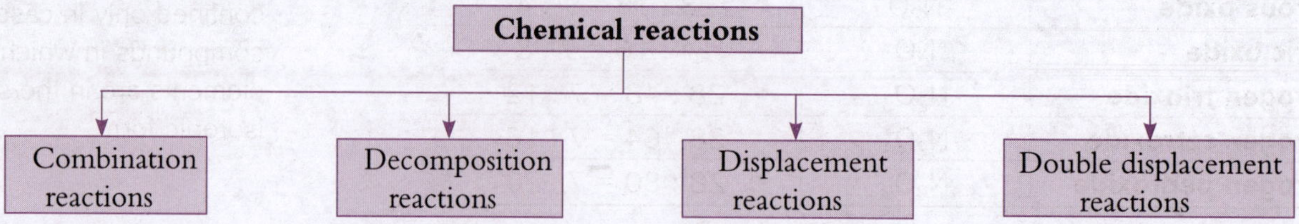

Combination Reactions

A chemical reaction in which two or more substances combine to form a single new substance is called a **combination reaction.**

Representation: A + B → AB

Examples:

(a) Element – element combination reaction. The formation of a compound from its constituent elements is called **synthesis**.

Example: $N_2(g) + 3H_2(g) \rightarrow 2NH_3(g)$

(b) Element – compound combination reaction.

Example: $2SO_2(g) + O_2(g) \rightarrow 2SO_3(g)$

(c) Compound – compound combination reaction.

Example: $NH_3(aq) + HCl(aq) \rightarrow NH_4Cl(s)$

$$\underset{\text{Quick lime}}{CaO(s)} + H_2O(l) \rightarrow \underset{\text{Slaked lime}}{Ca(OH)_2(aq)} + \text{heat}$$

Info Bytes!

The fastest chemical reactions can occur in picoseconds (10^{-12} seconds). One such reaction is the proton transfer during acid-base reactions

Decomposition Reactions

The reaction in which a single compound splits into two or more simpler substances is known as **decomposition reaction.**

Representation: AB → A + B

Examples: $2KNO_3(s) \xrightarrow{\text{Heat}} 2KNO_2(s) + O_2$

$$2FeSO_4(s) \xrightarrow{\text{Heat}} Fe_2O_3(s) + SO_2(g) + SO_3(g)$$

Types of Decomposition Reaction

- If the decomposition of the substance takes place by the absorption of heat, it is called **thermal decomposition**.

Examples: $2Pb(NO_3)_2(s) \xrightarrow{\Delta} 2PbO(s) + 4NO_2(g) + O_2(g)$

$$MgCO_3(s) \xrightarrow{\Delta} MgO(s) + CO_2(g)$$

$$CaCO_3(s) \xrightarrow{\text{Heat}} CaO(s) + CO_2(g)$$

CaO (quick lime) produced in the above reaction is made use of in the manufacture of cement.

- If the decomposition of a substance takes place in the presence of light, it is called **photolytic decomposition (photolysis)**.

Examples: $2AgCl(s) \xrightarrow{\text{Sunlight}} 2Ag(s) + Cl_2(g)$

$$2AgBr(s) \xrightarrow{\text{Sunlight}} 2Ag(s) + Br_2(g)$$

Info Bytes!

These reactions are used in the black and white photography.

- If the decomposition of the substance takes place by the passage of electricity, it is called **electrolytic decomposition (electrolysis)**.

Example: $MgCl_2 \xrightarrow[\text{current}]{\text{electrical}} Mg + Cl_2$

Electrolytic Decomposition of Water

A glass beaker with two holes at the centre of the bottom is taken. Two carbon rods are inserted into the two holes through rubber stoppers. These rods are connected to the opposite terminals of a battery which act as cathode and anode. Water containing few drops of dilute H_2SO_4 is taken in the beaker. Two test tubes filled with water are inverted over the two carbon electrodes. When current is passed through this water, water decomposes to give hydrogen and oxygen. This is indicated by the formation of bubbles in the test tubes. The gases can also be tested by keeping a burning splinter at the mouth of the test tubes after removing from the apparatus.

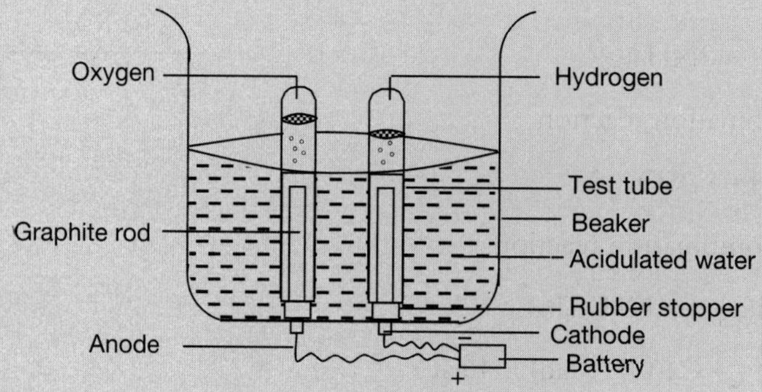

As the balanced equation corresponds to $2H_2O \rightarrow 2H_2 + O_2$, the volumes of hydrogen and oxygen formed will be in the ratio of 2 : 1.

Displacement Reaction

In a displacement reaction, the more reactive element displaces the less reactive element from its compound.

Representation: $AB + C \rightarrow CB + A$ Metal displacement reaction

$XY + Z \rightarrow XZ + Y$ Halogen displacement reaction

The ability of an element to displace another element is known by its relative position in the **reactivity series.**

Potassium	K	(Most reactive metal)
Sodium	Na	
Calcium	Ca	
Magnesium	Mg	
Aluminium	Al	
Zinc	Zn	Reactivity decreases ↓
Iron	Fe	
Nickel	Ni	
Tin	Sn	
Lead	Pb	
Hydrogen	H	
Copper	Cu	
Mercury	Hg	
Silver	Ag	
Gold	Au	
Platinum	Pt	(Least reactive metal)

Figure 2.1 Metal Reactivity Series

F_2	Reactivity decreases ↓
Cl_2	
Br_2	
I_2	

Figure 2.2 Halogen Reactivity Series

The more reactive metal displaces the less reactive metal from its compound in its aqueous solution.

Example: $Fe + CuSO_4 \rightarrow FeSO_4 + Cu$

Copper sulphate — Ferrous sulphate

As iron is more reactive than copper, it displaces copper from copper sulphate solution, thereby forming ferrous sulphate. In general, displacement reactions are exothermic in nature.

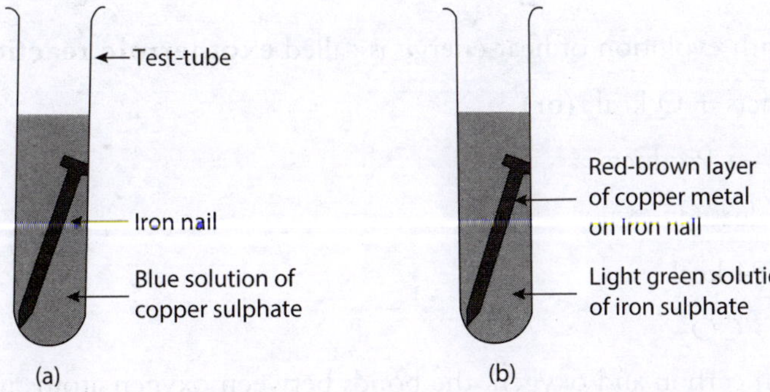

Figure 2.3 Displacement reaction between iron (nail) and copper sulphate solution

Halogen Reactivity Series

The more reactive halogen displaces the less reactive halogen from its compound.

Example: $2NaBr + Cl_2 \rightarrow 2NaCl + Br_2$

Chlorine is more reactive than bromine, hence it displaces bromine from sodium bromide, and reddish brown bromine gas is formed.

Double Decomposition/Double Displacement Reactions

The chemical reaction in which two reactants combine to form two new substances by mutual exchange of their radicals is called **double decomposition** or **double displacement reaction.**

$AB + CD \rightarrow AD + CB$

Examples: $2NaNO_3(aq) + CuSO_4(aq) \rightarrow Na_2SO_4(aq) + Cu(NO_3)_2(aq)$

$NaOH(aq) + HCl(aq) \rightarrow NaCl(aq) + H_2O(aq)$

$K_2SO_4(aq) + Cu(NO_3)_2(aq) \rightarrow 2KNO_3(aq) + CuSO_4(aq)$

If the reaction takes place between an acid and a base, it is called **neutralization reaction**. Salt and water are formed in this reaction.

Examples: $NaOH + HCl \rightarrow NaCl + H_2O$

$2NH_4OH + H_2SO_4 \rightarrow (NH_4)_2SO_4 + 2H_2O$

In a double decomposition reaction, if one of the products is insoluble, it is called precipitate and the reaction can be called **precipitation reaction**.

Photo Credit: Trevor Clifford. Pearson Education Ltd

Figure 2.4 Precipitation of $BaSO_4$ due to the addition of $BaCl_2$ solution to Na_2SO_4 solution

Examples: $KCl + AgNO_3 \rightarrow KNO_3 + AgCl \downarrow$

$BaCl_2 + Na_2SO_4 \rightarrow 2NaCl + BaSO_4 \downarrow$

The chemical reactions may be associated with release or absorption of energy. If the reaction involves release of energy, the reaction is said to be **exothermic reaction.** If the reaction involves absorption of energy, the reaction is said to be **endothermic reaction.**

Exothermic Reactions

A chemical reaction associated with evolution of heat energy is called **exothermic reaction.**

Reactants → Products + Q kcal **(or)**

Reactants – Q kcal → Products

Q = Heat energy released

Example: $C + O_2 \rightarrow CO_2 + 94$ kcal

$C + O_2 - 94$ kcal $\rightarrow CO_2$

For the formation of CO_2 from carbon and oxygen, the bonds between oxygen atoms in oxygen molecules should be broken. For the breaking of this bond, some amount of energy is absorbed. At the same time, some amount of energy is released during the formation of new bonds between carbon and oxygen.

If energy released is more than the energy required during the reaction, the difference in energy is released as heat energy.

Decomposition of vegetable matter into compost is also an exothermic reaction.

Respiration: The process of breaking down of glucose molecules into simpler molecules is also accompanied by release of heat energy.

$$C_6H_{12}O_6(aq) + 6O_2(aq) \rightarrow 6CO_2(g) + 12H_2O(l) + \text{energy.}$$

Endothermic Reactions

A chemical reaction which proceeds with the absorption of heat energy is called an **endothermic reaction.**

Representation: Reactants + Q kcal → Products **(or)**

Reactants → Products – Q kcal

Q = Heat energy absorbed

Examples: $N_2 + O_2 \rightarrow 2NO - 44$ kcal

$N_2 + O_2 + 44$ kcal $\rightarrow 2NO$

$C + 2S + 22$ kcal $\rightarrow CS_2$

For the formation of nitric oxide from nitrogen and oxygen, some amount of energy is required to break the bonds between nitrogen and oxygen atoms present in the respective molecules. Some amount of energy is released during the formation of bonds between nitrogen and oxygen. In this case, the energy absorbed is more than the energy released. Hence, the difference in energy is absorbed as heat energy during the reaction.

Most of the decomposition reactions are endothermic.

Oxidation and Reduction Reactions

In addition to the above categories, chemical reactions are categorized as redox reactions, as they involve both oxidation and reduction reactions.

Oxidation and reduction are an important class of reactions.

Oxidation	Reduction
Addition of oxygen or electronegative element to a substance. *Example:* $2Mg + O_2 \rightarrow 2MgO$	Removal of oxygen or electronegative element from a substance. *Example:* $2Hg_2O \xrightarrow{\Delta} 4Hg + O_2$
Removal of hydrogen or electropositive element from a substance or electrons from an element. *Example:* $H_2S + Cl_2 \rightarrow 2HCl + S$	Addition of hydrogen or electropositive element to a substance or electrons to an element *Example:* $H_2 + Cl_2 \xrightarrow{\text{Light}} 2HCl$

Oxidation and reduction are simultaneous processes since oxidation of a substance is accompanied by reduction of another substance. Hence, these reactions are said to be **redox reactions.** In a redox reaction, the substance which undergoes oxidation is called **reducing agent** and the substance which undergoes reduction is called **oxidizing agent.**

$$CuO + H_2 \xrightarrow{\Delta} Cu + H_2O$$

CuO is called oxidizing agent and hydrogen is called reducing agent.

Effects of Oxidation Reactions in Daily Life

Since the atmosphere contains large proportion of oxygen, certain substances spontaneously undergo oxidation. The most important effects of oxidation involve corrosion of metals and rancidification of oils. The most common example for corrosion of metals is rusting of iron.

Corrosion of Metals: When iron is exposed to atmosphere for a long time, iron reacts with atmospheric oxygen in the presence of moisture to form hydrated ferric oxide known as **rust** which appears as dark brown flakes. This process is known as **rusting of iron.** Since rusting leads to destruction of iron, the iron articles are coated with paint.

$$4Fe + 3O_2 + 2xH_2O \rightarrow 2Fe_2O_3.xH_2O$$

Other examples of corrosion include the formation of black coating on silver and green coating on copper. Thus, the change undergone by some metals on exposure to moisture, acids, etc., is called **corrosion.** Sulphur in the polluted air attacks silver thereby forming silver sulphide. Copper on exposure to CO_2 and moisture forms copper hydroxycarbonate. Corrosion causes damage to the articles made up of metals.

Photo Credit: A_Lesik. Shutterstock

Figure 2.5 Rusting of iron

Photo Credit: Jens Mayer. Shutterstock

Figure 2.6 Green patches on copper articles

Photo Credit: glevalex. 123rf.com

Figure 2.7 Silver coins turned black

Rancidity of Oils: Oils and fats, on exposure to atmospheric oxygen for a long time, get oxidized to form certain substances by which the smell and taste of oils changes and they become unfit for consumption. Addition of antioxidants (which prevents the oxidation of the substance) or keeping in air tight containers or in an atmosphere of nitrogen prevents rancidification of oils.

EXAMPLE 2.11 Calculate the ratio by mass of nitrogen that combines with fixed amount of oxygen during the formation of NO and N_2O_3.

SOLUTION

In NO: 14 g of N combines with 16 g of O

Hence, 1 g of O combines with $\frac{14 \times 1}{16} g$ of N = $\frac{7}{6}$ g of N

In N_2O_3: 28 g of N combines with 48 g of O

Hence, 1 g of O combines with $\frac{28 \times 1}{48}$ g of N = $\frac{7}{12}$ g of N

$\therefore$ The ratio by mass of nitrogen that combines with fixed amount of oxygen in NO and $N_2O_3 = \frac{7}{6} : \frac{7}{12} = 2 : 1$

EXAMPLE 2.12 Why is reduction essential for oxidation to take place?

SOLUTION

For an atom or element to undergo oxidation, it must lose electrons. These released electrons cannot exist independently, so they need to be accepted by another atom or element. The process in which an element gains electrons is termed as reduction. Therefore, whenever oxidation occurs, there must be another species present that will undergo reduction by accepting the electrons lost. In this way, reduction is essential for oxidation to take place, ensuring that the electrons being released are immediately consumed.

EXAMPLE 2.13 Nitric acid is colorless but on long standing it turns yellow. How do you account for the following?

SOLUTION

On longstanding, HNO_3 undergoes photolytic decomposition and gives NO_2, which is a brown colored gas. This gas along with HNO_3 appears yellow.

$$HNO_3 \xrightarrow{hv} 4NO_2 + 2H_2O + O_2$$

EXAMPLE 2.14 Four beakers are labeled as A, B, C, and D. A, B, and C are filled with water whereas D is filled with copper sulphate solution. Potassium sulphate, ammonium nitrate, anhydrous copper sulphate, and fine iron fillings are added to A, B, C, and D, respectively. The temperatures of the four beakers are measured before and after the addition of the substances. Identify the change in temperatures of the beakers and justify.

SOLUTION

The reactions that occur in A and B containers are endothermic and that in C and D are exothermic.

Reasons:

(i) Potassium sulphate is not readily soluble in water. So, it requires heat for dissolution. So, the temperature of the beaker decreases after the reaction.

(ii) Ammonium nitrate requires heat for dissolution. So, the temperature of beaker B decreases after the reaction.

(iii) Anhydrous salts dissolve in water with the liberation of heat. So, the temperature of beaker C increases after the reaction.

(iv) All displacement reactions take place with the evolution of heat energy. Since the reaction in beaker D is a displacement reaction, the temperature of the beaker increases after the reaction.

Solutions and Solubility

Most of the chemical reactions occur in solution state. Therefore, understanding basic concepts regarding solutions forms an integral part in the study of chemistry.

A **solution** is a homogeneous mixture of two or more substances. The proportion of the constituents of the solution can be varied within certain limits. The solutions comprising of two components are called **binary solutions.**

That component of a solution which is in the same physical state (that is solid, liquid, or gas) as the solution is called **solvent**, the other component which undergoes change in physical state when dissolved in a solvent is called the **solute.**

If both the components are in the same state, the component which is present in larger proportions is called **solvent** and the one which is present in minor proportions is called **solute**.

Classification of Solutions

Depending on the physical states of the solute and the solvent, solutions can be classified into various types.

Solvent	Solute	Example
Solid	solid	Alloys of metals
	liquid	Hydrated crystalline salts
	gas	Hydrogen gas adsorbed on platinum or palladium
Liquid	solid	Common salt in water
	liquid	Petrol in kerosene
	gas	Aerated water or soft drinks
Gas	gas	Air

When the solvent is a gas and the solute is a solid or a liquid, the resultant mixture becomes heterogeneous. These two types of mixtures being heterogeneous are called **suspensions**.

Examples: Fog, mist, dust particles in air.

All other solutions being homogeneous are called true solutions. .

The study of solutions is generally confined to the solutions of solid solute in liquid solvent.

In most of the cases, water is taken as the solvent since it can dissolve a wide range of chemical compounds. Those solutions in which water is taken as the solvent are called **aqueous solutions.**

Apart from water, other liquids can also be taken as solvents. Examples of such solvents are alcohol, petrol, ether, benzene etc. Those solutions in which a liquid other than water is taken as solvent are called **non-aqueous solutions.**

Saturated Solution: A solution which contains the maximum amount of solute that can be dissolved in the solvent at a given temperature is called **saturated solution** at that particular temperature. This solution can no longer dissolve any more solute under the given conditions.

Unsaturated Solution: The solution containing lesser amount of solute than the saturated solution at a given temperature is called an **unsaturated solution.** In an unsaturated solution, the solvent has the capacity of dissolving more amount of solute at that particular temperature.

Supersaturated Solution: If a solution holds more solute than the saturated solution at a given temperature, it is called a **supersaturated solution.**

When more solute is made to dissolve in a saturated solution by raising its temperature and then cooling it slowly without causing any disturbances (like shaking, scratching the wall of the container), then the resultant solution holds more solute than the saturated solution. Supersaturated solution is metastable and slight disturbances like shaking, stirring, scratching the wall of the container or adding a solute crystal to the solution make the additional amount of solute precipitate out, resulting in the formation of a saturated solution again.

Solubility

The process of dissolving a substance in a given solvent is called **dissolution.** The amount of solute dissolved in a definite quantity of a solvent depends upon the nature of the solute as well as the nature of the solvent.

The maximum amount of a solute in grams, which can dissolve in 100 g of a solvent at a given temperature is called **solubility.**

$$\text{Solubility} = \frac{\text{Mass of solute}}{\text{Mass of solvent}} \times 100$$

Example: Solubility of copper sulphate in water at 20°C is 20 × 7 and solubility of potassium chloride in water at 20°C is 34.

> **Info Bytes!**
>
> - At room temperature, around 357 grams of sugar can dissolve in 1 litre of water, making it one of the most soluble everyday substances.

EXAMPLE 2.15 25 g of a saturated solution of NaCl at 25°C when evaporated to dryness, leaves 5 g of solid. Calculate the solubility of NaCl.

SOLUTION

The mass of H_2O in solution = 25 – 5 = 20 g

20 g of H_2O dissolves in 5 g of a solid

100 g of H_2O will dissolve = $\frac{5}{20} \times 100 = 25\%$

∴ Solubility of NaCl in H_2O at 25°C is 25

Factors Affecting Solubility

1. **Nature of Solute:** Ionic compounds or polar compounds are more soluble in polar solvents like water. Non-polar compounds are more soluble in non-polar solvents like benzene.
2. **Nature of Solvent:** The solvents which have high dielectric constants can dissolve polar and ionic compounds to a greater extent than the solvents with low dielectric constants.

   Example: NaCl is highly soluble in water but sparingly soluble in benzene.
3. **Temperature:** For most of the substances, solubility increases with the increase in temperature. However, the solubility of some substances decreases with increase in temperature. In case of some substances, the temperature has no or little effect on the solubility.

Solubility Curves

The graphs which show variation of solubility with temperature are called **solubility curves.**

Importance of Solubility Curves

1. The solubility of a solute in a given solvent at a given temperature can be found out.
2. Solubilities of different solutes in a given solvent at a particular temperature can be compared.
3. It is possible to determine the amount of solute that can be precipitated by cooling the saturated solution of that solute to a certain temperature.

4. From the solubility curves, it is possible to know the preferential precipitation of different salts during the fractional crystallization process if the solution contains more than one salt dissolved in it.

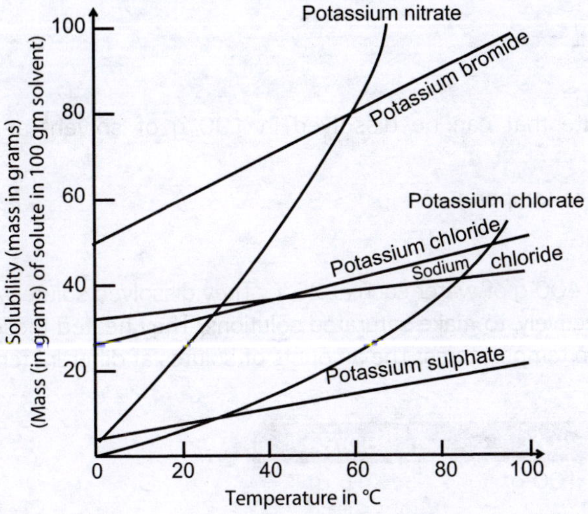

Variation of solubility of various solids with temperature

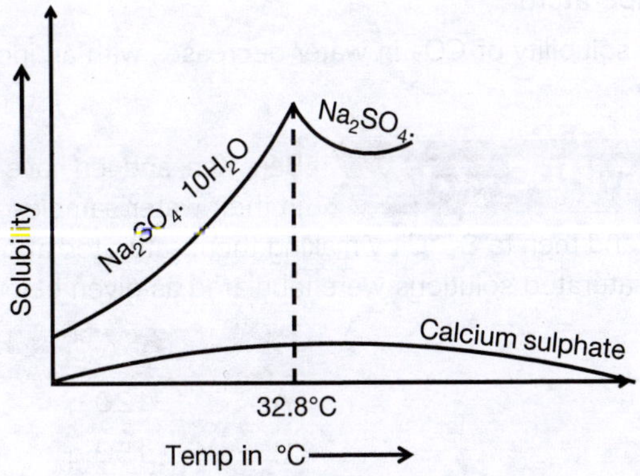

Solubility curves of $Na_2SO_4.10H_2O$ and $CaSO_4$

Figure 2.8 Solubility curves

Rate of Dissolution of a Solid in a Liquid

Though each solute has a certain fixed value of solubility, the rate at which a solute dissolves in a particular solvent depends on certain factors.

1. **Size of the Solute Particles:** The smaller the solute particles, the faster is the rate of dissolution. This is because division into smaller particles increases the surface area of contact between the solute and solvent particles. Greater area of contact increases the rate of dissolution.
2. **Agitation of Solution:** Agitation or stirring improves the contact between the solute and solvent molecules. Consequently, the rate of dissolution increases.
3. **Temperature:** Rate of dissolution of most of the solids increases with the increase in temperature because the solubility of the solid increases with the increase in temperature. However, in case of some solids, the rate of dissolution increases with the increase in temperature upto a certain point and decreases beyond a certain point.

   Example: $Na_2SO_4.10H_2O$ and $CaSO_4$

Factors Affecting the Solubility of Gases in a Liquid

The solubilities of gases in liquids show a different trend with regard to the effect of temperature. In these solutions, the solubility is also influenced by the pressure.

Effect of Temperature: With the increase in temperature, the solubility of a gas in a liquid decreases.

Effect of Pressure: The effect of pressure on the solubility of a gas in a liquid is given by **Henry's law,** which states that at constant temperature the increase in pressure on the surface of the liquid increases the solubility of the gas in the liquid.

Example: Soda water – Excess CO_2 remains dissolved in water at high pressure.

EXAMPLE 2.16 Correct the following sentences by the addition or deletion of an appropriate term in the given sentences.

(a) Solubility is defined as the maximum amount of the solute that can be dissolved in 100 grams of solvent.

(b) The solubility of CO_2 in water decreases with temperature.

SOLUTION

(a) Solubility is defined as the maximum amount of solute that can be dissolved in 100 g of solvent at a specific temperature.

(b) The solubility of CO_2 in water decreases with an increase in temperature.

EXAMPLE 2.17 Ben, Ken, and Jen have taken 400 g of water each at 20°C. They dissolved solutes A, B, and C in their water samples, respectively, to make saturated solutions. They heated these solutions to 40°C and then to 80°C by making them saturated at both the temperatures. The amounts of solutes at different temperatures in their saturated solutions were tabulated as given below.

	20°C	40°C	80°C
A	120 g	100 g	115 g
B	150 g	180 g	190 g
C	140 g	160 g	150 g

Their teacher asked them to cool the solutions of A, B, and C to 20°C again and observe the changes. Predict the changes observed by them at the given temperature. Give appropriate reasons.

SOLUTION

Sample A: When the solution is cooled from 80°C to 40°C solute forms a precipitate of 15 g and when it is cooled from 40°C to 20°C the solubility increases from 100 g to 120 g and the solution becomes unsaturated.

Sample B: When the solution is cooled from 80°C to 40°C, the solute forms a precipitate of 10 g and when cooled from 40°C to 20°C, solubility decreased from 180 g to 150 g forming 30 g precipitate.

Sample C: When the solution is cooled from 80°C to 40°C solubility increase from 150 g to 160 g forming unsaturated solution and from cooling from 40°C to 20°C solubility decreases from 160 g to 140 g forming 10 g precipitate.

EXAMPLE 2.18 Why does a soda bottle fizz upon opening?

SOLUTION

A soda bottle contains carbonated water, which means water in which carbon dioxide gas has been dissolved under pressure. When the bottle is sealed, the carbon dioxide is in equilibrium with the water, maintaining a high concentration due to the high pressure inside. According to Henry's Law, the solubility of a gas in a liquid is directly proportional to the pressure of the gas above the liquid. When the bottle is opened, the pressure inside drops rapidly. As a result, the solubility of the carbon dioxide decreases, and the excess gas comes out of the solution in the form of bubbles, leading to the characteristic fizz.

POINTS TO REMEMBER

- Chemistry has its own language in terms of symbols and formulae, which are shorthand notations of elements and compounds, respectively.
- While deriving the formula of a particular compound, one should keep in mind the following points:
  - (i) As a whole, the compound or molecule is neutral that means the total positive charge is equal to the total negative charge.
  - (ii) Metal should take the first place followed by a non-metal.
  - (iii) When both are nonmetals, less electronegative element takes the first place followed by more electronegative element.
- The chemical changes are represented by a chemical equation which has to be balanced. While balancing a chemical equation, the number of atoms of all elements on either side of a reaction are balanced by keeping appropriate coefficients.
- The metals placed above hydrogen are more reactive and liberate hydrogen with acids. The metals which are placed below hydrogen are less reactive and do not liberate hydrogen from acids. Thus, more reactive metal displaces less reactive metal from its compound.
- An element which is said to be oxidized acts as a reducing agent while an element which is said to be reduced acts as an oxidizing agent.
- Any reaction which is accompanied by the loss of heat is called exothermic reaction and a reaction accompanied by absorption of heat is called endothermic reaction. In an exothermic reaction, the energy of products is less than the energy of reactants and it is vice versa for endothermic reaction. The formation of new bonds is associated with the release of energy and the breakage of bonds is associated with the absorption of energy.
- Solubility has a fixed value for a specific solute in a specific solvent at a specific temperature.
- For most of the solids, solubility increases with the increase in temperature (exceptions: Glauber salt ($Na_2SO_4 . 7H_2O$) and calcium sulphate). Therefore, the cooling of hot saturated solutions in most cases results in crystallization.
- By studying the solubility curves, it is possible to find out the amount of solute which crystallizes in a given temperature range.
- Solubility of gases in liquids shows a decreasing trend with the increase in temperature. Solubility of a gas in a liquid increase with the increase in pressure at a constant temperature.
- $\text{Atomic mass} = \dfrac{\text{Mass of one atom of an element}}{\text{Mass of } ^1/_{12}\text{th of carbon atom}}$
- Molecular mass = $\dfrac{\text{Mass of one molecule of an element of compound}}{\text{Mass of } ^1/_{12}\text{th of carobn atom}}$
- $\text{Equivalent mass} = \dfrac{\text{Atomic mass}}{\text{Valency}}$
- $\text{Solubility} = \dfrac{\text{Mass of solute}}{\text{Mass of solvent}} \times 100$

PRACTICE QUESTIONS CLASSROOM WING

Very Short Answer Type Questions

Direction for questions from 1 to 3:
State whether the following statements are true or false.

1. Decomposition of silver is a thermal decomposition reaction.
2. Alloys are solid-solid heterogeneous mixture.
3. The solubility of a gas in a liquid decreases with the increase in temperature.

Direction for questions from 4 to 25:
Fill in the blanks.

4. Chemistry is the branch of science where we deal with different types of________, ________, and ________.
5. The 118 elements discovered so far have been assigned unique ________.
6. A formula in chemistry represents the number of ________ of each element present in the ________.
7. When a metallic ion with a higher charge is named, it gets the suffix ________.
8. The naming of inorganic compounds can be classified into three categories: ________, ________, and ________.
9. The atomic mass of a hydrogen atom is ______.
10. The molecular mass of Na_2CO_3 is ________.
11. Equivalent mass of calcium in calcium carbonate is ________.
12. The reaction between Fe_2O_3 and carbon produces ______ and ______.
13. An unbalanced chemical equation is called a ________ equation.
14. Electrolysis of water is a ______ reaction.
15. The products obtained due to the reaction between K_2SO_4 and $Cu(NO_3)_2$ are ______ and ______.
16. If in a chemical reaction one of the products precipitates out from the solution, the reaction is called ______ reaction.
17. The precipitate formed during the reaction between KCl and $AgNO_3$ is ________.
18. The chemical reaction in which heat is released is called ________ reaction.
19. Reaction $\rightarrow$ Product – Q kcal. It is an ______ reaction.
20. Energy is ______ when nitrogen combines with oxygen to form NO.
21. In an aqueous solution, the solvent is _____.
22. A ______ is a homogeneous mixture of two or more substances.
23. The solution comprising of two components is called a ______ solution.
24. The process of dissolving a substance in the given solvent is called ________.
25. The graph which shows variation of solubility with ______ is called a solubility curve.

Direction for questions from 26 to 49:
For each of the questions, four choices have been provided. Select the correct alternative.

26. Which of the following is NOT a way in which an element's symbol is derived?
    (a) The initials of the name of the element.
    (b) Latin or Greek names.
    (c) The last letter of the element's name.
    (d) When two elements have the same initial letter, another letter is taken from the name.
27. The combining capacity of an atom is known as its:
    (a) Radical
    (b) Symbol
    (c) Valency
    (d) Ion
28. Which ion is formed by the gain of electrons?
    (a) Cation
    (b) Anion
    (c) Radical
    (d) Neutron

29. Which ion among the following is divalent?
(a) Chloride (Cl^-)
(b) Permanganate (MnO_4^-)
(c) Chromate (CrO_4^{2-})
(d) Nitrate (NO_3^-)

30. For the element Copper, which of the following corresponds to Copper (I)?
(a) Cuprous
(b) Cupric
(c Ferrous
(d) Ferric

31. Which of the following represents the formula of calcium hydroxide?
(a) CaOH
(b) $Ca(OH)_3$
(c) $Ca(OH)_2$
(d) $Ca_2(OH)$

32. Which of the following defines the valency of an element?
(a) The quantity of electrons in the atom.
(b) The number of hydrogen atoms with which one atom of the element can combine.
(c) The atomic mass of the element.
(d) The equivalent mass of the element.

33. The formula of hypochlorous acid is
(a) HClO (b) $HClO_2$
(c) $HClO_3$ (d) $HClO_4$

34. How many atoms are present in calcium biphosphate?
(a) 5 (b) 6
(c) 7 (d) 8

35. The number of nitrogen atoms present in one molecule of zinc nitrite is:
(a) 1 (b) 2
(c) 3 (d) 4

36. Mercurous oxide is:
(a) HgO (b) HgO_2
(c) Hg_2O (d) Hg_2O_2

37. How many ammonium radical(s) is/are present in one molecule of ammonium phosphate?
(a) 1 (b) 2
(c) 3 (d) 4

38. The molecular mass of potassium dihydrogen phosphate is:
(a) 136 (b) 140
(c) 152 (d) 135

39. The gram molecular mass of oxygen is:
(a) 16 g (b) 32 g
(c) 64 (d) 48 g

40. Equivalent mass of zinc is:
(a) 32.6 (b) 65.3
(c) 16.32 (d) 21.7

41. The gas produced on heating $CaCO_3$ is:
(a) O_2 (b) CO_2
(c) CO (d) O_3

42. In a balanced chemical equation, _____ are the same.
(a) the number of molecules of reactants and products
(b) the number of atoms of each constituent element of reactants and products
(c) the valences of the constituent ions of reactants and products
(d) All the above

43. $C + O_2 \rightarrow CO_2$
The above reactions is a __________ reaction.
(a) combination
(b) decomposition
(c) displacement
(d) double displacement

44. The ratio of the volumes of hydrogen to oxygen obtained during the electrolysis of water is:
(a) 1 : 2 (b) 2 : 1
(c) 3 : 2 (d) 2 : 3

45. The most reactive halogen is:
(a) F_2 (b) Cl_2
(c) Br_2 (d) I_2

46. Which of the following is not a solution?
(a) Sugar syrup (b) Air
(c) Alloy (d) Mixture of petrol in water

47. In soda water the solute is:
(a) a solid (b) a gas
(c) a liquid (d) water

48. Unsaturated solution
(a) can dissolve more solute
(b) cannot dissolve any more solute
(c) is not homogeneous
(d) becomes saturated on standing

49. An aqueous solution contains NaCl and sugar. It does not have the ability to dissolve any more solute. What kind of solution is it?
(a) Saturated solution
(b) Unsaturated solution
(c) Super saturated solution
(c) Binary solution

Direction for question 50:
Match the entries in Column A with the appropriate ones in Column B.

50.

	Column A		Column B
(i)	Thermal decomposition	(A)	Liberation of O_2 from KNO_3
(ii)	Exothermic	(B)	Formation of silver due to the reaction between copper and AgCl
(iii)	Endothermic	(C)	Reaction between $Ca(OH)_2$ + HCl
(iv)	Neutralization	(D)	Formation of CS_2 from carbon and sulphur
(v)	Displacement	(E)	Combustion

Direction for questions from 51 to 71:
Answer the following questions.

51. Define symbol.
52. Write the valencies of the following radicals:
(a) Phosphate (b) Zincate
(c) Biphosphate (d) Silicate
53. Among the following, identify the elements which show a variable valency.
Cu, Zn, Co, Fe, Sn, Pb, Ba, and Al
54. How are chemical changes represented in short form?
55. (a) Identify the diatomic molecule(s) from the following:
Hydrogen, Sulphur, Phosphorous, Chlorine, Ozone, Iodine.
(b) Identify the polyatomic molecules from the following.
Ozone, Phosphorus, Sulphur, Carbon, Zinc, Hydrogen, Neon
56. Define:
(a) relative atomic mass
(b) equivalent mass
(c) atomicity
(d) atomic mass unit
(e) gram atomic mass
57. What is the relation between equivalent mass and the atomic mass of an element?
58. State the law of conservation of mass with respect to a chemical reaction.
59. How do you indicate a gas in a balanced chemical equation?
60. What does the symbols '$\rightleftharpoons$' and 'Δ' indicate in a balanced chemical equation?
61. State the law of reciprocal proportion.
62. What is a synthesis reaction?
63. Formation of NH_4Cl from NH_3 and HCl is a synthesis reaction. Comment on the statement.
64. Name the most reactive and the least reactive metals.
65. Which halogen cannot replace any other halogen from their compounds?
66. Give two examples for a neutralization reaction.
67. Why do oils and fats become unfit for consumption if they are exposed to atmosphere for a long time?
68. Define:
(a) solvent
(b) solute.
(c) solubility.
69. Give examples for non-aqueous solvents.
70. Differentiate between a saturated and an unsaturated solution.
71. Mention three factors affecting the rate of dissolution.

Short Answer Type Questions

72. Why is the study of nomenclature important in the field of chemistry?
73. Explain the significance of symbols in chemistry.
74. Why do some metals show variable valency?
75. For each of the following reactions, identify the products formed and balance the equations.

(a) $C_4H_{10} + O_2 \rightarrow$ (b) $Na_2CO_3 + HCl \rightarrow$
(c) $Zn + HCl \rightarrow$ (d) $Ca(OH)_2 + H_2CO_3 \rightarrow$
(e) $AgNO_3 + Cu \rightarrow$

76. Complete the following reactions and then balance.

(a) lead nitrate + potassium iodide → ______ + ______

(b) Barium chloride(aq) + sodium sulphate (aq) → ______ + ______

77. Classify the following reactions into combination, displacement, decomposition, and double displacement.

(a) $NH_4Cl \rightarrow NH_3 + HCl$

(b) $2NO + O_2 \rightarrow 2NO_2$

(c) $ZnCO_3 \rightarrow ZnO + CO_2$

(d) $Ag_2SO_4 + 2Fe \rightarrow 2Ag + Fe_2(SO_4)_3$

(e) $2NH_3 \rightarrow N_2 + 3H_2$

(f) $AgNO_3 + HCl \rightarrow AgCl + HNO_3$

(g) $2SO_2 + O_2 \rightarrow 2SO_3$

78. $Zn + CuSO_4 \rightarrow ZnSO_4 + Cu^-$

$Cu + 2AgNO_3 \rightarrow Cu(NO_3)_2 + Ag^-$

$Zn + FeSO_4 \rightarrow ZnSO_4 + Fe^-$

$Cu + FeSO_4 \rightarrow$ No reaction

(a) Arrange Zn, Cu, Fe, Ag in the order of their increasing reactivity. Give reason.

(b) Mention the type of reactions.

79. (a) What do you mean by exothermic reactions?

(b) What do you mean by endothermic reactions?

(c) Give one example for each of the two reactions given above.

Essay Answer Type Questions

80. Describe different types of chemical reactions with examples.

81. Define solubility and explain the factors affecting the solubility.

82. Discuss the importance and methods of representation of chemical changes in the language of chemistry.

83. Describe the method and rules followed in naming inorganic compounds, citing appropriate examples.

PRACTICE QUESTIONS COMPETITION WING

Level 1: Apply your Concepts

Direction for questions from 1 to 5:
State whether the following statements are true or false.

1. Sulphate radical is a dipositive radical.
2. The formula of chloric acid is $HClO_3$.
3. Phosphorus is a triatomic element.
4. Equivalent mass of magnesium is 24.
5. Slaking of lime is a compound-compound combination reaction.

Direction for questions from 6 to 23:
Answer the following questions.

6. The formula of a metal carbonate is MCO_3. Determine the formula of its (a) chloride and (b) nitride.
7. Explain the difference between gram atomic mass and gram molecular mass.
8. What does the 'ous' and 'ic' suffix indicate in the naming of metallic ions?
9. Why is a molecule considered electrically neutral when writing the formulae of compounds?
10. Explain the difference between equivalent mass and gram equivalent mass.
11. If a magnesium ribbon undergoes combustion, it gains weight. Does this phenomenon violate the law of conservation of mass?
12. Determine the coefficient of HCl when it reacts with one molecule of $K_2Cr_2O_7$. Two metallic chlorides, chlorine gas and water are obtained in this reaction.
13. Write the balanced chemical equation for the following:
    (a) The liberation of nitrous oxide by the reaction between zinc and nitric acid. Other products are water and a metallic nitrate.
    (b) The liberation of hydrogen gas and the solid metallic nitrate due to the reaction between manganese and very dilute nitric acid.
14. Verify the law of multiple proportions in the case of oxides of nitrogen.
15. A pair of gases can be formed from $Cu(NO_3)_2$. What kind of reaction is it? CuO can be obtained from both $Cu(NO_3)_2$ and $CuCO_3$. Which law can be verified by the given observation?
16. What kind of reaction is slaking of lime?
17. $A + BX \rightarrow AX + B$
    $B + CX \rightarrow$ No reaction.
    $C + DX \rightarrow$ No reaction.
    $C + AX \rightarrow CX + A$
    Identify the least reactive metal among A, B, C, and D and give reason.
18. Name the type of reactions involved in black and white photography.
19. In the presence of light, nitric acid turns yellowish. Give reason.
20. What kind of reaction is rusting of iron? Explain.
21. Identify the oxidizing and reducing agents in the following reaction.
    $H_2S + Cl_2 \rightarrow HCl + S$
22. Effect of pressure on the dissolution of a gas in liquid is observed while opening a sealed bottle of aerated drink. Explain.
23. Freshly prepared distilled water is devoid of O_2. From this observation, what inference can you draw regarding the effect of temperature on the dissolution of a gas in a liquid?

Level 2: Review your Concepts

24. What is the significance of the law of definite proportions?
25. Describe an exothermic reaction with an example.
26. Why are solubility curves important?
27. A salt X, on heating releases CO_2 gas. If one molecule of this salt reacts with 2 molecules of HCl(acid), calculate

the number of metal atoms present in one molecule of X and determine the formula of X.

28. One molecule of an oxyacid of sulphur has 3 oxygen atoms. When it reacts with two molecules of KOH, a salt is formed. Calculate the total number of atoms present in 5 molecules of this salt and the number of atoms of each of the constituent elements.

29. The relative molecular mass of an element is x a.m.u. if its atomicity is 3, find out the mass of 5 atoms of the element in grams.

30. x grams of a metal react with 32 g of oxygen and the atomic weight of the metal is 0.5x. Calculate the valency of the metal.

31. A salt contains calcium and a negative radical containing nitrogen. If three molecules of the salt contain 18 atoms of oxygen, identify the acid and base from which it is produced.

32. The equivalent mass of an element A is x. x grams of A react with y grams of another element B. If the valency of B in the product is 2, what is the atomic mass of B?

33. Find the number of phosphine molecules formed when 5 molecules of Ca_3P_2 reacts with water. Slaked lime is another product.

34. One molecule of calcium phosphate reacts with silica and coke and gives rise to calcium silicate, phosphorus and carbon monoxide. Calculate the mass of carbon monoxide obtained.

35. Why are combination reactions generally exothermic?

36. Why are halides of silver stored in dark colored bottles?

37. An element X reacts with a substance and another element is obtained as one of the products. What type of a chemical reaction is it with respect to its nature?

38. Silver articles gain weight in polluted atmosphere having H_2S. Give reason.

39. When ferrous sulphate undergoes thermal decomposition:

(A) O_2 is obtained as one of the products.

(B) both the oxides of sulphur are evolved.

(C) a salt containing a sulphide radical is produced.

(D) higher oxide of iron is formed.

(E) the valency of iron changes form 2 to 3

40. Solubility of a salt in water is 22 at 25°C. Calculate the amount of the salt required to saturate 500 g water at 25°C.

41. Calculate the solubility of the solute, if x g of solute is present in y g of saturated solution at a given temperature.

42. The solubility of a solute is 35 at 60°C and 25 to 30°C. If 200 g of solvent is made to saturate with the solute at 60°C, what is the amount of precipitate formed at 30°C?

43.

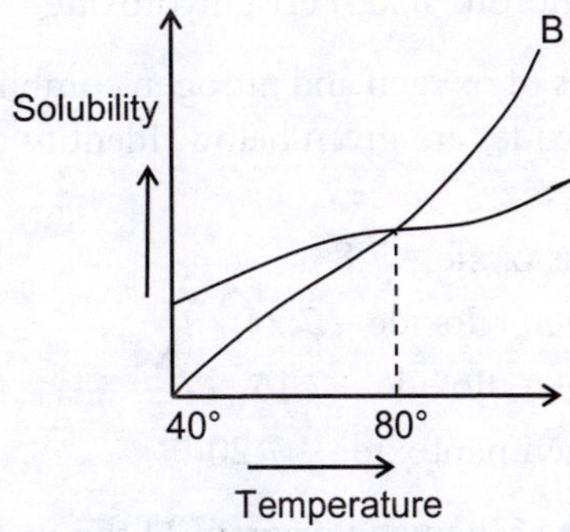

Observe the given curves. Saturated solutions of A and B are cooled from 80°C to 40°. Which of the above curves is associated with the formation of more amount of precipitate?

Level 3 : Assess Your Concepts

44. Elaborate on the types of chemical reactions, citing examples for each.

45. Discuss the factors that affect the solubility of a substance in a solvent.

46. Assume that the solubilities of KCl and KNO_3 are the same at a given temperature. A saturated solution of KCl is taken at that temperature and solid $AgNO_3$ is added to it. The amount of $AgNO_3$ added is such that all the Cl^- ions present in the solution get precipitated as AgCl. What will be the state of the solution in terms of saturation?

47. Dissolution of a solid X in water is exothermic. How does its solubility change with temperature?

48. The percentage of oxygen in air is about 21%. But the oxygen cylinder meant to be carried by deep sea divers contains about 4% oxygen. Why is there a difference in the percentage of oxygen?

49. CO_2 gas is passed through water under pressure. What type of reaction is it with respect to the nature of the reaction?

PRACTICE QUESTIONS JEE-NEET SPECIAL WING

Multiple-Answer Type Questions

Directions for Questions number 1 to 5:
Select one or more correct alternative(s) from the given choices.

1. Identify the compounds in which the total positive charge and the negative charge would be equal to 6 units.
   (a) Magnesium phosphate (b) Aluminium carbonate
   (c) Ferric chromate (d) Barium nitride
2. In a neutralisation reaction, 3 molecules of acid are neutralised by 2 molecules of base. Identify the set (s) of acids and bases which comply with the above neutralisation reaction.
   (a) Phosphoric acid; Calcium hydroxide
   (b) Carbonic acid; Ferric hydroxide
   (c) Chromic acid; Aluminium hydroxide
   (d) Phosphorous acid; Ferric hydroxide
3. The masses of oxygen and nitrogen combining to form different oxides are given below. Identify the correctly matched sets.
   (a) Nitrous oxide – 7:8
   (b) Nitrogen trioxide – 7:24
   (c) Nitrogen dioxide – 7:16
   (d) Nitrogen pentoxide – 7:20
4. Observe the schematic diagram of the metal reactivity series. Identify the options with correct probable sets of metals.

(a)	A- K	I-Pb	N-Pt	J-Cu
(b)	B-Na	M-Au	H-Sn	K-Hg
(c)	L-Ag	C-K	J-Fe	D-Mg
(d)	C-Ca	E-Zn	N-Cu	I-Ag

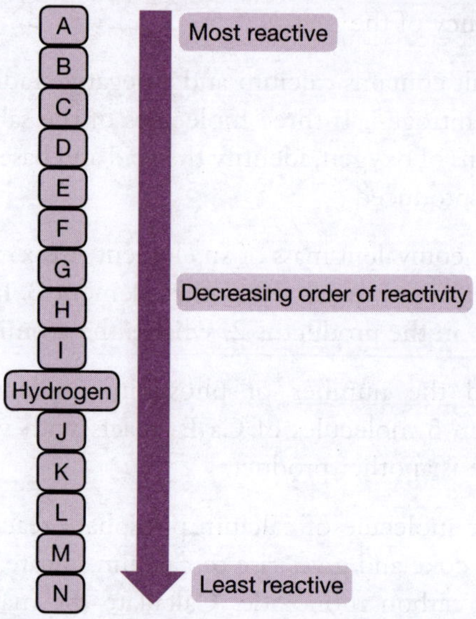

5. Which of the following sets of compounds can be used to illustrate the law of reciprocal proportions?
   (a) NH_3; NCl_3; HCl (b) SO_2; SO_3; H_2S
   (c) CO_2; SO_2; CS_2 (d) H_2S; SO_2; H_2O

Comprehension-Based Questions

Directions for questions 6 to 10
Read the content given in the following passage and answer the questions given below.

One gram atom of metal 'M' reacts with 16 g of oxygen to form an oxide. The gram atomic mass of the metal is '*x*'g. The stable ion of this metal forms compounds with various oxyacids of chlorine-A;B;C;D. The oxyacids A, B, C, D are in the decreasing order of percentage of oxygen. The salts formed can be represented as P;Q;R;S respectively.

6. Calculate the approximate percentage of chlorine in the compound 'S' if the metal taken is considered to be the constituent of limestone.
   (a) 67% (b) 50%
   (c) 30% (d) 35%
7. Identify the total number of atoms present in a molecule of 'Q'.
   (a) 11 (b) 6
   (c) 9 (d) 5
8. The ratio of mass of oxygen between two of the salts is 2:3. Identify the set of oxides among the following.
   (a) S and Q (b) Q and P
   (c) S and R (d) R and P

9. Consider that the equivalent mass of the metal is 12. What would be the gram molecular mass of the salt 'R'?

(a) 190 (b) 107.5
(c) 91.5 (d) 159

10. Predict the coefficients of the reactants and the products in the balanced chemical equation for the reaction of thermal decomposition of the compound 'Q'.

(a) 1; 1; 2 (b) 2; 2; 3
(c) 1; 1; 3 (d) 2; 1; 3

Directions for questions 11 to 16:

Read the content given in the following passage and answer the questions given below.

Chemical reactions follow the various laws of chemical combination apart from the law of conservation of mass.

The law of definite proportions states that the ratio of mass of combining elements will be same irrespective of the method of preparation of the compound.

Illustration

Method 1: $C + O_2 = CO_2$

Ratio of mass of carbon and oxygen = 12:32 = 3:8

Method 2: $CaCO_3 \rightarrow CaO + CO_2$

Ratio of mass of carbon and oxygen = 12:32 = 3:8

The law of multiple proportions

When two elements combine to form two or more compounds, the weights of one of the elements which combine with a fixed weight of the other, bear a simple whole number ratio.

Illustration

Formation of water and hydrogen peroxide

Water: Mass ratio of hydrogen and oxygen 2:16 or 1:8.

Hydrogen peroxide : Mass ratio of hydrogen and oxygen 2:32 or 1:16.

Ratio of mass of oxygen combining with fixed mass of hydrogen = 16:32 = 1:2

The law of reciprocal proportions

When two different elements separately combine with the same weight of a third element, the ratio in which they combine will be the same or some simple multiple of the ratio in which the first two elements combine.

Illustration

Methane and Carbon dioxide

Methane - 4 g hydrogen combines with 12 g carbon.

CO_2 – 32 g oxygen combines with 12 g carbon.

CO – 16 g oxygen combines with 12 g carbon.

Ratio of hydrogen and oxygen combining with fixed mass of carbon = 4:16 or 4:32 =1:4 or 1:8

Compounds of hydrogen with oxygen – Water and Hydrogen peroxide

Ratio of hydrogen and oxygen in water = 2:16 or 1:8

Ratio of hydrogen and oxygen in H_2O_2 = 2:32 or 1:16

11. Which among the following sets of compounds illustrate the law of reciprocal proportions?

(a) N_2O; NO_2; N_2O_5 (b) SO_2; SO_3; H_2S
(c) N_2O_3; NH_3; H_2O (d) CuO; Cu_2O; CuS

12. 22 g of an oxide of a nonmetal contains 8 g of oxygen. The percentage of oxygen in other oxides of the same nonmetal are given below. Find out the mass ratio of the oxygen which combines with fixed mass of nonmetal.

Oxide	% of oxygen
X	53.3
Y	74
Z	69.6

(a) 4:10:5 (b) 2:5:4
(c) 2:10:3 (d) 4:5:2

13. Two elements X and Y have gram atomic masses equal to 31 g and 16 g respectively. 12.4 g of X combines with 9.6 g of Y. What would be the amount of Y which combines with the same amount of X in another binary compound of X and Y?

(a) 12.7 g (b) 4 g
(c) 16 g (d) 32 g

14. A metal forms two oxides X and Y in which the metal shows the valencies of 1 and 2 respectively. These two oxides on heating separately in a current of hydrogen form the metal. Identify the true statement(s) regarding the given activity.

(a) This activity proves the law of definite proportions.
(b) The mass of the metal produced will be in 2:1 ratio if same number of moles of X and Y are taken.
(c) The activity illustrates the law of multiple proportions.
(d) Both (b) and (c)

15. Identify the correct statement regarding the homologous series of saturated hydrocarbons (alkanes).

(a) The mass of hydrogen reacting with the same amount of carbon would be in simple numerical ratio for all the compounds in the series.
(b) In the first two members the mass ratio of hydrogen combining with fixed amount of carbon would be 2:3.
(c) The higher members of the series do not obey the law of multiple proportions.
(d) The formation of the compounds of this series violate all the laws of chemical combination.

16. Consider the following reactions. Assuming that these reactions take place to completion, identify the statements which does not comply with the given reactions.

Reaction A: Burning of magnesium ribbon which weighs 7.2 g

Reaction B: Strong heating of 78 g of magnesium sulphite (18 g)

Reaction C: Strong heating of 73 g magnesium bicarbonate

Reaction D: Strong heating of magnesium carbonate obtained in reaction C

(a) The amount of magnesium obtained in the product of reaction A is same as the product of reaction B and D.

(b) The products obtained in the reactions A, B and D have the same percentage of magnesium.

(c) All the reactions can illustrate the law of definite proportions.

(d) The amount of magnesium in the products of reactions A, B, C and D would be in the order D<B<A<C.

Directions for question 17:

Read the content given in the following passage and answer the question given below.

The following graph shows the solubilities of four solids A,B,C and D at different temperatures. The saturated solutions of all the solids are taken at 70ºC and are cooled slowly up to 10º C.

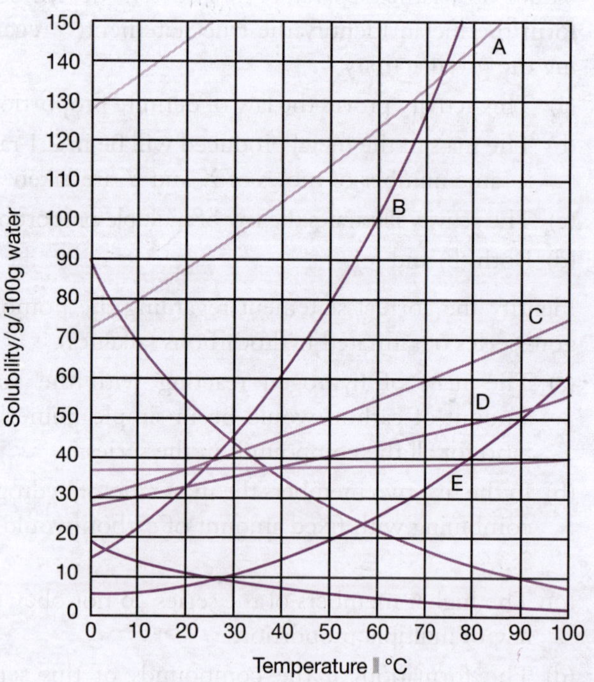

17. Based on the information given above, match the entries in column A with those in column B.

Column A Solids taken	Column B Amount of solid precipitated
(a) Solid A	(i) 32 g
(b) Solid B	(ii) 15 g
(c) Solid C	(iii) 27 g
(d) Solid D	(iv) 72 g
(e) Solid E	(v) 107 g

Directions for question 18:

Read the content given in the following passage and answer the question given below.

The various metals form binary compounds with oxygen. Some of the metals form more than one binary compound also. The binary compounds of metals with oxygen could be oxides or peroxides. The very highly active metals form peroxides in addition to the oxides. The metals which show variable valency form lower oxides as well as higher oxides. The formulae of these oxides depend on the valencies exhibited by the respective metals. Very few metals form mixed oxides also.

18. Based on the information given above, match the entries in column A with those in column B.

Column A Metal	Column B Formulae of binary compounds with oxygen
(a) Barium	(i) M_2O; M_2O_2
(b) Lead	(ii) MO; M_2O_3; M_3O_4
(c) Copper	(iii) MO; MO_2
(d) Sodium	(iv) M_2O; MO
(e) Iron	(v) MO; MO_2; M_3O_4

ANSWER KEYS

Crossword

Across

2. Photolysis 3. Nitric acid 4. Hydrargyrum 8. Precipitate 9. Oxide
10. Ammonium

Down

1. Electrolytic 6. Ide 5. Potassium 7. Greater

Classroom Wing

Very Short Answer Type Questions

1. False 2. False 3. True 4. elements, compounds, mixtures
5. symbols 6. atoms, molecule 7. 'ic' 8. acids, bases, salts 9. 1 amu
10. 106 11. Ca 12. Iron and CO 13. skeletal
14. electrolytic decomposition 15. KNO_3 and $CuSO_4$ 16. precipitation
17. AgCl 18. exothermic 19. endothermic 20. absorbed 21. water
22. solution 23. binary 24. dissolution 25. temperature 26. (c)
27. (c) 28. (b) 29. (c) 30. (a) 31. (c)
32. (b) 33. (a) 34. (c) 35. (b) 36. (c)
37. (c) 38. (a) 39. (b) 40. (a) 41. (b)
42. (b) 43. (a) 44. (b) 45. (a) 46. (d)
47. (b) 48. (a) 49. (a)
50. (i) : A, (ii) : E, (iii) : D, (iv) : C, (v) : B

Competition Wing

Level 1: Apply your Concepts

1. False 2. True 3. False 4. False 5. True
22. (c) 23. (b)

JEE-NEET Special Wing

Multiple-Answer Type Questions

1. (a; b; c; d) 2. (b; c; d) 3. (c; d) 4. (a; b) 5. (a; c; d)
6. (c)

Comprehension-Based Questions

7. (c) 8. (c; d) 9. (d) 10. (c) 11. (c)
12. (b) 13. (c) 14. (a) 15. (a) 16. (c)
17. (a) ↔ (iv), (b) ↔ (v), (c) ↔ (i), (d) ↔ (iii), (e) ↔ (ii)
18. (a) ↔ (iii), (b) ↔ (v), (c) ↔ (iv), (d) ↔ (i), (e) ↔ (ii)

Hints and Explanations

Classroom Wing

Very Short Answer Type Questions

1. Decomposition of silver is a photolytic decomposition reaction.
2. Alloys are solid-solid homogeneous mixture that is they are solid in solid solution.
3. The solubility of a gas in a liquid decreases with the increase in temperature.
4. elements, compounds, mixtures
5. symbols
6. atoms, molecule
7. 'ic'
8. acids, bases, salts
9. Atomic mass of a hydrogen atom is 1 amu.
10. Molecular mass of Na_2CO_3, is 106.
11. Equivalent mass of Ca $= \frac{40}{2} = 20$
12. The reaction between Fe_2O_3 and carbon produces iron and CO.
13. An unbalanced chemical equation is called a skeletal equation.
14. Electrolysis of water is an electrolytic decomposition reaction.
15. The products obtained due to the reaction between K_2SO_4 and $Cu(NO_3)_2$ are KNO_3 and $CuSO_4$
16. If in a chemical reaction, one of the products precipitates out, the reaction is called precipitation reaction.
17. The precipitate formed during the reaction between KCl and $AgNO_3$ is of AgCl.
18. The chemical reaction in which heat is released is called an exothermic reaction.
19. It is an endothermic reaction.
20. Energy is absorbed when nitrogen combines with oxygen to form NO.
21. In an aqueous solution, the solvent is water.
22. A solution is a homogeneous mixture of two or more substances.
23. The solution comprising of two components is called a binary solution.
24. The process of dissolving a substance in the given solvent is called dissolution.
25. The graph which shows variation of solubility with temperature is called a solubility curve.
26. (c). Element symbols are derived from the first letter of their name, Latin, German, or Greek names, or another letter from the name when two elements have the same initial letter.
27. (c). Valency refers to the combining capacity of an atom, indicating how many other atoms it can bond with.
28. (b). Anions are formed by the gain of electrons and are negatively charged.
29. (c). Among the given options, only Chromate (CrO_4^{2-}) has a valency of 2 or is divalent.
30. (a). Copper (I) refers to the ion Cu+ which is also named as Cuprous.
31. (c). Calcium hydroxide has a formula of $Ca(OH)_2$ where calcium is divalent.
32. (b). The valency of an element can be defined as the number of hydrogen atoms with which one atom of the element can combine to form a compound.
33. The formula of hypochlorous acid is HClO.

    Hence, the correct answer is (a).
34. Formula of calcium biphosphate is $CaHPO_4$, number of atoms = 7.

    Hence, the correct answer is (c).
35. The number of nitrogen atoms present in one molecule of zinc nitrite $Zn(NO_2)_2$, is 2.

    Hence, the correct answer is (b).
36. Mercurous oxide is Hg_2O.

    Hence, the correct answer is (c).

37. Ammonium phosphate $(NH_4)_3PO_4$ contains 3 ammonium radicals.

Hence, the correct answer is (c).

38. Molecular mass of $KH_2PO_4 = 39 + 2 + 31 + (16 \times 4)$

$= 39 + 2 + 31 + 64 = 136.$

Hence, the correct answer is (a).

39. Gram molecular mass of O_2 is 32 g.

Hence, the correct answer is (b).

40. Equivalent mass of zinc is $\frac{65.3}{2} = 32.6.$

Hence, the correct answer is (a).

41. The gas produced on heating $CaCO_3$ is CO_2.

Hence, the correct answer is (b).

42. In a balanced chemical equation the number of atoms of each constituent element is the same.

Hence, the correct answer is (b).

43. $C + O_2 \rightarrow CO_2$

The above reaction is a combination reaction.

Hence, the correct answer is (a).

44. The ratio of the volume of H_2 and O_2 produced during electrolysis is 2 : 1.

Hence, the correct answer is (b).

45. The most reactive halogen is fluorine.

Hence, the correct answer is (a).

46. Mixture of petrol in water is not a solution since it is not homogeneous. They are immiscible liquids.

Hence, the correct answer is (d).

47. In soda water, the solute is a gas.

Hence, the correct answer is (b).

48. Unsaturated solution can dissolve more solute in it.

Hence, the correct answer is (a).

49. The solution is a saturated solution.

Hence, the correct answer is (a).

50. (i) $\rightarrow$ A

(ii) $\rightarrow$ E

(iii) $\rightarrow$ D

(iv) $\rightarrow$ C

(v) $\rightarrow$ B

51. Symbols are the shorthand notations representating a single atom of an element.

52. (a) Valency of phosphate (PO_4^{-3}) is 3

(b) Valency of zincate (ZnO_2^{-2}) is 2

(c) Valency of biphosphate (HPO_4^{-2}) is 2

(d) Valency of silicate (SiO_3^{-2}) is 2

53. Among the given metals Cu, Fe, Sn, Pb and Co elements show variable valency.

54. Chemical changes are represented in short form in the form of chemical equations by using symbols and formulae.

55. (a) Hydrogen, chlorine, and iodine are diatomic molecules.

(b) Ozone, phosphorus and sulphur are poly atomic molecules.

56. (a) The mass of the atom of an element is calculated with respect to the number of times the atom of the element is heavier than $\frac{1}{12}^{th}$ part of a carbon 12 isotope. This is called relative atomic mass of the element.

(b) The equivalent mass of an element is defined as the number of parts by mass, of that element which can displace or combine with 1.008 parts by mass of hydrogen or 8 parts by mass of oxygen or 35.5 parts by mass of chlorine.

(c) The number of atoms present in the molecule of an element is called its atomicity.

(d) The mass of $\left(\frac{1}{12}\right)^{th}$ part of a C – 12 isotope is called atomic mass unit (amu).

(e) The relative atomic mass of an element expressed in grams is called gram atomic mass.

57. Equivalent mass of an element

$$= \frac{\text{Atomic mass of the element}}{\text{Valency}}$$

58. The law of conservation of mass states that the total mass of the reactants taking part in a chemical reaction is equal to the total mass of the products obtained.

59. A gas is indicated by an upward arrow (↑).

60. The symbol $\rightleftharpoons$ indicates that the reaction is reversible.

Symbol Δ represents heating.

61. The law of reciprocal proportion states that when two elements combine separately with a definite mass of another element, the ratio of the mass of the two combining elements is an integral multiple of the ratio in which they combine with each other.

62. The formation of a compound from its constituent elements is called synthesis.

63. No, the given reaction is not a synthesis reaction because in this reaction two compounds combine to form another compound.

64. The most reactive and the least reactive metals are potassium and platinum, respectively.

65. I_2 cannot replace any other halogens from their compounds.

66. Two examples of neutralization reaction are:

$NaOH + HCl \rightarrow NaCl + H_2O$

$2NH_4OH + H_2SO_4 \rightarrow (NH_4)_2SO_4 + 2H_2O$

67. Oils and fats, on exposure to atmospheric oxygen for a long time, get oxidized and become unfit for consumption.

68. (a) The component of a solution which is in the same physical state as the solution is called solvent. If both the components are in the same phase, the component which is present in larger proportion is called a solvent.

(b) The component of the solution which undergoes change in physical state is called a solute. If both the components are in the same phase, the component which is present in minor proportions is called a solute.

(c) The maximum amount of a particular solute in grams, which get dissolved in 100 g of the solvent at a given temperature is called solubility.

69. Alcohol, petrol, ether, benzene are examples for non-aqueous solvents.

70. A solution which contains the maximum amount of solute that can be dissolved in the solvent at a given temperature is called a saturated solution.

The solution that contains lesser amount of solute than the saturated solution at a given temperature, is called an unsaturated solution.

71. Factor affecting the rate of dissolution:

(i) Size of the solute particles

(ii) Agitation of solution

(iii) Temperature

Short Answer Type Questions

72. The study of nomenclature is important in chemistry because every chemical substance has a unique composition, and to communicate about these chemicals universally, a standardized naming system is essential.

73. Symbols in chemistry are shorthand notations representing individual atoms of an element. They offer a concise way to depict elements without writing out their full names, making chemical representations more efficient and universally recognized.

74. Some metals exhibit variable valency because, in these metals, electrons from the penultimate shell can also participate in bond formation, leading to the formation of multiple ions with different charges.

75. (a) $2C_4H_{10} + 13O_2 \rightarrow 8CO_2 + 10H_2O$

(b) $Na_2CO_3 + 2HCl \rightarrow 2NaCl + H_2O + CO_2$

(c) $Zn + 2HCl \rightarrow ZnCl_2 + H_2$

(d) $Ca(OH)_2 + H_2CO_3 \rightarrow CaCO_3 + 2H_2O$

(e) $2AgNO_3 + Cu \rightarrow Cu(NO_3)_2 + 2Ag$

76. (a) $Pb(NO_3)_2 + 2KI \rightarrow PbI_2 + 2KNO_3$

(b) $BaCl_2(aq) + Na_2SO_4(aq) \rightarrow BaSO_4{}^- + 2NaCl$

77. (a) Decomposition reaction

(b) Combination reaction

(c) Thermal decomposition reaction

(d) Displacement reaction

(e) Decomposition reaction

(f) Double displacement reaction

(g) Combination reaction

78. (a) Ag < Cu < Fe < Zn is the increasing order of their reactivity.

Reason: zinc replaces copper and iron from their salt solutions. So zinc is more reactive than copper and Fe. Copper replaces silver from $AgNO_3$. So Cu is more reactive than silver. between copper and iron, copper is less reactive because it cannot replace iron from $FeSO_4$ solution.

(b) All these reactions are displacement reactions.

79. (a) Exothermic reaction: Reactions which take place with the release of heat along with the formation of products are called exothermic reactions.

(b) Endothermic reaction: Reactions which take place with the absorption of heat along with the formation of products are called endothermic reactions.

(c) *Example:* Burning of natural gas is an exothermic reaction

$CH_4(g) + 2O_2(g) \rightarrow CO_2(g) + 2H_2O(g) + \text{energy}$

Decomposition of $CaCO_3$ is an endothermic reaction.

$CaCO_3(s) \rightarrow CaO(s) + CO_2(g)$

Essay Answer Type Questions

80. Different types of reactions are combination, decomposition, displacement, and double displacement reactions.

Combination reactions: A chemical reaction in which two or more substances combine to form a single new substance is called a combination reaction.

Representation: $A + B \rightarrow AB$

Examples:

(i) Element – element combination reaction. The formation of a compound from its constituent elements is called synthesis.

Example: $N_2(g) + 3H_2(g) \rightarrow 2NH_3(g)$

(ii) Element – compound combination reaction.

Example: $2SO_2(g) + O_2(g) \rightarrow 2SO_3(g)$

(iii) Compound – compound combination reaction.

Example: $NH_3(aq) + HCl(aq) \rightarrow NH_4Cl(s)$

Decomposition reactions: The reaction in which a single compound splits into two or more simpler substances is known as decomposition reaction.

Representation: $AB \rightarrow A + B$

Examples: (i) $2KNO_3(s) \xrightarrow{\text{Heat}} 2KNO_2(s) + O_2$

(ii) $2FeSO_4(s) \xrightarrow{\text{Heat}} Fe_2O_3(s) + SO_2(g) + SO_3(g)$

If the decomposition of the substance takes place by the absorption of heat, it is called thermal decomposition.

Examples: (i) $2Pb(NO_3)_2(s) \xrightarrow{\Delta} 2PbO(s) + 4NO_2(g) + O_2(g)$

(ii) $MgCO_3(s) \xrightarrow{\Delta} MgO(s) + CO_2(g)$

(iii) $CaCO_3(s) \xrightarrow{\text{Heat}} CaO(s) + CO_2(g)$

CaO (quick lime) produced in the above reaction is made use of in the manufacture of cement.

If the decomposition of a substance takes place in the presence of light, it is called photolytic decomposition (photolysis).

Examples: (i) $2AgCl(s) \xrightarrow{\text{Sunlight}} 2Ag(s) + Cl_2(g)$

(ii) $2AgBr(s) \xrightarrow{\text{Sunlight}} 2Ag(s) + Br_2(g)$

The above reactions are used in the black and white photography.

If the decomposition of the substance takes place by the passage of electricity, it is called electrolytic decomposition (electrolysis).

Example: $MgCl_2 \xrightarrow[\text{current}]{\text{electrical}} Mg + Cl_2$

Displacement reaction: In a displacement reaction, the more reactive element displaces the less reactive element from its compound.

Representation: $AB + C \rightarrow CB + A$

Metal displacement reaction

$XY + Z \rightarrow XZ + Y$ Halogen displacement reaction

Example: $Fe + CuSO_4 \rightarrow FeSO_4 + Cu$

As iron is more reactive than copper, it displaces copper from copper sulphate solution, thereby forming ferrous sulphate. In general, displacement reactions are exothermic in nature.

The more reactive halogen displaces the less reactive halogen from its compound.

Example: $2NaBr + Cl_2 \rightarrow 2NaCl + Br_2$

Double decompositions/Double displacement reactions: The chemical reaction in which two reactants combine to form two new substances by mutual exchange of their radicals is called double decomposition or double displacement reaction.

Representation: $AB + CD \rightarrow AD + CB$

Examples: (i) $2NaNO_3(aq) + CuSO_4(aq) \rightarrow Na_2SO_4(aq) + Cu(NO_3)_2(aq)$

(ii) $NaOH(aq) + HCl(aq) \rightarrow NaCl(aq) + H_2O(aq)$

(iii) $K_2SO_4(aq) + Cu(NO_3)_2(aq) \rightarrow 2KNO_3(aq) + CuSO_4(aq)$

If the reaction takes place between an acid and a base, it is called neutralization reaction. Salt and water are formed in this reaction.

Examples: (i) $NaOH + HCl \rightarrow NaCl + H_2O$

(ii) $2NH_4OH + H_2SO_4 \rightarrow (NH_4)_2SO_4 + 2H_2O$

In a double decomposition reaction, if one of the products is insoluble, it is called precipitate and the reaction can be called precipitation reaction.

Examples: (i) $KCl + AgNO_3 \rightarrow KNO_3 + AgCl^-$

(ii) $BaCl_2 + Na_2SO_4 \rightarrow 2NaCl + BaSO_4^-$

81. Solubility: The maximum amount of a solute in grams, which can dissolve in 100 g of solvent at a given temperature is called solubility.

$$\text{Solubility} = \frac{\text{Mass of solute}}{\text{Mass of solvent}} \times 100$$

Factors affecting solubility

1. Nature of solute: Ionic compounds or polar compounds are more soluble in polar solvents like water. Nonpolar compounds are more soluble in nonpolar solvents like benzene.

2. Nature of solvent: The solvents which have high dielectric constants can dissolve polar and ionic compounds to a greater extent than the solvents with low dielectric constants.

   Example: NaCl is highly soluble in water but sparingly soluble in benzene.

3. Temperature: For most of the substances, solubility increases with the increase in temperature. However, the solubility of some substances decreases with increase in temperature. In case of some substances the temperature has no or little effect on the solubility.

82. The representation of chemical changes is pivotal in the realm of chemistry. It provides a systematic way to detail reactions, simplifying complex processes. Using names of substances can become cumbersome, especially with numerous elements and compounds in the mix. Hence, shorthand notations, symbols for elements, and formulae for compounds were introduced. Berzelius's method, for example, proposed using the first letter of an element's name or incorporating Latin, German, or Greek roots for clarity. Similarly, a molecule's formula gives information about the number of atoms of each element present, streamlining the portrayal of chemical compositions. Another crucial aspect is the concept of valency, which indicates an atom's combining capacity. Introducing ions or radicals further enriched the chemical language, highlighting the charged entities in reactions. Overall, the language of chemistry, through symbols, formulae, and other representations, enhances the precision, clarity, and universality of chemical communication.

83. Inorganic compounds are generally classified into three main categories: acids, bases, and salts.

Naming of Acids: Acids typically contain the hydrogen ion (H^+) as the positive radical. The name of an acid is often determined by its negative radical. If the acid's negative radical consists of a single non-metal, it is a binary acid and has the 'ic' suffix prefixed by 'hydro'. For instance, HCl is called Hydrochloric acid. Oxyacids have a negative radical made up of non-metal and oxygen. The naming depends on the oxygen's percentage. Acids with less oxygen get the 'ous' suffix (e.g., H_2SO_3 is Sulphurous acid), while those with more oxygen get the 'ic' suffix (e.g., H_2SO_4 is Sulphuric acid).

Naming of Bases: Bases contain the hydroxyl radical (OH^-) as their negative radical and a metal ion as their positive radical. The name of the base starts with the metal's name, followed by 'hydroxide'. For instance, $Ca(OH)_2$ is named Calcium hydroxide.

Naming of Salts: Salts derive their positive radical from a base and their negative radical from an acid. The salt's name starts with the metal's name (the positive radical) and is followed by the name of the negative radical. This name depends on the acid from which the salt originates. Salts from 'ous' acids have the 'ite' suffix (e.g., $CaSO_3$ is Calcium sulphite), while those from 'ic' acids have the 'ate' suffix (e.g., $ZnSO_4$ is Zinc sulphate).

Competition Wing

Level1: Apply your Concepts

1. Sulphate radical is a dinegative radical.
2. The formula of chloric acid is $HClO_3$.
3. Phosphorus is a tetratomic element.
4. Equivalent mass of magnesium is 12 since its valency is 2.
5. Slaking of lime is a compound-compound combination reaction.
6. The valency of the metal in the metal carbonate is 2. The formula of metal chloride is MCl_2 and metal nitride is M_3N_2.
7. Gram atomic mass refers to the relative atomic mass of an element expressed in grams. It represents the mass of one mole of atoms of the element. On the other hand, gram molecular mass is the molecular mass of a substance expressed in grams and it represents the mass of one mole of molecules of the substance.
8. The 'ous' suffix indicates the ion with the lower charge while the 'ic' suffix denotes the ion with a higher charge when a metal exhibits variable valency.
9. A molecule is considered electrically neutral because the total positive charge on the positive radicals (or cations) should be balanced by the total negative charge on the negative radicals (or anions). This ensures the neutrality of the compound.
10. The equivalent mass of an element is a measure of the number of parts by mass of that element which can displace or combine with a certain standard mass of another element. Equivalent mass has no units. When the equivalent mass is expressed in grams, it is called gram equivalent mass.
11. Magnesium on burning, combines with oxygen and forms MgO. Hence, it gains weight. But it does not violate the law of conservation of mass because the balanced chemical reaction is:

    $2Mg + O_2 \rightarrow 2MgO$

    Oxygen gets added to Magnesium. If the process is carried out in a closed vessel, the mass of the substances before the reaction and after the reaction remain the same.
12. $K_2Cr_2O_7 + 14HCl \rightarrow 2KCl + 2\ CrCl_3 + 3Cl_2 + 7H_2O$

    The coefficient of HCl is 14
13. (a) $4Zn + 10HNO_3 \rightarrow 4Zn(NO_3)_2 + N_2O + 5H_2O$

    (b) $Mn + 2HNO_3 \rightarrow Mn(NO_3)_2 + H_2$
14. Nitrogen forms 5 different oxides

    Their formulae are

    N_2O, NO, NO_2, N_2O_3, and N_2O_5

    The ratio of mass of oxygen present in different oxides with respect to the fixed mass of nitrogen $= 8 : 16 : 32 : 24 : 40$

    $= 1 : 2 : 4 : 3 : 5$

    which is a simple whole number ratio.

    Thus, the law of multiple proportions is verified.
15. $Cu(NO_3)_2 \xrightarrow{\Delta} CuO + NO_2 + O_2$

    It is a thermal decomposition reaction.

    It is experimentally observed that CuO obtained from both $CuCO_3$ and $Cu(NO_3)_2$ has the same composition that is the ratio by mass of copper and oxygen is the same. Hence, the law of definite proportion is verified.
16. $CaO + H_2O \rightarrow Ca(OH)_2$

    The above reaction is slaking of lime.

    It is a combination reaction as well as an exothermic reaction.
17. A is more reactive than B since it displaces B from its compound.

    B cannot displace C from its compound, hence B is less reactive than C.

    C cannot displace D from its compound, but it can displace A.

    Therefore, the reactivity order is $B < A < C < D$.
18. The reaction involved in black and white photography is a photolytic decomposition of silver bromide. It is also a redox reaction.

    In this reaction, silver ions get reduced to silver metal and chloride ions get oxidized to chlorine.
19. In the presence of light, nitric acid undergoes decomposition to form brown coloured gaseous NO_2 which dissolves in nitric acid, there by turning it yellow. The colour of NO_2 is brown.
20. Rusting of iron is an oxidation–reduction reaction since iron gets converted to iron oxide by the reaction with aerial oxygen. In this reaction, iron gets oxidized and aerial oxygen gets reduced.

21. H_2S reduces Cl_2 to HCl. Hence it is the reducing agent, Cl_2 oxidizes H_2S. Hence it is an oxidizing agent.

22. When a sealed bottle of an aerated drink is opened, CO_2 fizzes out because in aerated drinks CO_2 gas is made to dissolve in water under high pressure. When the bottle is opened, pressure is released and solubility of CO_2 in water decreases.

23. Distillation involves boiling that is heating. During heating all the dissolved gases are expelled. This proves that increase in temperature decreases t he solubilities of gases in water/liquid.

Level 2: Review Your Concepts

24. The law of definite proportions states that a pure compound always contains the same elements combined together in the same proportion by weight, regardless of how the compound was prepared or sourced. This emphasizes the fixed and consistent composition of pure substances.

25. The release of heat energy in a chemical reaction is a characteristic of an exothermic reaction. The energy released during the reaction is typically in the form of heat.

For example, the combustion of carbon with oxygen to form carbon dioxide is exothermic:

$C + O_2 \rightarrow CO_2 + 94$ kcal.

26. Solubility curves are crucial because they show the variation of solubility with temperature. They help in determining solute solubility at different temperatures, comparing the solubilities of different solutes, understanding the amount of solute that can be precipitated by cooling a solution, and in knowing the preferential precipitation of various salts.

27. Let the metal atom be M.

The chloride salt produced is MCl_2. Hence valency of the metal atom is 2

$\therefore$ The salt X is MCO_3 one metal atom is present in one molecule of the salt.

28. The acid is H_2SO_3.

$2KOH + H_2SO_3 \rightarrow K_2SO_3 + 2H_2O$

One molecule of K_2SO_3 contains total 6 atoms

$\therefore$Number of atoms in 5 molecules = 30

$K \rightarrow 2$ atoms

$S \rightarrow 1$ atom

$O \rightarrow 3$ atoms

29. Relative atomic mass of the element = $\frac{x}{3}$ amu $\frac{x}{3}$ a m

$u = \left(\frac{x}{3} \times 1.6 \times 10^{-24}\right)$ g

The mass of 5 atoms of the element

$= \left(\frac{x}{3} \times 5 \times 1.6 \times 10^{-24}\right)$ g

$= \left(x \times \frac{8}{3} \times 10^{-24}\right)$ g = 2.66 x $\times 10^{-24}$ g

30. 32 g of oxygen reacts with x g of the metal

$\therefore$ 8 g of oxygen reacts with $\frac{x}{4}$ g of the metal

$\therefore$ Gram equivalent weight of the metal is $\frac{x}{4}$ g.

Atomic weight of the metal is 0.5 x

$$\text{Valency} = \frac{\text{Atomic wt of the metal}}{\text{Eq wt of the metal}}$$

$$= \frac{0.5x}{\frac{x}{4}} = \frac{0.5x}{0.25x} = 2$$

31. The salt is $Ca(NO_3)_2$

The base is $Ca(OH)_2$

The acid is HNO_3

32. Equivalent mass of B is y.

$\because$ The valency of B is 2, the atomic mass of B is 2y.

33. $Ca_3P_2 + 6H_2O \rightarrow 3Ca(OH)_2 + 2PH_3$

5 molecules of Ca_3P_2 reacts with 30 molecules of water to produce 10 molecules of PH_3

34. $2Ca_3(PO_4)_2 + 6SiO_2 + 10C \rightarrow 6CaSiO_3 + P_4 + 10CO$

1 molecule of $Ca_3(PO_4)_2$ forms 5 molecules of CO.

$\therefore$ The mass of carbon monoxide obtained in g

$= (5 \times 28) \times 1.6 \times 10^{-24} = 224 \times 10^{-24}$g

35. A combination reaction is usually associated with the formation of new bonds which is in turn associated with the release of energy.

36. Halides of silver undergo photolytic decomposition. Hence, they are stored in a dark coloured bottle.

37. The reaction in which an element reacts with a compound and displaces one of the constituent elements of that compound is known as a displacement reaction.

38. In a polluted atmosphere, silver reacts with H_2S to form Ag_2S. Hence, it gains weight.

39. $FeSO_4 \rightarrow Fe_2O_3 + SO_3 + SO_2$
Both the oxides of sulphur are obtained, but O_2 is not evolved. No sulphide salt is formed. Higher oxide of iron that is Fe_2O_3 is formed.
In $FeSO_4$, the valency of iron is 2 and in Fe_2O_3, it is 3. Solution B, D, and E

40. 100 g of water dissolves 22 g of salt and gets saturated. 500 g of water dissolves $22 \times 5 = 110$ g of the salt.

41. y g solution contains x g solute
$\therefore$ $(y - x)$ g solvent contains x g solute
$\therefore$ 100 g solvent contains $\dfrac{x}{y-x} \times 100$ g solute
The solubility is $\dfrac{100x}{y-x}$

42. 200 g of solvent dissolves maximum $(35 \times 2) = 70$ g of solute. At 30°C it can contain maximum $(25 \times 2) = 50$ g solute. Hence $(70 - 50)$ g $= 20$ g solute will be precipitated.

43. Curve B is associated with the formation of more amount of precipitate than A since its solubility decreases to a greater extent in the given temperature range.

Level 3 : Assess Your Concepts

44. Chemical reactions can be broadly classified into several types:
   - ***Combination Reactions:*** In which two or more substances combine to form a single new substance.
     Example: $N_2(g) + 3H_2(g) \rightarrow 2NH_3(g)$.
   - ***Decomposition Reactions:*** A single compound splits into two or more simpler substances.
     For instance, 2KNO3(s) when heated decomposes to $2KNO_2(s) + O_2$.
   - ***Displacement Reactions:*** The more reactive element displaces the less reactive element from its compound.
     An example would be the reaction between iron and copper sulphate: $Fe + CuSO_4 \rightarrow FeSO_4 + Cu$.
   - ***Double Decomposition/Double Displacement Reactions:*** Two reactants combine to form two new substances by mutual exchange of their radicals.
     For example, $2NaNO_3(aq) + CuSO_4(aq) \rightarrow Na_2SO_4(aq) + Cu(NO_3)_2(aq)$.

   In addition to these main types, reactions can also be classified based on their energy characteristics. Exothermic reactions release heat, such as the combustion of carbon, while endothermic reactions absorb heat, like the formation of nitric oxide from nitrogen and oxygen.

45. Solubility, which refers to the maximum amount of a solute that can dissolve in a solvent at a given temperature, is influenced by various factors. First, the nature of the solute plays a role: Ionic or polar compounds are more soluble in polar solvents like water, whereas non-polar compounds prefer non-polar solvents. Secondly, the solvent's nature matters. Solvents with high dielectric constants can dissolve polar and ionic compounds more than those with low dielectric constants. Another influencing factor is temperature. Generally, the solubility of most substances increases with temperature, but there are exceptions. Lastly, for the solubility of gases in liquids, pressure is a crucial factor. As per Henry's law, at a constant temperature, an increase in pressure on the liquid's surface enhances the solubility of the gas in the liquid. This is why beverages like soda water have excess CO_2 dissolved at high pressures.

46. Cl^- ion will be precipitated in the form of AgCl. Hence, the solution contains only KNO_3. The molecular mass of KNO_3 is more than KCl. Therefore, the solution will be supersaturated since their solubility is the same at that temperature

47. If the dissolution process is exothermic, at higher temperature the solubility of the solute becomes less. Hence with the increase in temperature the solubility of X decreases.

48. Deep sea divers go in to the deep sea where the pressure is high due the depth of the water. Hence the solubility of oxygen in blood increases. But the requirement of oxygen for respiration does not increase. Therefore, the percentage of oxygen in the cylinder carried by them ought to be less.

49. When CO_2 gas is passed through water under pressure, it reacts with H_2O to form carbonic acid, H_2CO_3.

$$H_2O + CO_2 \rightarrow H_2CO_3$$

It is a combination reaction.

JEE-NEET Special wing

Multiple-Answer Type Questions

1.

Compound	Formula	Total positive charge	Total Negative charge
Magnesium phosphate	$Mg_3(PO_4)_2$	6 units	6 units
Aluminium carbonate	$Al_2(CO_3)_3$	6 units	6 units
Ferric chromate	$Fe_2(CrO_4)_3$	6 units	6 units
Barium nitride	Ba_3N_2	6 units	6 units

2. 3 molecules of acid should possess 6 H^+ ions while 2 molecules of base possess $3OH^-$ ions. That means acid should be dibasic acid and the base should be triacidic base. Among the given ones, carbonic acid, chromic acid and phosphorous acid are the dibasic acids. Similarly, aluminium hydroxide and ferric hydroxide are the triacidic bases.

3.

Nitrous oxide	28:16 = 7:4
Nitrogen dioxide	14:32 = 7:16
Nitrogen trioxide	28:48 = 7:12
Nitrogen pentoxide	28:80 = 7:20

4.

A- K	I-Pb	N-Pt	J-Cu
B-Na	M-Au	H-Sn	K-Hg

5. NH_3; NCl_3; HCl
CO_2; SO_2; CS_2
H_2S; SO_2; H_2O

Comprehension-Based Questions

6. The mass of the metal which reacts with 8 g of oxygen is called its gram equivalent mass. Since one gram atom reacts with 16 g oxygen, the equivalent mass should be half of the atomic mass. The valency of the metal should be 2. The oxyacids of chlorine should be
A-$HClO_4$; B-$HClO_3$; C-$HClO_2$; D-HOCl
S-Ca $(OCl)_2$ GMM–143 % of chlorine ≈ 50

7. Q-$Ca(ClO_3)_2$ No. of atoms = 9

8.

Salt	Salt	% of oxygen
P	Ca $(ClO_4)_2$	54
Q	Ca $(ClO_3)_2$	46
R	Ca $(ClO_2)_2$	36
S	Ca $(ClO)_2$	22

Ratio of percentage of oxygen in S and R = 22:36 ≈ 2:3
Ratio of percentage of oxygen in R and P = 36:54 ≈ 2:3

9. The metal should be Mg. The salt 'R' should be having the formula $Mg(ClO_2)_2$. The molecular mass of the salt could be 159.

10. $Ca(ClO_3)_2 \rightarrow CaCl_2 + 3O_2$

11. Ratio of nitrogen and oxygen in N_2O_3 = 7:12
Ratio of nitrogen and hydrogen in NH_3 = 14:3
Ratio of hydrogen and oxygen combining with 14 g nitrogen = 24:3 = 8:1.
Ratio of hydrogen and oxygen in H_2O = 1:8

12. The mass of nonmetal = 22 – 8 = 14 g.
The ratio of nonmetal to oxygen = 14:8 = 7:4.
The nonmetal can be assumed as nitrogen.

Oxide	% of oxygen	Formula of oxide	Mass ratio of nitrogen and oxygen
X	53.3	NO	7:8
Y	74	N_2O_5	7:20
Z	69.6	NO_2	7:16

Mass ratio of oxygen which combines with fixed mass of nitrogen = 8:20:16 = 2:5:4

13. The nonmetals mentioned would be phosphorus and oxygen.
Mass ratio of phosphorus and oxygen in P_2O_3 = 62:48.
Mass ratio of phosphorus and oxygen in P_2O_5 = 62:80.
12.4 g Phosphorus combines with 9.6 g oxygen in P_2O_3.
12.4 g Phosphorus combines with 16 g oxygen in P_2O_5.

14. The given activity illustrates the law of definite proportions.

15. The mass of hydrogen reacting with the same amount of carbon would be in simple numerical ratio for all the compounds in the series.

16. Since the products formed in the reactions A, B, C and D are different, they do not illustrate the law of definite proportions.

17.

(a)	Solid A	(iv)	72 g
(b)	Solid B	(v)	107 g
(c)	Solid C	(i)	32 g
(d)	Solid D	(iii)	27 g
(e)	Solid E	(ii)	15 g

18.

Column A (Metal)	Column B (Formulae of binary compounds with oxygen)		
(a) Barium	(iii)	MO; MO_2	BaO; BaO_2
(b) Lead	(v)	MO; MO_2; M_3O_4	PbO; PbO_2; Pb_3O_4
(c) Copper	(iv)	M_2O; MO	Cu_2O; CuO
(d) Sodium	(i)	M_2O; M_2O_2	Na_2O; Na_2O_2
(e) Iron	(ii)	MO; M_2O_3; M_3O_4	FeO; Fe_2O_3;Fe_3O_4

Hence, the correct options are:

(a) ↔ (iii), (b) ↔ (v), (c) ↔ (iv), (d) ↔ (i), (e) ↔ (ii)

CHAPTER

3

Mole Concept, Stoichiometry, and Behaviour of Gases

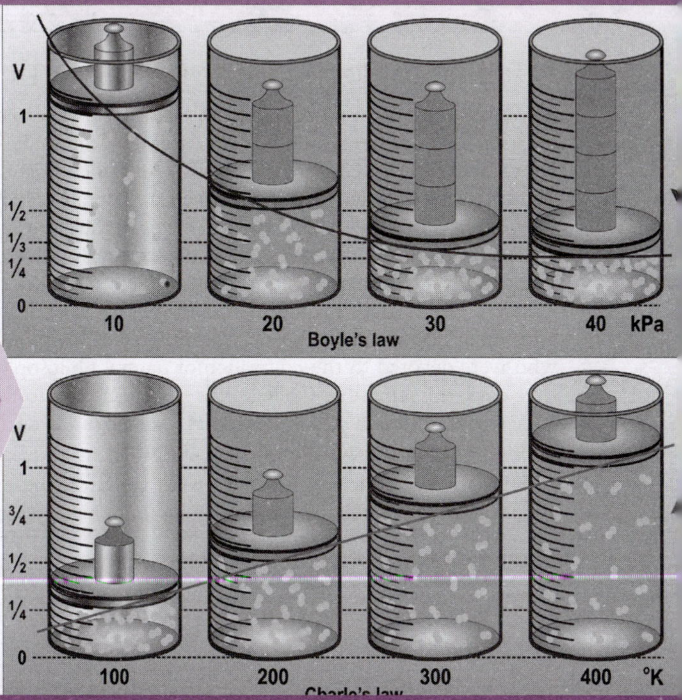

Remember

Before beginning this chapter, you should be able to:

- highlight basic concepts of matter and its classification.
- understand the concepts of chemical reactions.

Key Ideas

After completing this chapter, you should be able to:

- derive the formulae of compounds and understand the naming of compounds.
- describe the laws pertaining to the inter-relation of measurable properties of gases along with ideal gas equation.
- develop numerical ability in mole concept.
- explain the types of chemical reactions.
- balance the chemical equations and study the stoichiometric relation in correlation with the concept of mole

Scientific Crypt

A Tribute to Robert Boyle (1627–1691)

Boyle was born at Lismore Castle, in Ireland. He received private tutoring in Latin, Greek and French. After the death of his mother, he was sent to Eton College in England. After spending over three years there, he travelled abroad and stayed at Florence in Italy during the winter. There he studied the paradoxes of the great star-gazer, Galileo Galilei who was still alive at that time. Boyle returned to England from continental Europe with a keen interest in scientific research. He devoted his life to scientific research and acquired a prominent place in the band of inquirers called 'Invisible College' who were devoted to the cultivation of natural philosophy. In the later days, this 'Invisible College' was transformed into the Royal Society of London in which Boyle was a member. He declined the honour of being elected President of the society.

His early scientific investigations were based on the principles enunciated by Francis Bacon. In spite of his initial belief regarding the possible transmutation of metals, in the later period, he endorsed the view of elements being the undecomposable constituents of material bodies. Boyle accomplished many important works in Physics and Chemistry. Some of them include the enunciation of Boyle's law, the role of air in the propagation of sound, the expansion of freezing water, specific gravities, and refractive powers of crystals etc., he brought out the distinction between compounds and mixtures and evolved methods for the detection of ingredients of a chemical substance. He published a famous book *'Sceptical Chemist'*.

He made a wish list of 24 possible inventions among which few could be realized.

Boyle died from paralysis in 1691 and was buried in the churchyard of St. Martin. Boyle endowed a series of lectures which came to be known as Boyle Lectures.

FUN TIME

CROSSWORD

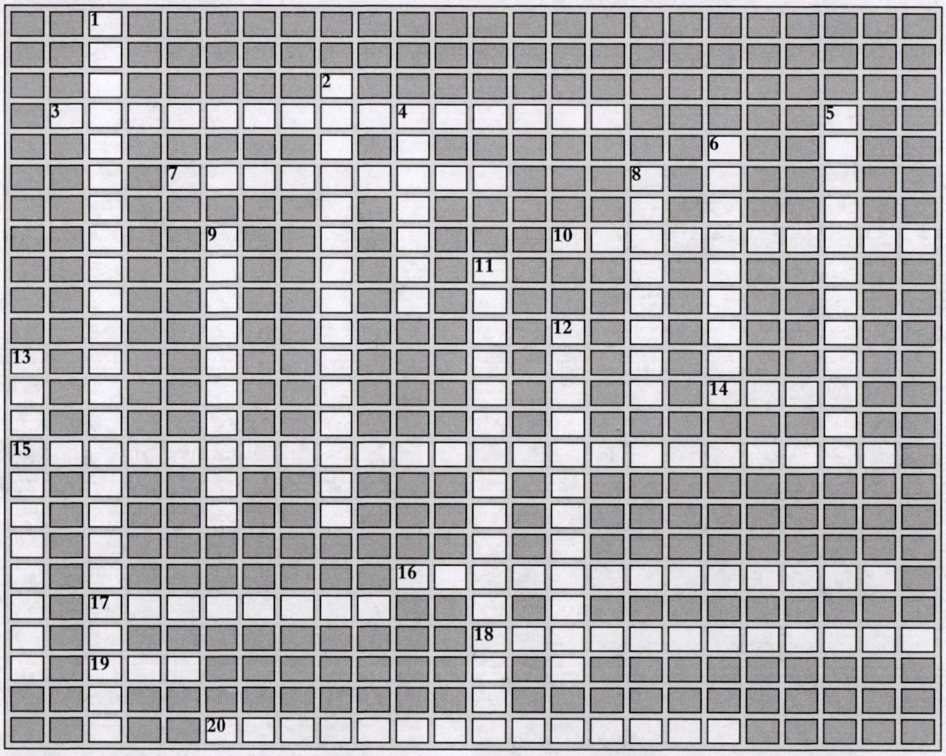

Across

3. Volume occupied by one gram molecule of any gas at STP
7. Relationship between pressure and volume of a given amount of gas at a constant temperature
10. Law pertaining to the rate of diffusion of gases
14. Weight of Avogadro number of particles
15. Decomposition of the compound in the presence of light
16. Study of quantitative relationship among reactants and products
17. Gas that obeys the gas equation under all conditions of temperature and pressure
18. The ratio of the number of moles of one component to the total number of moles of all the components
19. Suffix used for naming of binary compounds
20. Units in which relative atomic mass is expressed

Down

1. Decomposition of compound in the presence of heat
2. The volume of gas diffused in unit time at a given temperature
4. Combining the capacity of an atom
5. The temperature at which the volume of a gas becomes zero
6. The most reactive metal in the metal reactivity series
8. Atomic mass expressed in grams
9. Relationship between temperature and volume of a given amount of gas at constant pressure
11. Formula that gives the simplest ratio of the atoms of different constituent elements
12. Molecular mass expressed in grams
13. The kinetic energy of the gas molecules is proportional to ______

INTRODUCTION

Chemistry is the branch of science which deals with the study of matter that involves various aspects, the most important aspect. The study of chemical reactions. A chemical reaction involves transformation of matter associated with change in molecular composition. For the sake of convenience, we represent chemical reactions in the form of chemical equations. In these chemical equations, the various substances involved in the reactions are written in the form of symbols and formulae which are the shorthand notations of the respective elements and compounds. The study of naming various compounds and derivation of formulae for the compounds is an inevitable part in the study of chemical reactions, which is considered the language of chemistry.

Symbols and Formulae

There are 118 elements discovered till now and all of them have been given symbols on the basis of their English or Latin names. A **symbol** represents an atom of an element.

Table 3.1 Examples of symbols

English Names		Latin Names	
Name	**Symbol**	**Name**	**Symbol**
Chlorine	Cl	*Aurum* (gold)	Au
Carbon	C	*Argentum* (silver)	Ag
Beryllium	Be	*Stannum* (tin)	Sn
Magnesium	Mg	*Plumbum* (lead)	Pb

The **formulae** of elements and compounds are written by making use of the symbols of the respective elements. It represents the actual number of atom(s) of each element present in one molecule of the substance (element or compound).

Table 3.2 Examples of formulae

Names	Formulae
Nitrogen	N_2
Ozone	O_3
Barium sulphate	$BaSO_4$

Radicals or Ions

An atom or a group of atoms gets converted to the corresponding ions or radicals by losing or gaining electrons. These are called positive and negative radicals, respectively. Based on the amount/number of charge on the radicals, they are categorized as monovalent, bivalent, trivalent, and tetravalent ions or radicals.

Table 3.3 Some important positive radicals

Names of radicals	Formulae of radical	Types
Hydrogen	H^+	Monovalent
Sodium	Na^+	Monovalent
Potassium	K^+	Monovalent
Cuprous	Cu^+	Monovalent
Mercurous	Hg^+	Monovalent

(Continued)

Info Bytes!

Radicals are groups of atoms that behave as a single unit in a chemical reaction. They can be either positive (cations) or negative (anions) and determine the properties of the compound.

Table 3.3 Continue

Names of radicals	Formulae of radical	Types
Ammonium	NH_4^+	Monovalent
Argentous	Ag^+	Monovalent
Zinc	Zn^{2+}	Bivalent
Magnesium	Mg^{2+}	Bivalent
Cupric	Cu^{2+}	Bivalent
Ferrous	Fe^{2+}	Bivalent
Calcium	Ca^{2+}	Bivalent
Barium	Ba^{2+}	Bivalent
Mercuric	Hg^{2+}	Bivalent
Stannous	Sn^{2+}	Bivalent
Plumbous	Pb^{2+}	Bivalent
Argentic	Ag^{2+}	Bivalent
Aluminium	Al^{3+}	Trivalent
Ferric	Fe^{3+}	Trivalent
Stannic	Sn^{4+}	Tetravalent
Plumbic	Pb^{4+}	Tetravalent

Table 3.4 Some important negative radicals

Names of radicals	Formulae of radicals	Types
Hydroxyl	OH^-	Monovalent
Fluoride	F^-	Monovalent
Chloride	Cl^-	Monovalent
Bromide	Br^-	Monovalent
Iodide	I^-	Monovalent
Nitrite	NO_2^-	Monovalent
Nitrate	NO_3^-	Monovalent
Hypochlorite	ClO^-	Monovalent
Chlorite	ClO_2^-	Monovalent
Chlorate	ClO_3^-	Monovalent
Perchlorate	ClO_4^-	Monovalent
Acetate	CH_3COO^-	Monovalent
Formate	$HCOO^-$	Monovalent
Bisulphide	HS^-	Monovalent
Bisulphite	HSO_3^-	Monovalent
Bisulphate or hydrogen sulphate	HSO_4^-	Monovalent
Hydride	H^-	Monovalent
Bicarbonate or hydrogen carbonate	HCO_3^-	Monovalent
Sulphide	S^{2-}	Bivalent
Sulphate	SO_4^{2-}	Bivalent
Carbonate	CO_3^{2-}	Bivalent
Oxide	O^{2-}	Bivalent
Peroxide	O_2^{2-}	Bivalent
Sulphite	SO_3^{2-}	Bivalent
Phosphate	PO_4^{3-}	Trivalent

Derivation of Formulae of Compounds

Two basic principles are followed in writing the formulae of the compounds. Firstly, the more electropositive element (positive radical) is written first followed by the electronegative element or negative radical. Secondly, the total charge on the positive radicals should be balanced by the total charge on the negative radicals since a molecule is electrically neutral.

Table 3.5 Compounds and their formulae

Examples	Formulae
K^+ Cl^- 1 1 1 1	KCl
Fe^{2+} O^{2-} 2 2	FeO
Fe^{3+} O^- 3 2 2 3	Fe_2O_3
Si^{4+} O^- 4 2 2 1 1 2	SiO_2
Ca^{2+} NO_3^- 2 1 1 2	$Ca(NO_3)_2$

Naming of Compounds

Binary Compounds

The compounds that are formed by the combination of two elements are called **binary compounds**.

In naming binary compounds, the electropositive atom (generally metal) is specified first by giving its ordinary English name. The name of the second element which is generally a non-metal is obtained by adding the suffix 'ide' to its name.

Examples:

$MgCl_2$	Magnesium chloride
$CaCl_2$	Calcium chloride
BaO	Barium oxide
H_2S	Hydrogen sulphide

In case of metals showing variable valency, it is necessary to specify which of the positive ions are present.

Examples:

FeO	Ferrous oxide or Iron (II) oxide
Fe_2O_3	Ferric oxide or Iron (III) oxide
CuCl	Cuprous chloride or Copper (I) chloride
$CuCl_2$	Cupric chloride or Copper (II) chloride

For binary covalent compounds, generally formed by two nonmetallic elements, it is required to specify the number of atoms of more electronegative element a prefix.

Table 3.6 Prefixes for binary covalent compounds

Number of atoms	Prefixes
One	Mono
Two	Di
Three	Tri
Four	Tetra
Five	Penta
Six	Hexa
Seven	Hepta
Eight	Octa
Nine	Nona
Ten	Deca

The less electronegative element is specified first, followed by the more electronegative element. The prefix is generally added to the more electronegative element to specify its number of atoms.

SO_2	Sulphur dioxide
N_2O_5	Nitrogen pentoxide
SF_6	Sulphur hexafluoride
PCl_3	Phosphorus trichloride
CO	Carbon monoxide

Naming of Acids

Acids usually contain hydrogen ion (H^+) as the positive radical. Hence, the name of the acid is determined by the constituent(s) of its negative radical.

Table 3.7 Prefixes for binary covalent compounds

Types of Acids	Types of negative radicals	Suffixes
Binary acid	Negative radical consists of a single non-metal *Examples:* HCl, HBr, etc.	'ic' (prefix hydro) Hydrochloric acid Hydrobromic acid
Oxy acid	Negative radical consists of a nonmetal and oxygen. The name of the oxyacid is determined by the percentage of the oxygen associated with a specific non-metal. Acids with comparatively less percentage of oxygen *Examples:* H_2SO_3, HNO_2, H_3PO_3, etc.	'ous' Sulphurous acid, nitrous acid phosphorous acid
	Acids with comparatively more percentage of oxygen Examples: H_2SO_4, HNO_3, H_3PO_4, etc.	'ic' Sulphuric acid, nitric acid, phosphoric acid, etc.

If the acid contains lesser number of oxygen atoms than the corresponding 'ous' acid, 'hypo' prefix is given to the negative radical, whereas 'per' prefix is given to the negative radical when the acid contains greater number of oxygen atoms than the corresponding 'ic' acid.

Examples:

Hypochlorous acid	$HClO$
Chlorous acid	$HClO_2$
Chloric acid	$HClO_3$
Perchloric acid	$HClO_4$

Konnect

The longest-named compound according to the IUPAC nomenclature rules has over 189,000 letters.

Naming of Bases

Bases generally contain hydroxyl radical (OH^-) as the negative radical and a metal ion as the positive radical (M^+). While writing the name of the base, the name of the metal is written first followed by hydroxide.

Examples:

Calcium hydroxide	$Ca(OH)_2$
Magnesium hydroxide	$Mg(OH)_2$
Sodium hydroxide	$NaOH$
Aluminium hydroxide	$Al(OH)_3$

Naming of Salts

The positive radical present in the salt comes from the corresponding base and the negative radical comes from the corresponding acid.

The name of the salts starts with the name of the metal present as positive radical which is followed by the name of the negative radical. The name of the negative radical is determined by the name of the acid from which the salt is produced.

Table 3.8 Naming of salts

Acids from which the salt is produced	Suffix and name of the salts	
'ous' acid	'ite'	
Examples:	$CaSO_3$	Calcium sulphite
Sulphurous acid (H_2SO_3)	$Zn(NO_2)$	Zinc nitrite
Nitrous acid (HNO_2)	$Mg(PO_3)_2$	Magnesium phosphite
Phosphorous acid (H_3PO_3)		
'ic' acid	'ate'	
Examples:		
Sulphuric acid (H_2SO_4)	$ZnSO_4$	Zinc sulphate
Nitric acid (HNO_3)	$NaNO_3$	Sodium nitrate
Phosphoric acid (H_3PO_4)	$AlPO_4$	Aluminium phosphate

If NH_4^+ is present as a positive radical in the base or in the salt, ammonium is written in place of the name of the metal.

Examples:

Ammonium hydroxide (base)	NH_4OH
Ammonium phosphate (salt)	$(NH_4)_3PO_4$

EXAMPLE 3.1 The ratio of number of metal atoms to total number of constituents present in a metal (M) phosphate is 3 : 13. Calculate the total number of constituent atoms present in metal.

(i) Oxide (ii) Bisulphate (iii) Sulphide

SOLUTION

Let the metal be M and its valency be x

$\therefore$ Metal phosphate = $M^{x+}\ PO_4^{3-} \Rightarrow M_3(PO_4)_x$

The ratio of number of metal atoms to total number of constituents = $\dfrac{3}{3+5x} = \dfrac{3}{13}$

$\Rightarrow 3 + 5x = 13 \Rightarrow x = 2$

(i) Metal oxide is $M^{2+}O^{2-} \Rightarrow MO$

$\therefore$ Total number of constituents is 2

(ii) Metal bisulphite is $M^{2+}HSO_3^- \Rightarrow M(HSO_3)_2$

$\therefore$ Total number of constituents is 11

(iii) Metal sulphide is $M^{2+}S^{2-} \Rightarrow MS$

$\therefore$ Total number of constituents is 2

EXAMPLE 3.2 The valencies of elements A, B, C, and D with respect to chlorine in compounds P, Q, R, and S are 3, 4, 1, and 2, respectively. Find out the number of oxygen atoms present in the one molecule of binary compounds formed by A, B, C, and D with same valencies and also mention the formulae of binary compounds.

SOLUTION

The valencies of elements A, B, C, and D with respect to chlorine in compounds P, Q, R, and S are 3, 4, 1, and 2, respectively. The formulae of binary compounds with oxygen are A_2O_3, BO_2, C_2O, and DO, respectively. So, the number of oxygen atoms present in each molecule of those oxides is 3, 2, 1, and 1, respectively.

Kinetic Theory of Gases

A chemical formula gives scope for the study of matter with respect to the molecular composition. The other aspect of the study of matter involves the study with respect to the three distinct physical states. The three physical states, namely, solids, liquids and gases are basically distinguished on the basis of their molecular arrangement.

Solids are characterized by closely packed molecular arrangement which gives them definite shape. Therefore, the intermolecular forces of attraction are very high in solids. In liquids, the molecules are relatively loosely packed and hence, they exhibit less intermolecular forces of attraction. Matter in gaseous state is characterised by a very loosely packed arrangement of molecules. Due to this molecular arrangement, there is negligible intermolecular forces of attraction in gaseous state.

Konnect

The Kinetic Theory of Gases was a revolutionary idea that proposed gas molecules are in constant random motion and that this motion is related to the temperature of the gas.

Characteristics of Gases Based on the Kinetic Theory of Gases

The postulates of kinetic theory of gases are the following:

1. Gases contain large number of tiny particles known as molecules.
2. The force of attraction between the molecules is very low.
3. The intermolecular space is large.

4. Molecules of a gas are in the state of random motion resulting in continuous collisions among themselves and with the walls of the container, exerting pressure.
5. The kinetic energy of molecules is proportional to the temperature.

From the kinetic theory of gases, we can conclude that the following are the characteristics of gases:

1. Gases do not possess definite volume and shape.
2. Gases possess low density compared to liquids and solids.
3. Gases exert pressure equally in all directions.
4. Gases are capable of great expansion. They occupy the entire volume of any given container.
5. Gases are highly compressible compared to liquids and solids.
6. Gases exhibit the property of diffusion.

Konnect

The volume and physical behavior of a given mass of a gas depend on its temperature and pressure over it.

Gas Laws

Based on experiments, certain relations among the variables of gas (volume, temperature, and pressure) are established. These are stated as **gas laws**.

Boyle's Law

The volume of a given mass of a gas is inversely proportional to its pressure at constant temperature.

If a given mass of a gas occupies a volume (V) at pressure (P) and temperature (T), then from Boyle's law:

$$V \propto \frac{1}{P} \text{ (T is constant);}$$

$$V = \frac{K}{P} \text{ or}$$

$$PV = \text{K (K is proportionality constant)}$$

If at constant temperature, a certain mass of a gas occupies a volume (V_1) at pressure (P_1), and a volume (V_2) at pressure (P_2), then from Boyle's law, $\mathbf{P_1V_1 = P_2V_2}$, at constant temperature.

Graphical Representation of Boyle's Law

1. Volume (V) vs pressure (P)

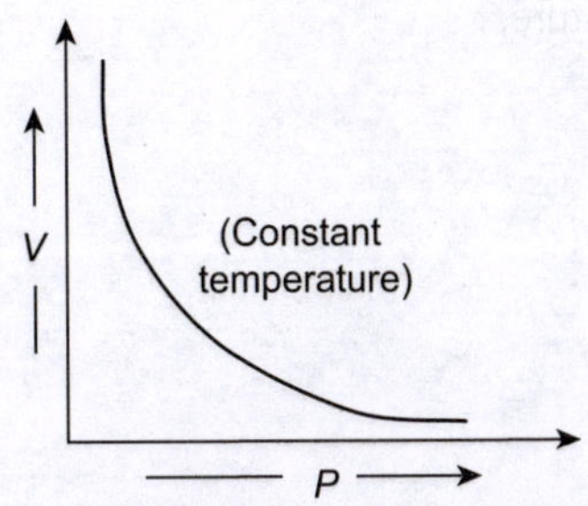

Figure 3.1 P-V curve

2. Volume (V) vs $\dfrac{1}{\text{Pressure }(P)}$

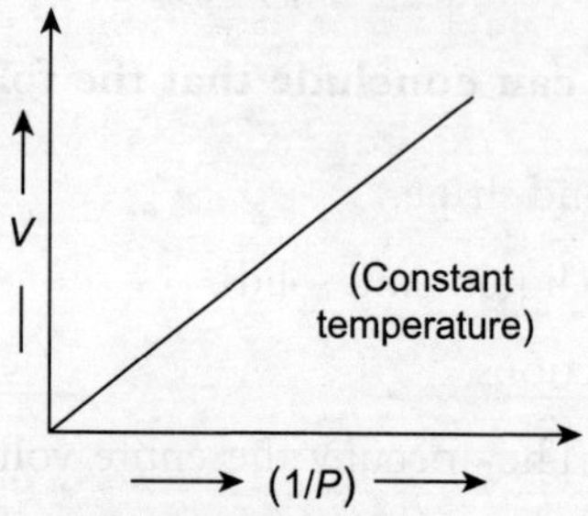

Figure 3.2 V-1/P curve

3. The product of pressure and volume (PV) vs. pressure (P)

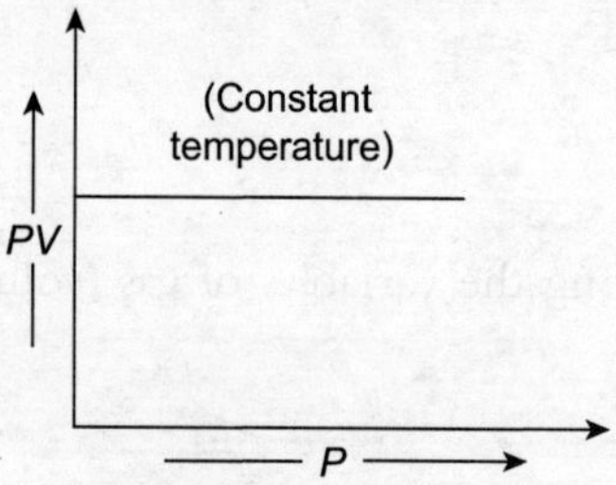

Figure 3.3 PV-P curve

Explanation of Boyle's Law on the Basis of Kinetic Molecular Theory

At constant temperature, the molecules of gas possess constant kinetic energy and hence the same velocity. When the volume of the gas is changed (say increased), the average distance between the molecules and walls of the container increases since a given mass of a gas contains a definite number of molecules. When the distance between the molecules and walls of the container increases while keeping the velocity of molecules constant, the number of collisions on the walls of the container decreases which results in a decrease in the pressure with an increase in volume.

EXAMPLE 3.3 What will be the volume of a certain mass of a gas at a pressure of 56 cm of Hg if it occupies 300 mL at a pressure of 168 cm of Hg while maintaining the temperature constant?

SOLUTION

P_1 = Initial pressure = 56 cm of Hg

P_2 = Final pressure = 168 cm of Hg

V_2 = Final volume = 300 mL

V_1 = Initial volume

According to Boyle's law, at a constant temperature,

$P_1V_1 = P_2V_2$

$P_1 \times V_1 = P_2 \times V_2$

$56 \times V_1 = 168 \times 300$

$V_1 \; \dfrac{168 \times 300}{56}$

$V_1 = 900\ mL$

So, the volume of the gas at 56 cm of Hg is 900 mL.

EXAMPLE 3.4 If 100 mL of oxygen at a certain temperature is compressed to a volume of 40 mL under a pressure of 5 atmospheric pressures, what was the original pressure of the oxygen?

SOLUTION

P_1 = Initial pressure

Given,

V_1 = Initial volume = 100 mL

P_2 = Final pressure = 5 atm

V_2 = Final volume = 40 mL

According to Boyle's law, at a constant temperature,

$P_1V_1 = P_2V_2$

$P_1 \times V_1 = P_2 \times V_2$

$P_1 \times 100 = 5 \times 40$

$P_1 = \frac{200}{100}$ 2 atm

So, the original pressure of the oxygen was 2 atm.

Charles' Law

At constant pressure, the volume of a given mass of a gas increases or decreases by (1/273) of its volume at 0°C for every 1°C increase or decrease in temperature, respectively.

$$V_t = V_0\left(1 + \frac{t\ \text{C}}{273}\right)$$

Let the volume of a given mass of the gas at 0°C be V_0. Its volume increases to V_t at t°C under constant pressure.

Hence, from Charles' law,

$$V_t = V_0\left(\frac{273 + t°\text{C}}{273}\right)$$

$V_t = V_0\left(\frac{T}{273}\right)$; T is the absolute temperature (Kelvin temperature)

$$V \propto T, \text{ as } \frac{V_0}{273} = \text{constant}$$

Hence, Charles' law can also be stated as follows:

For a fixed mass of gas, the volume of a gas (V) is directly proportional to the absolute temperature (T), at constant pressure,

i.e., $V \propto T$ (P is constant)

or $\frac{V}{T}$ = K (K is the proportionality constant)

Info Bytes!

The lowest ever man-made temperature was achieved in a lab at MIT, where scientists cooled sodium-potassium molecules to just 500 nanokelvins or 500 billionths of a Kelvin above absolute zero.

If at constant pressure, a certain mass of a gas occupies a volume (V_1) at temperature (T_1) and a volume (V_2) at temperature (T_2), then according to Charles' law:

$$\frac{V_1}{T_1} = \frac{V_2}{T_2} \text{ (at constant pressure)}$$

Graphical Representation of Charles' Law

1. Volume (V) vs absolute temperature (T)

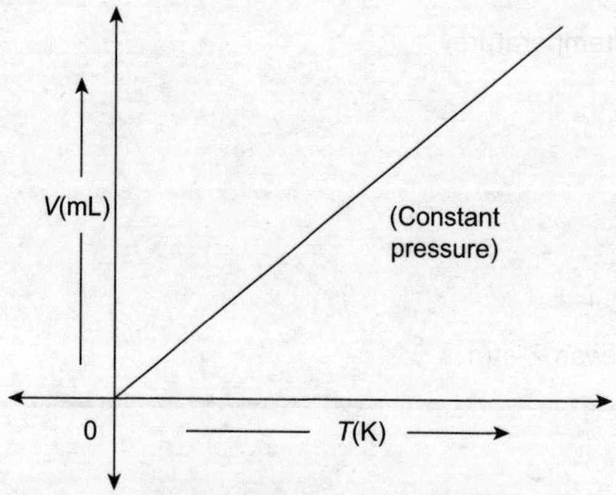

Figure 3.4 V-T(K) curve

2. Volume (V) vs temperature (T) in Celsius scale

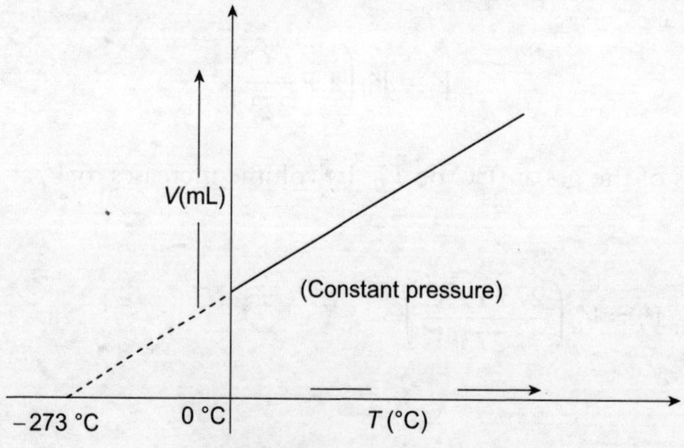

Figure 3.5 V-T(°C) curve

From Charles' law:

$$V_t = V_o\left(\frac{273 + t°C}{273}\right)$$

As t in this equation approaches 273°C, the volume approaches zero. Below 273°C, the volume of a gas would become negative which is practically not feasible.

Therefore, 273°C is the lowest temperature that can be attained theoretically. However, practically before reaching this temperature itself all gases either get liquefied or solidified. Therefore, 273°C is taken as zero point on a new temperature scale called **absolute temperature scale.**

Info Bytes!

Temperature in Kelvin scale can be obtained by adding 273 to the temperature measured in the Celsius scale.

T (Kelvin) = 273 + t°C (Celsius)

t°C(Celsius)= T (Kelvin) – 273

Explanation of Charles' Law on the Basis of Kinetic Molecular Theory

A given mass of a gas contains a definite number of molecules. When the temperature of a gas increases, the kinetic energy of the molecules also increases. Since the gas is at constant pressure, the number of collisions on the unit area of the walls of the container remains unaltered. That means there should be a corresponding increase in the average distance between the molecules and the walls of the container. Therefore, volume of the gas increases with increase in temperature at constant pressure.

Contrary to this, when the temperature of a gas increases at a constant volume, the number of collisions on unit area of the walls of the container increases thereby resulting in an increase in pressure.

EXAMPLE 3.5 At what temperature will a given mass of a gas occupy a volume of 75 L if it occupies a volume of 100 L at a temperature of 27°C, pressure remaining constant?

SOLUTION

According to Charles' law at constant pressure,

$$\frac{V_1}{T_1} = \frac{V_2}{T_2}$$

Where,

V_1 = Initial volume V_2 = Final volume

T_1 = Initial temperature T_2 = Final temperature

Given,

$V_1 = 75$ L $V_2 = 100$ L

$T_1 = ?$ $T_2 = 300$ K

$$\frac{V_1}{T_1} = \frac{V_2}{T_2}$$

$$\frac{75}{T_1} = \frac{100}{300}; \quad T_1 = \frac{300 \times 75}{100} = 225\text{K}$$

EXAMPLE 3.6 The volume of a certain mass of gas is 50 L at 50°C. What will its volume be at 250°C, assuming the pressure remains constant?

SOLUTION

V_2 = Final volume

Given,

V_1 = Initial volume = 50 L

T_1 = Initial temperature = 50°C = 50 + 273 = 323 K

T_2 = Final temperature = 250°C = 250 + 273 = 523 K

According to Charles' law, at a constant pressure,

$$\frac{V_1}{T_1} = \frac{V_2}{T_2}$$

$$\frac{50}{323} = \frac{V_2}{523}$$

$$V_2 = \frac{50 \times 523}{323} = 80.95L$$

The Gas Equation

For a given mass of a gas, the gas equation gives a relationship among the volume, pressure, and temperature, and can be derived by combining the laws of Boyle and Charles.

The volume of a given mass of a gas is (V) at temperature (T) and pressure (P).

Applying Boyle's law: $V \propto \frac{1}{P}$ (T is constant) (3.1)

Applying Charles' law: $V \propto$ T (P is constant) (3.2)

Combining (3.1) and (3.2),

$$V \propto \frac{1}{P} \times T \text{ (when both } T \text{ and } P \text{ change)}$$

$$V = K\frac{T}{P}$$

$$\frac{PV}{T} = K \text{ (K is a proportionality constant)}$$

If the volume of a given mass of a gas changes from V_1 to V_2, pressure from P_1 to P_2 and temperature from T_1 to T_2, then from the gas equation, we have $\frac{P_1V_1}{T_1} = \frac{P_2V_2}{T_2}$.

EXAMPLE 3.7 A certain mass of gas occupies 250 cm^3 at 25°C and 760 mm of Hg pressure. What will be its volume at 35°C and 380 mm of Hg pressure?

SOLUTION

V_2 = Final volume

Given,

V_1 = Initial volume = 250 cm^3

T_1 = Initial temperature = 25°C = 25 + 273 = 298 K

T_2 = Final temperature = 35°C = 35 + 273 = 308 K

P_1 = Initial pressure = 760 mm of Hg

P_2 = Final pressure = 380 mm of Hg

According to gas law,

$$\frac{P_1V_1}{T_1} = \frac{P_2V_2}{T_2}$$

$$\frac{760 \times 250}{298} = \frac{380 \times V_2}{308}$$

$$V_2 = \frac{308 \times 760 \times 250}{298 \times 380} = 516.7 cm^3$$

EXAMPLE 3.8

(i) A given mass of a gas at 27°C and 400 mm of Hg of pressure, occupies a volume of 238 mL. At what temperature the gas will occupy a volume of 119 mL at 600 mm of Hg pressure.

(ii) The pressure exerted by 328 mL of a gas at 55°C is 224 cm of Hg. What is the pressure of the gas at 117°C, if the volume is reduced to 168 mL?

(iii) At 27°C and 5 atm pressure, the volume of a given mass of a gas is 220 L. Find the temperature at which the gas occupies 110 L of volume at 10 atm pressure?

SOLUTION

(i) From the gas equation,

$$\frac{P_1V_1}{T_1} = \frac{P_2V_2}{T_1},$$

$P_1 = 400$ mm of Hg

$V_1 = 238$ mL

$T_1 = 27°C = 27 + 273 = 300$ K

$P_2 = 600$ mm

$V_2 = 119$ mL

$T_2 = ?$

$$\frac{400 \times 238}{300} = \frac{600 \times 119}{T_2}$$

$$T_2 = \frac{600 \times 119 \times 300}{400 \times 238} = 225\text{ K} = (225 - 273)\ °\text{C} = -48\ °\text{C}$$

(ii) From the gas equation,

$$\frac{P_1V_1}{T_1} = \frac{P_2V_2}{T_1},$$

$P_1 = 224$ cm of Hg, $V_1 = 328$ mL, $T_1 = 55$ °C $= 55 + 273 = 328$ K

$P_2 = ?$, $V_2 = 168$ mL, $T_2 = 117$ °C $= 117 + 273 = 390$ K

$$\frac{224 \times 328}{328} = \frac{P_2 \times 168}{390}$$

$$P_2 = \frac{224 \times 328 \times 390}{168 \times 328} = \frac{4}{3} \times 390 = 520\text{ mm of Hg}$$

(iii) From the gas equation,

$$\frac{P_1V_1}{T_1} = \frac{P_2V_2}{T_1},$$

$P_1 = 5$ atm, $V_1 = 220$ L

$T_1 = 27$ °C $= 27 + 273 = 300$ K

$P_2 = 10$ atm, $V_2 = 110$ L

$T_2 = ?$

$$\frac{5 \times 220}{300} = \frac{10 \times 110}{T_2}$$

$$T_2 = \frac{10 \times 110 \times 300}{5 \times 220} = 300\text{ K} = 300 - 273 = 27\ °\text{C}$$

Standard/Normal Temperature and Pressure (STP or NTP)

Temperature and pressure have great influence on the volumes of gases. It is necessary to choose a suitable value of each as standards refer to the volume of a gas.

The conditions of standard temperature and pressure are given below:

Standard temperature = 0°C = 273 K

Standard pressure = 760 mm of Hg (mercury)

= 76 cm of Hg = 1 atm

A gas which strictly obeys the gas equation under all the conditions of temperature and pressure is called an **ideal gas**. However, all gases are real gases, i.e., they do not perfectly obey the gas equation under all the conditions of temperature and pressure.

The behavior of gases can be expressed by the laws of Boyle and Charles when the gases are subjected to change in pressure and temperature. Another law, namely, Gay-Lussac's law of combining volumes describes the relationship among the volumes of gaseous reactants and products.

Gay-Lussac's Law of Combining Volumes of Gases

When gases react chemically, they do so in volumes which bear a simple whole number ratio to each other and to the volumes of the products, provided the products are also in the gaseous state and the temperature and pressure of the reactant and product gases are the same. For example:

In the reaction of carbon monoxide with oxygen, two volumes of carbon monoxide react with one volume of oxygen to give two volumes of carbon dioxide:

$$\underbrace{CO + CO}_{2\,vol} + \underbrace{O_2}_{1\,vol} \longrightarrow \underbrace{CO_2 + CO_2}_{2\,vol}$$

The volume ratio of carbon monoxide, oxygen, and carbon dioxide is 2 : 1 : 2.

Info Bytes!

In 1811, Amedo Avogadro established a relationship between the volumes of gases and the number of molecules present in them provided the volumes are measured at similar conditions of temperature and pressure.

Avogadro's law

Under similar conditions of temperature and pressure, equal volumes of all gases contain equal number of molecules.

Under similar conditions of temperature and pressure, 1 L of any gas, hydrogen, helium, or hydrogen chloride contains the same number of molecules.

From Avogadro's law, the number of particles present in a given mass of a substance (solid, liquid, or gas) and the volume of the substance is calculated, if it is in gaseous state.

The mass of a substance is nothing but the total mass of its constituent particles, i.e., atoms or molecules.

Mathematically, it can be represented as:

$V \propto n$

Where, V is the volume of the gas; n is the number of moles of the gas.

If you have two states of a gas (1 and 2), the relationship can be further represented as:

$V_1/n_1 = V_2/n_2$

Assuming temperature and pressure remain constant.

The Ideal Gas Law

The Ideal Gas Law (or Equation of State for an ideal gas) is a fundamental principle that describes the behavior of ideal gases. It is given by:

$PV = nRT$

Where:

P is the pressure of the gas.

V is the volume of the gas.

n is the number of moles of the gas.

R is the universal gas constant. ($R \approx 8.314 J/mol \cdot K$)

T is the temperature in Kelvin (K).

Measurement of the Mass of Atoms and Molecules

- **Atomic Weight or Relative Atomic Mass:** The mass of $\frac{1}{12}$th of a carbon-12 isotope has been taken as the standard. The mass of the atoms of other elements is calculated with respect to the number of times an atom of an element is heavier than $\frac{1}{12}$th part of the carbon-12 isotope. This is called **atomic weight** or the **relative atomic mass**. Since the weight of $\frac{1}{12}$th part of the carbon-12 is called **atomic mass unit**, the **relative atomic mass** is expressed in amu.
- **Gram Atomic Weight or Gram Atom:** The relative atomic mass expressed in grams is called **gram atomic weight (GAW)** or **gram atom.**

  Example: Atomic weight of oxygen = 16 amu

  Gram atomic weight of oxygen = 16 g
- **Molecular Weight or Relative Molecular Mass:** Molecular weight is a number which indicates how many times a molecule of a substance is heavier in comparison to $\frac{1}{12}$th the mass of one carbon-12 isotope.
- **Gram Molecular Weight:** Molecular weight expressed in grams is called **gram molecular weight**. The molecular weight of a substance can be easily determined from its formula by adding up the atomic weights of its constituent atoms.

  Example:

  Calculation of molecular weight of calcium carbonate ($CaCO_3$):

  Atomic weight of calcium is 40 amu

  Atomic weight of carbon is 12 amu

  Atomic weight of oxygen is 16 amu

  Molecular weight of calcium carbonate

  $= 40 + 12 + (16 \times 3) = 100$ amu
- **Gram Molecular Volume:** One gram molecule of any dry gas at standard, temperature and pressure (STP) occupies the same volume, i.e., 22.4 L or 22.4 dm^3. This is called gram molecular volume or GMV. For example:

  1 g molecule of dry chlorine gas occupies 22.4 L at STP.

  Since GMW of chlorine is 71 g, 71 g of chlorine gas occupies 22.4 L at STP.

Avogadro's Number and Mole Concept

Mole is the unit of amount of substance and it is a number or fixed quantity like dozen. By using mole as a unit of amount of substance, it is possible to calculate the number of atoms, molecules, and ions of a given mass of a substance.

Mole

Mole is defined as the amount of substance that contains the same number of units (atoms, molecules, or ions) as there are atoms in exactly 12 g of carbon-12 isotope. This number is called **Avogadro number**.

Experimentally, it was found that this number is 6.023×10^{23}.

From the concept of mole, it can be concluded that:

1. 1 g atom of any substance is equivalent to one mole of atoms of that substance and contains Avogadro number of atoms.
2. 1 g molecule of any substance is equivalent to one mole of molecules of that substance and contains Avogadro number of molecules.

> **Konnect**
>
> One mole of any substance contains Avogadro number of chemical units.

Example:

(i) One mole of hydrogen atoms
$= 6.023 \times 10^{23}$ hydrogen atoms
$= 1$ g of hydrogen

(ii) One mole of carbon atoms
$= 6.023 \times 10^{23}$ carbon atoms
$= 12$ g of carbon

(iii) One mole of NaCl
$= 6.023 \times 10^{23}$ Na^+ ions and 6.023×10^{23} Cl^- ions
$= 58.5$ g of NaCl

(iv) One mole of ammonia gas
$= 6.023 \times 10^{23}$ ammonia gas
$= 17$ g of NH_3

(v) One mole of sodium
$= 6.023 \times 10^{23}$ hydrogen molecules
$= 23$ g of sodium

(vi) One mole of hydrogen
$= 6.023 \times 10^{23}$ hydrogen molecules
$= 2$ g of hydrogen

Relation between GMV, Mole and Avogadro Number

One gram molecule of any dry gas occupies 22.4 L volume at STP. Hence, 22.4 L of a dry gas at STP is equivalent to 1 mole of that gas and contains 6.023×10^{23} molecules, i.e., Avogadro number of molecules.

Example: 1 gram molecule or 32 g or 1 mole of dry oxygen gas occupies 22.4 L at STP and contains 6.023×10^{23} molecules of oxygen.

Example: 1 gram molecule or 4 g or 1 mole of dry helium gas occupies 22.4 L at STP and contains 6.023×10^{23} atoms because helium is a monoatomic gas.

For all solid and liquid substances, mole can be converted into weight or number of atoms or molecules. For gaseous substances, mole can also be converted into volume in addition to weight and number of particles.

Examples:

(i) One mole of bromine liquid

$= 6.023 \times 10^{23}$ bromine molecules

$= 160$ g of bromine

(ii) One mole of chlorine gas

$= 6.023 \times 10^{23}$ chlorine molecules

$= 71$ g of chlorine

$= 22.4$ L chlorine at STP

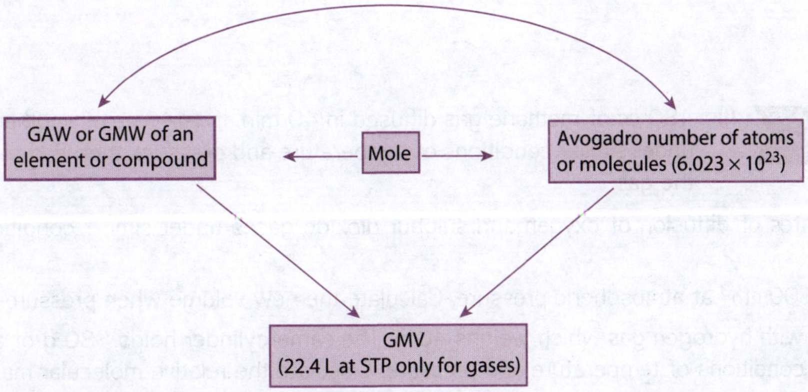

Figure 3.6 Schematic Representation of Different Relationships for Mole

EXAMPLE 3.9 (i) Calculate the number atoms present in 112 g of N_2 and also find its volume at STP.

(ii) Calculate the mass of water which contains the same number of molecules as that of 667.5 g of aluminium chloride.

SOLUTION

(i) Gram molecular weight of $N_2 = 28$ g.

112 g of N_2 is equivalent to $\frac{112}{28} = 4$ moles of nitrogen

112 g of N_2 contains $4 \times 6.023 \times 10^{23}$ molecules $= 24 \times 10^{23}$ (approx) molecules

The volume of the given mass $N_2 = (4 \times 22.4)$ L $= 89.6$ L at STP

(ii) Molecular weight of aluminium chloride ($AlCl_3$) $= 133.5$ g/mol

667.5 g of aluminium chloride is equivalent to $\frac{667.5}{133.5} = 5$ moles of aluminium chloride.

Numbers of molecules present in 667.5 g of aluminium chloride is equivalent to that present in 5 moles of water.

The mass of 5 moles of water $= 18 \times 5 = 90$ g

Graham's Law of Diffusion

Another characteristic property shown by gases is the process of diffusion. The spreading of the fragrance of perfume in a specific area can be attributed to this property of gases.

The volume of the gas diffused in unit time at certain temperature and pressure through unit area is called **rate of diffusion of the gas.**

Thomas Graham, based on his observations, established a quantitative relationship between the rate of diffusion of gases and their densities.

Graham's law of diffusion states that the rates of diffusion of different gases are inversely proportional to the square roots of their densities, under similar conditions of temperature and pressure.

$$r = \frac{1}{\sqrt{d}} \text{ (constant temperature and pressure)}$$

$$\frac{r_1}{r_2} = \sqrt{\frac{d_2}{d_1}} = \sqrt{\frac{M_2}{M_1}}$$

EXAMPLE 3.10 (i) 480 cc of methane gas diffused in 40 min. If 1440 cc of another gas diffused in 60 min under similar conditions of temperature and pressure, then find out the molecular mass of the gas.

(ii) Find out the relative rates of diffusion of oxygen and sulphur dioxide gases under similar conditions of temperature and pressure.

(iii) Volume of a gas was 600 cm^3 at atmospheric pressure. Calculate the new volume when pressure increases by 25%.

(iv) A gas cylinder is filled with hydrogen gas which weighs 40 g. The same cylinder holds 880 g of a gas A and 560 g of a gas B under the same conditions of temperature and pressure. Calculate the relative molecular masses of A and B.

SOLUTION

(i) Rate of methane and unknown gas can be given as:

$$r_{methane} = \frac{V_{methane}}{time} \qquad r_x = \frac{V_x}{time}$$

$$r_{methane} = \frac{480}{40} = 12\,cc/min$$

$$r_x = \frac{1440}{60} = 24\,cc/min$$

$$\frac{r_{CH_4}}{r_x} = \sqrt{\frac{M_x}{M_{CH_4}}}$$

$$= \sqrt{\frac{M_x}{16}} = \frac{12}{24}$$

$$= M_x = \frac{12^2}{24^2} \times 16 = 4\,g$$

Gram molecular mass of the gas = 4 g

(ii)

$$\frac{r_{O_2}}{r_{SO_2}} = \sqrt{\frac{M_{SO_2}}{M_{O_2}}} = \sqrt{\frac{64}{32}} = \sqrt{2} : 1$$

(iii) Initial pressure of gas (P_1) = 760 mm

25% of initial pressure = 25 × 760/100 = 0.25 × 760 = 190 mm

Final pressure (P_2) = 760 + 190 = 950 mm

Initial volume (V_1)= 600 cm^3; Final volume (V_2) = ?

According to Boyle's Law, $P_1 V_1 = P_2 V_2 \Rightarrow V_2 = \frac{P_1 V_1}{P_2} = \frac{760 \times 600}{950} = 480\ cm^3$

(iv) Since the volume of cylinder is same for all gases, they contain same number of molecules that means equal number of moles under the same conditions of temperature and pressure.

2 g of hydrogen → 1 mole; 40 g of hydrogen → 20 moles; 880 g of gas A also constitutes 20 moles

Mass of gas A corresponding to 1 mole = $\frac{880}{20}$ = 44 g ∴ Molecular mass of A = 44

560 g of gas B also constitutes 20 moles

Mass of gas B corresponding to 1 mole = $\frac{560}{20}$ = 28 g ∴ Molecular mass of B = 28

EXAMPLE 3.11 Equal masses of four different gases A, B, C, and D are taken in separate containers of same volume. The molecular masses of the gases are in the order B < D < A < C. Compare the pressures exerted by the respective gases at constant temperature.

SOLUTION

The pressure exerted by a gas depends upon the number of molecules present in the given amount of gas. The greater the molecular mass, the lesser the pressure exerted by the gas. Since the order of molecular masses is B < D < A < C, the order of number of molecules could be C < A < D < B. The pressures exerted by the gases is also in the same order.

Stoichiometry

The chemical reactions are represented in the form of chemical equations. Since these chemical equations should comply with the law of conservation of mass, they should be balanced with respect to the number of atoms of each element involved in the reaction. Therefore, a quantitative relationship can be established between the various reactants and products. The area of study pertaining to the study of this quantitative relationship among reactants and products is called **stoichiometry**.

Example of a balanced chemical equation: $NaOH + HCl \rightarrow NaCl + H_2O$

Reactants	Products
One atom of sodium	One atom of sodium
One atom of chlorine	One atom of chlorine
One atom of oxygen	One atom of oxygen
Two atoms of hydrogen	Two atoms of hydrogen

Balancing of Chemical Equations by Trial and Error Method

1. The number of times an element appears on the reactant side and the product side of the equation is counted.
2. The element which appears the least number of times is balanced first.
3. The other elements are balanced in the increasing order of their frequency.
4. In case any two or more elements have the same frequency, the metallic element is balanced first in preference to the nonmetallic element.

Example:

Skeleton equation:

$$KI + H_2SO_4 + MnO_2 \rightarrow KHSO_4 + MnSO_4 + H_2O + I_2$$

Balancing sulphur:

$$2KI + 3H_2SO_4 + MnO_2 \rightarrow 2KHSO_4 + MnSO_4 + H_2O + I_2$$

Balancing oxygen and hydrogen:

$$2KI + 3H_2SO_4 + MnO_2 \rightarrow 2KHSO_4 + MnSO_4 + 2H_2O + I_2$$

A balanced chemical equation provides:

1. weight–weight relationship of the reactants and products.
2. weight–volume relationship when some of the reactants and products in gaseous state.
3. volume–volume relationship when all the reactants and products in gaseous state.

EXAMPLE 3.12 What is the amount of NH_3 formed when 14 g of N_2 combines with 6 g of H_2?

SOLUTION

N_2	+	$3H_2$	→	$2NH_3$
1 mol		3 mol		2 mol
28 g		3×2 g		2×17 g

From the balanced equation, 1 mol of N_2 reacts with 3 mol of H_2 or 28 g of N_2 reacts with 6 g of hydrogen. The amount of nitrogen is less than that required for complete reaction with H_2. Hence, N_2 is called **limiting reactant** or **limiting reagent**. However, H_2 is an excess reactant. Further, 28 g of N_2 forms 34 g of NH_3

14 g of N_2 forms $\frac{14 \times 34}{28}$ g of NH_3

Amount of ammonia formed = 17 g

EXAMPLE 3.13 When calcium carbonate is strongly heated, 28 g of calcium oxide is obtained, calculate the volume of CO_2 liberated at STP.

$$CaCO_3 \xrightarrow{\Delta} CaO + CO_2$$

SOLUTION

The above chemical equation shows that 1 mole of $CaCO_3$ decomposes to form 1 mole of CaO and 1 mole of CO_2.

Hence, if 56 g of CaO is obtained by heating $CaCO_3$, the volume of CO_2 liberated is 22.4 L or dm^3 at STP.

Therefore, when 2 g of CaO is obtained, the volume of CO_2 is $\left(22.4 \times \frac{28}{56}\right)$L $= 11.2$L or dm^3.

EXAMPLE 3.14 Calculate the volume of CO_2 at STP, when 22.4 L of CO under STP completely burns in the presence of excess oxygen.

$$2CO + O_2 \rightarrow 2CO_2$$

SOLUTION

The above chemical equation shows that 2 gram molecular volume of CO reacts with 1 gram molecular volume of O_2, and hence, 2 gram molecular volume of CO_2 is produced.

Hence, $(22.4 \times 2) = 44.8$ L of CO at STP burns in oxygen and produces $(22.4 \times 2) = 44.8$ L of CO_2 at STP

Therefore, 22.4 L of CO at STP on complete combustion gives 22.4 L of CO_2.

Calculation of Empirical and Molecular Formulae of Compounds

Another important aspect of stoichiometry is the elemental analysis of a substance. The proportion by mass of each element present in a compound is called its **percentage composition**. The elemental analysis helps to determine the mass of each element present in 100 g of known compound and it also establishes the chemical formula of unknown compound.

$$\text{Percentage of an element by mass present in a compound} = \frac{\text{mass of element in one mole of the compound}}{\text{gram molecular mass of the compound}} \times 100$$

The chemical formula of the compound that can be calculated from the elemental analysis data (percentage by mass of each element in the compound) is called **empirical formula.**

Empirical formula represents the simplest whole number ratio of the atoms of different constituent elements present in one molecule of the compound. The molecular formula of a compound can be calculated if both the empirical formula and the molecular mass are known.

Molecular formula represents the actual number of atoms of different constituent elements present in one molecule of the compound.

The molecular and empirical formula of any chemical compound are related as:

$n \times$ Empirical formula = Molecular formula, where n is a positive integer

$$n = \frac{\text{Molecular mass of compound}}{\text{Empirical formula mass}}$$

Info Bytes!

If you had a compound with an empirical formula of CH (like ethyne), it might seem like it has the same empirical formula as benzene (C_6H_6), but their molecular formulas and structures are vastly different.

EXAMPLE 3.15

(i) Calculate the percentage composition of calcium bicarbonate.

(ii) An organic compound on analysis has been found to have following percentage composition:

Percentage of carbon = 40%

Percentage of hydrogen = 6.66%

If the vapour density of the compound is 30, find out the molecular formula of the compound.

SOLUTION

(i) GMW of calcium bicarbonate [$Ca(HCO_3)_2$] = 162

Amount calcium in 162 g of calcium bicarbonate = 40 g

Amount of calcium in 100 g of calcium bicarbonate = $\dfrac{40 \times 100}{162} = 24.7\%$

Amount of hydrogen in 162 g of calcium bicarbonate = 2 g

Amount of hydrogen in 100 g of calcium bicarbonate = $\dfrac{2 \times 100}{162} = 1.23\%$

Amount of carbon in 162 g of calcium bicarbonate = 24 g

Amount of carbon in 100 g of calcium bicarbonate = $\dfrac{24 \times 100}{162} = 14.8\%$

Amount of oxygen in 162 g of calcium bicarbonate = 96 g

Amount of oxygen in 100 g of calcium bicarbonate = $\dfrac{96 \times 100}{162} = 59.2\%$

Percentage composition of calcium bicarbonate:

Percentage of calcium	24.7%
Percentage of hydrogen	1.23%
Percentage of carbon	14.8%
Percentage of oxygen	59.2%

(ii)

Elements	Percentages	Atomic masses	Atomic ratios	Simplest ratios
Carbon	40	12	40/12 = 3.33	$\frac{3.33}{3.33} = 1$
Hydrogen	6.66	1	$\frac{6.66}{1} = 6.66$	$\frac{6.66}{3.33} = 2$
Oxygen	53.34	16	$\frac{53.34}{16} = 3.33$	$\frac{3.33}{3.33} = 1$

Empirical formula is CH_2O

Vapour density = 30

Mol. wt. = 2 × vapor density = 30 × 2 = 60

Empirical formula wt. = 30

$$\text{Molecular formula} = CH_2O\left(\frac{60}{30}\right) = CH_2O2$$

$$= C_2H_4O_2$$

EXAMPLE 3.16 Calculate the volume of CO_2 formed at STP and the weight of zinc oxide formed in grams, when 2.32 g of zinc carbonate decomposes with no further loss in weight.

SOLUTION

$ZnCO_3 \rightarrow ZnO + CO_2$

125.3 g of $ZnCO_3 \rightarrow$ 81.3 g of ZnO and 22.4 L of CO_2 at STP

2.32 g of $ZnCO_3$ gives ? of ZnO and ? of CO_2 at STP

$\frac{2.32 \times 81.3}{125.3}$ g of ZnO and $\frac{2.32 \times 22.4}{125.3}$ L of CO_2 = 1.5 g of ZnO and 0.41 L of CO_2.

EXAMPLE 3.17 One mole of hydrocarbon is subjected to combustion. The product obtained is condensed and the resulting gaseous product occupied a volume of 89.6 L at STP. Oxygen required for this combustion is 145.6 L at STP. What should be the molecular formula of x?

SOLUTION

Equation for the combustion of hydrocarbon is $C_xH_y + \left(x + \frac{y}{4}\right) O_2 \rightarrow xCO_2 + \frac{y}{2} H_2O$.

The gaseous product left after condensation of water vapour is CO_2.

89.6 L $CO_2 = \frac{89.6}{22.4} = 4$ moles;

$\therefore x = 4$

1 mole of O_2 occupies 22.4 L of volume at STP

145.6 L of O_2 1 corresponds to $= \frac{145.6 \times 1}{22.4} = 6.5$ moles of O_2

$\therefore x + \frac{y}{4} = 6.5 ; 4 + \frac{y}{4} = 6.5 \Rightarrow y = 10 \therefore$ Hydrocarbon is C_4H_{10}

EXAMPLE 3.18 24.58 g of 80% pure potassium chlorate gives certain amount of oxygen which is sufficient for the combustion of how many grams of acetylene at STP? (Molecular formula of acetylene is C_2H_2).

SOLUTION

$2KClO_3 \rightarrow 2KCl + 3O_2$

Amount of pure $KClO_3$ in 24.58 g of 80 % sample = $\dfrac{80 \times 24.58}{100} = 19.66$ g

245 g $KClO_3$ gives 96 g O_2

19.66 g $KClO_3$ gives $\dfrac{96 \times 19.66}{245} = 7.7$ g O_2 $\therefore$ No. of moles of $O_2 = \dfrac{7.7}{32} = 0.24$

$C_2H_2 + 5/2O_2 \rightarrow 2CO_2 + H_2O$

2.5 moles of oxygen reacts with 1 mole acetylene

0.24 moles of oxygen reacts with $\dfrac{0.24 \times 1}{2.5} = 0.096$ mol

Amount of acetylene subjected to combustion = 0.096 × 26 = 2.504 g

EXAMPLE 3.19 A mixture of sodium carbonate and sodium bicarbonate was subjected to heating. Some loss in weight was found. How does this information help us to find out the composition of mixture?

SOLUTION

Between sodium carbonate and sodium bicarbonate, only sodium bicarbonate decomposes to given sodium carbonate, CO_2 and H_2O. The gaseous products (CO_2 and H_2O) escape out into the atmosphere. Therefore, an apparent loss in weight occurs during the reaction.This loss in weight corresponds to the amount of gaseous products formed. From the mass of gaseous products formed, amount of sodium bicarbonate in the mixture can be obtained, and thus, composition of the mixture can be found out.

EXAMPLE 3.20 The percentage of oxygen in a metallic oxide of an alkali metal is 20.1%. The molecular mass of the compound is 79.5. Write the molecular formula of the compound considering the symbol of the metal as M and find out the atomic mass of the metal.

SOLUTION

The molecular mass of that compound = 79.5

The number of oxygen atoms present in one molecule of oxide = $\dfrac{79.5 \times 20.1}{100 \times 16} = 1$

The metal is univalent since it is alkali metal. The formula could be M_2O

The atomic mass of metal be x; $79.5 = 2x + 16 \Rightarrow x = 31.75$

POINTS TO REMEMBER

- ✔ A symbol represents an atom of an element.
- ✔ The formulae of elements and compounds are written by making use of the symbols of the respective elements.
- ✔ An atom or a group of atoms gets converted to the corresponding ions or radicals by losing or gaining electrons. These are called positive and negative radicals, respectively.
- ✔ Acids usually contain hydrogen ion (H^+) as the positive radical.
- ✔ Bases generally contain hydroxyl radical (OH^-) as the negative radical and a metal ion as the positive radical (M^+).
- ✔ Based on experiments, certain relations among the variables of gas (volume, temperature, and pressure) are established. These are stated as gas laws.
- ✔ Boyle's Law states that the volume of a given mass of a gas is inversely proportional to its pressure at constant temperature.
- ✔ Charles' Law states that, for a fixed mass of gas, the volume of a gas (V) is directly proportional to the absolute temperature (T), at constant pressure.
- ✔ For a given mass of a gas, the gas equation gives a relationship among the volume, pressure, and temperature, and can be derived by combining the laws of Boyle and Charles.
- ✔ A gas which strictly obeys the gas equation under all the conditions of temperature and pressure is called an ideal gas.
- ✔ Avogadro's law states that, under similar conditions of temperature and pressure, equal volumes of all gases contain equal number of molecules.
- ✔ The mass of the atoms of other elements is calculated with respect to the number of times an atom of an element is heavier than 1/12th part of the carbon-12 isotope. This is called atomic weight or the relative atomic mass.
- ✔ Mole is defined as the amount of substance that contains the same number of units (atoms, molecules or ions) as there are atoms in exactly 12 g of carbon-12 isotope. This number is called Avogadro number.
- ✔ The volume of the gas diffused in unit time at certain temperature and pressure through unit area is called rate of diffusion of the gas.
- ✔ The area of study pertaining to the study of this quantitative relationship among reactants and products is called stoichiometry.
- ✔ The proportion by mass of each element present in a compound is called its percentage composition.
- ✔ The chemical formula of the compound that can be calculated from the elemental analysis data (percentage by mass of each element in the compound) is called empirical formula.
- ✔ Molecular formula represents the actual number of atoms of different constituent elements present in one molecule of the compound

PRACTICE QUESTIONS CLASSROOM WING

Very Short Answer Type Questions

Direction for questions from 1 to 3:
Fill in the blanks.

1. The temperature at which molecular motion ceases is _____°C or _____ K.
2. Pressure of gas molecules is due to _____.
3. The SI unit of temperature is _____.

Direction for questions from 4 to 12:
Answer the following questions.

4. What is the mole ratio of reactants in the reaction:

   Reduction of ferric oxide with coke?

5. On heating, ammonia gives nitrogen and hydrogen. Hydrogen on treatment with chlorine gas forms hydrogen chloride gas. Hydrogen chloride gas on dissolution in water forms hydrochloric acid. Hydrochloric acid, on treatment with sodium hydroxide, forms sodium chloride and water. Sodium chloride, thus, formed on treatment with silver nitrate forms silver chloride and sodium nitrate

   Various types of reactions involved in the above process are given below. Arrange them in a proper sequence as given above.

   (A) Combination (B) Neutralization
   (C) Precipitation (D) Decomposition

6. Is the volume ratio of reactants in the formation of SO_3 from SO_2 and O_2, the same as in the formation of CO_2 from CO and O_2?
7. Calculate the molecular weight of
   (i) ammonium sulphate $[(NH_4)_2SO_4]$
   (ii) Cryolite $[Na_3AlF_6]$
8. What is STP? Give the values of temperature and pressure at STP.
9. In each of the given, a positive and a negative radical is listed. Using the criss-cross method, write the formula for the compound that is formed and name the compound.
   a. Ag^+ Br^-
   b. K^+ OH^-
   c. NH_4^+ HPO_4^{2-}
   d. Ca^{2+} HSO_4^-
   e. Sn^{4+} S^{2-}
10. Balance the following chemical equations:
    a. $NaNO_3 \rightarrow NaNO_2 + O_2$
    b. $BeO + NaOH \rightarrow Na_2BeO_2 + H_2O$
    c. $LiNO_3 \rightarrow Li_2O + NO_2 + O_2$
    d. $KI + H_2SO_4 \rightarrow K_2SO_4 + SO_2 + I_2 + H_2O$
    e. $NaBr + H_3PO_4 \rightarrow Na_3PO_4 + HBr$
    f. $SO_2 + H_2S \rightarrow H_2O + S$
11. For each of the following reactions, identify the products formed and balance the equations:
    a. $Na_2O_2 + H_2O \rightarrow$
    b. $S + HNO_3 \rightarrow$
    c. $MnO_2 + HCl \rightarrow$
    d. $HNO_3 + CaCO_3 \rightarrow$
    e. $Fe_2(SO_4)_3 + NaOH \rightarrow$
12. Empirical formula of a compound is C_2H_4O. If its empirical formula weight is equal to its vapor density, calculate the molecular formula of the compound.

Short Answer Type Questions

13. An oxyacid contains two hydrogen atoms, one sulphur atom and four oxy-gen atoms. Write the formula of the compound formed by the negative rad-ical of the acid with ferric ion.'
14. Calculate the number of atoms for 15×10^{25} molecules of SO_3 and 2.5×10^{25} molecules of N_2O_5.
15. 175 g of calcium carbonate on thermal decomposition gives 33.6 L CO_2 at STP. Calculate the percentage purity of calcium carbonate.

16. Calculate the percentage of
    (i) magnesium in magnesium carbonate
    (ii) oxygen in calcium hydroxide

17. State Gay-Lussac's law of combining volumes of gases. Give an example.

18. $2C_2H_6 + 7O_2 \rightarrow 4CO_2 + 6H_2O$
    60 dm^3 of ethane is mixed with 448 dm^3 of pure oxygen at STP. If the mixture is ignited and reacts as illustrated in the above reaction, calculate the volume of CO_2 formed.

19. The relation between gram molecular mass and gram molecular volume is established by Avogadro's law. Explain.

20. Calculate the weight of the following gases which occupy a volume 3.36 dm^3 at STP:
    (i) nitrogen
    (ii) hydrogen
    (iii) helium

21. Calculate the number of moles in
    (i) 29.4 g of H_2SO_4
    (ii) 31.9 g of hydrated copper sulphate
    (iii) 5 g of $CaCO_3$

22. (a) Calculate the weight (g) of 5×10^{24} molecules of nitrogen dioxide.
    (b) A metal 'M' forms a compound with a non-metal with atomic number 8 and the ratio of non-metal to total number of atoms is 1 : 3. Derive the formulae of the following compounds of the succeeding element of M.
    (A) Hydrogen phosphate (B) Bicarbonate
    (C) Silicate (D) Nitride

23. Two flasks A and B of equal volumes are kept under similar conditions of temperature and pressure. If flask A holds 16.2 g of gas X while flask B holds 1.35 g of hydrogen, calculate the relative molecular mass of gas X.

24. A gaseous hydrocarbon of vapor density 14 contains 85.2% of carbon. Calculate its molecular formula.

25. Calculate the amount of mercury obtained by the decomposition of 2.16 kg of mercuric oxide.

26. Give the values for the following:
    (a) Gram molecule of helium = ________ g of helium.
    (b) Gram atom of chlorine = ________ g of chlorine.
    (c) Gram atom of potassium = ________ g of potassium.

27. Calculate the amount of potassium chloride obtained by the thermal decomposition of 12.25 kg of potassium chlorate.

Essay Answer Type Questions

28. 300 mL of ethene is subjected to complete combustion. Calculate the volumes of O_2 required and CO_2 produced under same conditions.

29. The percentage composition of a compound is 80% C, 20% H. The weight of 1.5×10^{23} molecules of the compound is 7.5 g. Determine the molecular formula of the compound.

30. How many litres of CO_2 gas at STP are given by 70% pure 105 g of $NaHCO_3$?

31. Calculate the volume of CO_2 formed at STP and the weight of zinc oxide formed in grams, when 2.32 g of zinc carbonate decomposes with no further loss in weight.

32. Calculate the volume of CO_2 formed at STP and weight of calcium oxide formed, in grams, when 5.5 g of calcium carbonate crystals decompose with no further loss in weight.

33. Equal masses of three gases, ammonia, nitrogen dioxide and methane are taken in three cylinders having a volume ratio of 2 : 5 : 7 at a certain temperature. Draw a comparison of the pressures exerted by those gases.

PRACTICE QUESTIONS COMPETITION WING

Level 1: Apply your Concepts

Direction for questions from 1 to 10:
State whether the following statements are true or false.

1. Pressure of a gas is measured using a barometer.
2. Volume of the given mass of a gas is directly proportional to pressure at constant temperature.
3. The number of molecules present in 16 g of sulphur dioxide is 3×10^{23}.
4. The volume of 32 g of oxygen at STP is 224 L.
5. Under similar conditions of temperature and pressure the ratio of rate of diffusion of methane and sulphur dioxide is 2 : 1.
6. The vapour density of hydrogen peroxide is equal to molecular weight of NH_3.
7. Real gases obey gas laws under all conditions.
8. Boyle's law states that, for a given mass of a gas, the volume of a gas (V) is directly proportional to the absolute temperature (T) at constant pressure.
9. Avogadro's law states that under similar conditions of temperature and pressure, equal volumes of all gases contain equal number of molecules.
10. Charles' law states that the rate of diffusion of a gas is inversely proportional to the square root of its density at constant temperature and pressure.

Direction for questions from 11 to 19:
Fill in the blanks.

11. 1 mm of Hg = ________ torr.
12. T (Kelvin) = ________ + °C (Celsius)
13. 9.2 g of sodium contains ______ atoms.
14. Marsh gas in coal mines is detected by using ______ law.
15. The volume of 5 gram molecules of methane gas is ________ at STP.
16. 1 mole of argon gas contains ______ number of fundamental particles.
17. The ratio of a gram atomic weight of nitrogen and oxygen is __________.
18. Empirical formula of a compound is C_2H_5 and its molecular weight is 58, then its molecular formula is ______.
19. The measurable properties of a gas are ______, ______ and ______.

Direction for question 20:
Match the entries given in Column A with appropriate ones in Column B.

20. Match the statements of Column A with those of Column B.

	Column A (Relationship)		Column B (Gas Law)
(i)	Pressure–volume.	(A)	Charles
(ii)	Volume–temperature.	(B)	Boyle
(iii)	Volume–number of molecules.	(C)	Graham
(iv)	Rate of diffusion–density.	(D)	Avogadro

Direction for questions from 21 to 43:
For each of the questions, four choices have been provided. Select the correct alternative.

21. **Assertion (A):** Temperature in the Kelvin scale is always positive.

    Reason (R): The least possible temperature in the Kelvin scale is 0 K (or) −273°C.

    (a) Both A and R are true and R is the correct explanation of A.

    (b) Both A and R are true, but R is not the correct explanation of A.

    (c) A is true and R is false.

    (d) A is false and R is true.

22. Which of the following graphs is true for the given mass of a gas at constant temperature?

(a) 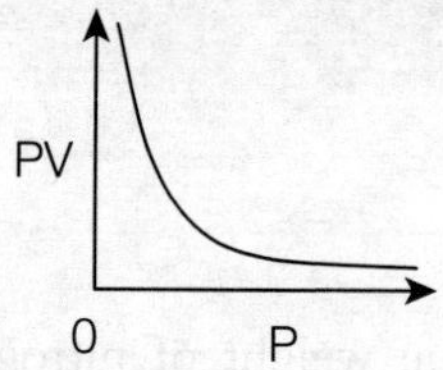

(b) 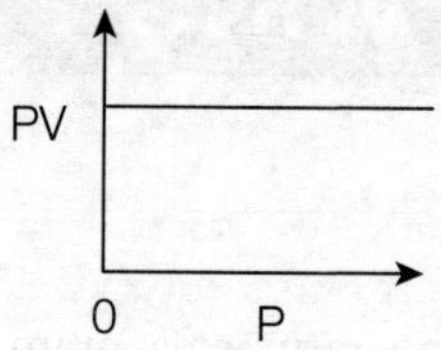

(c) 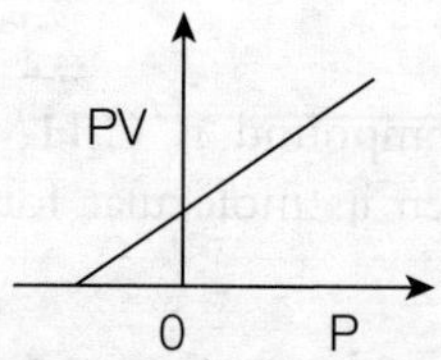

(d) 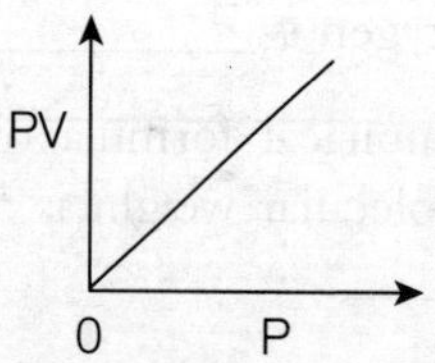

23. The formula of calcium dihydrogen phosphate is
(a) CaH_2PO_4 (b) $Ca(HPO_4)_2$
(c) $Ca(H_2PO_4)_2$ (d) $Ca_3(PO_4)_2$

24. The number of oxygen atoms present in 0.25 moles of magnesium perchlorate is
(a) 4N (b) 8N
(c) 6N (d) 2N

25. Vapor density of SO_3 is ______.
(a) 80 (b) 48
(c) 32 (d) 40

26. If equal volumes of two gases, CH_4 and O_2, are allowed to diffuse, then the time taken for diffusion of CH_4 is found to be:
(a) $\frac{1}{2}$ times that of O_2
(b) $\frac{1}{\sqrt{2}}$ times that of O_2
(c) $\sqrt{2}$ times that of O_2
(d) 2 times that of O_2

27. If the rate of diffusion of a gas is r and its density is d, then under similar conditions of pressure and temperature ______.
(a) $r \propto d$ (b) $r \propto \sqrt{d}$
(c) $r \propto \frac{1}{\sqrt{d}}$ (d) $r \propto \frac{1}{d}$

28. The volume of CO_2 liberated at STP on burning 24 g of carbon in excess oxygen is ______.
(a) 22.4 L (b) 44.8 L
(c) 16.8 L (d) 67.2 L

29. Which among the following contain 43.4% of sodium?
(a) sodium bicarbonate
(b) sodium nitrate
(c) sodium carbonate
(d) sodium chloride

30. The number of atoms present in 16 g of O_2 is ______.
(a) 6.023×10^{23}
(b) 3.011×10^{23}
(c) 12.046×10^{23}
(d) 3.011×10^{22}

31. In which of the following cases, empirical formula is the same as molecular formula?
(a) Sucrose (b) C_6H_6
(c) C_2H_5COOH (d) Glucose

32. 50 g of magnesium on treatment 40 g of carbon dioxide gives magnesium oxide. In this amount of excess reagent taken is
(a) 8.5 g (b) 6.37 g
(c) 5.5 g (d) 7.5 g

33. Identify the correct sequence of relevant steps to write the formula of cupric bisulphate.
(1) Writing the symbol of a negative radical as HSO_4^{2-}.
(2) Writing the symbol of a positive radical as Cu^{2+}.
(3) Writing the symbol of a negative radical as HSO_4^-.
(4) Writing the symbol of a positive radical as Cu^+.
(5) Interchanging the valencies of positive and negative radicals and writing subscripts as 1 and 2.
(6) Interchanging the valencies of positive and negative radicals and writing subscripts as 2 and 1.
(7) Keeping HSO_4 in parenthesis.
(8) Keeping Cu in parenthesis.
(a) 2 1 5 8 (b) 2 3 5 7
(c) 4 3 6 8 (d) 4 1 6 7

34. Arrange the following relevant points in a proper sequence to explain why gases exert pressure.
(1) Gas molecules are in random motion.
(2) Kinetic energy of gas molecules is proportional to absolute temperature.
(3) A gas is made up of tiny particles called molecules.
(4) Intermolecular forces of attraction are negligible in gases.
(5) During random motion, the gas molecules collide with each other.

(6) During random motion, the gas molecules collide with the walls of a container.

(a) 3 1 4 5 6 (b) 3 2 4 6 5
(c) 3 4 1 6 (d) 3 4 1 5 6

35. Arrange the following relevant points in a proper sequence for explaining why Kelvin scale is preferred to Celsius scale in the study of gases.

(1) −273°C is the least possible temperature.
(2) A graph of volume vs temperature is a straight line passing through origin.
(3) A graph of volume vs temperature (°C) is a straight line which intersects volume axis at some point.
(4) Extrapolation of straight line touches the volume axis at −237°C.
(5) −237°C is called absolute zero or 0 K.
(6) All values of temperature are positive in Kelvin scale.
(7) Usage of negative values for temperature gives negative values for other properties, like, pressure and volume.

(a) 3 4 1 5 6 (b) 2 4 1 5 6 7
(c) 3 4 6 5 1 7 (d) 2 4 6 5 1 2

36. The ratio of phosphorus atoms present in calcium phosphide and magnesium phosphate is

(a) 1 : 2 (b) 2 : 1
(c) 1 : 3 (d) 1 : 1

37. For which of the following reactions, is Gay-Lussac's law not applicable?

(a) formation of HI from its constituents
(b) formation of NH_3 from its constituents
(c) formation of CO_2 from its constituents
(d) formation of SO_3 from SO_2 and O_2

38. The ratio of number of molecules present in a given mass of oxygen and sulphur trioxide is

(a) 2 : 1 (b) 5 : 2
(c) 2 : 5 (d) 1 : 2

39. At constant temperature, a gas is at a pressure of 940 mm of Hg. At what pressure, its volume decreases by 40%?

(a) 564 mm of Hg (b) 1860 mm of Hg
(c) 2350 mm of Hg (d) 1567 mm of Hg

40. The ratio of rates of diffusion of two gases X and Y is $4 : \sqrt{11}$. If the molecular mass of Y is double to the molecular mass of oxygen, then X is:

(a) CO (b) SO_3
(c) CO_2 (d) NO

41. 160 mL of carbon monoxide is mixed with 100 mL of oxygen and the mixture is ignited. What volume of oxygen is left behind? (Assume that all volumes are measured under same conditions.)

(a) 80 mL (b) 60 mL
(c) 20 mL (d) 40 mL

42. Assertion (A): One gram molecule of any gas occupies 22.4 L volume at STP

Reason (R): Under similar conditions of temperature and pressure equal masses of all gases occupy equal volumes.

(a) Both A and R are correct and R is the correct explanation for A
(b) Both A and R are correct but R is not the correct explanation for A
(c) A is correct, but R is wrong
(d) A is wrong, but R is correct

43. What is the volume of oxygen liberated at STP when 24.5 g of potassium chlorate is subjected to heating?

(a) 3.36 L (b) 5.6 L
(c) 6.72 L (d) 16.8 L

Level 2: Review your Concepts

44. Arrange the following compounds in the increasing order of number of oxygen atoms.

(a) Plumbic carbonate (b) Ferric chromate
(c) Zinc silicate (d) Aluminium sulphite

45. 96 g of 'X' contains 9×10^{23} molecules, and 0.32 g of gas 'Y' contains 1.2×10^{22} molecules. Compare the rate of diffusion (r) of X and Y at the same temperature and pressure.

46. Arrange the following compounds in the decreasing order of the total number of atoms.

(A) Mercuric phosphate
(B) Magnesium nitride
(C) Cupric chlorite
(D) Auric sulphite

47. The volume of a given mass of gas is 400 mL at 3 atm pressure. Calculate the new volume when pressure increases by 15% at a constant temperature.

48. Calculate the volume of CO_2 required for the complete combustion of 30 g of coke at STP, if the percentage conversion is 80%.

49. Compare the rates of diffusion of oxygen, sulphur trioxide and ozone at constant temperature and pressure.

50. In an organic compound the percentage of carbon and hydrogen are 40 and 6.7, respectively. If the vapor density of the compound is 30, what is the molecular formula of the compound?

51. (a) How many grams of oxygen contain the same number of molecules as present in 352 g of CO_2?

(b) Three gas cylinders of equal capacity are filled with oxygen and two unknown gases X and Y respectively at the same temperature and pressure. Calculate the gram molecular masses of X and Y if the mass of oxygen in the cylinder is 8 g and X and Y are 5 g and 20 g respectively.

52. The volume occupied by oxygen at STP obtained on heating the 490 g of $KClO_3$ is 130 L. Calculate the percentage purity of $KClO_3$ ($KClO_3$ on heating produces KCl and O_2).

53. Balance the following chemical reactions by identifying the products:

(a) $CuSO_4 + HI \rightarrow CuI_2 +$ ___

(b) $PCl_5 + H_2O \rightarrow H_3PO_4 +$ ___

(c) $Fe_3O_4 + HCl \rightarrow FeCl_2 + FeCl_3$ ___

(d) $Al_2O_3 + N_2 + C \rightarrow AlN +$ ___

54. How many moles of water are required to be dissociated to produce oxygen which is just sufficient to form 800 g of magnesium oxide by burning magnesium? (atomic weight of Mg is 24)

55. The mass of 256 mL of a triatomic elemental gas at 27°C and 4 atm is 2 g. Calculate the weight of one atom.

56. 710 g of chlorine gas contains X atoms of chlorine. Calculate the mass of sodium chloride which contains X number of chloride radicals. (atomic weight of Na is 23 g)

57. Two gases A and B, which do not chemically react, are taken in two 1 L containers. They are found to exert pressures P_1 and P_2, respectively. When the mixture of the gases A and B is taken in another 1 L container, the pressure exerted is found to be (P_1 + P_2). How can you justify this on the basis of kinetic molecular theory?

58. A particular compound contains only nitrogen and hydrogen. The percentage of nitrogen in that compound is 87.5%. Further, 96 g of that compound contains 18×10^{23} molecules of that substance. Find out the molecular formula of that compound.

Directions for questions from 59 to 67:

Application-Based Questions

59. The ratio of non-metal atoms to the number of atoms of two nonmetallic oxides A and B are 0.33 and 0.25, respectively. Find the valencies of non-metals present in those nonmetallic oxides.

60. Two moles of chlorine atoms are present in how many grams of chlorine gas?

61. A cylinder is filled with a mixture of equal number of molecules of oxygen, carbon dioxide, and helium. When leakage occurs, do equal amounts of gases come out? Give a reason.

62. At what centigrade temperature, will the volume of a given mass of a gas at 0°C triple itself if pressure is kept constant?

63. Two gases A and B are kept in two cylinders and allowed to diffuse through a small hole. If the time taken by gas A is four times the time taken by gas B for diffusion of equal volume of gas under similar conditions of temperature and pressure, what will be the ratio of their molecular masses?

64. (a) If the volume occupied by a certain mass of gas is decreased by 60%, what would be the percentage change in pressure at the same temperature?

(b) A certain amount of calcium nitrate is subjected to heating. The oxygen obtained get completely exhausted on reaction with 4.8 g of magnesium. Calculate the amount of calcium nitrate taken and also the amount of final product obtained.

65. The percentage of a trivalent metal in a metallic oxide is 53%. How many grams of this metallic oxide should be required to produce 22.8 g of salt when treated with excess sulphuric acid?

66. 44.8 L of ammonia at STP on decomposition gives X g of nitrogen. How many molecules of oxygen are required to produce NO_2 from X g of nitrogen?

67. Calculate the number of molecules of gaseous product obtained on heating 8.8 g of CO_2 with coke if the conversion of CO_2 is 80% by mass.

Level 3: Assess Your Concepts

68. If the volume occupied by a certain mass of gas is decreased to 70%, what would be the percentage change in pressure at the same temperature?

69. What is the volume of gaseous products obtained by the thermal decomposition of 59.2 g of magnesium nitrate at STP?

70. (a) Under what conditions can ideal gases be liquefied? Give reasons to support your answer.

(b) A 53 g sample of a mixture of sodium carbonate and sodium bicarbonate is subjected to heating till there is no further loss in weight. The gaseous products occupied 11.2L volume at STP. Calculate the relative percentage of the two components in the mixture.

71. 210 g of sodium bicarbonate is subjected to thermal decomposition in an open vessel and in a container fitted with a condenser separately. Calculate the change of loss in weight.

72. If 1 mole of each reactant is taken, then calculate the loss of weight of reactants, on thermal decomposition for $KClO_3$ and $CaCO_3$ and find out whose loss in weight is more.

Directions for questions from 73 to 77:
Application-Based Questions

73. A certain volume of O_2 gas is kept in a cylinder fitted with a movable piston. If all the O_2 molecules present in that cylinder get converted to O_3 molecules at the same temperature and pressure, will you observe any change in the system? Calculate the percentage change if any change takes place. Justify your answer with appropriate reasons.

74. Equal volumes of CO and O_2 are kept in a closed cylinder under certain temperature and pressure. The mixture is heated till all the CO gets converted to CO_2. Then, the temperature of the gases is brought to the previous temperature. Will there be any change in any parameter of the gas or gases present in the cylinder? Justify your answer with appropriate reasons. If any change takes place, calculate the percentage change.

75. A sample of a mixture of Na_2CO_3 and $NaHCO_3$ is subjected to heating till there is no further loss in weight. Assuming that the loss in weight of the sample is 22% of the initial weight of the mixture due to the evolution of CO_2, find out the relative percentages of the two components in the mixture.

76. A patient Vasu had to survive for a month on artificial respiration before he passed away. A nurse was instructed to give him 7.5 g of glucose per hour for consumption to meet the energy requirement. What volume of carbogen (95% O_2 + 5% CO_2) had to be supplied for Vasu assuming that he was kept under the conditions of 27°C and normal atmospheric pressure?

77. 64.5% pure sample of zinc when treated with excess of dil. HCl liberated some volume of hydrogen gas at STP. This hydrogen is utilized for the reduction of 23.2 g Fe_3O_4. Find out the amount of iron obtained and also amount of impure zinc taken. [atomic mass of Zn = 65.5 and Fe = 56].

AT

PRACTICE QUESTIONS JEE-NEET SPECIAL WING

Multiple-Answer Type Questions

Directions for questions 1 to 5:

Select one or more correct alternative(s) from the given choices.

1. Identify the molecular formulae which correspond to the empirical formula 'CH_2O'
   (a) CH_3COOH (b) HCHO
   (c) C_2H_5OH (d) CH_3CHO
2. Which among the following pairs have almost equal rates of diffusion under similar conditions of temperature and pressure?
   (a) Methane and Ammonia
   (b) Carbon monoxide and Nitrogen
   (c) Nitric oxide and Ethane
   (d) Carbon dioxide and Nitrous oxide
3. A hydrocarbon on complete combustion gives carbon dioxide and water vapour. Identify the sets of hydrocarbons from the given choices which utilise equal number of moles of oxygen for combustion reactions:
   (a) 2 mole C_4H_8 ; 3 mole C_3H_4
   (b) 4 mole C_2H_6 ; 2 mole C_4H_6
   (c) 4 mole C_5H_{10} ; 5 mole C_3H_8
   (d) 2 mole C_3H_8 ; 4 mole C_2H_2
4. Which among the following gases occupy a volume of 6.72 litre volume at STP?
   (a) 19.2 g sulphur dioxide (b) 13.8 g nitrogen dioxide
   (c) 18 g ethane (d) 3.4 g ammonia
5. Identify the correctly matched pairs among the following.

	Compound	Percentage of carbon
(a)	Acetic acid	40
(b)	Calcium bicarbonate	24
(c)	Ethyl alcohol	52
(d)	Sodium carbonate	11

Comprehension-Based Questions

Directions for questions 6 to 10:

Read the given paragraph and answer the questions given below.

A mixture of oxygen gas and carbon monoxide gas is taken in 2 : 1 ratio in a cylinder with movable piston at 27°C. They are made to react to give CO_2 gas which occupied a volume of 33.6 litre at STP. The gaseous mixture at the end of the reaction is transferred into a 6 litre cylinder at the same temperature. This mixture is then used to fill the balloons each having a volume of 200 mL.

6. What would be the percentage change in the pressure in the cylinder at the end of the reaction?
   (a) Pressure increases by 16.6%
   (b) Pressure decreases by 16.6%
   (c) Pressure decreases by 22.6%
   (d) Pressure increases by 22.6%
7. Identify the number of balloons which can be filled by the gaseous mixture transferred from the cylinder.
   (a) 150 (b) 120
   (c) 100 (d) 180
8. What are the values of partial pressures of oxygen and CO_2 in the cylinder at the end of the reaction?
   (a) 3 atm; 2 atm (b) 3 atm; 3 atm
   (c) 2 atm; 4 atm (d) 4 atm; 4 atm
9. The gaseous mixture formed is allowed to be transferred into a cylinder. If 40 ml of oxygen present in the mixture coming out of the reaction vessel in unit time, what would be the volume of CO_2 in the mixture?
   (a) 17 mL (b) 34 mL
   (c) 25 mL (d) 10 mL
10. If the gaseous mixture is allowed to pass through calcium hydroxide, what would be the amount of white precipitate obtained assuming complete reaction?
   (a) 166.5 g (b) 100 g
   (c) 450 g (d) 150 g

Directions for questions 11 to 16:

Read the given paragraph and answer the questions given below.

The following table gives the list of 5 elements with the number of times their atoms is heavier than an atom of carbon 12 isotope. Based on the information given in the table, answer the questions given below.

Element	No. of times an atom is heavier than carbon-12 atom
A	1.167
B	2.67
C	2.59
D	3.34
E	4.67

11. Identify the set of ions which cannot be formed by the element 'C'.

(a) $H_2CO_3^-$; HCO_4^{-2}
(b) CO_4^{-3}; HCO_3^{-2}; HCO_4^{-2}
(c) CO_3^{-3}; HCO_4-
(d) C^{-3}; HCO_3^{-2}

12. Identify the statements which comply with the characteristics of element 'E'.

(a) It shows variable valency by forming E^{+2} and E^+ ions.
(b) Two stable oxides with formulae EO and E_2O_3 are formed.
(c) The molecular mass of the compound formed with B could be approximately 88
(d) It is highly vapourisable metal at relatively lower temperatures.

13. Identify the correctly matched sets pertaining to the element B.

(i)	Lower oxide	32 g occupies 11.2 L volume at STP
(ii)	Higher oxide	32 g occupies 4.48 L volume at STP
(iii)	Higher oxyacid	56 g oxide dissolved in water gives 68.6 g of acid
(iv)	Lower oxyacid	16.4 g contain 1.2 $\times 10^{23}$ atoms

(a) (i), (ii) (b) (ii), (iii)
(c) (ii), (iv) (d) (i), (iii)

14. One among the given elements forms a compound of the formula XH_4XO_3. Identify the element.

(a) E (b) C
(c) B (d) A

15. Identify the set of elements which form the compound of the formula X_3Y_2.

(a) E; C (b) D; C
(c) E; A (d) D; A

16. Which among the following oxides have equal proportions of oxygen and the other element?

(a) AO_2 (b) BO_2
(c) E_2O_3 (d) C_2O_3

Directions for question 17:

Read the content given in the following passage and match the entries in column I with those in column II.

Oxygen gas can be obtained by four different methods by subjecting the compounds A, B, C and D to thermal decomposition. The description of the compounds is given below.

A- The binary compound in which hydrogen and oxygen atoms combine in 1 : 1 ratio

B, C and D are the salts of a monovalent metal with gram equivalent mass of 39 g.

B- The salt of ic acid of chlorine

C- A purple coloured compound of the given metal

D- The salt of higher oxy acid of nitrogen

The oxygen gas in each case is collected separately and the volumes are measured at 273°C temperature and 2 atm pressure.

17. Based on the information given above, match the entries in column I with those in column II.

	Column I Amount of compound taken		Column II Volume of O_2 obtained
(a)	10.2 g of compound A	(i)	8.96 L
(b)	73.5 g of comound B	(ii)	560 mL
(c)	7.9 g of compound C	(iii)	3.36 L
(d)	80.8 g of compound D	(iv)	20.16 L

ANSWER KEYS

Crossword

Across

3. Gram molar volume
7. Boyle's law
10. Graham's law
14. Mole
15. Photolytic decomposition
16. Stoichiometry
17. Ideal gas
18. Mole fraction
19. Ide
20. Atomic mass unit

Down

1. Thermolytic decomposition
2. Rate of diffusion
4. Valency
5. Absolute zero
6. Potassium
8. Gram atom
9. Charles law
11. Empirical formula
12. Gram molecule
13. Temperature

Classroom Wing

Very Short Answer Type Questions

1. –273, 0
2. Collisions on the walls of container
3. Kelvin

Competition Wing

Level 1: Apply your Concepts

1. True
2. False
3. False
4. True
5. True
6. True
7. False
8. False
9. True
10. False
11. one
12. 273
13. 2.4×10^{23}
14. Grahams
15. 112 L
16. 54 N
17. 7 : 8
18. C_4H_{10}
19. Pressure, volume, temperature
20. (i) → (B); (ii) → (A); (iii) → (D); (iv) → (C)
21. (a)
22. (b)
23. (c)
24. (d)
25. (d)
26. (b)
27. (c)
28. (b)
29. (c)
30. (a)
31. (a)
32. (b)
33. (b)
34. (c)
35. (b)
36. (d)
37. (c)
38. (b)
39. (d)
40. (c)
41. (c)
42. (c)
43. (c)

JEE-NEET Special Wing

Multiple-Answer Type Questions

1. (a; b)
2. (a; b; c; d)
3. (a; d)
4. (a; b)
5. (a; c; d)

Comprehension-Based Questions

6. (c)
7. (b)
8. (a)
9. (b)
10. (d)
11. (c)
12. (b)
13. (d)
14. (d)
15. (b)
16. (b)
17. (a) ↔ (iii); (b) ↔ (iv); (c) ↔ (ii); (d) ↔ (i)

Hints and Explanations

Classroom Wing

Very Short Answer Type Question

1. –273, 0
2. Collisions on the walls of container
3. Kelvin
4. $Fe_2O_3 + 3C \rightarrow 2Fe + 3CO$

   $\therefore$ Mole ratio of Fe_2O_3 and C is 1:3.
5. The correct order is DABC.
6. Yes.

   $2SO_2 + O_2 \rightarrow 2SO_3$

   Volume ratio of reactants = 2:1 ($\therefore n \alpha v$)

   $2CO + O_2 \rightarrow 2CO_2$

   Volume ratio of reactants = 2:1
7. (i) 132 g (ii) 210 g
8. The standard temperature and pressure which refer to the volume of gas.

   Standard temperature = 0°C = 273 K

   Standard pressure = 1 atm = 760 mm of Hg = 76 cm of Hg
9.
   a. AgBr
   b. KOH
   c. $(NH_4)_2HPO_4$
   d. $Ca(HSO_4)_2$
   e. SnS_2
10.
    a. $2NaNO_3 \longrightarrow 2NaNO_2 + O_2$
    b. $BeO + 2NaOH \longrightarrow Na_2BeO_2 + H_2O$
    c. $4LiNO_3 \longrightarrow 2Li_2O + 4NO_2 + O_2$
    d. $2KI + 2H_2SO_4 \longrightarrow K_2SO_4 + SO_2 + I_2 + 2H_2O$
    e. $3NaBr + H_3PO_4 \longrightarrow Na_3PO_4 + 3HBr$
    f. $SO_2 + 2H_2S \longrightarrow 2H_2O + 3S$
11.
    a. $2Na_2O_2 + 2H_2O \longrightarrow 4NaOH + O_2$
    b. $S + 6HNO_3 \longrightarrow H_2SO_4 + 6NO_2 + 2H_2O$
    c. $MnO_2 + 4HCl \longrightarrow MnCl_4 + 2H_2O.$
    d. $2HNO_3 + CaCO_3 \longrightarrow Ca(NO_3)_2 + H_2CO_3$
    e. $Fe_2(SO_4)_3 + 6NaOH \longrightarrow 3Na_2SO_4 + 2Fe(OH)_3$
12. Empirical formula weight = 12 + 2 + 4 + 16 = 44

    Empirical formula weight = Vapour density = 44

    Molecular weight = 2 × vapour density = 44 × 2 = 88

    Molecular formula = $C_4H_8O_2$.

Short Answer Type Questions

13. Oxyacid is H_2SO_4.

    $\therefore$ Negative radical is SO_4^{-2}.

    $\therefore$ Compound of Fe^{+3}, $SO_4^{-2} \Rightarrow Fe_2(SO_4)_3$.
14. No. of atoms in 15×10^{25} molecules of SO_3 $= 15 \times 10^{25} \times 4 = 6 \times 10^{26}$

    No. of atoms in 2.5×10^{25} molecules of N_2O_5 $= 2.5 \times 5 \times 10^{25} = 12.5 \times 10^{25}$
15. $CaCO_3 \rightarrow CaO + CO_2$

    100 g of $CaCO_3$ gives 22.4L of CO_2 at STP.

    x g of $CaCO_3$ gives 33.6L of CO_2 at STP.

    $$\Rightarrow x = \frac{100 \times 33.6}{22.4} = 150 \text{ g of 100\% } CaCO_3$$

    $$\therefore \text{\% purity} = \frac{150}{175} \times 100 = 85.7\%.$$
16. Formula used: Amount of element present in 100 g of the compound

    $$= \frac{\text{Amount of element} \times 100}{\text{Molecular weight}} \times 100$$
17. When gases react chemically, they do so in volumes which bear a simple whole number ratio to each other and to the volumes of the products, provided the products are also in the gaseous state and the temperature and pressure of the reactant and product gases are the same.

    Example: In the reaction of carbon monoxide with oxygen, two volumes of carbon monoxide react with one volume of oxygen to give two volumes of carbon dioxide

18. 2 moles of Ethane reacts with 7 moles of Oxygen to form 4 moles of Carbon dioxide.

1 mole of ethane = 30

2 moles of ethane = (2×30)=60 dm^3

1 mole of oxygen = 32

7 moles of oxygen = (7×32) =224 dm^3

2 moles of ethane = (2×30)= 60 dm^3 reacts with 7 moles of Oxygen = (7×32) = 224 dm^3 to form (4×44) =176 dm^3 of Carbon dioxide.

19. Avogadro reinterpreted Gay-Lussac's findings and proposed in 1811 that

(1) some molecules were diatomic and

(2) "equal volumes of all gases at the same temperature and pressure contain the same number of molecules"

20. Here given volume = 3.6 dm^3 = 3.36 L

Moles of gas = 3.36/22.4 = 3/20 = 0.15

(a) Nitrogen (N_2)

molecular weight of N_2 gas = 28 g/mol

Number of moles = 0.15

so, weight of N_2 gas = molecular weight × number of moles

= 28×0.15 = 4.2 g

(b) Hydrogen (H_2)

Molecular weight of H_2 gas = 2 g/mol

so, weight of H_2 gas = molecular weight × number of moles

= 2×0.15 = 0.3 g

(c) Helium (He)

Molecular weight of He gas = 4g/mol

so, weight of He gas = molecular weight × number of moles

= 4×0.15 = 0.6 g

21. (i) 29.4 g of H_2SO_4 = 29.4/98.07 = 0.3

(ii) 31.9 g of $CuSO_4.5H_2O$ = 31.9/249.7 = 0.127

(iii) 5 g of $CaCO_3$ = 5/100 = 0.05

22. (a) 381 g

(b) The formula of compound of metal and nonmetal (oxygen) should be M_2O. The metal ion should be monovalent (M^+). The succeeding element of M should be bivalent and forms M^{+2} ion.

(A) Formula of metal hydrogen phosphate $MHPO_4$

(B) Formula of metal bicarbonate $M(HCO_3)_2$

(C) Formula of metal silicate $MSiO_3$

(D) Formula of metal nitride M_3N_2

23. No. of moles in 2 g of hydrogen gas = 1

No. of moles in 1.01 g of hydrogen gas = 1/2

Now the weight of gas X that contains 1/2 moles = 16.2 g

Weight of gas X that contains 1 mole = 32 g

24. (i) Molecular weight = 2 × vapour density

(ii) Calculate the simplest ratio of the number of carbons and hydrogens.

(iii) Calculate empirical formula weight using the formula:

Molecular formula = n × Empirical formula,

(iv) Calculate molecular formula from empirical formula weight and molecular weight.

25. (i) $2HgO \rightarrow 2Hg + O_2$

(ii) 2(200 + 16) = 432 gm of HgO produces 2(200) = 400 gm of Hg

1 gm of HgO will produce 400/432 gm

2160 gm will produce = (400/432) × 2160 gm = 2160 gm of Hg

26. (a) 4.003

(b) 35.5

(c) 39

27. (i) $KClO_3 \rightarrow 2KCl + 3O_2$

(ii) 1 mole of potassium chlorate gives 2 moles of potassium chloride.

Mass of 1 mole of potassium chloride = 122.55 g

Mass of 1 mole of potassium chloride = 74.55 g

122.55 g of $KClO_3$ gives = 2 × 74.55 g of KCl

1 g of $KClO_3$ gives = 2 × 74.55 g of KCl

14.903 kg of KCl is produced.

Essay Answer Type Questions

28. $C_2H_4 + 3O_2 \rightarrow 2CO_2 + 2H_2O$

1 volume of C_2H_4 requires 3 volumes of O_2 and gives 2 volumes of CO_2.

⇒ 300 volume of C_2H_4 requires 900 volume of O_2 and gives 400 volume of CO_2.

29.

Element	Atomic Weight	Percentage	Atomic Ratio	Simplest Ratio
C	12	80	$\frac{18}{12} = 6.67$	$\frac{6.67}{6.67} = 1$
H	1	20	$\frac{20}{1} = 20$	$\frac{20}{6.67} = 3$

Empirical formula is CH_3.

Empirical formula mass = 15

1.5×10^{23} molecules → 7.5 g

6×10^{23} molecules → ?

$$= \frac{7.5 \times 6 \times 10^{23}}{1.5 \times 20^{23}} = 30 \text{ g}$$

$\therefore$ GMM = 30

$$\therefore n = \frac{30}{15} = 2$$

$\therefore$ Molecular formula = $(CH_3)_2 = C_2H_6$.

30. Amounts of pure $NaHCO_3$ in 105 g sample

$$\frac{70 \times 105}{100} = 73.5 \text{ g}$$

$$\text{No. of moles of } NaHCO_3 = \frac{73.5}{84} = 0.875$$

$2NaHCO_3 \rightarrow Na_2CO_3 + CO_2 = H_2O$

1 mole of $NaHCO_3 \rightarrow 0.5$ moles of CO_2

0.875 mole of $NaHCO_3 \rightarrow 0.875 \times 0.5 = 0.437$ mole CO_2

1 mole of $CO_2 \rightarrow 22.4\ \lambda$ at STP

0.437 mole of $CO_2 \rightarrow 22.4 \times 0.437 = 9.8\ \lambda$ at STP

31. $ZnCO_3 \rightarrow ZnO + CO_2$

32. $CaCO_3 \rightarrow CaO + CO_2$

33. Let mass of each gas be x g

$$n_{NH_3} = \frac{x}{17}$$

$$n_{NO_2} = \frac{x}{46}$$

$$n_{CH_4} = \frac{x}{16}$$

By using ideal gas equation, PV = nRT

$$P_{NH_3} = \frac{nRT}{V} = \frac{\frac{x}{17}}{2}RT = \frac{x}{34}RT$$

$$P_{NO_2} = \frac{\frac{x}{46}}{5}RT = \frac{x}{230}RT$$

$$P_{CH_4} = \frac{\frac{x}{16}}{7}RT = \frac{x}{112}RT$$

The pressures are in the order $NH_3 > CH_4 > NO_2$.

Competition Wing

Level 1: Apply your Concepts

20. Pressure – volume ⇒ Boyle law

Volume – number of molecules ⇒ Avogadro law

Volume – temperature ⇒ Charles law

Rate of diffusion – density ⇒ Graham law

Hence, the answer is (i) → (B); (ii) → (A); (iii) → (D); (iv) → (C).

21. The least possible temperature is –273°C or 0 K. Any centigrade temperature greater than –273°C will become positive when converted to absolute scale. Since a centigrade temperature of less than –273°C is not possible, Kelvin temperature cannot have a negative value.

Hence, the correct option is (a).

22. Since all values of temperature are positive in the Kelvin scale, the volume of gas is always positive. Hence, Kelvin temperature is used in studying gas laws.

Hence, the correct option is (a).

23. 2-gram molecules of oxygen = 2 moles = 2 × 22.4 λ = 44.8 λ at STP

1 mole of any gas contains 6×10^{23} particles.

Hence, the correct option is (d).

24. 44 g of CO_2 corresponds to 1 mole, which contains 6×10^{23} molecules.

1 mole of any gas occupies 22.4 L at STP.

Hence, the correct option is (d).

33. 2 writing the symbol of positive radical as Cu^{2+}

3 writing the symbol of negative radical as HSO_4^-

5 interchanging the valencies of positive and negative radicals and writing 1 and 2 as subscripts.

7 keeping HSO_4 in parenthesis

Hence, the correct answer is (b).

34. 3 Gas is made up of tiny particles called molecules.

4 Intermolecular forces of attraction are negligible in gases.

1 Gas molecules are in random motion.

6 During random motion, the gas molecules collide with the walls of the container.

Hence, the correct answer is (c).

35. 2 A graph of volume vs. temperature (°C) is a straight line which intersects volume axis at some point.

4 Extrapolation of straight line touches the volume axis at –273°C.

1 –273 °C is the least possible temperature.

5 –273°C is called absolute zero or 0 Kelvin.

6 All values of temperature are positive in Kelvin scale.

7 Usage of negative values gives negative values for other properties, like, pressure and volume.

Hence, the correct answer is (b).

36.

Ca_3P_2	$Mg_3(PO_4)_2$
3 Ca atoms	3 Mg atoms
2 P atoms	2 P atoms
	8 O atoms

The ratio of phosphorus atoms is 2 : 2 = 1 : 1

Hence, the correct answer is (d).

37. Constituents of CO_2 are carbon and oxygen where carbon is a solid, Gay-Lussac's law is applicable for only gaseous reactions.

Hence, the correct answer is (c).

38. 32 g of oxygen contains N molecules

32 g of SO_3 contains $\frac{80}{32}$ N molecules

Ratio of number of molecules present in 32 g

of O_2 and $SO_3 = N : \frac{80}{32}N = 2.5 : 1 = 5 : 2$

Hence, the correct answer is (b).

39. P_1 = 940 mm of Hg, V_2 = 60 L

V_1 = 100 L, P_2 = ?

$$P_2 = \frac{P_1V_1}{V_2} = \frac{940 \times 100}{60} = 1567 \text{ mm Hg}$$

Hence, the correct answer is (d).

40. $$\frac{r_x}{r_y} = \frac{4}{\sqrt{11}} = \sqrt{\frac{M_y}{M_x}} \Rightarrow \frac{4}{\sqrt{11}} = \sqrt{\frac{M_y}{M_x}} (1)$$

Molecular weight of O_2 = 32

∴ Molecular weight of Y = 2 × 32 = 64

$$\therefore \frac{4}{\sqrt{11}} = \sqrt{\frac{64}{M_x}} \Rightarrow \frac{16}{11} = \frac{64}{M_x} \Rightarrow M_x = 44$$

∴ Gas X is CO_2

Hence, the correct answer is (c).

41. $2CO + O_2 \rightarrow 2CO_2$

2 moles of CO react with 1 mole of O_2

160 mL (moles) of CO react with ? mL (moles) of O_2

$= \frac{160 \times 1}{2} = 80\,\text{ml of } O_2$

$\therefore$ Volume of O_2 left = 100 – 80 = 20 mL

Hence, the correct answer is (c).

42. One gram molecule of any gas occupies 22.4 L volume at STP.

According to Avogadro's law, under similar conditions of temperature and pressure equal moles but not equal mass of all gases occupy equal volumes.

Hence, the correct answer is (c).

43. $2KClO_3 \xrightarrow{\Delta} 2KCl + 3O_2 \uparrow$

2 moles of $KClO_3 \rightarrow$ 3 moles of O_2

$\frac{24.5}{122.5} = 0.2\,\text{moles} \rightarrow x = \frac{3 \times 0.2}{2}$

= 0.3 moles of O_2

1 mole $\rightarrow$ 22.4 L

$0.3 \rightarrow x = 6.72$ L

Hence, the correct answer is (c).

Level 2: Review your Concepts

44. Plumbic carbonate = Pb^{+4}, $CO_3^{-2} \Rightarrow Pb(CO_3)_2$ $\Rightarrow$ 6 oxygen atoms

Ferric chromate = Fe^{+3}, $CrO_4^{-2} \Rightarrow Fe_2(CrO_4)_3$ $\Rightarrow$ 12 oxygen atoms

Zinc silicate = Zn^{+2}, $SiO_3^{-2} \Rightarrow ZnSiO_3 \Rightarrow$ 3 oxygen atoms

Aluminium sulphite = Al^{+3}, $SO_3^{-2} \Rightarrow Al_2(SO_3)_3 \Rightarrow$ 9 oxygen atoms

45 96 g of X $\rightarrow 9 \times 10^{23}$ molecules

a g of X $\rightarrow 6 \times 10^{23}$ molecules

$\therefore a = \frac{96 \times 6 \times 10^{23}}{9 \times 10^{23}}$

$a = 64$ g

$\therefore$ GMM of X = 64 g

0.32 g of Y $\rightarrow 1.2 \times 10^{22}$ molecules

b g of Y $\rightarrow 6 \times 10^{23}$ molecules

$\Rightarrow b = \frac{0.32 \times 6 \times 10^{23}}{1.2 \times 10^{22}}$

$b = 16$ g

$\therefore$ GMM of Y = 16 g

According to Graham's law $\frac{rX}{rY} = \sqrt{\frac{GM\,MY}{GM\,MX}}$

$\Rightarrow \frac{rX}{rY} = \sqrt{\frac{16}{24}} = \frac{1}{2} \Rightarrow rY = 2rX$

46. Mercuric phosphate = Hg^{+2}, $PO_4^{-3} \Rightarrow Hg_3(PO_4)_2$ $\Rightarrow$ 13 atoms

Magnesium nitride = Mg^{+2}, $N^{-3} \Rightarrow Mg_3N_2 \Rightarrow$ 5 atoms

Cupric chlorite = Cu^{+2}, $ClO_2^{-1} \Rightarrow Cu(ClO_2)_2$ $\Rightarrow$ 7 atoms

Auric sulphite = Au^{+3} , $SO_3^{-2} \Rightarrow Au_2(SO_3)_2$ $\Rightarrow$ 10 atoms.

47. V_1 + 400 mL, $P_2 = 3 + \left(\frac{3 \times 15}{100}\right) = 3.45$ atm

$P_1 = 3$ atm, V_2 = ?

According to Boyle's law, $P_1V_1 = P_2V_2$

$\Rightarrow V_2 = \frac{P_1V_1}{P_2} = \frac{3 \times 400}{3.45} = 347$ mL

48. $C + CO_2 \rightarrow 2CO$

12 g of C requires 22.4L of CO_2 at STP.

30 g of C requires $= \frac{30 \times 22.4}{12}$

= 56λ of CO_2 at STP

100% conversion requires 56 L of CO_2 at STP.

$\therefore$ 80% conversion requires ? L of CO_2 at STP.

$\therefore V_{CO2} = \frac{56 \times 80}{100} = 44.8$L

49. According to Graham's law, $r \propto \frac{1}{\sqrt{GMM}}$

$\therefore r_{O_2} : r_{SO3} : r_{O_3} = \frac{1}{\sqrt{32}} : \frac{1}{\sqrt{80}} : \frac{1}{\sqrt{48}}$

$= \frac{1}{\sqrt{16 \times 2}} : \frac{1}{\sqrt{16 \times 5}} : \frac{1}{\sqrt{16 \times 3}}$

$= \frac{1}{4\sqrt{2}} : \frac{1}{4\sqrt{5}} : \frac{1}{4\sqrt{3}} = \frac{1}{\sqrt{2}} : \frac{1}{\sqrt{5}} : \frac{1}{\sqrt{3}}$

50. The empirical and molecular formula for the given organic compound is CH_2O and $C_2H_4O_2$

51. (a) 1 mole of sulphur = 32 + 2 × 16 = 64 gm

352 gram of sulphur = 1/64 × 352 = 5.5 mol

(b) According to Avogadro's law, equal volumes of all gases contain equal number of molecules under similar conditions of temperature and pressure.

The number of moles of X and Y should be equal to the number of moles of oxygen.

Number of moles of oxygen $= \frac{8}{32} = \frac{1}{4} = 0.25$

Mass of 0.25 mole X = 5 g

Mass of 1 mole X = 5/0.25 = 20 g

GMM of X = 20 g

Mass of 0.25 mole Y = 20 g

Mass of 1 mole Y $= \frac{20}{0.25} = 80\text{g}$

GMM of Y = 80 g

52. 96.7%

53. Balance the given equations by keeping appropriate coefficients

54. Mass of magnesium oxide = 800 g
Reaction equation is:
Moles of MgO = 800/40 = 20g/mol
One mole of MgO require 1 mol of O_2, 20 moles of MgO require 20 mole of O_2
20 moles of water used to produce oxygen.

55. P = 4 atm

T = 300 K

V = 256 mL

n = PV/RT = 4 × 0.25/0.082 × 300 = 0.040

Wt. of mole of gas would be = 1/0.040 = 25 g/mol

wt. of one atom of gas = 25g/mol/ 6.022 × 10^{23}
= 25/ N_A

56. 71 g of Cl_2 = 6.023 × 10^{23} molecules of Cl_2 gas
1 g of Cl_2 = (6.023 × 10^{23}) / 71 molecules of Cl_2 gas
So 710 g of Cl_2 = (6.023 × 10^{23} × 710) / 71 molecules of Cl_2 gas
= 6.023 × 10^{24} molecules of Cl_2 gas

Total number of atoms present in NaCl
= (6.023 × 10^{24} × 2) = 12.046 × 10^{24} atoms

57. Relation between the number of molecules of a gas and its pressure.

58. Molecular formula of the compound: N_2H_4

59. Let the nonmetallic oxide be X_xO_y.

$\therefore \frac{x}{x+y} = 0.33 \Rightarrow x = x(0.33) + y(0.33)$

$\Rightarrow 0.67x = 0.33y \Rightarrow x{:}y = 1{:}2$

Hence, the number of oxygen atoms is 2, as the valency of oxygen is' two, the valency of the nonmetal is four.

Let the nonmetallic oxide be $X_x O_y$.

In B

$\therefore \frac{x}{x+y} = 0.25 \Rightarrow x = 0.25x + 0.25y$

$\Rightarrow 0.75x = 0.25y$

$\Rightarrow x{:}y = 1{:}3$

Valency of non-metal

$= \frac{\text{valency of O} \times \text{No. of O atoms}}{\text{Number of non-metal atoms}} = \frac{2 \times 3}{1} = 6$

60. 1 molecule of chlorine gas consists of two chlorine atoms. Hence, 2 atoms of chlorine are present in 1 molecule of chlorine gas that is 71 g of Cl_2.

61. When leakage occurs in a cylinder containing a gaseous mixture containing equal masses of different gases, equal amounts of gases do not come out. This is because rate of diffusion of a gas depends on its molecular mass. The order of molecular masses of the gases is He < O_2 < CO_2.

The rate of diffusion is in the order He > O_2 > CO_2.

From the mixture, maximum amount of helium comes out, whereas minimum amount of CO_2 comes out.

62. 0°C corresponds to 273 K. Since volume of a gas is directly proportional to absolute temperature at constant pressure, the volume gets tripled when temperature is tripled.

$T_1 = 273$ K, $T_2 = ?$,

$V_1 = V$, $V_2 = 3V$,

$\frac{V_1}{T_1} = \frac{V_2}{T_2} \Rightarrow T_2 = \frac{V_2 T_1}{V_1} = \frac{3V \times 273}{V} = 819\,\text{K}$

$t = 819 - 273 = 546$°C

63. rate of diffusion(effusion)

$= \frac{\text{Volume of gas diffused } (v)}{\text{time taken } (t)}$

Let time taken by gas B be t.

Then, rate of diffusion of

$\text{B} = \frac{\text{Volume of gas B diffused } (V_1)}{t}$

According to the given data

time taken by gas A = 4 × time taken by gas B
= 4 × t

$\therefore$ Rate of diffusion of

$$A = \frac{\text{Volume gas A diffused } (V_2)}{4 \times t}$$

Volume of gas B diffused = Volume of gas A diffused

$\therefore V_1 = V_2$

$$\frac{\text{rate of diffusion of A}}{\text{rate of diffusion of B}} = \frac{r_A}{r_B} = \frac{V_1}{4t} \times \frac{t}{V_2} = \sqrt{\frac{M_B}{M_A}}$$

$$\therefore \frac{r_A}{r_B} = \frac{1}{4} = \sqrt{\frac{M_B}{M_A}}$$

Squaring on both sides $= \frac{1}{16} = \frac{M_B}{M_A}$

$M_A : M_B = 16 : 1$

64. (a) $P_1 = P,\ V_1 = V$

$$V_2 = V - \frac{60V}{100}$$

$P_2 = ?$

$P_1V_1 = P_2V_2,$

$$P_2 = \frac{PV}{V - \frac{60V}{100}} = 2.5P$$

Percentage change $= \frac{(2.5P - P)}{P} \times 100 = 150\%$

(b) $2Ca(NO_3)_2 \rightarrow 2CaO + 4NO_2 + O_2$

$2Mg + O_2 \rightarrow 2MgO$

No. of moles of magnesium $= \frac{4.8}{24} = 0.2$

2 mole magnesium $\rightarrow$ 1 mole oxygen

0.2 mole magnesium $\rightarrow$ 0.1 mole oxygen

1 mole oxygen $\rightarrow$ 2 mole calcium nitrate

0.1 mole oxygen $\rightarrow$ 0.2 mole calcium nitrate

Amount of calcium nitrate taken = 0.2 × 164 = 32.8 g

Amount of magnesium oxide formed = 0.2 × 40 = 8 g

65. The formula of metal oxide is M_2O_3.

Let the atomic weight of metal be x.

$$\therefore \left(\frac{2x}{2x + 48}\right)100 = 53 \Rightarrow x = 27.06$$

$\therefore$ The metal is Al and formula of oxide is Al_2O_3.

$Al_2O_3 + 3H_2SO_4 \rightarrow Al_2(SO_4)_3 + 3H_2O$

(54 + 48) g of Al_2O_3 gives [54 + 3(96)]g of $Al_2(SO_4)_3$

? $\leftarrow$ 22.8 g of $Al_2(SO_4)_3$

$$= \frac{22.8 \times 102}{342} = 6.87\text{ g.}$$

66. $2NH_3 \rightarrow N_2 + 3H_2$

2(22.4) L of $NH_3 \rightarrow$ 22.4 L of N_2

44.8 L $\rightarrow$?

$$= \frac{44.8 \times 22.4}{2 \times 22.4} = 22.4\text{ L}$$

28 g of N_2 corresponds to 22.4 L

? corresponds to 224 L

$$= \frac{28 \times 224}{22.4} = 280\text{ g}$$

$\therefore X = 280$ g

$N_2 + 2O_2 \rightarrow 2NO_2$

28 g of $N_2 \rightarrow$ 64 g of O_2

280 g $\rightarrow$?

$$= \frac{280 \times 64}{28} = 640\ g$$

32 g $\rightarrow 6 \times 10^{23}$ molecules

640 g $\rightarrow$?

$$= \frac{640 \times 6 \times 10^{23}}{32} = 12 \times 10^{24}\text{ molecules}$$

67. $CO_2 + C \rightarrow 2CO$

44 g of $CO_2 \rightarrow 2 \times 6 \times 10^{23}$ molecules of CO

8.88 g of $CO_2 \rightarrow$?

$$= \frac{8.8 \times 12 \times 10^{23}}{44} = 24 \times 10^{23}\text{ molecules}$$

100% conversion $\rightarrow 2.4 \times 10^{23}$ molecules

80% conversion $\rightarrow$?

$$= \frac{80 \times 2.4 \times 10^{23}}{100} = 1.92 \times 10^{23}\text{ molecules}$$

Level 3: Assess Your Concepts

68. Let $V_1 = 100\lambda,\ P_1 = 100$ atm

$V_2 = 70\lambda,\ P_2 = ?$

According to Boyle's law $P_1V_1 = P_2V2$

$\Rightarrow P_2 = \frac{P_1 V_1}{V_2} = \frac{100 \times 100}{70} = 143$ atm

$\therefore$ % change in pressure ≈ 43%.

69. $2Mg(NO_3)_2 \rightarrow 2MgO + 4NO_2 + O_2$

2 × 148 g of $Mg(NO_3)_2$ gives 5 moles of gases ($4 \rightarrow NO_2$; $1 \rightarrow O_2$).

$\Rightarrow$ 296 g of $Mg(NO_3)_2$ gives 5 × 22.4 l at STP.

59.2 g of $Mg(NO_3)_2$ gives? l at STP.

$= \frac{59.2 \times 5 \times 22.4}{296}$

= 22.4 l at STP

70. (a) Gases liquefy when their constituent molecules come into contact and interact with each other, this can only happen before absolute zero because real gas particles have volume. But in ideal gas, particles have zero volume, and no intermolecular interactions.

(b) Sodium carbonate is highly stable and does not undergo decomposition on heating. Only sodium bicarbonate undergoes decomposition which results in loss in weight due to the formation of gaseous products, CO_2 and H_2O.

Percentage of loss in weight = 29.2%

$2NaHCO_3 \rightarrow Na_2CO_3 + CO_2 + H_2O$

2 moles $NaHCO_3 \rightarrow$ 1 mole CO_2 + 1 mole H_2O = 2 mole gaseous products

No. of moles of $CO_2 = \frac{5.6}{22.4} = 0.25$

No. of moles of $H_2O = \frac{5.6}{22.4} = 0.25$

Mass of CO_2 = 0.25 × 44 = 11g

Mass of H_2O = 0.25 × 18 = 4.5 g

They correspond to 0.5 mole of $NaHCO_3$

$\therefore$ weight of $NaHCO_3$ = 0.5 × 84 = 42 g

The mixture contains 42g $NaHCO_3$ and 11g Na_2CO_3.

Percentage of $NaHCO_3 = \frac{4200}{53} \approx 79\%$

Percentage of $Na_2CO_3 = \frac{1100}{53} \approx 21\%$

71. In an open vessel, loss in weight is due to CO_2 and water vapour.

$2\ NaHCO_3 \rightarrow Na_2CO_3 + H_2O + CO_2$

2 × 84 g of $NaHCO_3 \rightarrow$ loss in weight is 44 = 18 = 62 g

$\Rightarrow$ 168 g $\rightarrow$ 62 g

210 g $NaHCO_3 = \frac{210 \times 62}{168} = 77.5$ g of weight loss

In a container fitted with condenser, loss of weight is due to CO_2.

$2NaHCO_3 \rightarrow Na_2CO_3 + H_2O + CO_2$

168 g of $NaHCO_3 \rightarrow$ 44 g of CO_2

210 g of $NaHCO_3 \rightarrow$?

$= \frac{210 \times 44}{168}$

= 55 g of weight loss

$\therefore$ Change in weight loss = 22.5 g

72. $2KClO_3 \rightarrow 2KCl + 3O_2$

2 moles of $KClO_3 \rightarrow$ 3 moles of O_2

1 mole of $KClO_3 \rightarrow$?

$= \frac{3}{2} = 1.5$ moles

= 48 g of O_2 (loss in weight)

$CaCO_3 \rightarrow CaO + CO_2$

1 mole of $CaCO_3 \rightarrow$ 1 mole of CO_2

= 44 g of CO_2 (loss in weight)

73. $3O_2 \rightarrow 2O_3$

3 moles of O_2 are converted to 2 moles of O_3.

$\therefore$ The volume will be reduced if the temperature and pressure are kept constant.

Let the volume of O_2 be x L.

$\therefore$ The volume of O_3 will be $\frac{2x}{3}$ L

$\therefore$ Percentage reduction of volume

$= \frac{x - \frac{2x}{3}}{x} \times 100$

$= \frac{\frac{x}{3}}{x} \times 100 = \frac{x}{3x} \times 100 = 33.33\%$

74. $2CO + O_2 \rightarrow 2CO_2$

Temperature is brought down to the previous temperature and the volume of the cylinder is fixed.

$\therefore$ Pressure will be reduced, because the number of molecules will be reduced.

Let $2n$ molecules of CO and $2n$ molecules of O_2 be there in that cylinder (an equal volume of any gas contains the same number of molecules under similar conditions of temperature and pressure).

$2n$ molecules of CO combine with n molecules of O_2 and form $2n$ molecules of CO_2, according to stoichiometric equation.

After the reaction $2n$ molecules of CO_2 are formed and n molecules of O_2 will be left over. If T and V are fixed, then pressure is directly proportional to the number of molecules.

$$\therefore \frac{p_1}{p_2} = \frac{4x}{3x}$$

$$\therefore p_2 = \frac{3p_1}{4}$$

Percentage change is equal to

$$= \frac{4x - 3x}{4x} \times 100 = 25\%$$

75. $2NaHCO_3 \rightarrow Na_2CO_3 + H_2O + CO_2$

Let 100 g be the weight of mixture amount of CO_2 produced = 22

Number of moles CO_2 = 0.5

Amount of $NaHCO_3$ present in the mixture $2 \times 0.5 \times 84 = 84$ g

Amount of Na_2CO_3 present in the mixture = 16 g

% of $NaHCO_3$ = 84%

% of Na_2CO_3 = 16%

76. $C_6H_{12}O_6 + 6O_2 \rightarrow 6CO_2 + 6H_2O$

Amount of glucose required for 30 days

= 7.5 × 24 × 30 = 5400 g

$$\therefore \text{No of moles of glucose} = \frac{5400}{180} = 30$$

Volume of O_2 required for combustion at STP

= 22.4 × 6 × 30 = 4032 L

STP	Given conditions
$T_1 = 273$ K	$T_2 = 300$ K
$P_1 = 1$atm	$P_2 = 1$ atm
$V_1 = 4032$ L	$V_2 = ?$

$$\frac{P_1V_1}{T_1} = \frac{P_2V_2}{T_2}$$

$$\therefore V_2 = \frac{1 \times 4032 \times 300}{273 \times 1} = 4430.76\,\text{L}$$

∴ oxygen required = 4430.76 L

95 L of oxygen is present in 100 L of carbogen

$$\therefore \text{4430 76 L of } O_2 \text{ is present in } = \frac{100 \times 4430.76}{95}$$

= 4663.95 L of carbogen

77. 2 g of Fe_3O_4 = 0.1 mole

1 mole of Fe_3O_4 requires 4 moles of H_2

0.1 mole of Fe_3O_4 requires 0.4 mole of H_2

To evolve 0.4 moles of H_2, 0.4 moles of Zn are required.

Mass of 0.4 mole of Zn = 0.4 × 65.5 = 26.2 g

$$\text{Amount of 64.5\% Zn} = \frac{26.2 \times 100}{65.5} = 40\ g$$

Amount of iron formed = 0.3 mol = 0.3 × 56

= 16.8 g

JEE-NEET Special wing

Multiple-Answer Type Questions

1. The molecular formulae of CH_3COOH and HCHO are obtained by multiplying the empirical formula CH_2O with an integer.

2. The gases which possess almost equal molecular mass show equal rates of diffusion.

Gas	Molecular mass
Methane	16
Ammonia	17
Carbon monoxide	28
Nitrogen	28
Nitric oxide	30
Ethane	30
Carbon dioxide	44
Nitrous oxide	44

3. $C_4H_8 + 6O_2 \rightarrow 4CO_2 + 4H_2O$ 2 mol requires 12 mol O_2

$C_3H_4 + 4O_2 \rightarrow 3CO_2 + 2H_2O$ 3 mol requires 12 mol O_2

$C_3H_8 + 5O_2 \rightarrow 3CO_2 + 4H_2O$ 2 mol requires 10 mol O_2

$C_2H_2 + 5/2O_2 \rightarrow 2CO_2 + H_2O$ 4 mol requires 10 mol O_2

4. Volume occupied by 19.2 g SO_2 at STP = (19.2/64)22.4 = 6.72 L

Volume occupied by 13.8 g NO_2 at STP = (13.8/46)22.4 = 6.72 L

Volume occupied by 18 g ethane at STP = (18/30)22.4 = 13.44 L

Volume occupied by 3.4 g NH_3 at STP = (3.4/17)22.4 = 4.48 L

5. Percentage of carbon in acetic acid = (24/60) 100 = 40

Percentage of carbon in calcium bicarbonate = (24/162) 100 = 14.8

Percentage of carbon in ethyl alcohol = $\left(\frac{24}{46}\right) \times 100$ = 52.1

Percentage of carbon in acetic acid = $\left(\frac{12}{106}\right) \times 100$ = 11.3

Comprehension-Based Questions

6. $2CO + O_2 \rightarrow 2CO_2$

1 vol 2 vol 1 vol

Mole ratio = Volume ratio

No. of moles of CO_2 obtained = $\frac{3.36}{22.4}$ = 1.5 mol

No. of moles of CO reacted = 1.5 mol

No. of moles of O_2 taken = 3 mol

No. of moles of O_2 reacted = 2.25 mol

Initial moles = 4.5

No. of moles at the end of the reaction = 3.75

Let initial pressure be P.

Pressure of gaseous mixture at the end of the reaction

$= \left(\frac{3.75P}{4.5}\right) = 0.83\ P$

Decrease in pressure = P – 0.83P = 0.17 P

Decrease in no. of moles = 0.75

Percentage decrease in pressure = $\left(\frac{0.17P}{0.75}\right)100$ = 22.6%

7. Volume of gas in the cylinder = 6 l

Total no. of moles of gas in the cylinder = 3.75

Temperature = 300 K

Pressure in the cylinder = $\frac{(3.75 \times 0.08 \times 300)}{6}$ = 5 atm

Volume occupied by the gas at 1 atm pressure = 30 L

The amount of gas that can be transferred = 30 – 6 = 24 L

Volume of balloon = 200 mL

No. of balloons filled = $\frac{24000}{200}$ = 120

8. No. of moles of CO_2 = 1.5 mol

No. of moles of O_2 = 2.25 mol

Partial pressure of CO_2 = $\left(\frac{1.5}{3.75}\right)5$ = 2 atm.

Partial pressure of O_2 = $\left(\frac{2.25}{3.75}\right)5$ = 3 atm.

9. Ratio of rate of diffusion of CO_2 and O_2 = $\frac{\sqrt{32}}{\sqrt{44}}$ = 0.85

Volume of oxygen present in the mixture diffused out in unit time = 40 mL

Volume of CO_2 present in the mixture diffused out in unit time.

= 0.85 × 40 mL = 34 mL

10. CO_2 reacts with Calcium hydroxide to form calcium carbonate.

$CO_2 + Ca(OH)_2 \rightarrow CaCO_3 + 2H_2O$

1 mol 1 mol 1 mol

No. of moles of $CaCO_3$ obtained = 1.5 mol

Mass of $CaCO_3$ obtained = 1.5 × 100 = 150 g

Common solutions for questions 11 to 16:

Element	No. of times an atom is heavier than carbon-12 atom	GAM	Element
A	1.167	14	Nitrogen
B	2.67	32	Sulphur
C	2.59	31	Phosphorus
D	3.34	40	Calcium
E	4.67	56	Iron

11. The element 'C' is phosphorus. It forms various ions or radicals.

P^{-3}	Phosphide
PO_4^{-3}	Phosphate
HPO_4^{-2}	Hydrogen phosphate
$H_2\ PO_4$-	Dihydrogen phosphate
HPO_3-	Hydrogen phosphite
$H_2\ PO_3^{-2}$	Dihydrogen phosphate

12. The element 'E' is iron. It forms two oxides of the formulae FeO and Fe_2O_3. The molecular mass of FeS is 76. It is a metal with high melting point and hence is not easily vapourisable.

13. The element 'B' is Sulphur.

Lower oxide is SO_2 with GMM = 64

The volume occupied by 32 g SO_2 = 11.2 l

Higher oxide is SO_3 with GMM = 80

The volume occupied by 32 g SO_3 = 8.96 l

Higher oxyacid is H_2SO_4 with GMM 98

56 g SO_3 = 0.7 mol

0.7 mole sulphuric acid = 0.7 × 98 = 68.6 g

Lower oxyacid is H_2SO_3 with GMM 82

16.4 g H_2SO_3 = 0.2 mol

No. of atoms = $0.2 \times 6 \times 10^{23} \times 6 = 7.2 \times 10^{23}$

14. Nitrogen is the only element which forms positive radical. Therefore, the compound given is is NH_4NO_3.

15. The element D is calcium. It forms a divalent ion. Hence it can form the compounds Ca_3N_2 and Ca_3P_2.

16. The element 'B' is sulphur. BO_2 is sulphur dioxide. One mole SO_2 has 32 g sulphur and 32 g oxygen.

17. A- H_2O_2

$2H_2O_2 \rightarrow 2H_2O + O_2$

No. of moles of O_2 obtained = $\dfrac{\left(\dfrac{10.2}{34}\right)}{2} = 0.15$

Volume occupied = 0.15 × 22.4 = 3.36 L

B- Potassium chlorate

$2KClO_3 \rightarrow 2KCl + 3O_2$

No. of moles of O_2 obtained = $\dfrac{\left(\dfrac{73.5}{122.5}\right)}{\left(\dfrac{3}{2}\right)} = 0.9$

Volume occupied = 0.9 × 22.4 = 20.16 L

C-Potassium permanganate

$2KMnO_4 \rightarrow K_2MnO_4 + MnO_2 + O_2$

No. of moles of O_2 obtained = $\dfrac{\left(\dfrac{7.9}{158}\right)}{2} = 0.025$

Volume occupied = 0.025 × 22.4 = 0.56 L

D- Potassium nitrate

$2KNO_3 \rightarrow 2KNO_2 + O_2$

No. of moles of O_2 obtained = $\dfrac{\left(\dfrac{80.8}{101}\right)}{2} = 0.4$

Volume occupied = 0.4 × 22.4 = 8.96 L

Column A (Amount of compound taken)		Column B (Volume of O_2 obtained)	
(a)	10.2 g of compound A	(iii)	3.36 L
(b)	73.5 g of comound B	(iv)	20.16 L
(c)	7.9 g of compound C	(ii)	560 mL
(d)	80.8 g of compound D	(i)	8.96 L

CHAPTER

4

Atomic Structure

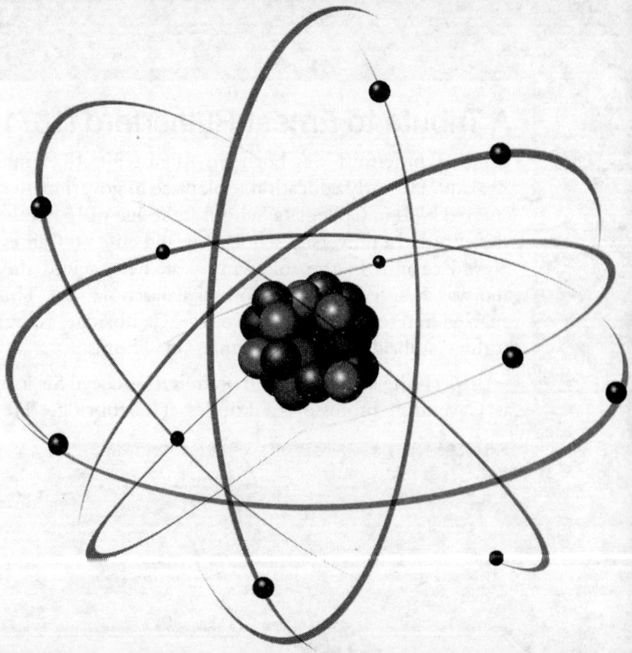

Remember

Before beginning this chapter, you should be able to:

- understand basic concept of matter and atom.
- identify presence of subatomic particles.
- describe the concept of atom as an indivisible particle.
- understand the concept of divisibility of atom and the characteristics of subatomic particles.
- recall the primary idea of the modern atomic model.

Key Ideas

After completing this chapter, you should be able to:

- understand the concept of divisibility of atom and the characteristics of subatomic particles.
- explain the stability of nucleus and nuclear reactions.
- conceptualize the model of atom based on the discovery of electrons.
- describe the concept of stationary orbits based on quantization of energy and approach towards the modern atomic model.
- observe gradual change in the perception of structure of atom based on experimental observations.
- understand the correlation between wave and particle nature of an electron.
- identify the difference between orbit and orbital based on Heisenberg's uncertainty principle.

Scientific Crypt

A Tribute to Ernest Rutherford (1871–1937)

Ernest Rutherford was born on August 30, 1871 in Nelson, New Zealand. His early education took place in government schools and he entered Nelson Collegiate School at the age of 16. At the age of 18, he was awarded a university scholarship and entered Canterbury College, New Zealand. In the following year, he received the B.Sc. degree and was awarded an exhibition science scholarship. This achievement enabled him to go to Trinity College, Cambridge, as a research student at the Cambridge laboratory under J.J. Thomson.

In 1919 he accepted an invitation to succeed Sir Joseph Thomson as Cavendish professor of Physics at Cambridge. He also became the director of the Royal Society Mond Laboratory, Cambridge. Professor Thomson readily recognized his talent on his arrival at Cambridge.

His greatest contribution is his investigation into the scattering of alpha rays and the nature of the inner structure of atoms which led to the postulation of his concept of the 'nucleus'. In 1908, he received the most prestigious award the Nobel Prize in Chemistry.

The discovery of the nucleus by Ernest Rutherford laid the foundation of the modern atomic model. He was an inspiring leader of the Cambridge laboratory and steered numerous future Nobel prize winners towards their great achievement.

FUN TIME

CROSSWORD

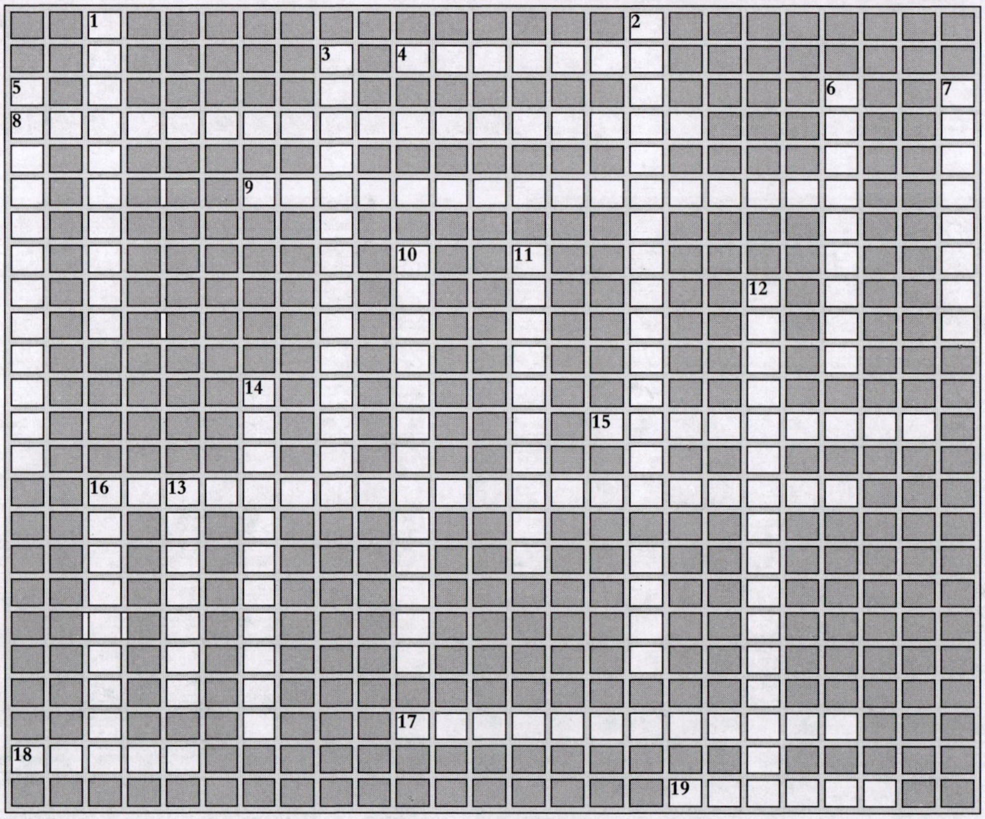

Across

4. Inert gas having electrons in 4th shells
8. Spectrum formed during the electronic transition from the lower energy level to the higher energy level
9. Spectrum formed during the electronic transition from the higher energy level to the lower energy level.
15. Quantum theory of radiation was given by
16. Spontaneous emission of characteristic radiations.
17. Splitting of spectral line under the influence of the magnetic field.
18. An atom having three electrons in the second shell
19. Inert gas with the lowest atomic number

Down

1. Sum of total number of protons and the total number of neutrons present in the nucleus of an atom.
2. Transmutation of a stable element into another radioactive element
3. Total number of protons present in the nucleus of an atom
5. Outermost shell
6. An atom having three electrons in the third shell.
7. Subatomic particle with the highest specific charge
10. Discovery of neutrons
11. Planetary model of the atom was given by _______
12. The second last shell with electrons in an atom
13. Plum pudding model of atom
14. Splitting of the spectral line under the influence of an electric field
16. Concept of stationary orbit

INTRODUCTION

The concept that atoms are the fundamental building blocks of matter dates back to very ancient times. John Dalton proposed his atomic theory on the basis of certain observations and experimental results. The basic principle of his theory was that it regarded an atom as the ultimate particle of matter.

Atoms are found to be mainly composed of three types of fundamental particles, namely, positively-charged protons, neutral particles known as neutrons, and negatively-charged electrons.

J. J. Thomson, after his discovery of the electron, proposed his atomic model according to which an atom is a spherical mass of positive charge in which electrons are embedded. Thomson's model of atom has been disproved by Rutherford's α-ray scattering experiment. This experiment resulted in the discovery of nucleus, which was a major breakthrough in the history of the structure of atom. Niels Bohr, in 1913, proposed his atomic model with the most crucial concept of stationary orbits for electrons. This concept of stationary orbits proposed by Bohr could successfully explain the stability of an atom, which was the major limitation of Rutherford's atomic model.

Discovery of Fundamental Particles

The elementary entities from which all matter has been made are fundamental particles.

Discovery of Electrons

The electron was the first fundamental particle that was discovered. The credit for the discovery of the electron goes to J. J. Thomson based on his experiments carried out in a discharge tube.

Sir William Crookes was the first scientist who designed the discharge tube which was called **Crooke's discharge tube** or **cathode ray tube**. It is a long glass tube having two metal plates connected to the oppositely charged poles of a battery. The pressure inside the discharge tube can be adjusted by means of an exhaust pump.

This discharge tube was later slightly modified by J. J. Thomson. When high voltage (HV) was applied between the cathode and the anode with a small hole at the centre of a partially evacuated tube at a pressure of 0.01 mm of Hg, a bright spot of light was formed on the zinc sulphide screen kept at the opposite end of the discharge tube. This was caused by the rays which originated from the cathode called **cathode rays.**

Info Bytes!

The term 'electron' was first coined by G. Johnstone Stoney in 1891 to describe the 'elementary quantity of electricity' during his studies on electrolysis.

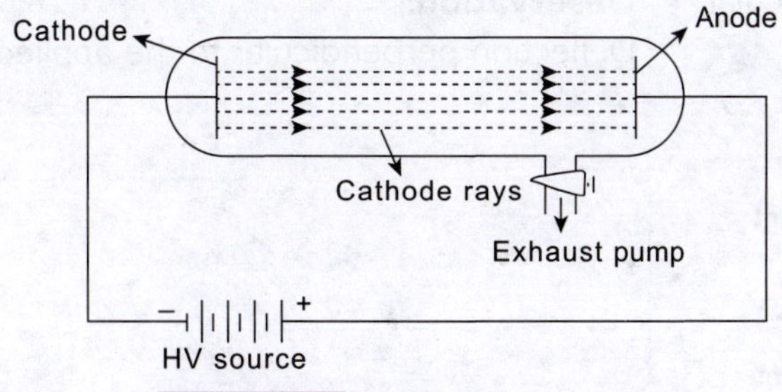

Figure 4.1 Cathode ray tube

J. J. Thomson conducted some experiments with a discharge tube for studying the properties of cathode rays.

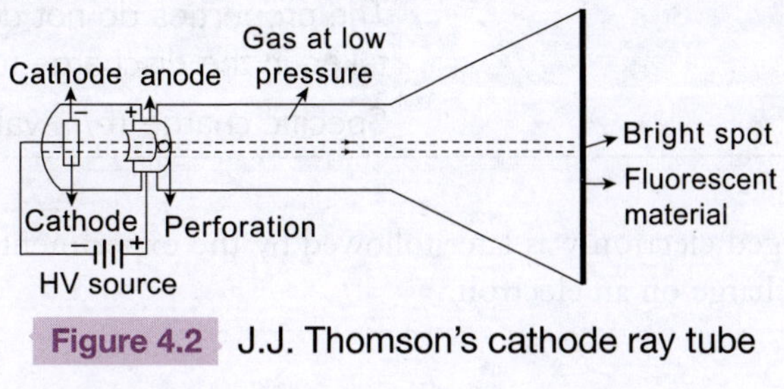

Figure 4.2 J.J. Thomson's cathode ray tube

Table 4.1 Experiments involved in discovery of fundamental particles

Experiments	Properties based on observation
Placing a small object in between the cathode and anode 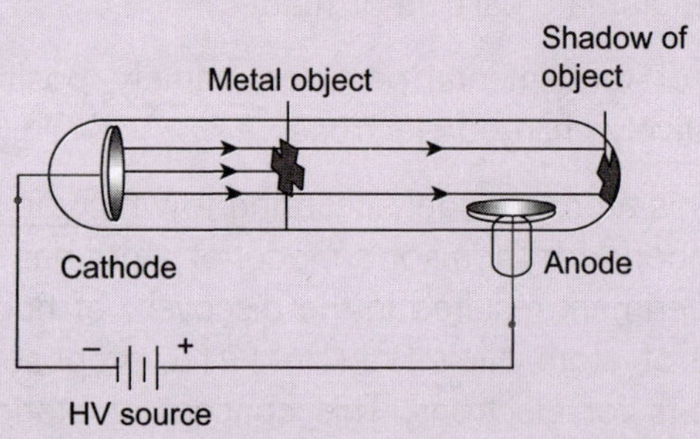	**Observation:** Formation of a shadow of the object on the opposite side of the cathode **Properties:** Cathode rays travel in straight lines
Placing a light paddle wheel between cathode and anode 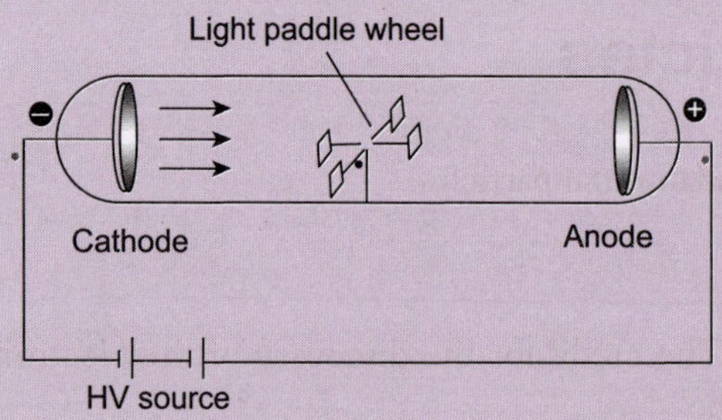	**Observation:** Rotation of light paddle wheel. **Properties:** Small particles having mass and kinetic energy
Passing through electric field 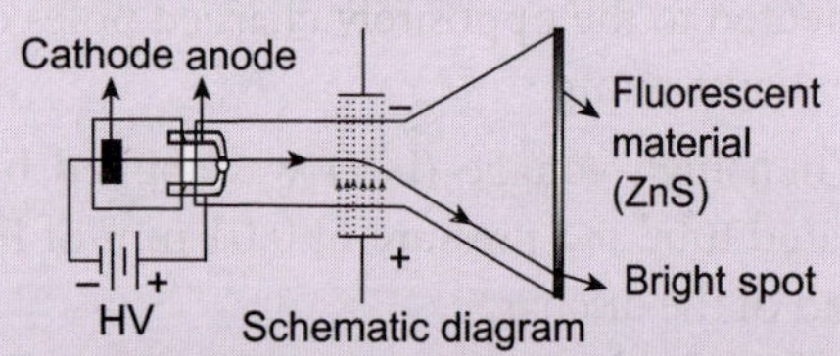	**Observation:** Bending of rays towards the positive plate **Properties:** Negatively-charged particles
Passing through magnetic field applied perpendicular to the path of the cathode rays 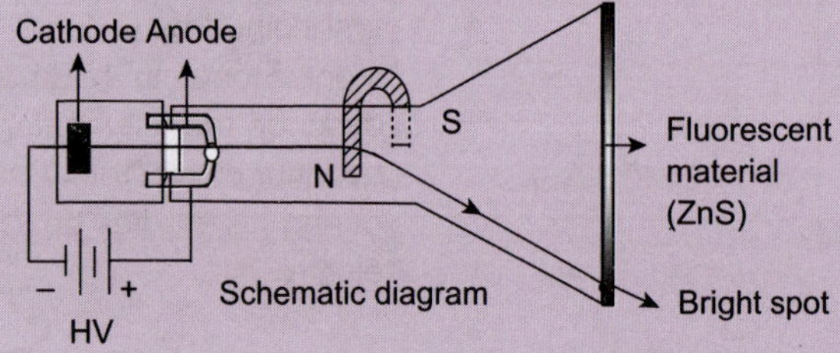	**Observation:** Deflection perpendicular to the applied magnetic field
The above experiments were carried out with different gases in the discharge tube.	No change in properties The properties do not depend on the nature of gas taken in the discharge tube. Specific charge (*e*/*m* value) remains the same.

The discovery of negatively-charged electron was later followed by the experiment conducted by Robert Millikan in 1909 to determine the quantity of charge on an electron.

Millikan's Oil Drop Experiment

Some fine oil droplets were allowed to be sprayed into the chamber by an atomizer. The air in the chamber was subjected to ionization by X-rays. The electrons produced by the ionization of air attached themselves to the oil drops. When sufficient amount of electric field is applied which can balance the gravitational force acting on an oil drop, the drop remains suspended in the air.

From this experiment, Millikan observed that the smallest charge found on them was approximately 1.59×10^{-19} coulombs and the charge on each drop was always an integral multiple of that value.

On the basis of this observation, he concluded that 1.59×10^{-19} coulombs is the smallest possible charge and considered that value as the charge of the electron.

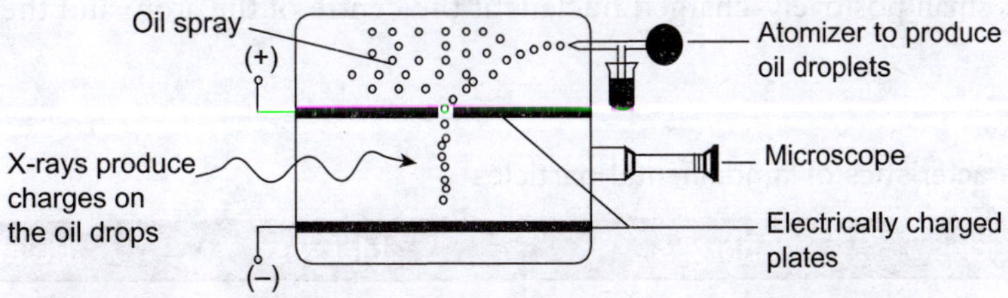

Figure 4.3 A schematic representation of the apparatus used by Millikan to determine the charge of an electron

Discovery of Protons

The presence of positively-charged particles in an atom has been predicted by Goldstein based on the electrical neutrality of an atom. The discovery of proton by Goldstein was done on the basis of the cathode ray experiment conducted by using a perforated cathode.

Just like the cathode rays, some rays were found to emanate from an anode. These are called **anode rays** or **canal rays.** Anode rays were found as a stream of positively-charged particles in contrast to the cathode rays. When hydrogen gas is taken in a discharge tube, these positively-charged particles were found to be protons.

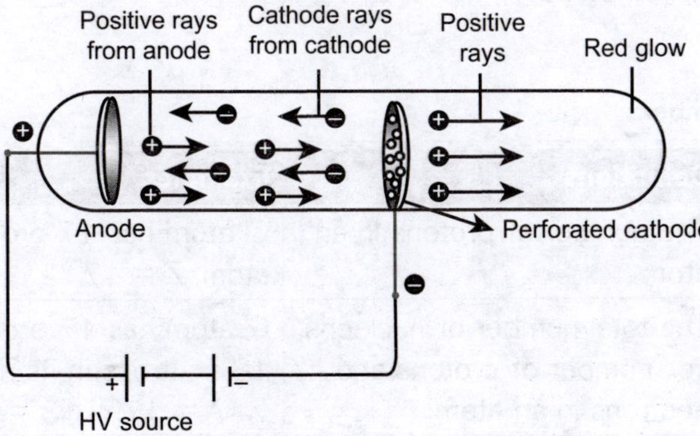

Figure 4.4 Discovery of Protons

Properties of Anode Rays

1. Anode rays travel in straight lines.
2. Anode rays possess positive charge since they were found to deflect towards negatively-charged electrodes.
3. The properties of anode rays depend upon the nature of the gas taken in the discharge tube.
4. The mass of the particles was same as the atomic mass of the gas inside the discharge tube.

Info Bytes!

The discovery of electrons and protons as subatomic particles inside the atom led to the conception of atomic models which depict the arrangement of fundamental particles in an atom.

Discovery of Neutrons

The electrons being particles having negligible mass and massive protons concentrated inside the nucleus, it could be predicted that the mass of an atom has to be equal to the mass of the total number of protons present in the atom. However, this was found to be true only in case of a hydrogen atom.

The difference in the predicted mass and actual mass of the atom has been found to be equal to the mass of the proton or multiples of the mass of a proton. These particles are supposed to have neutral charge since the atom is electrically neutral. They were called **neutrons** and they were discovered by James Chadwick by an experiment involving the bombardment of beryllium nucleus with α-particles.

The discovery of fundamental particles has ultimately resulted in the establishment of a basic atomic model. The basic model of an atom comprises small positively-charged nucleus at the centre of the atom and the electrons revolving round the nucleus in orbits.

Table 4.2 Characteristics of fundamental particles

Fundamental Particles	Charges	Masses	Relative Charges
Electron *(e−)*	-1.6×10^{-19} C -4.8×10^{-10} esu	9.1×10^{-31} kg or 0. 00055 amu	−1
Proton *(p+)*	$+ 1.6 \times 10^{-19}$ C $+ 4.8 \times 10^{-10}$ esu	1.67×10^{-27} kg or 1.0078 amu	+1
Neutron *(n)*	0	1.72×10^{-27} kg or 1.0083 amu	0

Table 4.3 Atomic number and mass number

	Representations	Definitions	Examples
Atomic number	Z	The number of protons in an atom	Cl atom has 17 protons in its atom, Z = 17
Mass number	A	The total number of nucleons, i.e., number of protons and neutrons in an atom	Cl atom has 17 protons and 18 neutrons in its nucleus. ∴ A = 17 + 18 = 35

An element when represented along with its atomic number and mass number is represented as ${}_ZX^A$. Elements are found to exist in their isotopic forms.

Isotopes are the atoms of the same element having different mass number. Based on their percentage abundance of each isotopic form, average atomic mass of an element is calculated.

Examples: ${}_1H^1$, ${}_1H^2$, ${}_1H^3$, etc.

It is also found that atoms of different elements have same mass number. These are called **isobars.**

Examples: ${}_{18}Ar^{40}$, ${}_{20}Ca^{40}$, etc.

EXAMPLE 4.1

Write different isotopes of hydrogen and nitrogen.

SOLUTION

The isotopes of hydrogen are ${}^{1}_{1}H$, ${}^{2}_{1}H$, (Deuterium), ${}^{3}_{1}H$ (Tritium).

The isotopes of nitrogen are ${}^{14}_{7}N$, ${}^{15}_{7}N$.

EXAMPLE 4.2

On what fundamental principle was Avogadro's hypothesis based?

SOLUTION

Avogadro's hypothesis was based on the fundamental principle that equal volumes of all gases, under the same conditions of temperature and pressure, contain an equal number of molecules.

EXAMPLE 4.3

(i) What are A, B, C, D, and E in the given figure?

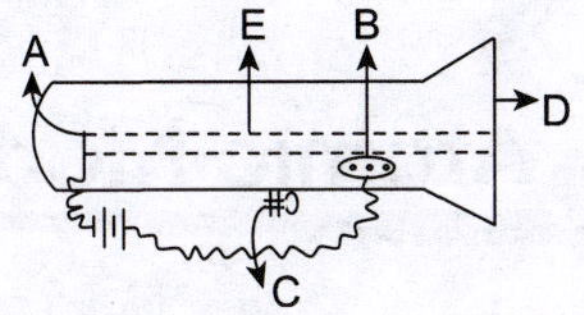

(ii) What is the purpose of C?

(iii) Explain the role of D in the phenomenon taking place in the discharge tube.

SOLUTION

(i) A is cathode, B is perforated anode, C is suction pump, D is zinc sulphide screen, and E is cathode ray.

(ii) C is suction pump which can help in reducing the pressure in the discharge tube.

(iii) D is zinc sulphide screen. Zinc sulphide is a fluorescent material. When cathode rays strike the zinc sulphide screen, bright spots are formed on the screen.

EXAMPLE 4.4

An atom of an element is represented as ${}_{Z}X^{A}$. After the emission of a β-particle, another element Y is formed. Represent Y with atomic number and mass number.

SOLUTION

${}_{Z}X^{A} \rightarrow {}_{Z+1}Y^{A} + \beta$ particle.

EXAMPLE 4.5

Calculate the specific charges *(e/m)* of the following particles and then arrange the particles in the ascending order of their specific charges.

(a) Electron **(b)** Proton **(c)** α-particle

SOLUTION

$$\text{Specific charge of an electron} = \frac{1.6\times10^{-19}}{9.1\times10^{-31}}\ \text{coulombs/kg}$$

$$= 0.176 \times 10^{12} = 17.6 \times 10^{10}\ \text{coulombs/kg}$$

$$\text{Specific charge of a proton} = \frac{1.6\times10^{-19}}{1.67\times10^{-27}}\ \text{coulombs/kg} = 0.96 \times 10^{8}\ \text{coulombs/kg}$$

$$\text{Specific charge of }\alpha\text{-particle} = \frac{2\times1.6\times10^{-19}}{2\times10^{-27}(1.67+1.72)} = \frac{1.6\times10^{8}}{3.39} = 0.472 \times 10^{8}\ \text{coulombs/kg}$$

Hence, ascending order of specific charges of electron, proton, and α-particles is α-particle < proton < electron.

EXAMPLE 4.6 Calculate the mass of a charged particle in CGS units if its charge is *x* coulomb and specific charge is *y* coulomb/g.

SOLUTION

The mass of the particle in CGS units is $\frac{e}{\frac{e}{m}} g = \frac{x}{y} g$.

EXAMPLE 4.7 The isotopes of an element have mass numbers: A, A + 1, A + 2. The ratio of abundance of these isotopes is 3 : 2 : 4. Calculate the average atomic mass of the element.

SOLUTION

$$\text{Average atomic mass} = \frac{A \times 3 + (A+1)2 + (A+2)4}{9} = \frac{3A + 2A + 2 + 4A + 8}{9} = A + \frac{10}{9}$$

Atomic Models

Various atomic models have been proposed by different scientists, like, J. J. Thomson, Rutherford, Bohr, and Sommerfeld.

Thomson's Atomic Model

J. J. Thomson proposed his atomic model soon after his discovery of electrons as listed hereunder.

1. An atom contains negatively-charged particles called electrons embedded uniformly throughout a thinly spread positively-charged mass.
2. Since the atom is electrically neutral, the total negative charge of electrons is balanced by the total positive charge.

Thomson's model of an atom is popularly known as **'plum pudding model'** or **'apple pie model'** or **'watermelon model'.**

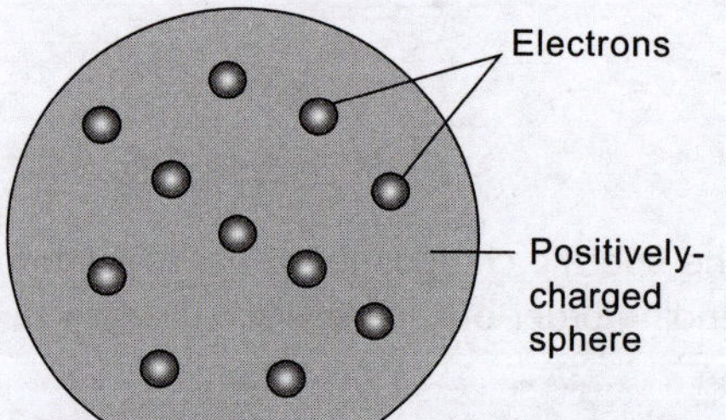

Figure 4.5 Thomson's atomic model

Validity of Thomson's Model

Thomson's model could successfully explain the electrical neutrality of atom. However, it failed to explain how the positively-charged particles are shielded from the negatively-charged electrons without getting neutralized.

Rutherford's α-ray Scattering Experiments

In order to test the validity of Thomson's atomic model, Rutherford conducted α-ray scattering experiment.

In this experiment, α-particles were allowed to pass through a pair of positively-charged parallel plates and the resultant narrow beam of α-particles was allowed to strike the gold foil which was surrounded by zinc sulphide screen.

The observations or results of this experiment completely disproved Thomson's model.

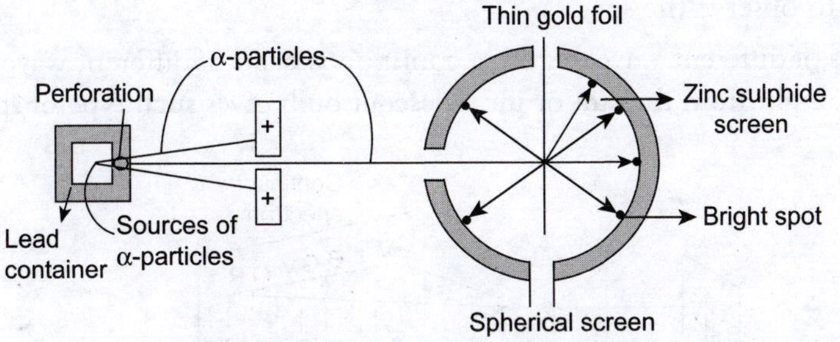

Figure 4.6 α-ray Scattering Experiment

Konnect

- Rutherford's α-ray Scattering Experiments led him to conclude that most of the atom's mass and all of its positive charge are concentrated in a core, which he termed the nucleus.

Table 4.4 Observations and conclusions of α-ray scattering experiment

Observations	Conclusions
Most of the particles passed straight through the gold foil without any deflection	Presence of large empty space in an atom
Very few α-particles completely rebounded and few α-particles showed large deflection	Presence of a central, positively-charged core known as nucleus

Rutherford's Atomic Model

The atom is mostly composed of empty space. The entire positive charge and mass of the atom is concentrated in the small, central part known as the **nucleus.** The size of the nucleus is so small that its diameter is 10^5 times less than that of the atom. The diameter of the nucleus has been estimated by Rutherford as 10^{-13} cm in contrast to that of the atom to be 10^{-8} cm. The electrons present outside the nucleus revolve round the nucleus with high velocities.

The electrons revolve round the nucleus with high velocities to counterbalance the electrostatic forces of attraction between protons and electrons. Rutherford's atomic model resembles the planetary motion in solar system. Therefore, Rutherford's model of an atom is also called **planetary model.**

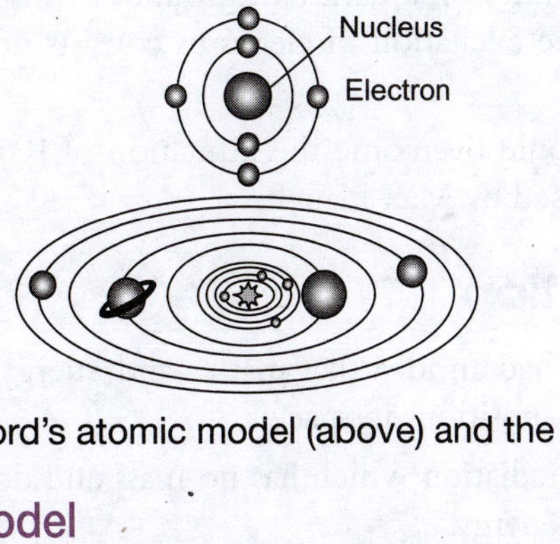

Figure 4.7 Rutherford's atomic model (above) and the solar system (below)

Validity of Rutherford's Atomic Model

Rutherford's atomic model could very well explain the presence of positively-charged nucleus and presence of electrons outside the nucleus in the atom. However, the failure of Rutherford's theory stemmed from two major objections.

1. This model is in contradiction to the principle of classical electrodynamics. According to this, any charged particle in a circular motion radiates energy continuously. The electron being a charged particle in the circular motion loses energy. This should ultimately result in its spiral path towards nucleus and the atom should then collapse.
2. The second major objection to Rutherford's model came from the pattern of atomic spectra.

When light passes through a prism, it gets split up into its components of different wavelengths, like, visible, ultraviolet, infrared light, etc. The arrangement of component light energies according to their wavelengths is called **spectrum** and spectroscope is the instrument designed to observe the spectra.

Since white light is composed of lights of different wavelengths, a continuous band of different wave lengths is obtained which is called **continuous spectrum.** Light from the sun or incandescent bulb gives such type of spectra.

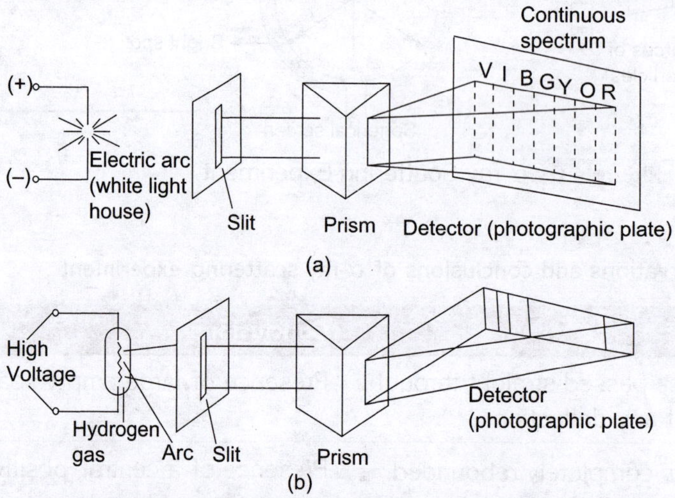

Figure 4.8 (a) Spectrum produced by the white light
(b) Atomic spectra of hydrogen

But when the spectrum is taken for the atoms of the gas present in the discharge tube, it is found to consist of discrete lines of different colours. This is called **line spectrum,** which is a discontinuous spectrum. Figure 4.8 (b) shows the atomic spectra of hydrogen gas.

According to Rutherford's atomic model, electrons revolving around the nucleus should lose energy continuously. Hence, the spectra of the atom should be a continuous spectrum, whereas the observed atomic spectrum was a line spectrum.

When the energy emitted by an atom due to the de-excitation of electrons is observed through a spectroscope, it appears as a spectrum consisting of bright lines on a dark background, this is emission spectrum. The spectrum formed due to the absorption of energy during the excitation of electrons consists of dark lines on a bright background, this is called absorption spectrum.

In 1913, Danish scientist, Niels Bohr could overcome the limitation of Rutherford's atomic model successfully based on the quantum theory of radiation proposed by Max Planck.

Quantum Theory of Radiation

At the end of the 19th century, physicists had an idea that matter and energy are distinctly different. Matter consists of particles which have mass and have specific positions in space.

Energy is the form of electromagnetic radiation which has no mass and does not have any specific position in space. Matter can absorb or emit any quantity of energy.

But in the beginning of the 20th century, these ideas were proved to be incorrect on the basis of some experimental results.

German physicist, Max Planck, in 1901 carried out the first important experiment by studying the radiation emitted by solid bodies heated to incandescence.

He concluded from his experimental observation that energy can be absorbed or radiated by a body in the form of small packets of energy called **quanta.**

Quanta = $nh\nu$

n = whole number multiples

h = Planck's constant = 6.625×10^{-34} J.s

ν = frequency of the radiation

This theory proves the particle nature of energy.

On the basis of this theory, Bohr proposed his atom model.

EXAMPLE 4.8 Following conclusions are drawn by observing α-ray scattering experiment. Write the respective observations based on which these conclusions are drawn.

(i) Non-uniform distribution of positive charge.

(ii) Presence of positively-charged core or nucleus.

(iii) Presence of large empty space in an atom.

SOLUTION

	Conclusions	Observations
(i)	Non-uniform distribution of positive charge	The angle of deflections of various α-particles were different
(ii)	Presence of positively-charged core or nucleus	Very few α-particles completely rebounded and few α-particles showed large deflection
(iii)	Presence of large empty space in an atom	Most of the α-particles passed through the gold foil without any deflection

EXAMPLE 4.9 Compare Thomson's atomic model with Rutherford's atomic model.

SOLUTION

Thomson's atomic model	Rutherford's atomic model
In Thomson's model positively-charged particles are thinly spread throughout the atom.	In Rutherford's model, positively-charged particles are concentrated in a small central part called nucleus.
Electrons are embedded in the thin positively-charged mass.	Electrons revolve around the nucleus with a high velocity.

EXAMPLE 4.10 The wavelength of particular radiation is 700 nm (1 nm = 10^{-9} m). Find its frequency (ν).

SOLUTION

λ = 700 nm = 700×10^{-9} m = 7×10^{-7} m. Also, c = velocity of light = 3×10^{8} m/s

$$\text{So, } \nu = \frac{c}{\lambda} = \frac{3\times10^{8}}{7\times10^{-7}} = 0.42 \times 10^{15}/\text{s}$$

Bohr's Model

Bohr proposed his atomic model based on the quantum theory of radiation.

According to Bohr's model:

1. Electrons move around the nucleus in specified circular paths called **orbits** or **shells** or **energy levels.**
2. Each orbit or shell is associated with a definite amount of energy. Hence, these are also called **energy levels** and are designated as K, L, M, and N shells.
3. The energy associated with a certain energy level increases with the increase in its distance from the nucleus. Hence, if the energies associated with the K, L, M and N shells are E_1, E_2, E_3, and E_4, respectively, then $E_1 < E_2 < E_3$ ………, and so on.
4. As long as the electron revolves in a particular orbit, the electron does not lose its energy. Therefore, these orbits are called **stationary orbits** and the electrons are said to be in stationary energy states.
5. An electron jumps from a lower to a higher energy level by absorbing energy. It jumps from a higher to a lower energy level by emitting energy in the form of electromagnetic radiation.
   The energy emitted or absorbed (ΔE) is given by Planck's equation, that is $\Delta E = h\nu$.
   For example, if E_1 and E_2 are the energies of first and second orbits, respectively, then the difference in energy is equal to $h\nu$:
   $$E_2 - E_1 = h\nu$$
6. An electron can revolve only in an orbit in which the angular momentum of the electron (mvr) is a whole-number multiple of $h/2\pi$. This is known as the **principle of quantization of angular momentum.**
   Hence, we can conclude the angular momentum an electron as
   $$mvr = \frac{nh}{2\pi},$$
   where n = integer (n = 1, 2, 3, 4, …….) and is called **principal quantum number.**
   m = mass of the electron,
   v = velocity of an electron in its orbit
   r = distance of the electron from the nucleus

   By applying the concept of quantization of energy, Bohr calculated the radius and the energy of the nth orbit of hydrogen atom (Z = 1).
   $$r_n = \frac{n^2h^2}{4\pi^2me^2 \cdot Z}, \quad E_n = \frac{-2\pi^2me^4}{n^2h^2} \cdot Z^2,$$
   where h = Planck's constant,
   m = mass of the electron
   e = charge of the electron.

   With the help of these expressions, Bohr gave a satisfactory explanation for the spectra of hydrogen and hydrogen-like species (ions having one electron, e.g., He^+, Li^{2+}, Be^{3+}, etc).

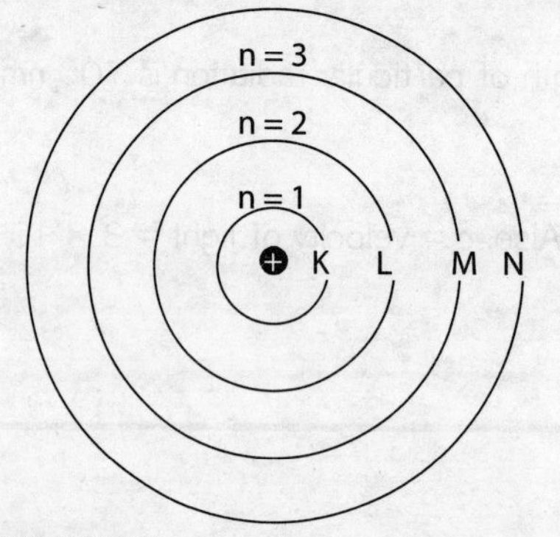

Figure 4.9 Stationary orbits of an atom

Limitations of Bohr's Atomic Model

1. Bohr could not explain the spectra of the multi-electronic species satisfactorily.
2. Bohr's model could not provide a satisfactory justification for the assumption that electron can revolve in those orbits where its angular momentum (mvr) is a whole-number multiple of $h/2\pi$, that is, he could not justify the quantization of angular momentum of the electron.
3. According to Heisenberg's uncertainty principle, it is impossible to determine simultaneously and accurately the exact position and the momentum of the moving particle. Bohr assumed that an electron of an atom is located at a definite distance from the nucleus and revolves around the nucleus with a definite velocity, which is against Heisenberg's uncertainty principle.
4. The atomic spectral lines are found to split into a number of closely packed lines in the presence of a magnetic and an electric field. These effects are called **Zeeman effect and Stark effect,** respectively. Bohr failed to explain these effects. Each spectral line in the atomic spectrum of hydrogen consists of still finer lines when it is observed by using the instrument with high resolving power. Bohr's model failed to explain this observation.

Sommerfeld's Extension of Bohr's Theory

In 1915, Arnold Sommerfeld extended Bohr's atomic theory to explain the fine structure of the spectral lines in the atomic spectra of hydrogen. He proposed that the electrons move in an elliptical orbit in addition to the circular orbit around the nucleus with the nucleus at one of the foci.

He suggested that the sub-energy levels or subshells associated with each main energy level (except the first main energy level) are responsible for the fine structure of the spectrum of hydrogen. These sub-energy levels or subshells exist due to the difference in energies of electrons revolving in different elliptical orbits belonging to the same main energy level.

He also proposed that the energy associated with the subshells is quantized and therefore, introduced a new quantum number called **azimuthal quantum number** to describe the angular momentum of the electrons revolving in different elliptical orbits.

To justify the assumption of the quantization of energy of the electron in the hydrogen atom, a French graduate student, Louis de Broglie, in 1924, suggested that the electrons have wave properties as well as particle properties.

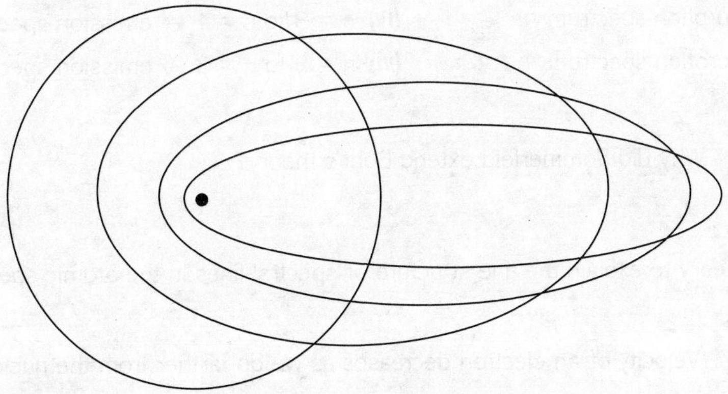

Figure 4.10 Sommerfeld's elliptical electron orbits. (Sub-energy levels for n = 4)

EXAMPLE 4.11 What do you mean by emission and absorption spectra?

SOLUTION

When the energy emitted by an atom due to the de-excitation of electrons is observed through a spectroscope, it appears as a spectrum consisting of bright lines on a dark background, this is emission spectrum. The spectrum formed due to the absorption of energy during the excitation of electrons consists of dark lines on a bright background, this is called absorption spectrum.

EXAMPLE 4.12 What do you mean by stationary orbit?

SOLUTION

According to Bohr's atomic model, an electron does not lose its energy as long as it revolves in a particular orbit. These orbits are called stationary orbits.

EXAMPLE 4.13 How did Bohr's model account for the stability of an atom?

SOLUTION

Bohr proposed that electrons in an atom move in specific, fixed orbits called energy levels or shells, without the emission or absorption of energy. An electron in a particular orbit has a definite energy and does not radiate energy, ensuring the stability of the atom. The electron can only move from one orbit to another by absorbing or emitting a discrete amount of energy, corresponding to the difference in energy between the two orbits.

EXAMPLE 4.14 Sunny and Bunny have taken spectra for the following transitions. Spectra taken by Sunny consisted of bright lines on a dark background. Spectra taken by Bunny consisted of dark lines on a bright background. Identify the electronic transitions corresponding to the spectra taken by Sunny and Bunny. What are those spectra called?

(i) n = 5 to n = 2 **(ii)** n = 4 to n = 6 **(iii)** n = 5 to n = 7

(iv) n = 3 to n = 1 **(v)** n = 1 to n = 2 **(vi)** n = 5 to n = 3

SOLUTION

When an electron in an atom gains energy, it gets excited to a higher energy state from the ground state. The electron being unstable in the excited state loses energy and comes back to the ground state either directly or in steps. During this process, the bright lines corresponding to the transitions are formed on the dark background. This is called emission spectrum. When the electrons get excited to higher energy levels, they absorb energy and dark lines corresponding to the transitions are formed on the bright background. This is called absorption spectrum.

(i) n = 5 to n = 2 → emission spectrum **(ii)** n = 4 to n = 6 → absorption spectrum

(iii) n = 5 to n = 7 → absorption spectrum **(iv)** n = 3 to n = 1 → emission spectrum

(v) n = 1 to n = 2 → absorption spectrum **(vi)** n = 5 to n = 3 → emission spectrum

EXAMPLE 4.15 Why did Sommerfeld extend Bohr's theory?

SOLUTION

Sommerfeld extended Bohr's theory to explain the fine structure of spectral lines in the atomic spectrum of hydrogen.

EXAMPLE 4.16 'Velocity of an electron decreases as we go farther from the nucleus'. Justify.

SOLUTION

According to Bohr, angular momentum is quantized.

$$mvr = \frac{nh}{2\pi} \Rightarrow v = \frac{hn}{2\pi mr}$$

From the above expression, it is obvious that the velocity decreases, as we go away from the nucleus. It is due to the decrease in nuclear forces of attraction.

As the nuclear forces of attraction decrease, less velocity is required for the electron to counter balance the nuclear force of attraction.

Dual Nature of Electron—de Broglie's Theory

De Broglie derived an expression for calculating wavelength (λ) of the wave, which is associated with the moving electrons. The expression is:

$$\lambda = \frac{h}{\text{momentum of electron}}$$

$$\text{or } \lambda = \frac{h}{mv},$$

where m = mass of electron
v = velocity of electron
h = Planck's constant

Info Bytes!

Louis de Broglie, in 1924, made the revolutionary proposal that particles such as electrons have both particle-like and wave-like properties, bridging the gap between classical and quantum physics.

This equation is called **de Broglie's equation,** and this hypothesis was experimentally confirmed by Davisson and Germer, who proved wave-like properties of electron in 1927. Hence, the dual nature of electron, that is particle nature as well as wave nature was established experimentally.

Louis de Broglie pointed out that the wave behavior of an electron is similar to that of a standing wave. The circumference of each of Bohr's orbit must be equal to an integral multiple of the wavelength of the wave associated with the moving electron. Orbits whose circumferences are not equal to the integral multiple of the wavelength are impossible for the existence of an electron in Bohr's atom model.

In 1927, the picture of electrons moving in fixed orbits was abandoned when the German physicist, Werner Heisenberg pointed out that both the position and the momentum of subatomic particles cannot be accurately determined simultaneously.

During this period, on the basis of the wave properties of electrons, Austrian physicist Erwin Schrödinger derived an equation called **Schrödinger wave equation** to describe the behaviour and energies of electrons in an atom. Based on this wave equation, the three-dimensional region in space around the nucleus, where the probability of finding an electron with a particular energy is determined to be maximum is called the **atomic orbital.**

On the basis of Schrödinger's wave equation, a quantum mechanical model of atom has been proposed. In this model, the state of an electron in an atom can be explained with respect to four quantum numbers. Among these, three quantum numbers namely the principal quantum number, azimuthal quantum number, and magnetic quantum number have been derived from Schrödinger's wave equation.

Quantum Numbers

Atoms and their electrons exhibit wave-like and particle-like behavior simultaneously, a concept introduced through wave-particle duality. Quantum mechanics was developed to describe and understand these behaviors. Within quantum mechanics, quantum numbers are used to describe the properties and positions of electrons in an atom. These numbers arise from mathematical solutions to the Schrödinger equation, which describes how electrons behave in an atom.

Principal Quantum Number

The principal quantum number determines the energy of the orbital and its size. Its value can be any positive integer. Larger the principal quantum number, higher the energy of the electron and greater the average distance of the electron from the nucleus. The principal quantum number is denoted by n, where n = 1, 2, 3.... and so on.

Azimuthal Quantum Number

The azimuthal quantum number determines the shape of the orbitals.

It is denoted by 'ℓ', where the value 'ℓ' can be any positive integer from 0 to (n – 1) (n is the principal quantum number). For example, the shell for which n = 4, has four subshells.

Konnect

The four quantum numbers - Principal, Azimuthal, Magnetic, and Spin - serve as 'addresses' for electrons, defining their exact locations and energies within an atom.

The azimuthal quantum number of these four subshells includes 0, 1, 2, and 3 and they are denoted by letters s, p, d, and f, respectively.

Table 4.5 Principal and azimuthal quantum numbers and representation of subshells

'n' values	'ℓ' values	Representations of subshells
1	0	1s
2	0, 1	2s, 2p
3	0, 1, 2	3s, 3p, 3d
4	0, 1, 2, 3	4s, 4p, 4d, 4f

Magnetic Quantum Number

The explanation for the splitting of a single spectral line of hydrogen atom into a number of closely spaced lines in the presence of a magnetic field or an electric field was given by Landé. He postulated that in the presence of an external electric field or a magnetic field, an electron can have different spatial orientations for a particular angular momentum. The magnetic quantum number was introduced to specify the further subdivisions of subshells or energy sublevels. It describes the spatial orientation of the orbital. The magnetic quantum number is denoted by 'm' and has integral values from $-\ell$ to $+\ell$. For example, +1, +2, and so on.

Table 4.6 Principal, azimuthal, and magnetic quantum numbers and representation of subshells

'n' values	'ℓ' values	'm' values	Representations of the orbitals
1	0	0	1s
2	0	0	2s
	1	−1, 0, +1	$2p_x\ 2p_y\ 2p_z$
3	0	0	3s
	1	−1, 0, +1	$3p_x\ 3p_y\ 3p_z$
	2	−2, −1, 0, +1, +2	$3d_{xy}\ 3d_{yz}\ 3d_{zx}\ 3d_{x^2-y^2}\ 3d_{z^2}$

Spin Quantum Number

It was observed with the help of an instrument with high resolving power that the spectral lines of some atoms consist of a pair of very closely spaced lines. To account for this fact, Austrian physicist Wolfgang Pauli suggested that these two closely spaced lines are the representation of the two different states of electrons. These states were later identified as the spin of the electron.

In 1925, Uhlenbeck and Goudsmit suggested that the electron rotates around its own axis either in a clockwise or in an anti-clockwise direction.

The angular momentum of the electron is not only due to its movement in the orbital but it also depends on its spinning around its own axis. Angular momentum under this condition is called **spin angular momentum,** which is also quantized and can have two values $+\frac{1}{2}$ and $-\frac{1}{2}$. $\left(+\frac{1}{2}\right)$ corresponds to the clockwise spinning and $\left(-\frac{1}{2}\right)$ corresponds to the anti-clockwise spinning of the electron.

Pauli's Exclusion Principle

Pauli's exclusion principle states that 'it is impossible for two electrons in a given atom to have all the quantum numbers identical.'

Table 4.7 Relation among quantum numbers following Pauli's exclusion principle

Values of principal quantum number	Values of azimuthal quantum number	Values of magnetic quantum number	Values of spin quantum number	Total number of electrons in main shells
$n = 1$ (K shell)	ℓ = 0 s subshell	m = 0	+1/2, –1/2	**2**
$n = 2$ (L shell)	ℓ = 0 s subshell	m = 0	+1/2, –1/2	2
	ℓ = 1 p subshell	m = –1 m = 0 m = +1	+1/2, –1/2 +1/2, –1/2 +1/2, –1/2	2 2 2 } 6
				2 + 6 = 8
$n = 3$ (M shell)	ℓ = 0 s subshell	m = 0	+1/2, –1/2	2
	ℓ = 1 p subshell	m = –1 m = 0 m = +1	+1/2, –1/2 +1/2, –1/2 +1/2, –1/2	2 2 2 } 6
	ℓ = 2 d subshell	m = –1 m = 0 m = –2 m = +1 m = +2	+1/2, –1/2 +1/2, –1/2 +1/2, –1/2 +1/2, –1/2 +1/2, –1/2	2 2 2 2 2 } 10 **2 + 6 + 10 = 18**
$n = 4$ (N shell)	ℓ = 0 s subshell	m = 0	+1/2, –1/2	2
	ℓ = 1 p subshell	m = –1 m = 0 m = +1 m = –2 m = –1	+1/2, –1/2 +1/2, –1/2 +1/2, –1/2	2 2 2 } 6
	ℓ = 2 d subshell	m = 0 m = +1 m = +2	+1/2, –1/2 +1/2, –1/2 +1/2, –1/2 +1/2, –1/2 +1/2, –1/2	2 2 2 2 2 } 10

(Continued)

Table 4.7 Continued

Values of principal quantum number	Values of azimuthal quantum number	Values of magnetic quantum number	Values of spin quantum number	Total number of electrons in main shells
	ℓ = 3 f subshell	m = −3 m = −2 m = −1 m = 0 m = +1 m = +2 m = +3	+1/2, −1/2 +1/2, −1/2 +1/2, −1/2 +1/2, −1/2 +1/2, −1/2 +1/2, −1/2 +1/2, −1/2	2, 2, 2, 2, 2, 2, 2 } 14 **2 + 6 + 10 + 14 = 32**

Representation of an Orbital

Since atomic orbital is a three-dimensional space that represents the maximum probability of finding an electron, it is difficult to give a pictorial representation of the orbital.

An atomic orbital can be generally represented by a shaded figure in which the intensity of shading indicates the probability of finding an electron in that area.

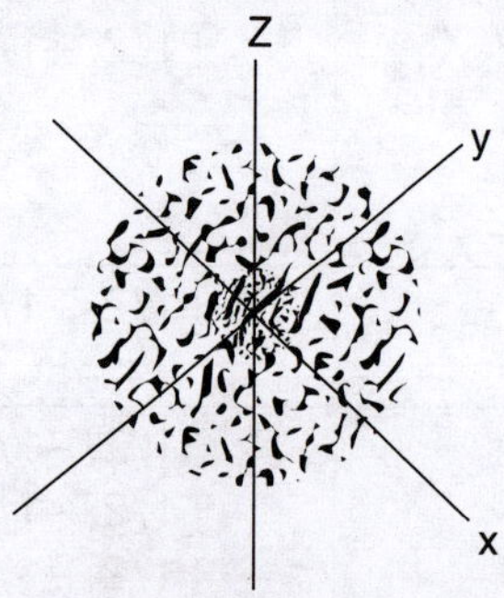

Figure 4.11 s-orbital

Info Bytes!

Orbitals are not solid structures but rather mathematical representations of where an electron is likely to be found 90% of the time.

Shapes of the Orbitals

When a boundary is drawn enveloping the region with maximum intensity of shading, the resultant orbital diagram is called the boundary surface diagram. The atomic orbitals can be conveniently represented by these boundary surface diagrams.

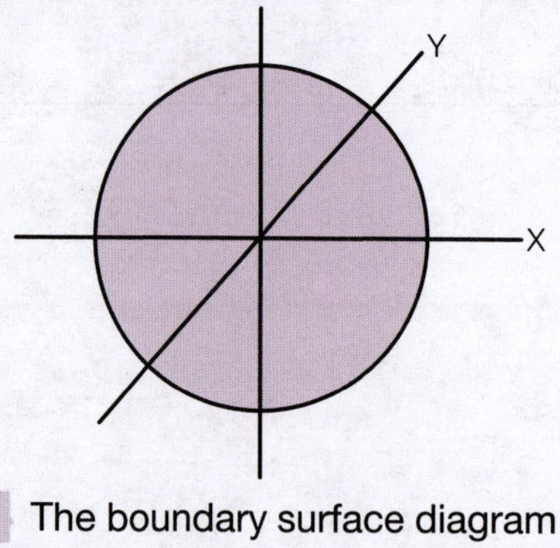

Figure 4.12 The boundary surface diagram of 1s orbital

s-orbitals: These orbitals have only one orientation and they are spherical (Figure 4.12). The spherical regions where in the probability of finding an electron is zero are called **nodal regions.** For an s-orbital of nth main energy level, the number of nodal regions is given by (n – 1), where n indicates the main energy level.

p-orbitals: They have two lobes and there are three orientations for *p*-orbitals represented as p_x, p_y, and p_z (Figure 4.13). The subscripts *x*, *y*, and *z* refer to the co-ordinate axes along which the density of the electrons of the respective orbitals is maximum. The p-orbitals are dumbbell shaped. The surface in which the probability of finding an electron is zero is called **nodal plane.** For example, for the p_x orbital, '*yz*' is the nodal plane. Each '*p*' orbital has one nodal plane, irrespective of the main energy level.

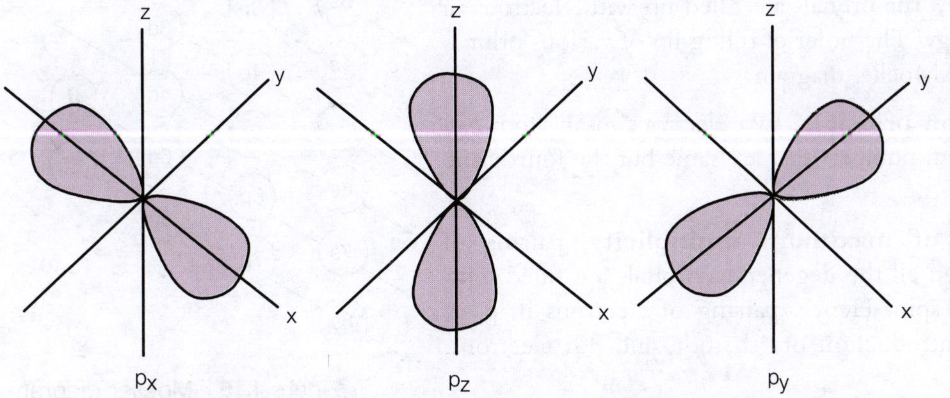

Figure 4.13 The boundary surface diagrams of the p-orbitals

Konnect

The shapes of the orbitals - s, p, d, and f - are derived from the solutions to the Schrödinger equation and depict the electron density distribution around the nucleus.

d-orbitals: There are five *d*-orbitals represented as d_{xy}, d_{yz}, d_{zx}, $d_{x^2-y^2}$, d_{z^2} .The orbitals d_{xy}, d_{yz} and d_{zx} have four lobes and these lobes lie symmetrically between the co-ordinate axes, for example, the lobes of d_{xy} lie symmetrically in between *x*-axis and *y*-axis (Figure 4.14).

The orbital $d_{x^2-y^2}$ also has four lobes along *x*-axis and *y*-axis. The orbital d_{z^2} has a unique shape with two lobes along *z*-axis and a 'belt-like' space centred in the $x - y$ plane. Each *d*-orbital has two nodal planes.

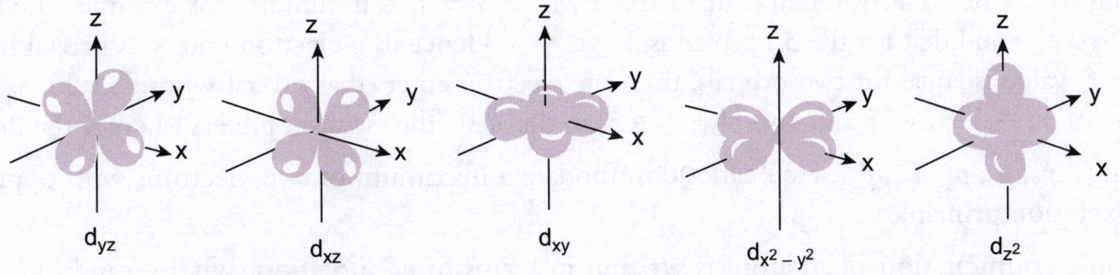

Figure 4.14 The boundary surface diagrams of five d-orbitals.

Electronic Configuration of Atoms

Shell	$2n^2$
K	2
L	8
M	18
M	32
O	50

The distribution of electrons in the different orbitals belonging to different energy levels of an atom is the electronic configuration of the atom of the given element. The electrons are arranged in an atom in the various shells around the nucleus. The last shell or the outermost shell from the nucleus with electrons is called **valence shell.** The shell inner to this is called **penultimate shell** and the one inner to the penultimate shell is called **anti-penultimate shell.** Some rules have been laid for writing the electronic configuration of elements. The filling of electrons in various shells can be done according to Bohr–Bury scheme. According to this, the maximum number of electrons that can be accommodated in any shell is given by $2n^2$, where n represents the number of the shell. The maximum number of electrons that can be filled in the valence shell is 8, that in the penultimate shell is 18 and the anti-penultimate shell has a maximum capacity of 32 electrons.

The study of the atomic spectra provided the information about the relative energies of the atomic orbitals. The increasing order of the energy of different orbitals belonging to different main energy levels was given by Aufbau principle.

'Aufbau' is a German expression that means building up or construction. According to **Aufbau principle,** 'the orbitals are filled up with electrons in the order of their increasing energy.' The order of filling up of various orbitals can be represented in the form of Moeller diagram.

According to **Pauli's exclusion principle,** two electrons in an atom can have a maximum of three quantum numbers that are same but the fourth one must be different.

According to **Hund's rule of maximum multiplicity**, pairing of electrons in a subshell starts when all the degenerate orbitals are filled with unpaired electrons with parallel spin. Hence, pairing of electrons in p, d, and f subshells starts with the introduction of 4th, 6th, and 8th electrons, respectively.

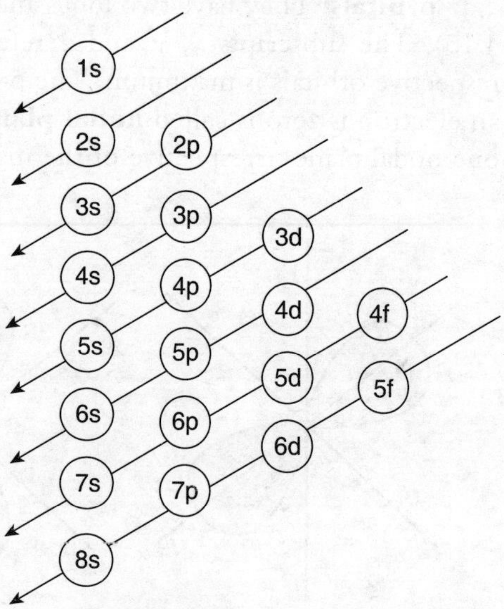

Figure 4.15 Moeller diagram

Rules for Filling Up of Electrons in the Orbitals

There are certain rules laid down for filling up of the electrons in the respective orbitals. These are as follows:

1. The maximum number of electrons in the main energy level is equal to $2n^2$, where n is the number of the main energy level.
2. The maximum number of electrons in a subshell or orbital like *s, p, d* and *f* is equal to $2(2\ell + 1)$, where the value of ℓ is 0, 1, 2 and 3, respectively for *s, p, d,* and *f* orbitals. Hence, the maximum number of electrons in s, p, d, and f orbitals is 2, 6, 10, and 14, respectively.
3. As a working rule, a new electron enters that orbital where $(n + \ell)$ is minimum, for example, the $(n + \ell)$ value of 4s orbital is $4 + 0 = 4$ and that for the 3d orbital is $3 + 2 = 5$. Hence, the electron enters 4s orbital before entering 3d. In case $(n + \ell)$ value is equal for two orbitals, then the electron enters that orbital whose n value is less. For example, $(n + \ell)$ value of $3d = 3 + 2 = 5$ and $4p = 4 + 1 = 5$, in this case, the electron prefers to enter the 3*d* orbital.
4. Each orbital (s, p_x, p_y, p_z, d_{xy}, d_{yz}, etc.) can accommodate a maximum of two electrons with opposite spin as given by Pauli's exclusion principle.

   The electronic configuration of an atom is written in terms of $n\ell^x$ notation, where n indicates the main energy level, ℓ indicates the subshells or orbitals (*s, p, d,* and *f*) and x indicates the total number of electrons present in the subshell.
5. Electrons enter the orbitals p_x, p_y, p_z, d_{xy}, d_{yz}, etc., in such a way that maximum number of unpaired electrons remain in the subshell and the unpaired electrons spin in the same direction.

   Hence, in the subshells *p, d,* and *f,* the electrons prefer to occupy separate orbitals rather than getting paired in an orbital.

   As a result of this, pairing takes place only with the entry of second electron in the s-orbital, fourth electron in the *p*-orbital, sixth electron in the *d*-orbital and eighth in the *f*-orbital. These orbitals are identical in energy in the absence of any electric or magnetic field and are called **degenerate orbitals.**
6. Half-filled or completely filled subshells impart greater stability to the atoms.

   Hence, actual electronic configurations of some transition elements are different from the expected electronic configuration.

Example: Expected electronic configurations of chromium and copper are $3d^44s^2$ and $3d^94s^2$, respectively. However, their actual electronic configurations are: chromium $3d^54s^1$ and copper $3d^{10}4s^1$. Most of the exceptions to the electron configuration predicted from the Aufbau principle occur among elements with atomic number Z > 20.

Table 4.8 Electronic configuration of elements up to Z = 54

Element	At. No.	K $n = 1$	L $n = 2$		M $n = 3$			N $n = 4$				O $n = 5$			
		1*s*	2*s*	2*p*	3*s*	3*p*	3*d*	4*s*	4*p*	4*d*	4*f*	5*s*	5*p*	5*d*	5*f*
H	1	1													
He	2	2													
Li	3	2	1												
Be	4	2	2												
B	5	2	2	1											
C	6	2	2	2											
N	7	2	2	3											
O	8	2	2	4											
F	9	2	2	5											
Ne	10	2	2	6											
Na	11	2	2	6	1										
Mg	12	2	2	6	2										
Al	13	2	2	6	2	1									
Si	14	2	2	6	2	2									
P	15	2	2	6	2	3									
S	16	2	2	6	2	4									
Cl	17	2	2	6	2	5									
Ar	18	2	2	6	2	6									
K	19	2	2	6	2	6		1							
Ca	20	2	2	6	2	6		2							
Sc	21	2	2	6	2	6	1	2							
Ti	22	2	2	6	2	6	2	2							
V	23	2	2	6	2	6	3	2							
Cr	24	2	2	6	2	6	5	1							
Mn	25	2	2	6	2	6	5	2							
Fe	26	2	2	6	2	6	6	2							
Co	27	2	2	6	2	6	7	2							
Ni	28	2	2	6	2	6	8	2							
Cu	29	2	2	6	2	6	10	1							
Zn	30	2	2	6	2	6	10	2							
Ga	31	2	2	6	2	6	10	2	1						
Ge	32	2	2	6	2	6	10	2	2						
As	33	2	2	6	2	6	10	2	3						
Se	34	2	2	6	2	6	10	2	4						
Br	35	2	2	6	2	6	10	2	5						

(Continued)

Table 4.8 Continued

Element	At. No.	K $n = 1$	L $n = 2$		M $n = 3$			N $n = 4$				O $n = 5$			
Kr	36	2	2	6	2	6	10	2	6						
Rb	37	2	2	6	2	6	10	2	6			1			
Sr	38	2	2	6	2	6	10	2	6			2			
Y	39	2	2	6	2	6	10	2	6	1		2			
Zr	40	2	2	6	2	6	10	2	6	2		2			
Nb	41	2	2	6	2	6	10	2	6	4		1			
Mo	42	2	2	6	2	6	10	2	6	5		1			
Tc	43	2	2	6	2	6	10	2	6	5		2			
Ru	44	2	2	6	2	6	10	2	6	7		1			
Rh	45	2	2	6	2	6	10	2	6	8		1			
Pd	46	2	2	6	2	6	10	2	6	10		0			
Ag	47	2	2	6	2	6	10	2	6	10		1			
Cd	48	2	2	6	2	6	10	2	6	10		2			
In	49	2	2	6	2	6	10	2	6	10		2	1		
Sn	50	2	2	6	2	6	10	2	6	10		2	2		
Sb	51	2	2	6	2	6	10	2	6	10		2	3		
Te	52	2	2	6	2	6	10	2	6	10		2	4		
I	53	2	2	6	2	6	10	2	6	10		2	5		
Xe	54	2	2	6	2	6	10	2	6	10		2	6		

EXAMPLE 4.17

An element has protons whose mass is equal to 23,881 times that of an electron. Identify the element and write its electronic configuration.

SOLUTION

Mass of a proton is 1837-times than that of an electron.

$$\text{Number of protons} = \frac{23{,}881}{1837} = 13$$

Atomic number of the element is 13.

So, the element is aluminium and its electronic configuration is 2, 8, 3.

EXAMPLE 4.18

Write the electronic configuration and the atomic number of the atom which becomes stable by gaining 3 electrons in fifth shell.

SOLUTION

The electronic configuration of the stable species is 2, 8, 18, 18, 8.

Hence, the electronic configuration of the atom which becomes stable after gaining 3 electrons in the fifth shell is 2, 8, 18, 18, 5 and the atomic number is 51.

EXAMPLE 4.19 What is the ratio of the amount of energy required to remove an electron from hydrogen and He^+ ion?

SOLUTION

Energy of electron (single electron species) $E_n = -\dfrac{13.6 \times Z^2}{n^2} eV$;

For hydrogen $\Rightarrow -13.6 \times \dfrac{1^2}{1^2} = -13.6 eV$; Energy required to remove this electron = +13.6 eV

For $He^+ \Rightarrow -13.6 \times \dfrac{2^2}{1^2} = -54.4 eV$; Energy required to remove this electron = +54.4 eV

Ratio of energy required = $\dfrac{13.6}{54.4} = \dfrac{1}{4}$ = 1 : 4.

EXAMPLE 4.20 Distinguish between orbit and orbital with respect to definition.

SOLUTION

Orbit	Orbital
Orbit is a definite circular path in which electrons revolve around the nucleus.	Orbital is the three-dimensional space around the nucleus in which the probability of finding an electron with a particular energy is maximum.

EXAMPLE 4.21 Why did Sommerfeld introduce azimuthal quantum number?

SOLUTION

Sommerfeld introduced azimuthal quantum number to explain the quantization of energy associated with each subshell. Azimuthal quantum number describes the angular momentum of the electrons revolving in different elliptical orbits.

EXAMPLE 4.22 How does de Broglie's theory support Bohr's theory?

SOLUTION

According to Bohr's atomic theory, electrons revolve around the nucleus in a circular path with a fixed angular momentum. According to de Broglie, electron has a dual nature – particle nature and wave nature. The nature of the wave should be like a stationary wave if the path of the electron is circular. The circumference of the circular path of the electron should be an integral multiple of the wavelength of the wave associated with the electron since the wave is a stationary wave. The energy of the wave associated with the electron moving in a particular orbit is quantized because the wavelength of it is fixed for that particular orbit.

EXAMPLE 4.23 Configurations and designations of some orbitals are given below. Identify those configurations that are not possible in an atom. Arrange the orbitals with possible configurations in the order in which they are filled with electrons 6*s*, 8*p*, 7*s*, 4*d*, 2*p*, 3*d*, 3*f*, 4*f*, 1*p*.

SOLUTION

1*p* and 3*f* are the configurations that are not possible for any orbitals in an atom. All others are possible. The orbitals are occupied by electrons in increasing order of their energies. The order of energy is decided by $n + \ell$ rule.

$n + \ell$ values of orbitals

$6s \rightarrow 6 + 0 = 6$ $4d \rightarrow 4 + 2 = 6$; $4p \rightarrow 4 + 1 = 5$ $2p \rightarrow 2 + 1 = 3$

$8p \rightarrow 8 + 1 = 9$ $3d \rightarrow 3 + 2 = 5$; $7s \rightarrow 7 + 0 = 7$ $4f \rightarrow 4 + 3 = 7$

$2p < 3d < 4p < 4d < 6s < 4f < 7s < 8p$

EXAMPLE 4.24 The valence electronic configuration of an atom is $6s^2$. If d-orbital of the penultimate shell contains two unpaired electrons, calculate the atomic number.

SOLUTION

Since the valence electronic configuration of the atom is $6s^2$ and d-orbital of the penultimate shell contains two unpaired electrons, the electronic configuration is $[Xe]6s^2 4f^{14} 5d^2$. Therefore, the atomic number of the element is 72.

EXAMPLE 4.25 An atom of an element has five electrons in the 3d subshell. Calculate the atomic number of the element.

SOLUTION

The electronic configuration of the element having five electrons in the 3d subshell is $[Ar]4s^2\ 3d^5$. Therefore, the atomic number is 25.

EXAMPLE 4.26 What is the maximum number of electrons present in the main energy level in which the '*g*' subshell appears for the first time? Find the atomic number of the element to be discovered in which the differentiating electron is the only electron in the first '*g*' subshell.

SOLUTION

Corresponding 'ℓ' value of '*g*' subshell is '4'. Principal quantum number in which '*g*' subshell can exist is '5'.

The maximum number of electrons that can be accommodated in fifth orbit is $2 \times 5^2 = 50$ electrons.

Orbitals to be filled before filling of '5*g*' subshell are: 1*s*, 2*s*, 2*p*, 3*s*, 3*p*, 4*s*, 3*d*, 4*p*, 5*s*, 4*d*, 5*p*, 6*s*, 4*f*, 5*d*, 6*p*, 7*s*, 5*f*, 6*d*, 7*p*, 8*s*, 5*g*. Atomic number of the element should be 121.

EXAMPLE 4.27 Arrange the following atomic numbers in the increasing order of number of unpaired electrons.

(i) 16 **(ii)** 32 **(iii)** 40 **(iv)** 57

SOLUTION

(i) Electronic configuration is $1s^2\ 2s^2\ 2p^6\ 3s^2\ 3p^4$; number of unpaired electrons is 2.

(ii) Electronic configuration is $1s^2\ 2s^2\ 2p^6\ 3s^2\ 3p^6\ 4s^2\ 3d^{10}\ 4p^2$; number of unpaired electrons is 2.

(iii) Electronic configuration is $1s^2\ 2s^2\ 2p^6\ 3s^2\ 3p^6\ 4s^2\ 3d^{10}\ 4p^6\ 5s^2\ 4d^2$; number of unpaired electrons is 2.

(iv) Electronic configuration is $[Xe]\ 6s^2\ 5d^1$; number of unpaired electrons 1

$\therefore$ order is (i) = (ii) = (iii) > (iv)

EXAMPLE 4.28 Account for the very stable nitrogen atom in contrast to its neighboring carbon and oxygen atoms.

SOLUTION

Nitrogen has half-filled configuration $2s^2\ 2p^3$, while carbon $2s^2\ 2p^2$ and oxygen $2s^2\ 2p^4$ have no half-filled configurations. The atoms with half-filled configurations are exceptionally stable. This is due to the symmetry in the arrangement of the electrons in the orbitals and mutual exchange of energy among the parallel spins of electrons that lowers the energy of system. Hence, it becomes more stable.

POINTS TO REMEMBER

- ✔ The electron was the first fundamental particle that was discovered by J. J. Thomson.
- ✔ Sir William Crookes was the first scientist who designed the discharge tube which was called Crooke's discharge tube or cathode ray tube.
- ✔ Millikan observed that the smallest charge found on them was approximately 1.59×10^{-19} coulombs and the charge on each drop was always an integral multiple of that value.
- ✔ Anode rays were found as a stream of positively-charged particles in contrast to the cathode rays.
- ✔ Thomson's model could successfully explain the electrical neutrality of atom. However, it failed to explain how the positively-charged particles are shielded from the negatively-charged electrons without getting neutralized.
- ✔ The entire positive charge and mass of the atom is concentrated in the small, central part known as the nucleus.
- ✔ Rutherford's atomic model resembles the planetary motion in solar system. Therefore, Rutherford's model of an atom is also called planetary model.
- ✔ The arrangement of component light energies according to their wavelengths is called spectrum and spectroscope is the instrument designed to observe the spectra.
- ✔ White light is composed of lights of different wavelengths hence, a continuous band of different wavelengths is obtained which is called continuous spectrum.
- ✔ The spectrum for the atoms of the gas present in the discharge tube, is found to consist of discrete lines of different colours. This is called line spectrum, which is a discontinuous spectrum.
- ✔ Energy can be absorbed or radiated by a body in the form of small packets of energy called quanta.
- ✔ Electrons move around the nucleus in specified circular paths called orbits or shells or energy levels.
- ✔ As long as the electron revolves in a particular orbit, the electron does not lose its energy. Therefore, these orbits are called stationary orbits and the electrons are said to be in stationary energy states.
- ✔ An electron can revolve only in an orbit in which the angular momentum of the electron (mvr) is a whole-number multiple of $h/2\pi$. This is known as the principle of quantization of angular momentum.
- ✔ The atomic spectral lines are found to split into a number of closely-packed lines in the presence of a magnetic and an electric field. These effects are called Zeeman effect and Stark effect, respectively.
- ✔ Azimuthal quantum number to describe the angular momentum of the electrons revolving in different elliptical orbits.
- ✔ Atoms of different elements have same mass number are called isobars.
- ✔ Austrian physicist Erwin Schrödinger derived an equation called Schrödinger wave equation to describe the behaviour and energies of electrons in an atom.
- ✔ The three-dimensional region in space around the nucleus, where the probability of finding an electron with a particular energy is determined to be maximum is called the atomic orbital.
- ✔ Pauli's exclusion principle states that 'it is impossible for two electrons in a given atom to have all the quantum numbers identical.'

- ✔ The spherical regions where in the probability of finding an electron is zero are called nodal regions.
- ✔ The surface in which the probability of finding an electron is zero is called nodal plane.
- ✔ The last shell or the outermost shell from the nucleus with electrons is called valence shell.
- ✔ The shell inner to this is called penultimate shell and the one inner to the penultimate shell is called anti-penultimate shell.
- ✔ According to Aufbau principle, 'the orbitals are filled up with electrons in the order of their increasing energy.'
- ✔ According to Pauli's exclusion principle, two electrons in an atom can have a maximum of three quantum numbers that are same but the fourth one must be different.
- ✔ According to Hund's rule of maximum multiplicity, pairing of electrons in a subshell starts when all the degenerate orbitals are filled with unpaired electrons with parallel spin.
- ✔ Quantum numbers are crucial for our understanding of the electron configuration and behavior within atoms. They lay the foundation for understanding atomic structure and, subsequently, the behavior of elements and compounds in various chemical reactions.

DW

PRACTICE QUESTIONS CLASSROOM WING

Very Short Answer Type Questions

Direction for questions from 1 to 17:

Fill in the blanks.

1. According to Rutherford's atomic model, electrons revolve around the nucleus with __________ velocities
2. According to Bohr's atomic model, a fixed amount of energy is emitted when an electron jumps from an __________ orbit to an __________ orbit
3. According to ________, the charges in an atom are arranged like the pulp and seeds of a watermelon.
4. With the increase in the radius of the orbit, the energy of an electron __________.
5. The circular paths in which electrons revolve are called ______.
6. The ______ consists of well-defined lines of definite frequencies.
7. In the formula $E = h\nu$, E is ______ and ν is ______.
8. The region having maximum probability of finding an electron in space is known as ______.
9. The value of ℓ for an orbital having five degenerate orbitals is ______.
10. The valence electronic configuration of magnesium is ______.
11. Magnetic quantum number specifies ________.
12. In the degenerate orbitals, unpaired electrons have ________ spin.
13. Nitrogen atom has ________ unpaired electrons, according to ______ rule.
14. The ratio between the number of neutrons present in C^{12} and Si^{30} atoms is __________.
15. The electronic configuration of copper is ______.
16. When a 4p orbital is completely filled then the next electron goes to __________.
17. The number of unpaired electrons present in $Fe^{3+}$is __________.

Direction for questions from 18 to 53:

Answer the following questions

18. Which of the postulates of Dalton's atomic theory was proved wrong with the discovery of radioactivity?
19. Which postulate of Dalton's atomic theory became contradictory after the discovery of isotopes?
20. α-ray scattering experiment was carried out to prove the correctness of which atomic model?
21. Who discovered protons? Based on what experiment was he able to discover these protons?
22. What was the mathematical equation given by Max Planck?
23. Who discovered neutrons? How was the discovery made?
24. What name did Max Planck give to energy packets?
25. What is Heisenberg's uncertainty principle?
26. Which theory supported the particle nature of an electron?
27. Give the value of Planck's constant in
    (1) erg-s
    (2) joule-s
28. Give equations to calculate the following:
    (a) the radius of the nth orbit of hydrogen atom
    (b) energy of the nth orbit of hydrogen atom
29. What happens when an electron jumps from a lower energy level to a higher energy level?
30. What is Zeeman effect?
31. What is Stark effect?
32. What is an α-particle?
33. What is a continuous spectrum?
34. Why are light rays known as electromagnetic waves?
35. How are the subatomic particles arranged in an atom according to modern structure of the atom?

36. What is a fine spectrum?

37. What was the requirement for introducing the magnetic quantum number?

38. What is the principal quantum number?

39. Why did the spin quantum number come into existence?

40. What do you mean by the dual nature of an electron?

41. According to de Broglie, what is the relation between the wavelength of the wave associated with the moving electron and momentum of the electron?

42. Define an atomic orbital.

43. What was the requirement for introducing the atomic orbital concept?

44. How many orbitals are there in K, L, M, and N shells? What are they?

45. What is the shape of an 's' orbital? Draw the diagram.

46. Why does L shell does not have d-orbitals?

47. What do you mean by degenerate orbitals? Give examples.

48. How many nodal surface(s) can 5s orbital have?

49. In the pictorial representation of an orbital, what is the role of different intensity of shading?

50. How is the order of the energy of the atomic orbitals established?

51. In how many d-orbitals do the lobes lie in between co-ordinate axes? What are those?

52. How will you find out the maximum number of electrons in the main energy level?

53. Which one of the following (a or b) electronic configuration is more stable and why?
(a) $3d^4\ 4s^2$
(b) $3d^5\ 4s^1$

Short Answer Type Questions

54. Identify the element from the given configuration. a, $4a$, $(6a + 1)$, and $(a - 1)$

55. The ratio of atomic numbers of two elements 'X' and 'Y' is 1:7. The radius of the third orbit of single electron species of X is 1.587 Å. Identify the penultimate shell of Y.

56. Does the configuration: x, $(x + y)$, $3y$, x, hold good for zinc

57. Trinegative ion of element 'X' is isoelectronic with inert gas 'Y'. If X has two completely filled shells, then identify Y.

58. What is the amount of energy needed to remove an electron from a hydrogen atom to produce an H^+ ion? Explain.

59. If Rutherford's atomic model is correct, then the atom should collapse. Why?

60. Describe Millikan's oil drop experiment in brief.

61. According to Rutherford's atomic model, where are the protons and electrons located in an atom?

62. Why was the presence of neutrons in an atom predicted? How were neutrons discovered?

63. Describe J. J. Thomson's atomic model.

64. Define angular momentum. In the relation $mvr = \frac{nh}{2\pi}$, what do m, v, r and h denote?

65. On what basis did Bohr assume the concept of stationary orbits for an electron?

66. The wavelength of a particular radiation is 700 nm (1 nm = 10^{-9} m). Find its frequency (ν).

67. Distinguish between continuous spectrum and discontinuous spectrum. Give some examples of sources for these spectra.

68. An electron revolving round in an orbit has angular momentum equal to $\frac{h}{2\pi}$. Can it lose energy?

69. What is azimuthal quantum number?

70. What are the drawbacks of Bohr's theory?

71. What leads to the establishment of the particle nature of electron?

72. What is Heisenberg's uncertainty principle?

73. According to Pauli's exclusion principle, what is the maximum number of electrons that can be present in d-orbitals and f-orbitals? Explain.

74. Write the electronic configuration of the following elements.

Element	Atomic number	Electronic configuration (nl^x)
A	23	
B	38	
C	35	
D	20	
E	18	

75. What does Hund's rule for maximum multiplicity state?

76. Explain how the Bohr's atomic model was contradictory to Heisenberg's uncertainty principle.

77. (a) Write the electronic configurations of the noble gases starting from helium and predict their atomic numbers.

(b) The number of electrons with $\ell = 0$ value in an atom of copper is ________.

(c) An atom of an element has six electrons with $\ell = 2$ value. The number of half-filled orbitals in its stable ion is ________.

78. How many nodes are present in 3s, 3p, and 3d orbitals?

79. Describe the shape of different p-orbitals.

80. Calculate the maximum number of electrons in 1st, 2nd, 3rd, and 4th shells.

81. Draw the diagram of different d-orbitals.

Essay Answer Type Questions

82. Two isotopes 'X' and 'Y' are present in a natural sample in 3:2 ratio. If the average atomic mass is (A + 0.8) and the atomic mass of the lighter isotope, that is, X is A, then calculate the atomic mass of the heavier isotope in terms of A.

83. Calculate the radius of the third orbit of a single electron species, if the energy of this orbit is –13.6 eV.

84. If the energy of the second orbit of a single electron species is $-x$ eV, then calculate the atomic number of that atom in terms of x.

85. Describe Rutherford's atomic model.

86. State the limitations of Bohr's model.

87. (a) Explain Zeeman and Stark effects.

(b) How are they related to magnetic quantum number? Explain

88. What are the different rules for filling up the orbitals? Explain each rule in detail.

89. Discuss the four quantum numbers. Explain the interrelationship among the four quantum numbers. Also explain the significance of a quantum number.

90. What was the basis for the origin of the concept of an atomic orbital? Define atomic orbital.

91. Explain the dual nature of an electron on the basis of de Broglie's theory. State Heisenberg's uncertainty principle. How did it contradict Bohr's theory?

92. The angular momentum of the electron in the third orbit of hydrogen atom is 31.74×10^{-28} g cm^2 s^{-1}. Calculate the wavelength of wave associated with the electron.

PRACTICE QUESTIONS COMPETITION WING

Level 1: Apply Your Concepts

Direction for questions from 1 to 14:
State whether the following statements are true or false.

1. According to Thomson's atomic model, electrons revolve round the nucleus.
2. In a discharge tube, anode rays originate when electrons collide with gas molecules.
3. $_{8}O^{16}$ and $_{8}O^{18}$ are isotopes while $_{20}Ca^{40}$ and $_{18}Ar^{40}$ are isobars.
4. Energy is absorbed when the electron jumps from K to L energy shells.
5. α-ray scattering experiment proved that the positive particles are present in the extra nuclear part of an atom.
6. Characteristic spectra of atoms are line spectra.
7. An electron in the excited state of an atom is highly unstable.
8. The dual nature of electron was given by Sommerfeld.
9. Among 4p, 4s, 3p, and 3d orbitals, 3d orbital has the least energy.
10. Azimuthal quantum number indicates the angular momentum of an electron.
11. Any two electrons in an atom can have maximum of three quantum numbers same.
12. Pairing of electrons in degenerate orbitals takes place only when the degenerate orbitals are filled with one electron each.
13. Bohr's theory can explain the spectra of multielectron species.
14. In iron, the differentiating electron enters into the orbital of a penultimate shell.

Direction for questions from 15 to 33:
Fill in the blanks.

15. A dipositive ion of element 'A' is isoelectronic with inert gas 'X'. X possesses three completely filled shells. The number of electrons present in the antepenultimate shell of the atom of element A is ______
16. In α-ray scattering experiment, α-rays are used because they are ______ charged particles and have mass.
17. The value of the Planck's constant '*h*' in erg-s is ______.
18. Rutherford's model is also called ______ model
19. Mass of the electron is calculated from ______ and ______ values of electron.
20. Anode rays are deflected towards the negative plate in the presence of an electric field because they consist of ______ particles.
21. Some of the α-rays deflect in acute and obtuse angles due to the presence of the ______ in the centre of the atom.
22. According to classical electrodynamics, if an electrically charged particle revolves in a circular path, it continuously ______ energy.
23. The energy of an electron present in the first orbit of an atom is ______ than the energy of electron in the other orbits.
24. Splitting of spectral lines in the presence of magnetic field is known as ______ effect.
25. The kinetic energy of an electron present in the first orbit of an atom is ______ than that of the electron in the last orbit.
26. The spectra produced by the deexcitation of an electron is called ______.
27. For a given value of 'ℓ,' the total number of 'm' values is ______.
28. If the azimuthal quantum number of an electron is 2 then the shape of orbital is ______.
29. The value of Planck's constant is ______.
30. The ratio of energy to frequency of electromagnetic radiation is equal to ______.
31. The minimum angular momentum of an electron with the magnetic quantum numbers −1, 0, +1 is ______.
32. Bohr's model introduced the concept of quantization of ______.

33. The ratio of the energies of two different radiations whose frequencies are 3×10^{14} Hz and 5×10^{14} Hz is ________.

Direction for questions from 34 to 35:

Match the entries given in Column A with appropriate ones from Column B.

34. Match the values of Column A with those of Column B.

Column A (Change in angular momentum of the electron during the transition in a hydrogen atom).	Column B (Number of spectral lines)
(i). $\frac{5h}{2p}$ to $\frac{h}{p}$.	(A) 1
(ii). $\frac{3h}{2p}$ to $\frac{h}{p}$.	(B) 3
(iii) $\frac{3h}{p}$ to $\frac{h}{2p}$.	(C) 6
(iv) $\frac{2h}{p}$ to $\frac{h}{p}$.	(D) 15

35.

Column A	Column B
A. Be	a. $[He]2s^22p^6$
B. Ne	b. $[He]2s^2$
C. Si	c. $[Ne]3s^23p^3$
D. P	d. $[Ne]3s^23p^5$
E. Cl	e. $[Ne]3s^23p^2$

Direction for questions from 36 to 85:

For each of the questions, four choices have been provided. Select the correct alternative.

36. **Assertion (A):** An element with atomic number 36 is unreactive.

Reason (R): 8 electrons in the outermost shell make the atom highly energetic.

(a) Both A and R are true and R is the correct explanation of A.

(b) Both A and R are true, but R is not the correct explanation of A.

(c) A is true and R is false.

(d) A is false and R is true.

37. **Assertion (A):** From Thomson's experiment and Millikan's oil drop experiment, mass as well as charge of an electron can be calculated.

Reason (R): Specific charge of an electron is obtained from Thomson's experiment, whereas the charge of an electron is obtained from Millikan's oil drop experiment.

(a) Both A and R are true and R is the correct explanation of A.

(b) Both A and R are true, but R is not the correct explanation of A.

(c) A is true and R is false.

(d) A is false and R is true.

38. **Assertion (A):** An ion is more stable than an atom.

Reason (R): An ion is a charged particle.

(a) Both A and R are true and R is the correct explanation of A.

(b) Both A and R are true, but R is not the correct explanation of A.

(c) A is true and R is false.

(d) A is false and R is true.

39. **Assertion(A):** The specific charge of α particle is less than H^+.

Reason(R): Hydrogen has only one proton.

(a) Both A and R are true and R is the correct explanation of A.

(b) Both A and R are true, but R is not the correct explanation of A.

(c) A is true and R is false.

(d) A is false and R is true.

40. **Assertion A:** An electron in the inner orbit is more tightly bound to the nucleus.

Reason B: The greater the absolute value of energy of an electron the more tightly the electron is bound to the nucleus.

(a) Both A and B are true but B is not the appropriate reason for A.

(b) Both A and B are individually correct and B is the correct reason for A.

(c) A is correct but B is not correct.

(d) Both A and B are not correct.

41. The electron revolves only in the orbits in which

(a) $mvr > \frac{nh}{2\pi}$ (b) $mvr \geq \frac{nh}{2\pi}$

(c) $mvr = \frac{nh}{2\pi}$ (d) $mvr < \frac{nh}{2\pi}$

42. Which among the following pairs are having different number of valence electrons?

(a) Na^+, Al^{3+} (b) P^{3-}, Ar

(c) Mg^{2+}, Ar (d) O^{2-}, F^-

43. If two naturally occurring isotopes of an element are $_7X^{15}$, $_7X^{11}$; what will be the percentage composition of each isotope of X occurring, respectively, if the average atomic weight accounts to 14?

(a) 95, 5 (b) 80, 20

(c) 75, 25 (d) 65, 35

44. According to quantum theory of radiation, which is false?

(a) radiations are associated with energy

(b) radiation is neither emitted nor absorbed discontinuously

(c) the magnitude of energy associated with a quantum is dependent on frequency

(d) photons are quanta of radiation

45. Select True/False among the following statements:

(i) Bohr's theory successfully explained stability of the atom.

(ii) Atoms give line spectra.

(iii) Velocity of electromagnetic waves depends on the frequency.

(iv) Bohr introduced the concept of orbital.

(a) (i) T, (ii) T, (iii) F, (iv) F

(b) (i) T, (ii) F, (iii) T, (iv) T

(c) (i) F, (ii) T, (iii) F, (iv) F

(d) (i) F, (ii) F, (iii) T, (iv) T

46. Which of the following particles do not produce electronic spectra?

(a) Li^{2+} (b) He^{2+}

(c) Be^{2+} (d) Na^+

47. An element has two isotopes with mass numbers 16 and 18. The average atomic weight is 16.5. The percentage abundance of these isotopes is ______ and ______, respectively.

(a) 75, 25 (b) 25, 75

(c) 50, 50 (d) 33.33, 66.67

48. Which among the following are isobars?

(a) $_bX^a$ and $_bY^{a+1}$

(b) $_bX^a$ and $_cY^b$

(c) $_bX^a$ and $_{b+1}Y^a$

(d) $_bX^a$ and $_{b-1}Y^{a-1}$

49. Some of the elements have fractional atomic masses. The reason for this could be

(a) the existence of isobars

(b) the existence of isotopes

(c) the nuclear reactions

(d) the presence of neutrons in the nucleus

50. Which of these pairs has almost similar masses?

(a) proton–electron (b) neutron–electron

(c) electron–$_1H^1$ (d) neutron–$_1H^1$

51. The energy of an electron revolving in the 3rd orbit of Be^{3+} ion is ________ eV

(a) –10.2 (b) –13.6

(c) –24.2 (d) –18.1

52. Which of the following concepts, was not considered in Rutherford's atomic model?

(a) the electrical neutrality of atom

(b) the quantization of energy

(c) electrons revolve around the nucleus at very high speeds

(d) existence of nuclear forces of attraction on the electrons

53. What is the ratio of radii of the first successive odd orbits of hydrogen atom?

(a) 9 : 1 (b) 1 : 9

(c) 1 : 3 (d) 3 : 1

54. An electron revolves round the nucleus in the 3rd orbit and jumped to a higher orbit X showing a difference in angular momentum equal to $\frac{h}{\pi}$. The value of 'X' could be

(a) 4 (b) 6

(c) 5 (d) 7

55. Rutherford's α-particle scattering experiment eventually led to the conclusion that

(a) mass and energy are related

(b) the point of impact with matter can be precisely determined

(c) neutrons are buried deep in the nucleus

(d) electrons are distributed in a large space around the nucleus

56. Arrange the following steps which are carried out in μ-ray experiment in the correct sequence:

(1) Passage of α-particles through a slit
(2) bombardment of α-particles with a gold foil
(3) deflection of α-particles
(4) production of α-particles

(a) 4 1 2 3 (b) 4 1 3 2
(c) 1 4 3 2 (d) 1 4 2 3

57. Which among the following pairs are having different number of total electrons?

(a) Na^+ and Al^{3+} (b) P^{3-} and Ar
(c) Mg^{2+} and Ar (d) O^{2-} and F^-

58. The postulates of Bohr's atomic model are given below. Arrange them in the correct sequence:

(1) As long as the electron revolves in a particular orbit, the electron does not lose its energy. Therefore, these orbits are called stationary orbits and the electrons are said to be in stationary energy states.
(2) Electrons revolve round the nucleus in specified circular paths called orbits or shells.
(3) The energy associated with a certain energy level increases with the increase of its distance from the nucleus.
(4) An electron jumps from a lower energy level to a higher energy level by absorbing energy. But when it jumps from a higher to lower energy level, energy is emitted in the form of electromagnetic radiation.
(5) Each orbit or shell is associated with a definite amount of energy. Hence, these are also called energy levels and are designated as K, L, M, and N, respectively.

(a) 1 3 4 5 2 (b) 2 3 5 1 4
(c) 2 5 3 1 4 (d) 2 1 4 3 5

59. The ratio of atomic numbers of two elements A and B is 1 : 2. The number of electrons present in the valence shell (3rd) of A is equal to the difference in the number of electrons present in the other two shells. Steps involved for the calculation of ratio of number of electrons present in a penultimate shell to anti-penultimate shell of B are given below. Arrange them in the correct sequence:

(1) calculation of atomic number of B
(2) calculation of valence electrons present in A
(3) calculation of atomic number of A
(4) calculation of number of electrons present in the penultimate and anti-penultimate shells of B
(5) writing electronic configuration of B

(a) 2 3 4 1 5 (b) 2 3 1 5 4
(c) 4 5 2 3 1 (d) 4 2 1 3 5

60. The Bohr's model could successfully explain:

(a) the stability of the atom
(b) the atomic spectra of hydrogen atom
(c) the calculation of energy of the electron in a particular orbit of hydrogen atom
(d) all the above

61. Among the following, the orbital that has the lowest energy is:

(a) 5*f* (b) 4*f*
(c) 6*s* (d) 6*p*

62. What is the maximum number of electrons, present in an orbit whose angular momentum is $\frac{2h}{\pi}$?

(a) 18 (b) 2
(c) 32 (d) 8

63. 'The simultaneous location of both the position and the velocity of an electron in motion cannot be found with desired accuracy.' This was proposed by:

(a) Bohr (b) Heisenberg
(c) Sommerfeld (d) de Broglie

64. Which of the following sets of quantum numbers represent electron in hydrogen atom?

(a) 1, 1, 0, + ½ (b) 1, 0, 0, + ½
(c) 3, 0, 0, – ½ (d) 4, 2, 1, – ½

65. The electronic configuration of chromium is:

(a) [Ar] $3d^5\,4s^1$ (b) $3d^5\,4s^1$
(c) [Ar] $3d^4\,4s^2$ (d) $3d^4 4s^2$

66. The electronic configuration in which Pauli's exclusion principle or Hund's rule is not violated is

(a)
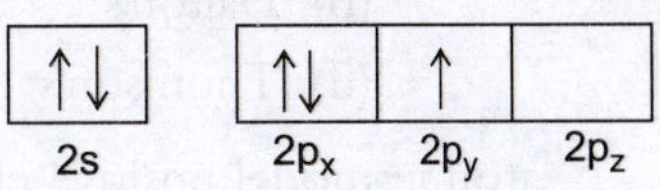

(b)
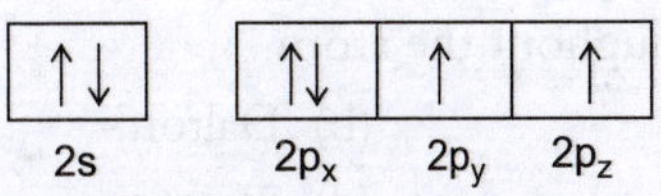

(c)
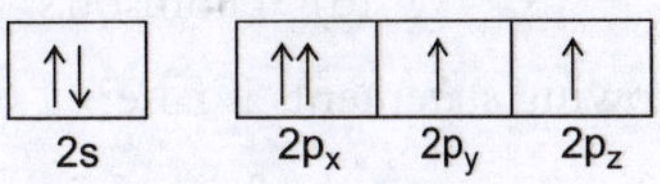

(d) 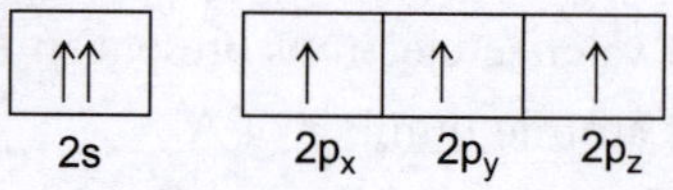

67. In the following pairs, identify the pair having a different $(n + \ell)$ value:

(a) 4*s*, 3*p* (b) 3*d*, 4*p*
(c) 4*s*, 3*d* (d) 4*d*, 5*p*

68. The maximum value of ℓ for $n = 4$ is:

(a) 2 (b) 4
(c) 3 (d) 5

69. The maximum number of electrons that can be accommodated in p-subshell is

(a) 2 (b) 4
(c) 6 (d) 10

70. Which of the following sets of quantum numbers is correct for an electron in 3d orbital?

(a) 3, 0, 0, + ½ (b) 3, 1, 1, – ½
(c) 3, 2, 1, + ½ (d) 3, 2, 3, – ½

71. Probability of finding a d_{yz} electron is zero along the

(a) *x*-axis (b) *y*-axis
(c) *z*-axis (d) all of these

72. Heisenberg's uncertainty principle is not applicable to:

(a) all the bodies moving with high speed
(b) protons
(c) electrons
(d) all the microparticles moving with high speed

73. If 20 electrons are present in the 4th orbit then the atomic number of that element is:

(a) 58 (b) 59
(c) 56 (d) 60

74. Zeeman and Stark effects can be explained by ______ quantum number.

(a) principal (b) azimuthal
(c) magnetic (d) spin

75. Discoveries of isotopes and isobars contradict some of the postulates of ______ atomic theory.

(a) Bohr's (b) Dalton's
(c) Rutherford's (d) Thomson's

76. According to ______ atomic model positive charge is thinly spread throughout the atom.

(a) Bohr's (b) Dalton's
(c) Rutherford's (d) Thomson's

77. Which of the following statements is false?

(a) Bohr's theory explains only the spectra of single electron species
(b) The energy of an electron remains constant during electronic transition
(c) The angular momentum of an electron is quantized
(d) According to Bohr's theory, electrons revolve around the nucleus in circular orbits

78. The difference in energy of radiation emitted absorbed during electronic transition is

(a) directly proportional to frequency
(b) directly proportional to wavelength
(c) inversely proportional to frequency
(d) inversely proportional to velocity of light

79. The statements given below are the postulates of various atomic models. Arrange them in their chronological order.

(1) Fine structure is due to the presence of subshells in the main energy level
(2) The size of an atom is much larger than the size of its nucleus
(3) As long as the electron is present in a particular orbit, its energy remains constant
(4) Negatively charged particles are uniformly spread in the lump of positive charge

(a) 4, 3, 2, 1 (b) 2, 3, 4, 1
(c) 4, 2, 3, 1 (d) 3, 4, 2, 1

80. (1) As long as an electron revolves in a particular orbit, the electron does not lose its energy. Therefore, these orbits are called stationary orbits and the electrons are said to be in stationary energy states

(2) Each orbit or shell is associated with a definite amount of energy. Hence, these are also called energy levels

(3) An electron jumps from a lower energy level to a higher energy level, by absorbing energy. It jumps from a higher energy level to a lower energy level by emitting energy in the form of electromagnetic radiation

(4) Electrons move around the nucleus in specified circular paths called orbits or shells or energy levels and are designated as K, L, M, and N shells, respectively

Arrange the above postulates of Bohr's theory in a correct sequence.

(a) 4, 1, 3, 2 (b) 4, 2, 1, 3
(c) 4, 1, 2, 3 (d) 2, 4, 1, 3

81. (1) The probability of finding an electron is maximum at certain places in space
(2) Energy change takes place only during excitation or deexcitation of electrons
(3) Electron has both particle and wave nature
(4) Angular momentum of the electrons revolving in different elliptical orbits is quantised
Arrange the above statements of different models or principles in the chronological order, which ultimately led to the development of modern structure of the atom.
(a) 1, 2, 3, 4 (b) 2, 4, 3, 1
(c) 4, 3, 2, 1 (d) 2, 3, 1, 4

82. Energy of an electron in a particular orbit of single electron species of beryllium is the same as the energy of an electron in the ground state of hydrogen atom. Identify the orbit of beryllium.
(a) 1 (b) 2
(c) 3 (d) 4

83. The difference between the angular momentum of two orbits of He^{2+} is $\frac{2h}{\pi}$. The energy of an electron present in the higher orbit is −1.51 eV. Identify the lower orbit.
(a) 1 (b) 2
(c) 3 (d) 4

84. Velocity of the electron in electron microscope is 1.6×10^6 m/s. What would be the wavelength of the electron?
(a) 5.39 Å (b) 4.55 Å
(c) 3.54 Å (d) 6.78 Å

85. An atom of an element has nine electrons with l = 0 value, 18 electrons with l = 1 value and 10 electrons with l = 2 value. Calculate the atomic number of the element.
(a) 37 (b) 41
(c) 38 (d) 39

Level 2: Review Your Concepts

86. Arrange the elements 'A', 'B', 'C' and 'D' in the ascending order of the number of valence electrons.
(A) A is the noble gas with the least number of shells.
(B) The number of electrons in B is 4 times that in A.
(C) C has 7 electrons more than that in B.
(D) D has 4 electrons less than that in C.

87. In a canal ray experiment, different gases were found to produce canal rays with the same specific charge. Explain.

88. When canal rays experiment is conducted with hydrogen gas, scientists were found to give particles with different $\frac{e}{m}$ values. Justify.

89. Energy of the electron in the atom is negative. Explain.
[Hint: Energy of a free electron is taken as zero.]

90. If the energy released when an electron jumped from the 4th orbit to the 3rd orbit of hydrogen is '*x*,' then what would be the energy difference when it jumps from the 3rd orbit to the 2nd orbit?

91. (a) Electronic spectra can distinguish isobars but not isotopes. Justify.
(b) The ratio of wavelengths of two electron waves in two different orbits of hydrogen atom is 3:4. Compare the kinetic energy of electrons in those orbits.

92. If the energy difference between the orbits when an electron in H atom gets excited to higher energy orbit from its ground state is 12.1 eV/atom, calculate the frequency of radiation emitted (1 eV = 1.602×10^{-19}J) when electron comes back to second energy level.

93. Is the energy difference between successive orbits the same for all orbits? Justify your answer.

94. Though there is only one electron in a hydrogen atom, the spectrum of hydrogen contains a number of lines. How do you explain this?

95. What is the ratio of the radius of the 1st orbit to 2nd orbit, if the velocity of the electron in the 1st orbit is twice that of the 2nd orbit.

96. A particular atom has the 4th shell as its valence shell. If the difference between the number of electrons between K and N shells and L and M shells is zero, find the atomic number of the element and electronic configuration of its stable ion.

97. A stable unipositive ion of an element contains three fully filled orbits. What is the atomic number of the element?

98. Explain why a blackened platinum strip when placed at the radius of curvature turns red hot, only when the cathode taken has concave shape.

99. The average atomic mass of two isotopes with mass numbers A and A + 2 is A + 0.25. Calculate the percentage abundance of the isotopes.

100. Spectral line given by an atom is a kind of signature of the respective atom. Comment on this statement.

[**Hint:** The nuclear charges of different atoms are different.]

Directions for questions from 101 to 110:
Application-Based Questions

101. Why was a spherical sulphide screen used in α-ray scattering experiment?

102. Why is the source of α-particles kept inside the lead block?

103. If Thomson's model is considered to be correct, what would be the observation of Rutherford's α-ray scattering experiment?

104. The ratio of the atomic numbers of two elements A and B is 2 : 3. A is an inert gas with the first 3 orbits completely filled. Identify A and B and write their electronic configurations.

105. A stable dipositive ion and a dinegative ion are isoelectronic with an octet configuration in the second shell of their atoms. Identify the preceding and succeeding elements and write their electronic configurations.

106. Predict the possible atomic number(s) of an atom in which the third shell is incompletely filled and maximum 3 more electrons can be added in that shell.

107. The radius of nth orbit of a single electron species is 0.132 n^2 A°. Identify the element.

108. What is the frequency of light emitted when an electron in a hydrogen atom jumps from the 3rd orbit to the 2nd orbit?

109. An electron having an angular momentum of 1.05×10^{-34} joules jumps to another orbit such that it has an angular momentum of 4.20×10^{-34} joules. Explain the possible transitions.

110. The mass number of a particular element which has equal number of protons and neutrons is 32. What is the electronic configuration of the atom and its stable ion?

111. 'p' orbital has a nodal plane while 's' orbital has a nodal region. Elaborate with the help of a diagram.

112. What is the common nodal plane of d_{xy} and d_{zx}?

113. The number of nodal regions for an 's' orbital is given by (n − 1). How do you account for this?

114. Compare the energy released during direct electronic transition from 4th orbit to 1st orbit with the energy released during successive electronic transitions between the same orbits in H-atom. Is the energy of all successive transitions between the 4th orbit and 1st orbit equal?

115. 'Wave nature of matter is applicable only for sub-atomic particles and not for larger objects.' Justify this statement.

116. Are the magnetic quantum number and angular momentum of an electron related to each other? Explain.

117. What is the maximum number of electrons present in the main energy level in which the 'g' subshell appears for the first time? Find the atomic number of the element to be discovered in which the differentiating electron is the only electron in the first 'g' subshell.

118. If the angular momentum of an electron is 3.16×10^{-34} kg m^2/s and the radius and energy of an orbit in which the above electron is present is 0.6×10^{-10} m and 2.4×10^{-18} J, respectively: then calculate the radius and energy of 2nd orbit of that atom.

119. 'When the electrons are successively filled in the orbitals of same shell, orbital, which is filled at the end, requires less energy to remove electron. Justify.

120. Atomic number of an element is 42. Find out the number of electrons present in the valence shell.

121. Arrange the following ions in the increasing order of unpaired electrons: Na^+, Cu^+, N^{3-}, O^-, P, and Cr.

122. Arrange the following orbitals in the order in which they are filled with electrons and justify the order: 6s, 5d, 6p, 7s, 5f.

123. Given that the N shell of an element contains 10 electrons, write the electronic configuration of the stable ion.

124. If an atom of an element has eight electrons in a subshell having five orientations of 4th energy level, write the electronic configuration of the element and four quantum numbers for valence electrons.

125. The energy of an electron in a particular orbit of Li^{2+} is –30.6 eV. What is the energy of an electron in the same orbit of Be^{3+}?

126. The angular momentum of an electron in a particular orbit of H-atom is 5.27×10^{-34} kg m^2/s. Calculate the radius of the particular orbit of lithium.

127. How did Sommerfeld explain the fine structure of hydrogen spectrum?

128. Electrons occupy the degenerate orbitals with parallel spins. How can you justify this statement with respect to stability?

129. (a) 'p-' orbital has a nodal plane while 's-' orbital has a nodal region. Elaborate with the help of a diagram.

(b) An electron in hydrogen atom has an angular momentum 3.16×10^{-34} kg m^2/s. It jumps to another orbit in which its velocity is 3.64×10^7 cm s^{-1}. Explain the possible transitions during excitation.

130. The atomic number of an atom A is x. Valence electronic configuration of another atom B is $6s^2 5d^3$ and its atomic number is (x + 5). Write the electronic configuration of A.

131. The ratio of atomic numbers of two elements X and Y is 1 : 7. Radius of 5th orbit of single electron species of X is 3.3 A°. Write the electronic configuration of Y and four quantum numbers for the valence electrons.

132. An electron is revolving in an orbit with a velocity of 5.46×10^7 cm s^{-1}. Calculate the wavelength associated with the electron.

133. A spherical orbital has three nodal regions and it contains a pair of electrons. If this is the only orbital that is occupied with electrons in that main energy level, and the penultimate shell is completely filled, calculate its atomic number.

134. The sum of all the quantum numbers of all the valence electrons of an atom of an inert gas is 22. Identify the inert gas.

Level 3: Assess Your Concepts

135. The ratio of atomic numbers of two elements 'P' and 'Q' is 2:7. The energy of the fourth orbit of single electron species of P is –13.6 eV. Calculate the difference in the number of electrons present in the valence and penultimate shells of Q.

136. The difference in weight between two isotopes of an element is 2 units and the average atomic mass is 1.25 units more than the lighter isotope. Calculate the ratio of the lighter to heavier isotope in the natural sample.

137. If the radius of the third orbit of a single electron species is *x* Ao, then find out its atomic number in terms of *x*.

138. The radius of the fourth orbit of single electron species is 2.116 Ao. Calculate the energy of the orbit.

139. If ${}^{y}_{x}A^{+1}$ or ${}^{y-2}_{x-1}B^{+1}$ were to be used instead of α-particles in Rutherford's experiment, which would be better and why?

Directions for questions from 140 to 152:

Application-Based Questions

140. Draw a comparison between the potential energy and kinetic energy of electrons in the 1st orbits of hydrogen and He^+ ion. Also comment on the total energy of the electrons in the above cases.

141. Though the kinetic energy of electrons decreases with an increase in the distance from the nucleus, the potential energy of the electron increases. How do you account for this?

142. Why is high voltage and low pressure maintained in the discharge tube?

143. If canal ray experiments are conducted with different isotopes of hydrogen gas, do the canal rays produced show the same deflection under the external electric field? Give reasons to support your answer.

144.

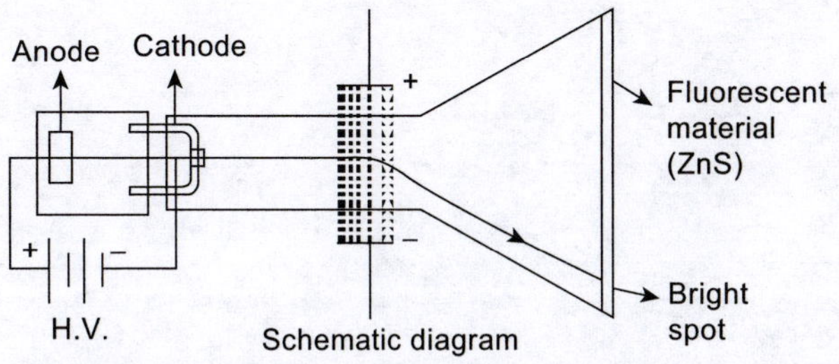

If the given schematic diagram represents Thomson's experiment and the corresponding observation, what would be his atomic model?

145. Energy of an electron increases with increase in distance from the nucleus. Comment on the change in kinetic energy and potential energy.

146. Do all the single electron species of various elements possess same energy for the electron in the ground state? Give reason.

147. Two electronic transitions were found to take place in a single electron species. One is deactivation of ele ctron from the 5th shell to the 4th shell and the other is from the 2nd shell to the 1st shell. Do the energies emitted due to the above transitions have the same wavelength? Justify.

148. An electron is present in a hydrogen atom in the ground state and another electron is present in a single electron species of beryllium. In both the species the distance between the nucleus and electron is same. Calculate the difference in their energies.

149. One electron is made to revolve around a proton and it possesses the least possible energy and another electron is made to revolve around an α-particle with the same energy. Calculate the ratio of the distances of the electrons from the respective species.

150. The principal and azimuthal quantum numbers associated with a subshell are a and $a - 4$, respectively. Predict the shape of that subshell if the shape of another subshell having azimuthal quantum number $a - 5$ is spherical. If that subshell is half-filled, predict the atomic number of the element.

151. Are the magnetic quantum number and angular momentum of an electron related to each other? Explain.

152. 'The larger the value of 'l' belonging to the same main energy, higher is the energy associated with it.' Comment on this statement.

153. Calculate the ratio of wavelength of radiation emitted when an electron jumps from 3rd orbit of He^+ to the ground state and 5th orbit of Be^{+3} to the ground state.

AT

PRACTICE QUESTIONS JEE-NEET SPECIAL WING

Multiple-Answer Type Questions

Directions for questions 1 to 5:

Select one or more correct alternative(s) from the given choices.

1. If the specific charge of proton is 'X' identify the particles with specific charge equal to '$\frac{x}{2}$'.
   (a) Deuteron
   (b) Unipositive helium ion
   (c) Alpha particle
   (d) Tritium ion

2. In a hypothetical Millikan oil drop experiment, the charges on some of the oil droplets have been found to be 1.15×10^{-17} Coulombs; 1.84×10^{-17} Coulombs; 2.76×10^{-17} Coulombs. Identify the true statements regarding the experiment.
   (a) The charge of the electron could be 1.15×10^{-17} Coulombs.
   (b) The possible charge on the oil droplet could be 4.6×10^{-17} Coulombs.
   (c) The minimum value of the charge possessed by the oil droplet would be 1.6×10^{-19} Coulombs
   (d) The charges on the oil droplet would be multiples of 1.6×10^{-19} Coulombs

3. Which among the following corresponds to the correctly matched sets of energy difference between the orbits?
   (a) $n = 2$ to $n = 1$ 10.2 eV
   (b) $n = 3$ to $n = 2$ 1.9 eV
   (c) $n= 4$ to $n = 2$ 7.0 eV
   (d) $n = 3$ to $n = 1$ 8.4 eV

4. Identify the angular momentum values corresponding to Bohr orbits.
   (a) $\frac{2h}{\pi}$ (b) $\frac{h}{2\pi}$
   (c) $\frac{h}{3\pi}$ (d) $\frac{h}{4\pi}$

5. Which sets of wavelengths fall in the visible region of the electromagnetic radiation?
   (a) 3800 Å (b) 2940 Å
   (c) 4370 Å (d) 6550 Å

Comprehension-Based Questions

Directions for the questions 6 to 10:

Read the following paragraph and answer the following questions.

When hydrogen gas is excited using an electric discharge and the light emitted is allowed to pass through a diffraction grating (prism), a spectrum is obtained. The spectrum is found to consist of discrete lines with specific wavelengths. Since these spectral lines are the characteristic of an element, they are considered as the atomic fingerprints. When an electric discharge is passed through hydrogen gas, the hydrogen molecules dissociate into atoms and then the electrons get energised to go to different excited states. These excited electrons travel back to the ground state by emitting electromagnetic radiation of different frequencies. This emission spectrum of hydrogen comprises of different series of spectral lines which are named after the scientists who discovered them. For example, all the electrons getting deexcited to the ground state from any higher energy states form spectral lines with frequencies corresponding to ultraviolet region. This is known as Lyman series. Similarly, the deexcitations corresponding to 2nd energy level and 3rd energy level fall in visible region [Balmer series] and infrared region [Paschen series] respectively. The rest of the transitions from higher energy levels fall in far infra red region. The Balmer series is the most studied one and the lines in this series are named as $H_\alpha;H_\beta;H_\gamma;H_\Delta$ in the increasing order of the higher values for 'n'.

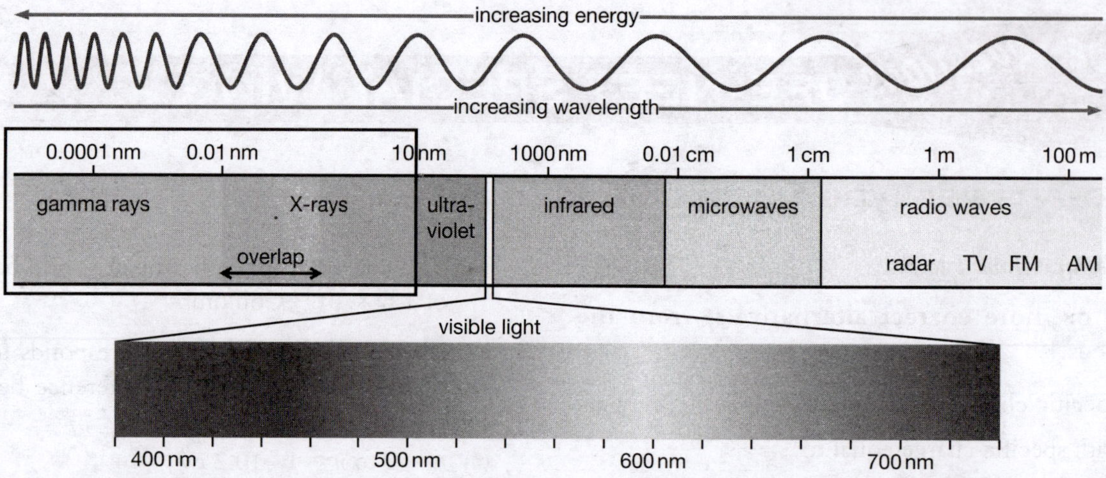

6. Identify the true statements regarding the spectral line corresponding to the wavelength of 656 nm.
   (a) It might represent the transition from $n = 3$ to $n = 2$
   (b) The spectral line may show red colour
   (c) This line corresponds to maximum wavelength transition
   (d) Both (a) and (c)

7. A spectral line represents an electronic transition from $n = 6$ to $n = 4$. Predict the most probable wavelength of the radiation emitted during the transition.
   (a) 285 nm (b) 466 nm
   (c) 828 nm (d) 1256 nm

8. Identify the transition corresponding to H_β line of Balmer series.
   (a) $n = 4$ to $n = 2$ (b) $n = 3$ to $n = 2$
   (c) $n = 5$ to $n = 2$ (d) $n = 6$ to $n = 2$

9. Which among the following transitions is associated with emission of lower energy radiation than H_α line?
   (a) $n = 3$ to $n = 2$ (b) $n = 2$ to $n = 1$
   (c) $n = 4$ to $n = 3$ (d) None of these

10. Identify the maximum wavelength electronic transition among the following.
   (a) $n = 6$ to $n = 1$ (b) $n = 5$ to $n = 2$
   (c) $n = 4$ to $n = 3$ (d) $n = 6$ to $n = 5$

Comprehension-Based Questions

Directions for the questions 11 to 15:

Read the following paragraph and answer the following questions.

The radius of an orbit for any single electron species can be given by the expression:

$$r_n = \frac{n^2h^2}{4\pi^2me^2.Z}$$

$$= 0.529 \times \frac{n^2}{Z}$$

The energy of an orbit of any single electron species can be given by the expression:

$$E_n = \frac{-2\pi^2me^4}{n^2h^2}.Z^2$$

$$= -13.6 \times \frac{n^2}{Z^2}eV$$

m = Mass of electron
e = charge of electron
n = Orbit or shell number
h = Planck's constant
Z = Nuclear charge

11. The radius of 2nd orbit of a single electron species is double the radius of 1st orbit of hydrogen atom. Identify the statement which does not comply with the same species.
   (a) The energy of the same orbit of that species is same as the first orbit of hydrogen atom.
   (b) The species carries one-unit positive charge.
   (c) 27.2 eV energy is required for the excitation of electron from the 1st orbit to 2nd orbit for that species.
   (d) None of these

12. Which among the following possesses the same energy for the electron as the 2nd orbit of hydrogen atom?
   (a) 4th orbit of He^+ ion
   (b) 2nd orbit of Be^{+3} ion
   (c) 4th orbit of Be^{+3} ion
   (d) Both a and b

13. The radius of 3rd orbit of single electron species of lithium is 'x' units. Calculate the radius of the same orbit of single electron species of beryllium.

(a) $3x$ (b) $3x/2$
(c) $x/4$ (d) $3x/4$

14. The energy of electron in nth orbit of a species is 0.44 times that of the 1st orbit of He+ ion. Identify the data which complies with the given information.

(a) 2nd orbit of Be^{+3} (b) 4th orbit of Li^{+2}
(c) 3rd orbit of Be^{+3} (d) 2nd orbit of Hydrogen

15. 13.6 eV energy is required to remove the electron from the hydrogen atom. What is the additional amount of energy required to remove the electron from the same orbit of Li^{+2} ion?

(a) 68 eV (b) 40.8 eV
(c) 108.8 eV (d) 122.4 eV

Match the Column

16. Based on the information given in the table, match the entries in column I with those in column II.

Element	No. of times an atom is heavier than electron in an atom
A	51436
B	45925
C	25718
D	38577
E	60621

Match the entries in column I with those in column II

	Element		No. of electrons in penultimate shell
(a)	A	(i)	8
(b)	B	(ii)	18
(c)	C	(iii)	16
(d)	D	(iv)	13
(e)	E	(v)	9

Directions for question number 17:

Based on the information given below, match the entries in column I with those in column II.

17. The arrangement of electrons in an atom is called electronic configuration. The electrons are arranged in such a way that the atom gets maximum stability. Therefore, certain rules are followed for writing the electronic configurations of the elements. Pauli's exclusion principle states that no two electrons can have the four quantum numbers identical. Aufbau principle states that the electrons are filled in the orbitals in the increasing order of their energies which is determined by the $(n + l)$ values of the orbitals. Hund's rule of maximum multiplicity states that the pairing up of electrons in the degenerate orbitals takes place only after all the orbitals are singly occupied. Half-filled and fully filled subshells provide extra stability to the atom and hence such elements violate Aufbau principle.

Match the entries in column I with those in column II.

	Column A (Element)		Column B (Number of electrons with l = 2)
(a)	Iron	(i)	5
(b)	Manganese	(ii)	3
(c)	Nickel	(iii)	6
(d)	Zinc	(iv)	8
(e)	Vanadium	(v)	10

ANSWER KEYS

Crossword

Across

4. Krypton
8. Absorption spectrum
9. Emission spectrum
15. Max Planck
16. Natural radioactivity
17. Zeeman effect
18. Boron
19. Helium

Down

1. Mass number
2. Induced radioactivity
3. Atomic number
5. Valence shell
6. Aluminium
7. Electron
10. James Chadwick
11. Rutherford
12. Penultimate shell
13. Thomson
14. Stark effect
16. Neils Bohr

Classroom Wing

Very Short Answer Type Questions

1. High
2. Outer, inner
3. Thomson's model
4. increases
5. orbits
6. line spectrum
7. E is the energy (quanta) ν is the frequency of the radiation
8. orbital
9. 4
10. $1s^2\ 2s^2 2p^6\ 3s^2$
11. Orientation of orbitals in space
12. same
13. three, Hund's
14. 3:8
15. [Ar] $3d^{10}4s^1$
16. 5s orbital
17. five

Competition Wing

Level 1: Apply Your Concepts

1. False
2. True
3. True
4. True
5. False
6. True
7. True
8. False
9. False
10. True
11. True
12. True
13. False
14. True
15. 18
16. positively
17. 6.625×10^{-27}
18. nuclear
19. e and e/m
20. positively-charged
21. positive charge
22. loses
23. less
24. Zeeman
25. more
26. emission spectrum
27. $2\ell + 1$
28. double dumbbell
29. 6.627×10^{-27} erg s or 6.627×10^{-34} J
30. Planck's constant
31. $\frac{h}{\pi}$
32. angular momentum and energy
33. 3:5
34. A → (iii), B → (i), C → (iv), D → (ii)
35. A : b, B : a, C : e, D : c, E : d
36. (c)
37. (a)
38. (b)
39. (a)
40. (a)
41. (c)
42. (c)
43. (c)
44. (b)
45. (a)
46. (b)
47. (a)
48. (c)
49. (b)
50. (d)
51. (c)
52. (b)
53. (b)
54. (c)
55. (d)
56. (a)
57. (c)
58. (c)
59. (b)
60. (d)
61. (c)
62. (c)
63. (b)
64. (b)
65. (a)
66. (b)
67. (c)
68. (c)
69. (c)
70. (c)
71. (d)
72. (a)
73. (b)
74. (c)
75. (b)
76. (d)
77. (b)
78. (a)
79. (c)
80. (b)
81. (b)
82. (d)
83. (d)
84. (b)
85. (a)

JEE-NEET Special Wing

Multiple-Answer Type Questions

1. (a; c) 2. (a; b) 3. (a; b) 4. (a; b) 5. (a; c; d)

Comprehension-Based Questions

6. (a) 7. (d) 8. (a) 9. (c) 10. (d)
11. (d) 12. (a) 13. (d) 14. (c) 15. (c)

Match the Column

16. (a) ↔ (iii); (b) ↔ (iv); (c) ↔ (i); (d) ↔ (v) ; (e) ↔ (ii)
17. (a) ↔ (iii); (b) ↔ (i); (c) ↔ (iv); (d) ↔ (v) ; (e) ↔ (ii)

Hints and Explanations

Classroom Wing

Very Short Answer Type Questions

1. According to Rutherford's atomic model, electrons revolve around the nucleus with high velocities.
2. According to Bohr's atomic model, a fixed amount of energy is emitted when an electron jumps from an outer orbit to an inner orbit.
3. Thomson's model
4. increases
5. orbits
6. line spectrum
7. *E* is the energy (quanta)

   v is the frequency of the radiation
8. orbital
9. 4
10. $1s^2\ 2s^2 2p^6\ 3s^2$
11. Orientation of orbitals in space
12. same
13. three, Hund's
14. 3:8
15. [Ar] $3d^{10}4s^1$
16. 5s orbital
17. five
18. Discovery of radioactivity proves the existence of sub-atomic particles. Therefore, it can be concluded that atoms are divisible.
19. Atoms of the same element are identical in all aspects.
20. α-ray scattering experiment was carried out to prove the correctness of J.J. Thomson's atomic model.
21. Goldstein, Discharge tube
22. $E = \eta\nu$
23. James Chadwick discovered neutrons by an experiment involving the bombardment of beryllium nucleus with α–particles
24. Quanta
25. Impossible to determine simultaneously the position and momentum of the particle.
26. Planck's quantum theory
27. 6.626×10^{-27} erg-s

    6.626×10^{-34} J-s
28. $r_n = \dfrac{n^2h^2}{4\pi^2me^2}, E_n = \dfrac{-2\pi^2me^4}{n^2h^2}$
29. Absorption of energy
30. Splitting of spectral lines in the presence of magnetic field.
31. Splitting of spectral lines in the presence of electric field.
32. Doubly ionized He ion.
33. A continuous band of different wavelengths.
34. Formed by vibration of mutually perpendicular electric and magnetic components
35. Electrons revolve around the nucleus, protons and neutrons are present in the nucleus.
36. Splitting of a spectrum into closely spaced lines.
37. To explain Zeeman and Stark effects.
38. The number indicating the main energy level.
39. Presence of pair of very closely spaced lines in the spectrum of an atom.
40. Electrons possess both wave and particle nature.
41. $\lambda = \dfrac{h}{mv}$
42. The three dimensional region where the probability of finding an electron is maximum around nucleus.
43. To explain the position of electron in three dimensional view.
44. For K shell one orbital; it is *s*

    For L shell two orbitals; they are *s* and *p*

    For M shell three orbitals; they are *s*, *p* and *d*

    For N shell four orbitals; they are *s*, *p*, *d* and *f*

45. Spherical

46. As n = 2, ℓ can have 2 values. They are "0" and "1". When L = 0 it is s sub-shell and L = 1 it is *p* sub-shell.

47. Orbitals of a given sub-shell having same energy Example: p_x, p_y, p_z.

48. 4 nodal surfaces.

49. To find the maximum probability of an electron.

50. Based on Aufbau principle

51. Three d_{xy}, d_{yz} and d_{zx}.

52. Based on formula $2n^2$

53. (b) because it is half-filled electronic configuration.

Short Answer Type Questions

54. The given configuration is *a*, 4*a*, (6*a* + 1), and (*a* – 1).

Since *a* = 2, the electronic configuration is 2, 8, 13, and 1.

This is the electronic configuration of chromium.

55. Given that Z_x:Z_y = 1:7

$$r^3 = \frac{0.529 \times n^2}{Z_x}$$

$$\Rightarrow 1.587 = \frac{0.529 \times 9}{Z_x}$$

$$\Rightarrow Z_x = 3$$

∴ Atomic number of Y is 21.

∴ Electronic configuration of Y is 2, 8, 9 and 2.

56. The electronic configuration of zinc is 2, 8, 18, 2 [*x*, (*x* + *y*), 3*y*, *x*]. Hence, it holds good.

57. Electronic configuration of X is 2, 8 and 5.

∴ Electronic configuration of Y is 2, 8 and 8.

Hence, Y is Ar.

58. Energy of electron = E_n = - 13.6 x Z^2/n^2

Energy required to remove this electron = +13.6 eV

59. According to Rutherford's model, any charged particle in a circular motion radiates energy continuously. The electron being a charged particle in the circular motion loses energy. This should ultimately result in its spiral path towards nucleus and the atom should then collapse.

60. Some fine oil droplets were allowed to be sprayed into the chamber by an atomizer. The air in the chamber was subjected to ionization by X-rays. The electrons produced by the ionization of air attached themselves to the oil drops.

When sufficient amount of electric field is applied which can balance the gravitational force acting on an oil drop, the drop remains suspended in the air.

From this experiment, Millikan observed that the smallest charge found on them was approximately 1.59 × 10^{-19} coulombs and the charge on each drop was always an integral multiple of that value.

On the basis of this observation, he concluded that 1.59 × 10^{-19} coulombs is the smallest possible charge and considered that value as the charge of the electron.

61. Protons are located in the centre of an atom and electrons occupy the extra-nuclear part.

62. The difference in the predicted mass and actual mass of the atom has been found to be equal to the mass of the proton or multiples of the mass of a proton. These particles are supposed to have neutral charge since the atom is electrically neutral. They were called neutrons and they were discovered by James Chadwick by an experiment involving the bombardment of beryllium nucleus with α-particles.

63. J.J. Thomson proposed his atomic model soon after his discovery of electrons as listed hereunder.

(i) An atom contains negatively charged particles called electrons embedded uniformly throughout a thinly spread positively charged mass.

(ii) Since the atom is electrically neutral, the total negative charge of electrons is balanced by the total positive charge.

64. Angular momentum is defined as the product of its moment of inertia and its angular velocity. *m* is the mass of the electron; *v* is the velocity of an electron in its orbit; *r* is the distance of the electron from the nucleus; *h* is the Planck's constant

65. As long as the electron revolves in a particular orbit, the electron does not lose its energy. Therefore, these orbits are called stationary orbits.

66. Frequency can be calculated by using the formula:

$c = \nu\lambda$

67. Continuous spectrum is a continuous band of different wavelengths. Light from the sun or incandescent bulb gives such type of spectrum. Discontinuous spectrum consists of discrete lines of different colours. For example, atomic spectra of hydrogen gas.

68. (i) Because of quantisation of energy.
 (ii) When electrons jump from one orbit to another, they emit or absorb only a certain amount of energy.

69. Azimuthal quantum number describes the angular momentum of the electrons revolving in different elliptical orbits

70. (i) Fine structure of atomic spectra.
 (ii) Spectra of multi electron species
 (iii) Zeeman effect and Stark effect

71. Quantum theory of radiation.

72. According to Heisenberg's uncertainty principle, it is impossible to determine simultaneously and accurately the exact position and the momentum of the moving particle

73. (i) Maximum number of electrons in any orbital is two
 (ii) L value for *d* and *f* orbital.

74. Ascending order of energies of different orbitals is $1s < 2s < 2p < 3s < 3p < 4s < 3d < 4p < 5s$

23: $1s^2 2s^2 2p^6 3s^2 3p^6 3d^3 4s^2$

38: $1s^2 2s^2 2p^6 3s^2 3p^6 3d^{10} 4s^2 4p^6 5s^2$

35: $1s^2 2s^2 2p^6 3s^2 3p^6 3d^{10} 4s^2 4p^5$

20: $1s^2 2s^2 2p^6 3s^2 3p^6 4s^2$

18: $1s^2 2s^2 2p^6 3s^2 3p^6$

75. Pairing of electrons in a sub-shell starts when all the degenerate orbitals are filled with unpaired electrons with parallel spin.

76. Bohr assumed that an electron of an atom is located at a definite distance from the nucleus and revolves around the nucleus with a definite velocity, which is against Heisenberg's uncertainty principle.

77. (a) (i) Similarity in the electronic configuration of noble gases.
 (ii) Relation between electronic configuration and atomic number.

(b) The electronic configuration of copper is $1s^2\ 2s^2\ 2p^6\ 3s^2\ 3p^6\ 3d^{10}\ 5s^1$, $\ell = 0$ corresponds to "s" sub-shell and the number of electrons is 7.

(c) The electronic configuration corresponding to the given description is $1s^2\ 2s^2\ 2p^6\ 3s^2\ 3p^6\ 3d^6\ 4s^2$. $3d^6$ can be represented as

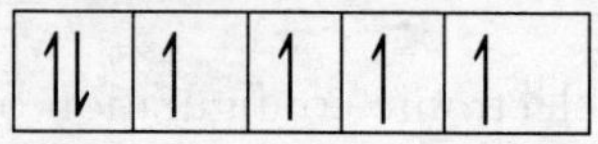

The stable ion formed should have the configuration with $3d^5$ after losing two 4s electrons and one 3d electron. There are five half-filled orbitals in the +3 ion.

78. 2 nodes are present in each 3*s*, 3*p*, and 3*d* orbitals.

80. $2n^2$, where n is principal quantum number.

81.

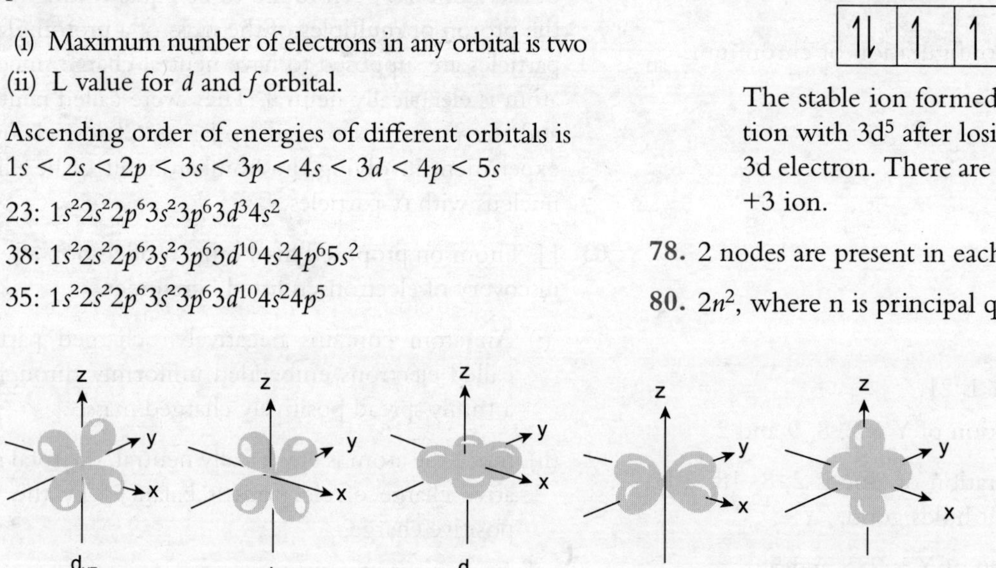

Essay Answer Type Questions

82. $$\frac{3A + 2(A + x)}{5} = A + 0.8$$

$\therefore 5A + 2x = 5A + 4$

$\therefore 2x = 4 \qquad \therefore x = 2$

$\therefore$ The mass of heavier isotope is $A + 2$.

83. $$-13.6 = \frac{-13.6 \times Z^2}{9}$$

$\therefore Z = 3$

$$\therefore r_3 = \frac{0.529 \times 3^2}{Z} = \frac{0.529 \times 3^2}{3} = 0.529 \times 3$$

$= 1.587$ A

84. $E_2 = \frac{-13.6 \times Z^2}{n^2}$

$\therefore -x = \frac{-13.6 \times Z^2}{4}$

$\therefore Z^2 = \frac{4x}{13.6}$

$\therefore Z = 2\sqrt{\frac{x}{13.6}}$

85. The atom is mostly composed of empty space. The entire positive charge and mass of the atom is concentrated in the small, central part known as the nucleus. The size of the nucleus is so small that its diameter is 10^5 times less than that of the atom. The diameter of the nucleus has been estimated by Rutherford as 10^{-13} cm in contrast to that of the atom to be 10^{-8} cm. The electrons present outside the nucleus revolve round the nucleus with high velocities.

86. The following are the limitations of Bohr's atomic model:

(i) Bohr could not explain the spectral series for the multi-electron atoms.

(ii) Bohr's model could not give a satisfactory justification for the assumption that electrons can revolve in those orbits where their angular momentum (*mvr*) is a whole number multiple of nh/2π, i.e., he could not justify quantization of angular momentum.

(iii) According to Heisenberg's uncertainty principle, it is impossible to determine simultaneously with certainty the exact position and the momentum of the particle. Bohr assumed that an electron of an atom is located at a definite distance from the nucleus and revolves around the nucleus with a definite velocity, i.e., the momentum of the electron is fixed which is against Heisenberg's uncertainty principle.

(iv) The atomic spectral lines split into a number of closely packed lines in the presence of a magnetic field and an electric field. These effects are called Zeeman effect and Stark effect, respectively. Bohr failed to explain these effects.

(v) When the hydrogen spectrum was observed with the spectroscope of high resolving power, it was found that the individual lines in the spectrum consisted of several fine lines lying close to each other. This is called fine spectrum and he failed to explain the fine structure of the spectrum.

87. (i) The atomic spectral lines are found to split into a number of closely packed lines in the presence of a magnetic and an electric field. These effects are called Zeeman effect and Stark effect, respectively.

(ii) Magnetic quantum number gives spatial orientations of orbital.

88. (i) Relative energies of orbitals on the basis of (n + ℓ) value.

(ii) Maximum number of electrons in any orbital.

(iii) Pairing of electrons in the degenerate orbitals.

89. (i) Relation between n and ℓ

(ii) Relation between ℓ and m

(iii) Location of electron

(iv) Maximum number of electrons accommodated

90. (i) Heisenberg's uncertainty principle

(ii) Dual nature of electron

(iii) Schrodinger wave equation

(iv) The space around the nucleus where the probability of finding electron is maximum is called atomic orbital.

91. (i) Electron has both wave nature and particle nature.

(ii) Determining simultaneously the exact position and momentum of the electron.

(iii) Definite energy levels for electron, velocities of electron in different energy levels.

92. Angular momentum mvr_3

$= \frac{nh}{2\pi} = 31.74 \times 10^{-28}\ \text{g cm}^2\ \text{s}^{-1}$

We know that $r_3 = \frac{0.529 \times n^2}{Z} \times 10^{-8}$ cm

$r_3 = \frac{0.529 \times 9 \times 10^{-8}}{1}$ cm

$\therefore$ mv$(0.529 \times 9 \times 10^{-8}) = 31.74 \times 10^{-28}$

$\Rightarrow \text{mv} = \frac{31.74 \times 10^{-28}}{0.529 \times 9 \times 10^{-8}}$

$= 6.666 \times 10^{-20}$ g.cm s^{-1}

$\therefore \lambda = \frac{h}{\text{mv}}$

$\lambda = \frac{6.625 \times 10^{-27}}{6.666 \times 10^{-20}}$

$= 0.99385 \times 10^{-7}$ cm $= 9.9385$ Å

Competition Wing

Level 1: Apply Your Concepts

15. Electronic configuration of X is 2, 8, 18 and 8.

Electronic configuration of A is 2, 8, 18, 8 and 2.

$\therefore$ No. of electrons in the antepenultimate shell = 18

16. In α-ray scattering experiment, α-rays are used because they are positively charged particles and have mass.

34. $\frac{5h}{2p}$ to $\frac{h}{p} \rightarrow 6$

$\frac{3h}{2p}$ to $\frac{h}{p} \rightarrow 1$

$\frac{3h}{p}$ to $\frac{h}{2p} \rightarrow 15$

$\frac{2h}{p}$ to $\frac{h}{p} \rightarrow 3$

A → (iii), B →(i), C → (iv), D → (ii)

36. 8 electrons in the last orbit make the atom stable (unreactive) because they remain in low-energy state.

Hence, the correct option is (c).

37. From J.J. Thomson's experiment, $\frac{e}{m}$ ratio (specific charge) can be calculated and from Millikan's oil drop experiment, charge of an electron can be calculated.

Hence, dividing e by $\frac{e}{m}$, mass of the electron can be calculated.

Hence, the correct option is (a).

38. Since an ion has electrons in the outermost shell, it is more stable than an atom. An ion is a charged particle.

Hence, the correct option is (b).

39. The specific charge of α-particle is $\frac{1}{2}$ of the specific charge of the H^+ because the charge of alpha particle is twice the charge of hydrogen ion and the mass of α-particle is 4 times the mass of H^+.

Hence, the correct option is (a).

43. Let the percentage of $_7X^{15}$ is x.

$\therefore$ The percentage composition of $_7X^{11}$ is 100 – x

Average atomic weight = 14

$$= \frac{x(15) + (100 - x)11x}{100}$$

$\Rightarrow 1400 = 15x + 1100 - 11x$

$\Rightarrow 1400 = 4x + 1100 \Rightarrow 4x = 300$

$x = \frac{300}{4} = 75$

$\therefore$ The percentage of $_7X^{11} = 100 - x$

$= 100 - 75 = 25$ and that of $_7X^{15}$ is 75

Hence, the correct answer is (c).

51. Energy, $E_n = \frac{-13.6Z^2}{n^2}$ eV

$$E_3 = \frac{-13.6 \times 16}{9} \text{eV} = -24.2\,\text{eV}$$

Hence, the correct answer is (c).

52. According to Rutherford's theory, an atom is electrically neutral and electrons revolve around the nucleus. Nuclear forces of attraction exist between the nucleus and electrons. The only assumption that Rutherford did not consider is quantization of energy.

Hence, the correct answer is (b).

53. $r_n = 0.529 \times n^2$ A°

Successive first odd orbits are 1 and 3

$$\frac{r_1}{r_3} = \frac{0.529 \times 1^2}{0.529 \times 3^2} = \frac{1}{9} = 1:9$$

Hence, the correct answer is (b).

54. Angular momentum in third orbit is given by

$$mvr = \frac{3h}{2\pi}$$

Angular momentum in X orbit is given by

$$mvr = \frac{Xh}{2\pi} \rightarrow (2)$$

$$\frac{Xh}{2\pi} - \frac{3h}{2\pi} = \frac{h}{\pi}$$

$$(X-3)\frac{h}{2\pi} = \frac{h}{\pi} \Rightarrow X = 5$$

Hence, the correct answer is (c).

55. The α-ray scattering experiment led to the discovery of nucleus which in turn helped him conclude that electrons revolve around the nucleus to overcome the strong electrostatic force of attraction.

Hence, the correct answer is (d).

56. 4 production of α-particles

1 production of a narrow beam of α-particles

2 bombardment of α-particles with gold foil

3 deflection of α-particles

Hence, the correct answer is (a).

57. The electronic configuration of Mg^{2+} is 2, 8

∴ Total no. of electrons = 10

The electronic configuration of Ar is 2, 8, 8

∴ Total no. of electrons = 18.

Hence, Mg^{2+} and Ar are having different number of total electrons.

Hence, the correct answer is (c).

58. 2 Electrons revolve around the nucleus in specified circular paths called orbits or shells.

5 Each orbit or shell is associated with a definite amount of energy. Hence, these are also called energy levels and are designated as K, L, M, and N, respectively.

3 The energy associated with a certain energy level increases with the increase of its distance from the nucleus.

1 As long as the electron revolves in a particular orbit, the electron does not lose its energy. Therefore, these orbits are called stationary orbits and the electrons are said to be in stationary energy states.

4 An electron jumps from a lower energy level to a higher energy level by absorbing energy. But when it jumps from a higher to lower energy level, energy is emitted in the form of electromagnetic radiation.

Hence, the correct answer is (c).

59. 2 calculation of valence electrons present in A

3 calculation of atomic number of A

1 calculation of atomic number of B

5 writing electronic configuration of B

4 calculation of number of electrons present in the penultimate and anti-penultimate shells of B

Hence, the correct answer is (b).

75. According to Dalton's atomic theory, atoms of same elements are identical in all respects, whereas atoms of different elements are different in all respects. But discovery of isotopes revealed that atoms of same element can have different mass. Discovery of isobars revealed that atoms of different elements can have same mass. These discoveries of isotopes and isobars contradict the above two postulates of Dalton's atomic theory.

Hence, the correct answer is (b).

76. In Thomson's model, positively charged particles are thinly spread throughout the atom. Electrons are embedded in the thin positively charged mass.

Hence, the correct answer is (d).

77. The energy of the electron remains constant only when it is revolving around nucleus in a particular orbit. During an electronic transition, it gains or loses energy.

Hence, the correct answer is (b).

78. Energy E = hν

$$\therefore\ E = h\frac{c}{\lambda}$$

that is, $E \propto \nu : E \propto \frac{1}{\lambda}, E \propto c$

Hence, the correct answer is (a).

79. 4 Negatively charged particles are uniformly spread in the lump of positive charge (Thomson's model).

2 The size of atom is much larger than the size of its nucleus (Rutherford's model).

3 As long as the electron is present in a particular orbit, its energy remains constant (Bohr's model).

1 Fine structure is due to the presence of subshells in the main energy level (Sommerfeld's model).

Hence, the correct answer is (c).

80. 4 Electrons move around the nucleus in specified circular paths called orbits or shells or energy levels and are designated as K, L, M and N shells, respectively.

2 Each orbit or shell is associated with a definite amount of energy. Hence, these are also called energy levels.

1 As long as the electron revolves in a particular orbit, the electron does not lose its energy. Therefore, these orbits are called stationary orbits and the electrons are said to be in stationary energy states.

3 An electron jumps from a lower to a higher energy level by absorbing energy. It jumps from a higher to a lower energy level by emitting energy in the form of electromagnetic radiation.

Hence, the correct answer is (b).

81. 2 Energy change takes place only during excitation or deexcitation of electrons.

4 Angular momentum of the electrons revolving in different elliptical orbits is quantised.

3 Electron has both particle and wave nature.

1 The probability of finding an electron is maximum at certain places in space.

Hence, the correct answer is (b).

82. Energy of an electron in Be^{3+} ion $= \frac{-13.6}{n^2} \times 4^2 eV$

Energy of the electron in ground state hydrogen atom $= -13.6$ eV

$$\therefore \frac{-13.6}{n^2} \times 4^2 = -13.6$$

$$\Rightarrow n^2 = 4^2$$

$$\Rightarrow n = 4$$

Hence, the correct answer is (d).

83. The energy of electron, $E = \frac{-13.6 \times Z^2}{n^2} eV$

$$\therefore 1.51 = \frac{-13.6 \times 4}{n^2}$$

$(\because Z = 2)$

$\therefore n = 6$

The difference in angular momentum of two orbits is

$$(mvr)_x - (mvr)_y = \frac{n_x h}{2\pi} - \frac{n_y h}{2\pi}$$

$$\therefore \frac{2h}{\pi} = (n_x - n_y)\frac{h}{2\pi}$$

$n_x - n_y = 4$

$\therefore$ The other orbit (n_x) is the 2nd orbit.

Hence, the correct answer is (d).

84. $v = 1.6 \times 10^6$ m/s

m = 9.1×10^{-31}kg

$$\lambda = \frac{h}{mv} = \frac{6.625 \times 10^{-34}}{9.1 \times 10^{-31} \times 1.6 \times 10} = 4.55 \text{ Å}$$

Hence, the correct answer is (b).

85. l = 0 corresponds to 's' subshell, l = 1 corresponds to 'p' subshell, l = 2 corresponds to 'd' subshell. The atom should possess '9' 's' electrons, 18 'p' electrons, and 10 'd' electrons. The electronic configuration of the element should be $1s^2\ 2s^2\ 2p^6\ 3s^2\ 3p^6\ 3d^{10}\ 4s^2\ 4p^6\ 5s^2$. The atomic number of the element should be 37.

Hence, the correct answer is (a).

Level 2: Review Your Concepts

86. Valence electron of A is 2.

Valence electron of B is 6.

Valence electron of C is 5.

Valence electron of D is 1.

$\therefore$ The order is DACB.

87. (i) factors affecting specific charge

(ii) conditions where different gases can have the same specific charge

88. (i) e/m depends on number of protons and neutrons

(ii) existence of isotopes

(iii) variation in e/m for isotopes

89. (i) comparing energy of free electron and energy of electron in an atom

(ii) change in energy when an electron is brought closer to the atom

(iii) reason for the change in the energy of an electron

90. The change in energy is given by

$$\Delta E = 13.6\left(\frac{1}{n_1^2} - \frac{1}{n_2^2}\right) \text{eV}$$

When the electron jumps from 4th orbit to 3rd orbit.

$$n_1 = 4, n_2 = 3, \Delta E = x$$

$$\Rightarrow x = 13.6\left(\frac{1}{4^2} - \frac{1}{3^2}\right)$$

$$\Rightarrow x = 13.6\left(\frac{9-16}{144}\right)$$

$$\Rightarrow x = -13.6\left(\frac{7}{144}\right) \rightarrow \text{(i)}$$

When the electron jumps from 3rd orbit to 2nd orbit.

$$\Delta E = 13.6\left(\frac{1}{3^2} - \frac{1}{2^2}\right)$$

$$\Rightarrow \Delta E = 13.6\left(\frac{4-9}{36}\right)$$

$$\Rightarrow \Delta E = -13.6\left(\frac{5}{36}\right) \rightarrow \text{(ii)}$$

Dividing equation (i) and (ii), we get,

$$\frac{x}{\Delta E} = \frac{-13.6}{-13.6} \times \frac{\frac{7}{144}}{\frac{5}{36}}$$

$$\Rightarrow \frac{x}{\Delta E} = \frac{7}{20}$$

$$\text{or, } \Delta E = \frac{20}{7}x$$

91. (a) (i) fundamental particle responsible for the spectra

(ii) relation between fundamental particle and structure of spectra

(iii) difference in number of the above particles between isobars and isotopes

(iv) effect of this on structure of spectra

(b) According to de Broglie theory

$$\lambda = \frac{h}{mv} \Rightarrow v = \frac{h}{m\lambda}.$$

$$\text{Kinetic energy } \quad K.E = \frac{1}{2}mv^2 \Rightarrow K.E = \frac{1}{2}m\left(\frac{h}{m\lambda}\right)^2$$

$$\Rightarrow K.E = \frac{h^2}{2m\lambda^2}$$

$$\Rightarrow K.E \propto \frac{1}{\lambda^2}$$

$$\therefore \frac{K.E_1}{K.E_2} = \frac{\lambda_2^2}{\lambda_1^2} = \frac{4^2}{3^2} = \frac{16}{9} = 16:9$$

92. (i) relation between energy and n

(ii) calculation of n_2 value from the difference in energy

(iii) calculation of frequency from energy

(iv) calculation of energy difference based on n values

(v) calculation of frequency

(vi) $\nu = 0.456 \times 10^{15}\ s^{-1}$

93. (i) factors affecting deflection

(ii) the effect of atomic number on deflection

(iii) the effect of kinetic energy on deflection

94. (i) Bohr's model of atom

(ii) relation between energy absorbed and excitation

(iii) relation between the path of electron during deexcitation and energy emitted

(iv) relation between energy emitted and spectrum

95. $r_1 : r_2 = 1 : 4$

96. atomic number = 20

97. 37

98. (i) factors responsible for the strip to turn red hot

(ii) The path in which the electrons travel from concave cathode.

99. (i) $(n_1 \times A) + (n_2 \times (A + 2)) = (n_1 + n_2)$

(A + 0.25) form

(ii) 87.5% and 12.5%

100. (i) calculation of energy of electrons in He^+ and Li^{2+} ions

(ii) 4 : 9

101. to observe scintillations even if the α-rays get deflected at large angles

102. α-particles cannot penetrate lead, but β- and γ-rays can. In order to screen α-particles from β- and γ-rays, lead block was used.

103. If Thomson's model is correct, all the α-particles would have penetrated the gold foil and their angle of deflection would be insignificant.

104. A → electronic configuration – 2, 8, 18, 8. Thus, the atomic number = 36.

A : B = 2 : 3

$$\therefore B = \frac{36 \times 3}{2} = 54$$

The electronic configuration of

B = 2, 8, 18, 18, 8.

105. Let the dipositive ion be X^{+2} and dinegative ion is Y^{-2}.

The octet in the second shell → 2, 8

The number of electrons in X = 10 + 2 = 12.

The number of electrons in Y = 10 – 2 = 8.

X is magnesium with an electronic configuration 2, 8, 2. Y is oxygen with a configuration 2, 6.

The element preceding magnesium is sodium and the succeeding one is aluminium. They have electronic configurations 2, 8, 1 and 2, 8, 3, respectively. The elements preceding and succeeding for oxygen are nitrogen and fluorine which have electronic configurations 2, 5 and 2, 7, respectively.

106. Electronic configuration of the atom which can accommodate three more electrons in the 3rd shell could be 2, 8, 5 and 2, 8, 15, 2. Hence, the probable atomic numbers are 15 and 27.

107. $r_n = \dfrac{Kn^2}{Z}$

$$\therefore 0.132n^2 = \frac{0.529 \times n^2}{Z}$$

$$\therefore Z = \frac{0.529}{0.132} = 4$$

Since the atomic number is 4, the element is beryllium.

108. $E_3 - E_2 = -21.72 \times 10^{-19}\left(\dfrac{1}{9} - \dfrac{1}{4}\right)$

$$= 21.72 \times 10^{-19} \times \frac{5}{36}$$

$\therefore$ Difference in energy, $E_3 - E_2 = 3.01 \times 10^{-19}$ J

According to Planck's equation, $\Delta E = h\nu$

$3.01 \times 10^{-19} = 6.625 \times 10^{-34}\ \nu$

$$\text{Frequency, } (\nu) = \frac{3.01 \times 13^{-19}}{6.625 \times 10^{-34}} = 4.5 \times 10^{14}\,\text{s}^{-1}$$

109. Angular momentum of an orbit

$$mvr = \frac{nh}{2\pi}$$

Initial angular momentum = 1.05×10^{-34} joules

$$1.05 \times 10^{-34} = \frac{n \times 6.625 \times 10^{-34}}{2 \times 3.14}, n = 1$$

The electron is present in the 1st orbit originally.

When the electron gets excited, the angular momentum

= 4.20×10^{-34} joules.

$$4.20 \times 10^{-34} = \frac{n \times 6.625 \times 10^{-34}}{2 \times 3.14}, n = 4$$

An electron can lose energy when it is present in the 4th orbit and not from the 1st orbit.

The possible transitions are $4 \rightarrow 3$, $4 \rightarrow 2$, $4 \rightarrow 1$, $3 \rightarrow 2$, $3 \rightarrow 1$ and $2 \rightarrow 1$.

110. Mass number = 32

No. of protons = No. of neutrons = 16

$\therefore$ Electronic configuration = 2, 8, 6

Element is sulphur and stable ion is S^{2-}

Electronic configuration of S^{2-} is 2, 8, 8

111. (i) shape of s-orbitals and p-orbitals

(ii) orientation of lobes of p-orbitals and s-orbitals in space

(iii) areas of zero probability of electron in s- and p-orbitals

(iv) comparison of these areas of s-orbitals and p-orbitals

112. (i) shape of d_{zx} and d_{xy} orbitals

(ii) orientation of lobes of d_{xy} and d_{xz} orbitals

(iii) planes where probability of finding an electron is zero

113. nodal region for 1s orbital

114. expression for energy of electron in nth orbit.

115. (i) de Broglie's wave equation

(ii) relation between mass and wavelength

(iii) relation between wavelength and nature of light

116. (i) significance of magnetic quantum number

(ii) degeneracy of orbitals

(iii) effect of a magnetic field

117. (i) 'ℓ' value for g subshell

(ii) total number of degenerate orbitals in 'g' subshell

(iii) number of electrons in 'g' subshell

(iv) main energy level in which 'g' subshell first appears

(v) orbitals that have lower energy than the first 'g' orbital

118. (i) quantization of angular momentum

(ii) calculation of principal quantum number from angular momentum

(iii) calculation of radius

(iv) calculation of energy of an electron

119. requisite for filling up of orbitals.

120. electronic configuration of the element.

121. electronic configuration of the respective ions.

122. (i) Aufbau principle

(ii) n + ℓ values of the given orbitals

(iii) relation between energy and n + ℓ value

(iv) relation between energy and the value of 'n' for the orbitals that have the same n + ℓ values

123. identification of atomic number.

124. identification of quantum numbers corresponding to the number of orientations.

125. (i) comparison of atomic numbers

(ii) –54.4 eV

126. Angular momentum, $mvr = \frac{nh}{2\pi}$

$\therefore\ 5.27 \times 10^{-34} = \frac{n \times 6.625 \times 10^{-34}}{2 \times \frac{22}{7}} \Rightarrow n = 5s$

Radius $r_n = \frac{0.529 \times n^2}{Z}$ Å

$= \frac{0.529 \times 25}{3} = 4.408$ Å or 4.408×10^{-8} cm

127. Sommerfeld suggested that the subenergy levels or subshells associated with each main energy level are responsible for the fine structure of hydrogen spectrum. These subenergy levels or subshells exist due to the difference in energies of electrons revolving in different elliptical orbits belonging to the same main energy level.

128. Degenerate orbitals are orbitals having equal energies belonging to same main energy level. Electrons can enter into any orbital. If an electron occupies one of the orbitals, the next electron necessarily takes the same spin and enters into the other vacant orbital instead of pairing up with the electron in the 1st orbital. The electrons always repel each other due to their same charge. If they rotate around their axis in the same direction, they will have similar magnetic moment and they will further repel each other and maintain maximum distance among each other that gives rise to the maximum stability.

129. (a) 's-' orbital is spherically symmetrical and non-directional. Hence, there is no nodal plane. Only a spherical region adjacent to the orbital where the probability of finding an electron is zero is found, which is called nodal region. 'p-' orbital is dumb bell shaped and directional and lies along the axis. Hence, for each p-orbital, there is one plane where the probability of finding an electron is zero.

(b) Angular momentum $mvr = \frac{nh}{2\pi} = 3.16 \times 10^{-34}$

$\frac{n \times 6.625 \times 10^{-34}}{2 \times 3.14} = 3.16 \times 10^{-34}$

$\Rightarrow n = 3$

Velocity $v_n = \frac{2\pi e^2 Z}{nh} = 3.64 \times 10^7$

$\Rightarrow \frac{2 \times 3.14 \times \left(4.8 \times 10^{-10}\right)^2 \times 1}{n \times 6.625 \times 10^{-27}} = 3.64 \times 10^7$

$\Rightarrow n = 6$

∴ The electron is jumped to 6th orbit from 3rd orbit.

∴ The possible transitions are $6 \rightarrow 3$, $6 \rightarrow 4$, $4 \rightarrow 3$, $6 \rightarrow 5$, $5 \rightarrow 4$, $5 \rightarrow 3$.

130. The atomic number of B is 73 because its electronic configuration is [Xe] $6s^2 4f^{14} 5d^3$.

∴ Atomic number of A is x, that is 73 – 5 = 68.

So, its electronic configuration is [Xe]$6s^2 5d^1 4f^{11}$

131. Radius, $r_n = \frac{0.529 \times n^2}{Z} \Rightarrow 3.3$

$= \frac{0.529 \times 25}{Z} \Rightarrow Z = 4$

∴ Atomic number of X is 4 and atomic number of Y is 28.

Electronic configuration of Y is $1s^2\ 2s^2\ 2p^6\ 3s^2\ 3p^6\ 4s^2\ 3d^8$ and valence electrons are $4s^2$ electrons.

Electron: $1 \rightarrow n = 4, l = 0, m = 0, s = \frac{1}{2}$

Electron: $2 \rightarrow n = 4, l = 0, m = 0, s = -\frac{1}{2}$

132. $\lambda = \frac{h}{mv}$

Given that v = 5.46×10^7 cm s^{-1}

h = 6.625×10^{-27} erg.s

m = 9.1×10^{-28} g

$\therefore \lambda = \frac{6.625 \times 10^{-27}}{9.1 \times 10^{-28} \times 5.46 \times 10^7}$

$= 0.1333 \times 10^{-6}$ cm

$\lambda = 13.3$ Å

133. A spherical orbital that has three nodal regions and contain a pair of electrons is $4s^2$. Since this is the only orbital of that main energy level that is occupied with electron, the valence shell is 4. All the penultimate shells are completely filled. Therefore, the electronic configuration is $[Ar]3d^{10}4s^2$. Therefore, the atomic number of that element is 30.

134. General valence electronic configuration of an inert gas is $ns^2\ np^6$. The sum of all four quantum numbers of the valence electrons of the inert gas is

Sum of principal quantum numbers = 8 × n

Sum of azimuthal quantum numbers

= (2 × 0) + (6 × 1)

Sum of magnetic quantum numbers = 0

Sum of spin quantum numbers = 0

∴ 8n + 6 = 22

$$\therefore\ n = \frac{16}{8} = 2$$

Valence electronic configuration of the inert gas is $2s^2\ 2p^6$ and hence the inert gas is neon.

Level 3: Assess Your Concepts

135. Given that $Z_p : Z_Q = 2:7$

$$r_4 = \frac{-13.6 \times Z^2}{n^2}$$

$$\Rightarrow -13.6 = \frac{-13.6 \times Z_p^{\ 2}}{4^2} \Rightarrow Z_p = 4$$

$\therefore Z_Q = 14$

Electronic configuration of Q is 2, 8, and 4.

∴ Difference in number of electrons = 8 – 4 = 4

136. $$\frac{A \times m + (A+2)n}{m+n} = A + 1.25$$

where A is the atomic weight of the lighter isotope.

$(A + Z)$ is the atomic weight of heavier isotope

m is % abundance of lighter isotope.

n is % abundance of heavier isotope.

$\therefore mA + nA + 2n = mA + nA + 1.25m + 1.25n$

$\therefore 0.75n = 1.25m$

$$\therefore \frac{m}{n} = \frac{0.75}{1.25} = \frac{3}{5}$$

137. $$r_3 = \frac{0.529 \times n^2}{Z}$$

$$\therefore x = \frac{0.529 \times 9}{Z}$$

$$\therefore Z = \frac{4.761}{x}$$

138. $$r_4 = \frac{0.529 \times 4^2}{Z}\ \text{Å}$$

$$\therefore 2.116 = \frac{0.529 \times 4^2}{Z}$$

$$\therefore Z = \frac{0.529 \times 4^2}{2.116} = 4$$

$$\therefore E_4 = \frac{-13.6 \times n^2}{Z^2} eV = \frac{-13.6 \times 4^2}{4^2} = -13.6\text{eV}$$

139. (i) the factors affecting angle of deflection

(ii) the characteristics in which the two particles differ

140. The electrons revolve round the nucleus with high velocities to counter balance the nuclear force of attraction. As nuclear force of attraction in the 1st orbit of He^+ is more than that in H atom. Kinetic energy of electron in He^+ is more (due to greater velocity) than in H atom. When an electron approaches towards an atom, it loses potential energy because it works towards the force of attraction. The greater the force of attraction, the more is the loss of potential energy. Hence, the electron in He^+ has lesser potential energy than the electron in H atom. But the loss of PE is more significant than the change in KE. Hence, total energy of helium is less than that of hydrogen.

141. The kinetic energy of an electron is proportional to its velocity. With the increase in distance from the nucleus, the velocity of the electron decreases as the electron has to overcome a lesser nuclear force of attraction. An electron loses its potential energy when it approaches towards an atom that is a nucleus because it works towards the force of attraction during this process. Hence, the potential energy of the electron decreases with decrease in distance between the nucleus and the electron and increases with increase in distance between the nucleus and electron.

142. Low pressure means that less number of gas molecules is present in the discharge tube. If the number of molecules is very less, the collisions between the electrons

which move towards the anode with a high velocity and the gas molecules become effective. These collisions lead to the dislodgement of electrons from gaseous molecules and formation of cathode rays takes place. Moreover, high voltage increases the kinetic energy of the electrons which in turn increases the probability of removal of electrons from the gaseous molecules.

143. Protium ($_1H^1$), deuterium ($_1H^2$) and tritium ($_1H^3$) are naturally occurring isotopes of hydrogen. Unipositive ions of protium, deuterium and tritium differ in their mass.

Thus, their e/m ratio is different. Therefore, they deflect at different angles in an external electric field.

144. Since in the given experiments, it is observed that positively-charged particles are detached from the molecules under low pressure and high voltage, Thomson's model would be the other way round, i.e., positively-charged particles would be embedded in a thinly spread negatively-charged mass.

145. As the electron moves away from the nucleus, its potential energy tends to increase. The potential energy of the electron is least at equilibrium distance from the nucleus. As this distance increases/decreases, its potential energy increases.

146. Energy of the electron depends only on the principal quantum number, n.

147. (i) calculation of energy emitted due to the above transition

(ii) calculation of difference in energy between 5th and 4th and 2nd and 1st shells

(iii) relation between the energy and the frequency of the electromagnetic radiation

(iv) relation between frequency and the wavelength of the electromagnetic radiation

148. radius of hydrogen atom in 1st orbit

$$^{r}H_1 = \frac{kn^2}{Z} = kn^2 = k \cdot 1^2 = k$$

Let radius of nth orbit of $Be^{3+} = k$

$$\therefore k = \frac{kn^2}{4}, \quad \therefore n^2 = 4, \quad \therefore n = 2$$

In order to maintain the same distance, the electron has to be present in the 2nd orbit of Be^{3+}. Energy of the electron in the 1st orbit of hydrogen

$$= \frac{-kZ^2}{n^2} = -k$$

Energy of the electron in the 2nd orbit of Be^{3+}

$$= \frac{-kZ^2}{n^2}$$

$$= -\frac{k \times 4 \times 4}{2 \times 2} = -4k$$

$\therefore$ Difference in energy = (4k – k) = 3k
= (3 × 13.6) eV
= 40.8 eV

149. Revolution of an electron around a proton at the closest distance implies that it is a hydrogen atom in its ground state.

Similarly, the other particle is He^+.

The energy of the electron revolving around the nucleus of He^+ should be –K.

$$\therefore -k = \frac{-kZ^2}{n^2}$$

$$\therefore n^2 = 4 [\because Z = 2]$$

$$\therefore n = 2$$

The ratio of radii of the first orbit of hydrogen to the second orbit of He^+ $= \dfrac{k \times 1^2}{\frac{k \times 2^2}{2}} = 1:2$

150. The shape of the subshell having azimuthal quantum number a – 5 is spherical. Hence, the value of a must be 5. Therefore, the subshell having principal and azimuthal quantum numbers a and (a – 4), that is, 5 and 1 is 5p. If 5p subshell is half-filled the electronic configuration is $[Kr]5s^2 4d^{10} 5p^3$. So, the atomic number of the element is 51. 5p orbital is dumbbell shaped with two lobes.

151. Magnetic quantum number represents the spatial orientation of the electrons that belong to same main and subenergy levels. Angular momentum is fixed for the orbitals associated with same 'n' and 'ℓ' values. The degeneracy of the orbitals gets disturbed by applying external magnetic field or electric field due to the change in angular momentum. Since the electrons are moving charged particles, they have their own magnetic field that has a particular direction and the direction of the magnetic field is different for different orbitals belonging to the same main and subenergy levels. Hence, the influence of the external magnetic or electric field is also different for different orbitals, which, in turn, changes the angular momentum of the electrons and their degeneracy gets lost.

152. When more than one electron is present in one main energy level, the energy of a particular electron is determined by the value of '0l.' When the electron enters into p-orbital from infinite distance, it has to work towards a weaker force of attraction than that in case of 's-' orbital due to the screening effect of the 's-' orbital belonging to the same energy level. Hence, the loss of energy is less in case of electron entering the 'p-' orbital than that entering the 's-' orbital. As a result, the electron belonging to 'p-' orbital has higher energy than that belonging to 's-' orbital. Similarly, 'd-' orbital is associated with higher energy than that of p and the energy of the 'f-' 'orbital' is the highest provided they all belong to the same main energy level.

153. $E_n = \dfrac{-13.6 \times Z^2}{n^2}\text{eV}$

$$(E_3)^{+}_{He} = \frac{-13.6\times 4}{9}\text{eV}; (E_1)_{He^+} = \frac{-13.6\times 4}{1}\text{eV}$$

$$\therefore E_3 - E_1 = \left(\frac{-13.6\times 4}{9} + 13.6\times 4\right)\text{eV}$$

$$= 54.4\text{ eV} - 6.04\text{ eV}$$

$$\therefore (\Delta E)^{+}_{He} = 48.3\,\text{eV}$$

$$(E_5)^{3+}_{Be} = \frac{-13.6\times 16}{25} = -8.704\,\text{eV}$$

$$(E_1)^{3+}_{Be} = -13.6\times 16 = -217.6\,\text{eV}$$

$$\therefore (\Delta E)^{3+}_{Be} = -8.704 + 217.6$$

$$= 208.89\text{ eV}$$

$$\Delta E = \frac{hc}{\lambda}$$

$$\therefore \frac{(\Delta E)^{+}_{He}}{(\Delta E)^{3+}_{Be}} = \frac{\lambda_{Be^{+3}}}{\lambda_{He^{+1}}}$$

$$\Rightarrow \frac{\lambda_{He^+}}{\lambda_{Be^{+3}}} = \frac{208.89}{48.3} = \frac{4.32}{1} = \frac{13}{3}$$

$$\therefore \lambda_{He^+} : \lambda_{Be^{3+}} = 13:3$$

JEE-NEET Special Wing

Multiple-Answer Type Questions

1. Specific charge of proton $(e/m) = x$
Specific charge of Deuteron = $e/2m = x/2$
Specific charge of Unipositive helium ion = $e/4m = x/4$
Specific charge of Alpha particle = $2e/4m = e/2m = x/2$
Specific charge of tritium ion = $e/3m = x/3$

2. The charge of the electron could be 5.75×10^{-18} Coulombs. The charge on the oil droplet with could be multiples of the given values. 4.6×10^{-17} is a multiple of 1.15×10^{17}.

3. $n = 2$ 3.4 eV $n = 1$ 13.6 eV difference = 10.2 eV
$n = 3$ 1.8 eV $n = 2$ 3.4 eV difference = 1.6 eV
$n = 4$ 0.85 eV $n = 2$ 3.4 eV difference = 2.55 eV
$n = 3$ 1.8 eV $n = 1$ 13.6 eV difference = 11.8 eV

4. $\frac{2h}{\pi}; \frac{h}{2\pi}$

5. The visible region of electromagnetic spectrum ranges from 3800Å to 7600 Å.

Comprehension-Based Questions

6. It might represent the transition from $n = 3$ to $n = 2$

7. The electronic transition from $n = 6$ to $n = 4$ corresponds to the spectral line in far infra-red region. Therefore, the most probable value of wavelength could be 1256 nm.

8. H_β line of Balmer series corresponds to $n = 4$ to $n = 2$.

9. $n = 4$ to $n = 3$ falls in infra-red region and hence has lower energy than H_α line of Balmer series.

10. $n = 6$ to $n = 5$ transition corresponds to maximum wavelength or minimum energy transition.

11. From the equation for radius of Bohr's orbit, we understand that the single electron species mentioned is He^+ ion with Z = 2.

$$r_n = 0.529 \times \frac{2^2}{Z} = 0.529 \times 2 \; Z = 2$$

$$E_n = -13.6 \times \frac{2^2}{2^2} = -13.6 \text{ eV [same as 1}^{st}\text{ orbit of hydrogen atom]}$$

$$E_n = -13.6 \times \frac{2^2}{1^2} = -40.8 \text{ eV [1}^{st}\text{ orbit of He}^+]$$

Difference in energy = 27.2 eV
All the given conditions comply with the data.

12. $$E_n = -13.6 \times \frac{1^2}{2^2} = \frac{-13.6}{4} \text{ eV [2}^{nd}\text{ orbit of hydrogen atom]}$$

$$E_n = -13.6 \times \frac{2^2}{4^2} = \frac{-13.6}{4} \text{ eV [4}^{th}\text{ orbit of He}^+]$$

13. $$r_n = 0.529 \times \frac{3^2}{3} = 0.529 \times 3 = x \text{ units}$$

$$r_n = 0.529 \times \frac{3^2}{4} = \frac{3x}{4} \text{ units}$$

14. $$E_n = -13.6 \times \frac{2^2}{1^2} = -13.6 \times 4 \text{ eV}$$

Energy of 3rd orbit of Be^{+3} = $En = -13.6 \times \frac{4^2}{3^2}$

$$= -13.6 \times 4 \times \frac{4}{9} = -13.6 \times 4 \times 0.44 \text{ eV}$$

15. $$E_n = -13.6 \times \frac{3^2}{1^2} = -13.6 \times 9 \text{ eV} = -122.4 \text{ eV}$$

[1st orbit of Li^{+2}]

Additional energy required = 122.4 – 13.6 = 108.8 eV

Match the Column

16.

Element	No. of times protons are heavier than electron in an atom	Z value	EC	No. of electrons in penultimate shell
A	51436	28	2,8,16,2	16
B	45925	25	2,8,13,2	13
C	25718	14	2,8,4	8
D	38577	21	2,8,9,2	9
E	60621	33	2,8,18,5	18

17.

	Column A (Element)		Column B (Number of electrons with $l = 2$)
a	Iron	(iii)	6
b	Manganese	(i)	5
c	Nickel	(iv)	8
d	Zinc	(v)	10
e	Vanadium	(ii)	3

CHAPTER

5

Chemical Kinetics and Equilibrium

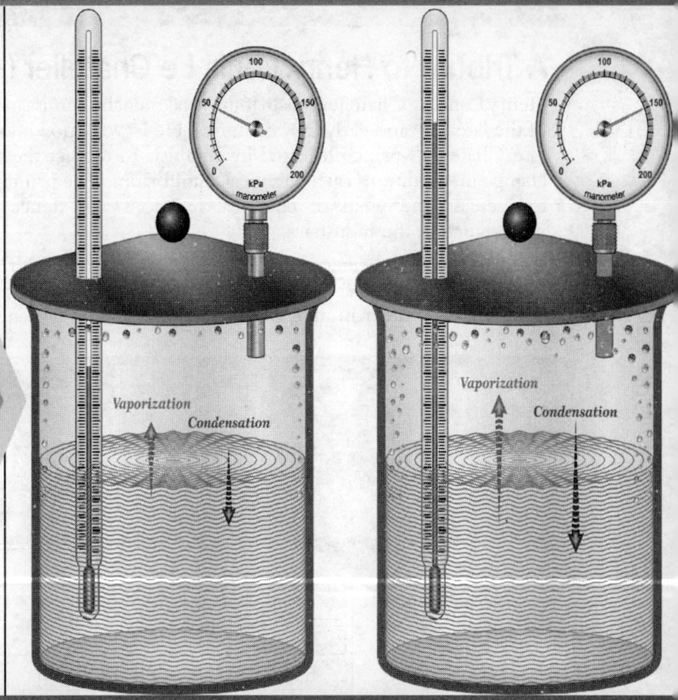

Remember

Before beginning this chapter, you should be able to:

- define a chemical reaction.
- recall the types of chemical reactions and how to formulate them.
- understand the concept of chemical changes and chemical properties of elements.
- review chemical reactions and conditions.

Key Ideas

After completing this chapter, you should be able to:

- explain the factors affecting rate of a chemical reaction and classification of chemical reactions based on it.
- describe the factors influencing rate of a reaction in the light of collision theory and study about the classification of chemical reactions based on the energy changes.
- classify chemical reactions based on reversibility.
- explain different aspects of equilibrium such as dynamic nature, characteristics, etc., and also the law of chemical equilibrium (law of mass action).
- understand Le Chatelier's principle and to study about factors affecting equilibrium.

A Tribute to Henry Louis Le Chatelier (1850–1936)

Henry Louis Le Chatelier was an influential French chemist and engineer of the late 19th and early 20th centuries. He is well known for devising "Le Chatelier's principle" used by chemists to predict the effect of a change in conditions on a chemical equilibrium. The principle is used to increase the yield of chemical reactions and hence has great importance in the industries.

Despite having been trained as an engineer and even with his interest in industrial problems, Le Chatelier chose to teach Chemistry rather than pursue a career in industry. In 1887, he was appointed as head of general chemistry at Ecole des Mines in Paris. Later he was also elected as a member of the Royal Swedish Academy of Sciences in 1907.

In Chemistry, Henry is known for his work on the chemical equilibrium and on the variation of the solubility of salts in an ideal solution. He published approximately thirty papers on these subjects between 1884 and 1914.

Henry Louis Le Chatelier who is known for the most famous principle on chemical equilibrium took the last breath on 17th September 1936.

FUN TIME

CROSSWORD

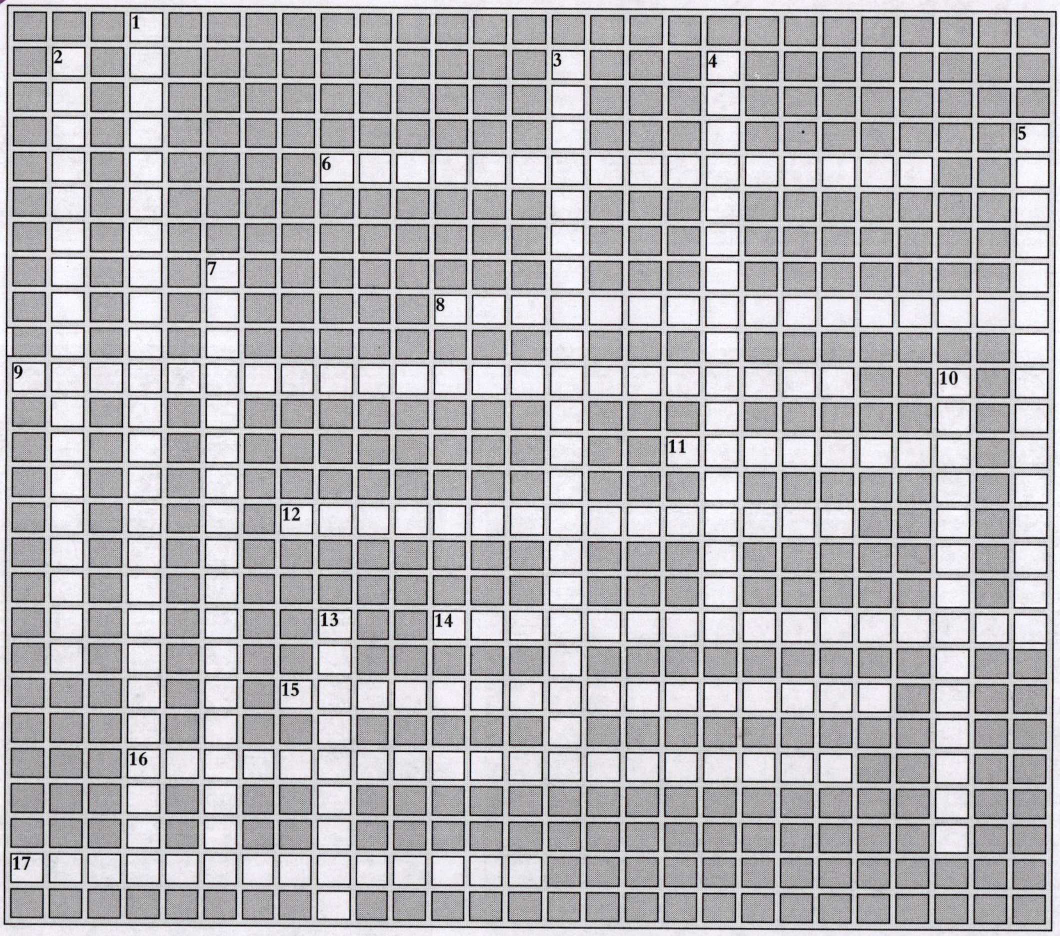

Across

6. The intermediate species formed during a chemical reaction
8. Reaction that requires a few hours for its completion
9. Equilibrium in which both the reactants and products are in the same phase
11. The chemical substance which alters the rate of reaction without participating
12. Sum of powers of concentration in the rate law expression
14. Ratio of the molar concentration of products to the reactants at any stage of the reaction
15. Extra amount of energy need to be supplied to the reactants to reach to the highest energy state
16. The slowest step of the reaction
17. Energy possessed by a substance by virtue of its chemical composition

Down

1. The rate of a reaction determined at a particular instant
2. Collisions lead to product formation
3. Reaction which takes place in the presence of light
4. The reaction in which the rate of reaction is independent of the concentration of reactants
5. The suppression of dissociation of a weak electrolyte by the addition of another electrolyte having one common ion
7. Reaction taking place in both the directions
10. Change in concentration with respect to time
13. With the increase in the concentration of the reactant the rate of reaction _______

INTRODUCTION

Life on earth is sustained because of the chemical reaction taking place around us. Digestion of food, burning of fuel and decomposition of organic matter are some such reactions that are very essential for the existence of life. The study of the chemical reactions can have different perceptions, one of the most important aspects of the this being 'rate of reactions.'

Every chemical reaction can be represented in the form of a balanced chemical equation. Nevertheless, writing a chemical equation does not imply that the reaction takes place necessarily at all the conditions. If that is the case, all gases in the atmosphere would react with one another and also with water. Obviously, that is not happening. For every reaction to occur, certain conditions are necessary. Moreover, some reactions may take short span of time and some may require longer time for completion. This means, different reactions take place at different speeds.

The study of rate of chemical reactions forms an integral part of chemistry. In the industry, the time taken for the completion of a particular reaction and the conditions employed to speed up the reaction determine the cost of production of a product and the economic viability of a process. Biological reactions in the presence of enzymes also take place at different rates. This aspect finds its application in the fields of medicine and agriculture.

The branch of chemistry that deals with the study of rates of reactions is called **chemical kinetics**. The area of chemical equilibrium deals with the kinetics of reversible reactions.

Classification of Reactions

A chemical reaction involves transformation of reactants into products. The time taken for this transformation of reactants into products is not the same for all reactions. Based on the time taken for the completion of a reaction, the chemical reactions are classified into three categories:

1. **Instantaneous Reactions**

   The reactions that reach completion within a fraction of a second are called **instantaneous reactions.**

   Examples:

   (a) Precipitation reactions

   $2AgNO_3 + BaCl_2 \rightarrow Ba(NO_3)_2 + 2AgCl\downarrow$

   (b) Burning of some active metals

   $2Na + O_2 \rightarrow Na_2O + \text{Heat}$

   (c) Acid–base neutralization reactions involving strong acids and bases.

   $HCl + NaOH \rightarrow NaCl + H_2O$

> **Info Bytes!**
>
> The most abundant type of chemical reaction on Earth is photosynthesis, where plants convert sunlight into energy.

2. **Moderate Reactions**

   The chemical reactions that require time ranging from a few minutes to hours to reach completion are called **moderate reactions.**

   Examples:

   (a) Digestion of food

   (b) Cooking of food

   (c) Photosynthesis in plants

3. **Slow Reactions**

Some chemical reactions require longer time ranging from days to months, or even years for completion. Such reactions are called **slow reactions.**

Examples:

(a) Rusting of iron
(b) Decomposition of organic matter
(c) Formation of coal and petroleum

Rate of a Chemical Reaction

For any chemical reaction, at the start of the reaction, the concentration of the reactants is maximum and the concentration of the products is zero. As the reaction proceeds, the concentration of the reactants decreases and the concentration of the products increases gradually. The change in concentration of the reactants or products with respect to time is known as the **rate of reaction**.

$$\text{Rate of reaction} = \frac{\text{Change in concentration of reactants or products}}{\text{Time interval}}$$

$$r = \frac{\Delta C}{\Delta t}$$

where, $\Delta C \rightarrow$ change in concentration of reactants or products

$\Delta t \rightarrow$ time interval

If the rate of reaction is measured with respect to reactants, it is given a negative sign, which indicates the decrease in the concentration of the reactants with time.

$$r = -\frac{\Delta C_{\text{Reactants}}}{\Delta t}$$

If the rate of reaction is measured with respect to products, it is given a positive sign, which indicates the increase in the concentration of the products with time.

$$r = +\frac{\Delta C_{\text{Products}}}{\Delta t}$$

Info Bytes!

Measuring the rate of a reaction is paramount in industries to optimize production rates, ensuring efficiency while minimizing resource wastage.

Units of Rate of Reaction

Since the concentration is expressed in moles/L and time is expressed in seconds, the rate of reaction is expressed in mole per litre per second (mol/L/s).

Average Reaction Rate versus Instantaneous Reaction Rate

The rate of reaction at the beginning of the reaction is proportional to the initial concentrations of the reactants. This is called the **initial rate of reaction.**

As the concentration of the reactants decreases continuously, the rate of reaction is not uniform throughout the reaction. It changes continuously during the course of reaction. The rate of reaction is always taken as the change in the concentration of reactants or products in a definite interval of time. This is called the **average reaction rate**. However, the average reaction rate does not give the exact idea of the rate of reaction at a particular instant of time.

At any instant, the rate of a reaction is proportional to the concentration of the reactants at that instant. As time progresses, the concentration of the reactants decreases. With decrease in the concentration of the reactants, the rate of a reaction also decreases. Therefore, the rate of a reaction determined at a particular instant is called the **instantaneous reaction rate**.

For measuring instantaneous reaction rate, a very small interval of time, which is almost equal to zero, should be taken and the change in the concentration in that small interval of time must also be taken.

For a reaction, $A \rightarrow B$

Rate of reaction $= \dfrac{\Delta C_B}{\Delta t}$, where

ΔC = change in concentration of the product B

Δt = time interval

When $\Delta t \rightarrow 0$ (Δt tends to zero)

$$\text{Instantaneous rate (r)} = -\frac{\Delta C_A}{\Delta t} \text{ or } +\frac{\Delta C_B}{\Delta t}$$

Info Bytes!

The difference between average and instantaneous reaction rates is similar to the distinction between average and instant speeds in physics.

Example:

If in a reaction $A \rightarrow B$, ΔC_B is 0.001 moles/L and Δt is 10 s.

$$\text{Average rate of reaction} = \frac{\Delta C_B}{\Delta t} = \frac{0.001}{10} = 10^{-4} \text{ mol/L/s}$$

Graphical Representation of Average Rate and Instantaneous Rate

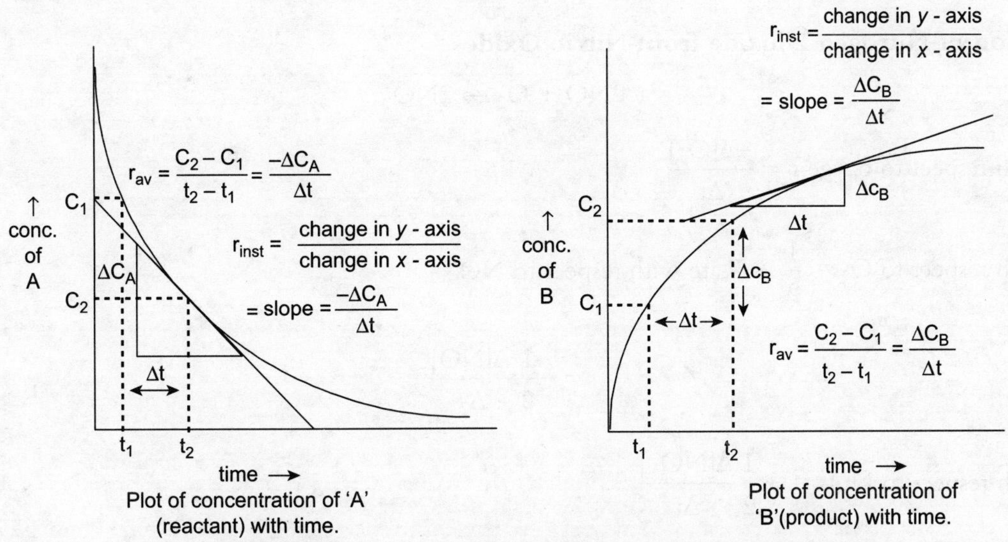

Figure 5.1 Determination of instantaneous reaction rate

Instantaneous rate at a particular time (t) can be obtained by determining the slope of the tangent drawn on the curve at the point where time = t.

$$\text{Slope of the tangent} = \frac{\text{Change in y-axis}}{\text{Change in x-axis}}$$

Change in 'y' axis ΔC_A or ΔC_B

Change in 'x' axis = Δt

Concentration of 'A' vs. t

$$r_{inst} = \text{slope} = -\frac{\Delta C_A}{\Delta t}$$

Concentration of 'B' vs. t

$$r_{inst} = \text{slope} = \frac{\Delta C_B}{\Delta t}$$

Example:

1. Formation of Hydrogen Iodide

$$H_2 + I_2 \rightarrow 2HI$$

The rate of the reaction may not be the same with respect to all the reactants and products. It depends upon the stoichiometric ratio of the reactants and the products. In the above case, one mole of hydrogen and one mole of iodine react to give two moles of hydrogen iodide. This means that the rate of consumption of hydrogen is equal to the rate of consumption of iodine:

$$r = \frac{-\Delta[H_2]}{\Delta t} = \frac{-\Delta[I_2]}{\Delta t}$$

Rate of formation of HI = 2 × Rate of consumption of hydrogen or iodine

$$\text{Rate of consumption of hydrogen or iodine} = \frac{1}{2} \times \text{Rate of formation of HI}$$

$$\therefore r = \frac{-\Delta[H_2]}{\Delta t} = \frac{-\Delta[I_2]}{\Delta t} = \frac{1}{2}\frac{\Delta[HI]}{\Delta t}$$

2. Formation of Nitrogen Dioxide from Nitric Oxide

$$2NO + O_2 \rightarrow 2NO_2$$

$$\text{Rate with respect to oxygen} = \frac{-\Delta[O_2]}{\Delta t}$$

$$\text{Rate with respect to } O_2 = \frac{1}{2} \times \text{Rate with respect to NO}$$

$$= -\frac{1}{2}\frac{\Delta[NO]}{\Delta t}$$

$$\text{Rate with respect to } NO_2 = +\frac{1}{2}\frac{\Delta[NO_2]}{\Delta t}$$

$$\therefore r = -\frac{1}{2}\frac{\Delta[NO]}{\Delta t} = \frac{-\Delta[O_2]}{\Delta t} = +\frac{1}{2}\frac{\Delta[NO_2]}{\Delta t}$$

Therefore, while writing the equation for the rate of reaction, the stoichiometric coefficients of reactants and products are also taken into consideration.

For a general reaction, aA + bB → cC +dD

$$r = -\frac{1}{a}\frac{\Delta C_A}{\Delta t} \qquad r = -\frac{1}{b}\frac{\Delta C_B}{\Delta t}$$

$$r = +\frac{1}{c}\frac{\Delta C_C}{\Delta t} \qquad r = +\frac{1}{d}\frac{\Delta C_D}{\Delta t}$$

where, ΔC_A, ΔC_B, ΔC_C and ΔC_D are small changes in the concentrations of A, B, C and D that occur in time, Δt.

Factors Influencing the Rate of a Reaction

Every chemical reaction has its own characteristic rate. Nevertheless, it is affected by some factors. The most important factors are listed below:

1. Concentration of reactants
2. Temperature
3. Catalyst

Konnect

Catalysts work like magic. They speed up reactions without getting consumed, playing a pivotal role in processes like the production of ammonia.

The reason behind different rates for different chemical reactions and factors influencing the rate of a reaction has been interpreted in terms of **collision theory of gases**. The basic concept behind the theory lies is the kinetic molecular theory of gases.

The basic assumption of this theory is that the collisions between the reactant molecules give rise to the product.

However, it is experimentally observed that the rate of reaction is much less than the frequency of collisions between the gas molecules (reactants). This observation was explained by proposing that the reactant molecules must collide with a certain minimum energy to give the product.

In 1880, Svante Arrhenius proposed that during collisions, the reactant molecules must attain certain minimum amount of energy called **threshold energy** for the reaction to occur.

The collision model postulates that required threshold energy for the reaction can be attained from the kinetic energy of the reactant molecules before the collision.

The extra amount of energy required for the chemical reaction to occur is called the **activation energy**.

However, every collision with sufficient energy cannot result in the formation of the product because collision should take place with right orientation of reactants so that the product molecule(s) can be formed.

The collisions that successfully produce the product are known as **effective collisions** and others are **ineffective collisions**. When the collision between the reactant molecules is effective, an intermediate species called **activated complex** is formed before the formation of the product.

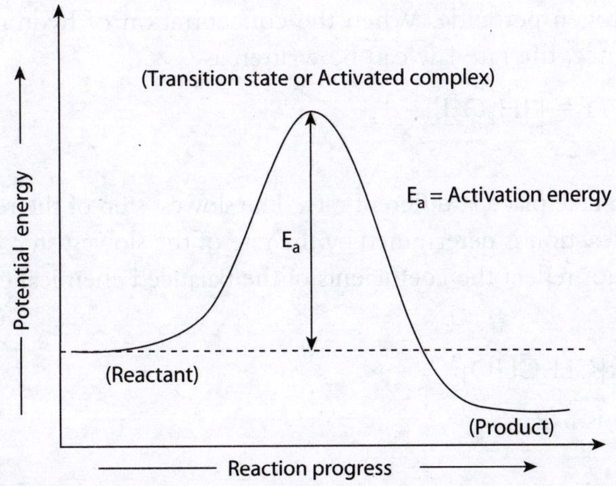

Figure 5.2 Energy profile diagram representing collision theory

Konnect

Collision theory satisfactorily accounts for the effect of change of concentration, temperature as well as the effect of catalyst on the rate of chemical reactions.

The energy of the system during the course of reaction increases and the energy associated with the activated complex is the highest. Then the energy of the system again decreases during the formation of the product from the activated complex.

Difference in the rates of different chemical reactions, that is, slow and fast reactions can be explained satisfactorily with the help of the concept of activation energy.

The magnitude of the activation energy depends on the nature of the reactants. In case of reactions associated with high activation energy, only a small fraction of the reactant molecules possess sufficient kinetic energy and can give corresponding number of effective collisions. Such reactions are considered as slow reactions.

Alternatively, in the reactions wherein the activation energy is less, an increased percentage of molecules causes effective collisions thereby giving a greater number of product molecules. These reactions are called **fast reactions.**

Effect of Concentration

With the increase in the concentration of the reactants, the number of reactant molecules per unit volume increases. Furthermore, the number of collisions increases, which results in the net increase in the effective collisions. Therefore, the rate of a reaction increases.

Rate Law

Rate law is an expression that gives a quantitative estimation of the change in the rate of reaction with the change in concentration of reactants. The establishment of quantitative relationship between the rate of reaction and concentration of the reactants cannot be obtained from the balanced chemical equation. This is because all the reactants participating in the reaction need not necessarily affect the rate of chemical reaction to the same extent. It can be done only by experimental methods.

For the general reaction,

$$aA + bB \rightarrow \text{products}$$

$$r = k[A]^x [B]^y \text{ (where k is the rate constant)}$$

The power 'x' is called order of the reaction with reference to 'A' and the power 'y' is called the order of the reaction with reference to 'B.' The sum of the powers (x + y) is called **overall order of the reaction**. It may or may not be equal to (a + b).

Order of a reaction can be defined as the sum of the powers to which the concentration terms are raised in the rate expression for that reaction.

Examples:

1. $2H_2O_2 \rightarrow 2H_2O + O_2$. The rate law is $r = k[H_2O_2]^1$.

   This reaction represents the dissociation of hydrogen peroxide. When the concentration of hydrogen peroxide is doubled, the rate of reaction is also doubled. Hence, the rate law can be written as

$$r = k[H_2O_2]^1.$$

2. $CH_3CHO \rightarrow CH_4 + CO$

   This reaction takes place in several steps. Each step take place at different rate. The slowest step of the reaction is called the **rate-determining step**. The overall rate of reaction is determined by the rate of the slowest step of the reaction. Consequently, the rate law for this reaction does not reflect the coefficients of the balanced chemical equation.

   Rate law for this reaction is

$$r = k[CH_3CHO]^{3/2}$$

   The order of reaction with respect to CH_3CHO is 3/2.

3. $2HI \rightarrow H_2 + I_2$

$$r = k[HI]^2$$

   The decomposition of hydrogen iodide in aqueous solution takes place in the above manner. This means that doubling the concentration of HI increases the rate of the reaction by four times. The rate law follows the stoichiometric equation.

4. $H_2 + Cl_2 \xrightarrow{\text{light}} 2HCl$

   In case of the above reaction of the formation of hydrogen chloride from hydrogen and chlorine, the rate of reaction is independent of concentrations of both hydrogen and chlorine. Therefore, the rate law can be written as

$$r = k[H_2]^0 [Cl_2]^0$$

Effect of Temperature

For most of the chemical reactions, the rate of the reaction increases with increase in number of effective collisions. When the temperature increases, the kinetic energy of molecules increases. More number of molecules attain threshold energy thereby increasing the number of fruitful collisions and hence, the rate of reaction.

Experiment to Study the Effect of Temperature and Concentration on the Rate of Reaction

1. Two boiling test tubes are taken with 3 g of zinc granules each. Graduated syringes are attached to the boiling test tubes. Further, 5 mL of 1M HCl and 5 mL of 2M HCl are added into the two test tubes. The volumes of hydrogen gas evolved in the two syringes at various time intervals are noted. It is observed that the volume of hydrogen gas evolved is more in the second case when compared to the first case. This shows that the rate of reaction increases with concentration.
2. The same experiment can be done by taking the same concentration of HCl at two different temperatures. Then, it is found that the volume of hydrogen evolved is more at higher temperature.

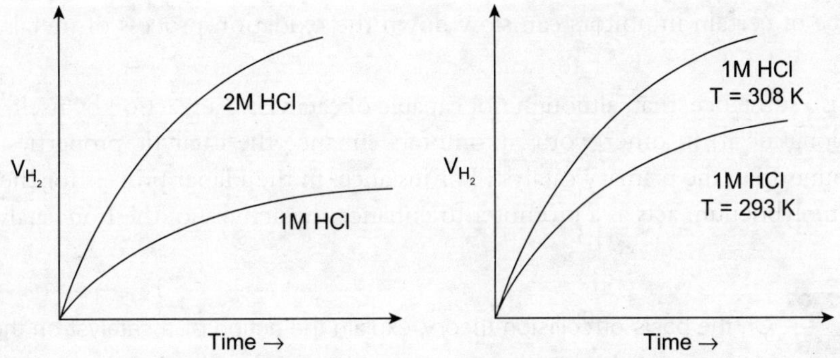

Figure 5.3 Energy profile diagram representing the effect of catalyst on rate of reaction

Effect of Catalyst

The chemical reactions can be carried out at a faster rate by increasing the temperature, but this is not possible in case of all reactions. Moreover, some reactions can be carried out at a lower temperature by using a catalyst. Since the process takes place at a lower temperature, the cost of production gets reduced.

A **catalyst** increases the rate of reaction by providing an alternative path for the reaction.

This alternative path is associated with lower activation energy when compared to the uncatalyzed reaction.

In most of the reactions, catalysts increase the rate of reactions. These type of catalysts are called **positive catalysts.**

Examples:

$$2SO_2 + O_2 \xrightarrow{NO} 2SO_3$$

$$2KClO_3 \xrightarrow{MnO_2} 2KCl + 3O_2$$

In case of some reactions, a catalyst only acts as a carrier of one of the reactants to the reaction site.

Example: Hydrogenation of unsaturated hydrocarbons.

$$\underset{\text{Ethylene}}{H_2C = CH_2} + H_2 \xrightarrow[\text{or Pd}]{\text{Ni or Pt}} \underset{\text{Ethane}}{H_3C - CH_3}$$

In the above case, the hydrogen gas gets adsorbed on the metal surface and thus hydrogen gas comes into contact with the other reactant.

In some reactions, the catalyst takes part in the chemical reaction at the initial stage and gets regenerated at the end of the reaction.

Example:

$$2SO_2 + O_2 \xrightarrow{NO} 2SO_3$$

In the following reaction, nitric oxide reacts with atmospheric oxygen to produce nitrogen dioxide (NO_2). This NO_2 oxidizes sulphur dioxide to sulphur trioxide. Nitric oxide is regenerated. This means, nitric oxide acts as an oxygen carrier in this reaction:

$$2NO + O_2 \rightarrow 2NO_2$$

$$SO_2 + NO_2 \rightarrow SO_3 + NO$$

There are few reactions in which catalysts slow down the process. Such type of catalysts are called **negative catalysts.**

Example:

Decomposition of hydrogen peroxide can be slowed down if some substances like glycerine, urea, acetanilide, sodium pyrophosphate, etc., are added to H_2O_2.

While catalysts play an important role in speeding up chemical reactions, there are other substances known as inhibitors that can slow down reactions. On the other hand, promoters are substances that enhance the activity of catalysts.

Inhibitors: An inhibitor is a substance that decreases the rate of a chemical reaction. It does so by either interacting with the reactants or the catalyst, effectively preventing them from participating in the reaction efficiently. For instance, in metal corrosion, the presence of certain inhibitors can slow down the oxidation process of metals, thus protecting them from rapid corrosion.

Promoters: A promoter is a substance that, although not capable of catalyzing a reaction by itself, increases the efficiency of a catalyst when present alongside it. In other words, promoters enhance the catalytic properties of a catalyst. They are typically used in smaller amounts than the primary catalyst. For instance, in the Haber process for the synthesis of ammonia, iron is used as a catalyst and molybdenum acts as a promoter to enhance the activity of the iron catalyst.

EXAMPLE 5.1 On the basis of collision theory, explain the action of a catalyst on the rate of reaction.

SOLUTION

The chemical reactions can be carried out at a faster rate by increasing the temperature, but this is not possible in case of all reactions. Moreover, the reactions can be carried out at a lower temperature by using a catalyst. Since the process takes place at a lower temperature, the cost of production gets reduced. A catalyst increases the rate of reaction by providing an alternative path for the reaction. This alternative path is associated with lower activation energy compared to the uncatalyzed reaction, which is evident from the following graph.

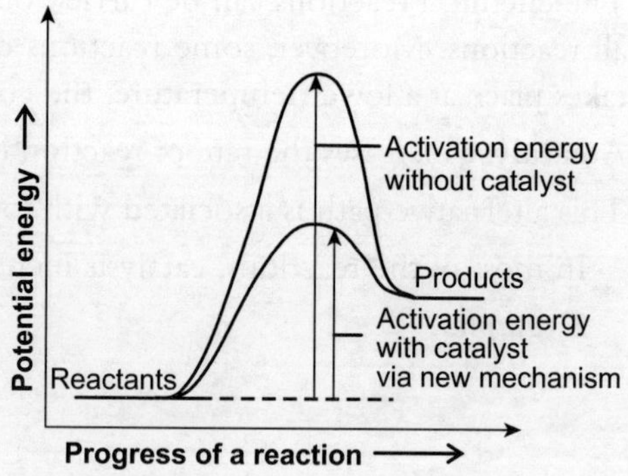

In most of the reactions, catalysts increase the rate of reactions. These type of catalysts are called positive catalysts. Example:

$$2SO_2 + O_2 \xrightarrow{NO} 2SO_3$$

There are few reactions in which catalysts slow down the rate of reactions. These type of catalysts are called negative catalysts. Example:

Decomposition of hydrogen peroxide can be slowed down if some substances like glycerine, urea, acetanilide, sodium pyrophosphate etc. are added to H_2O_2.

EXAMPLE 5.2 Sulphuric acid can decompose to produce sulphur dioxide and water. The uncatalyzed reaction has an activation energy of 95 kJ/mol. The activation energy value in the presence of ferrocene is 120 kJ/mol and in the presence of platinum, it is 60 kJ/mol. What conclusion can you draw from the above observations?

SOLUTION

The activation energy of a catalyzed reaction in the presence of platinum is 60 kJ/mol, which is much less than the activation energy of the uncatalyzed reaction, which is 95 kJ/mol. This indicates that the rate of decomposition of sulfuric acid is increased in the presence of platinum, making it a positive catalyst. On the other hand, the activation energy of the catalyzed reaction in the presence of ferrocene is 120 kJ/mol, which is significantly greater than that of the uncatalyzed reaction. This demonstrates that the rate of decomposition of sulfuric acid is decreased in the presence of ferrocene, marking it as a negative catalyst.

EXAMPLE 5.3 Assuming that $2H_2 + O_2 \rightarrow 2H_2O$ is a single-step reaction, what will be the rate of reaction when the volume of the reaction vessel is reduced to 1/3rd of the initial value? The original rate of reaction is 27 mol/L/s.

SOLUTION

$$2H_2 + O_2 \rightarrow 2H_2O$$

The rate of the reaction $r = k[H_2]^2[O_2]$, as it is a single-step reaction.

When the volume of the reaction vessel is reduced to 1/3rd of the initial volume, the concentration of each reactant is increased by three times. Since the reaction is a second order with respect to H_2 and first order with respect to O_2, the rate of reaction increases by 9 times for H_2 and 3 times for O_2.

On the whole, the rate of reaction increases by 27 times. The original rate of reaction is 27 mol/L/s and the new rate of reaction is 27 times more than this.

$r^2 = 27 \times 27 = 729$ which is 7.29×10^2 mol/L/s.

Chemical Equilibrium

When any liquid is taken in a closed container, the surface molecules go into vapor state due to evaporation. At the same time, at some stage, the vapor molecules condense and return to liquid state. Therefore, the level of liquid in the container remains constant when the rate of evaporation and the rate of condensation become equal. This state is called **equilibrium.**

The state of equilibrium is also attained in case of chemical reactions that may take place in either direction. The reaction the takes place in both the directions are called reversible reactions. Due to the attainment of equilibrium state, these reactions do not reach completion.

Reversible and Irreversible Reactions

Reactions in which the reactants are converted to products and the products are converted back to reactants are called **reversible reactions.** The reaction in which the reactants are converted to products is called **forward reaction**. The reaction in which the products are converted back to reactants is called **backward reaction**.

Reactions in which the reactants are converted into products but the products cannot be converted back to reactants are called **irreversible reactions.** These reactions take place only in one direction.

Info Bytes!

In an ideal world, all reactions are reversible. However, due to energy constraints and irreversible changes, some just don't reverse naturally.

Table 5.1 Comparative study of reversible and irreversible reactions

Reversible reactions	Irreversible reactions
Can take place in both directions Equilibrium is established Can be made irreversible under some conditions Represented by two half-arrows in opposite directions ($\rightleftharpoons$)	Can take place in one direction only No equilibrium is established Cannot be made reversible under any conditions. Represented by a full arrow pointing towards the products ($\rightarrow$)
Examples: $N_2(g) + 3H_2(g) \rightleftharpoons 2NH_3(g)$ $H_2(g) + I_2(g) \rightleftharpoons 2HI(g)$ $2SO_2(g) + O_2(g) \rightleftharpoons 2SO_3(g)$ $PCl_5(g) \rightleftharpoons PCl_3(g) + Cl_2(g)$ $2NO(g) + O_2(g) \rightleftharpoons 2NO_2(g)$ $CaCO_3(s) \rightleftharpoons CaO(s) + CO_2(g)$	***Examples:*** $4Fe(s) + 3O_2(g) \rightarrow 2Fe_2O_3(s)$ $NaCl + AgNO_3 \rightarrow AgCl + NaNO_3$ $Zn + H_2SO_4 \rightarrow ZnSO_4 + H_2$ $Sn + 2HCl \rightarrow SnCl_2 + H_2$

Dynamic Equilibrium

The rate of a reaction at any instant is proportional to the concentration of the reactants.

At the start of the reaction, the concentration of the reactants is maximum and thus the rate of forward reaction is maximum. When the chemical reaction is in progress, the concentration of reactants decreases and hence the rate of forward reaction also decreases. Along with this, during the course of reaction, the concentration of products increases thereby increasing the rate of backward reaction.

As time proceeds, a stage is reached when the rate of forward reaction becomes equal to the rate of backward reaction. At this stage, there is no net change in the molar concentrations of the reactants and the products. This means that the system has attained the state of equilibrium. As the composition of the reactants and the products remains constant at this stage, it appears that the reaction has come to a standstill. However, this is not the case. The forward and backward reactions take place with equal speeds without any net change in the concentrations of reactants and products.

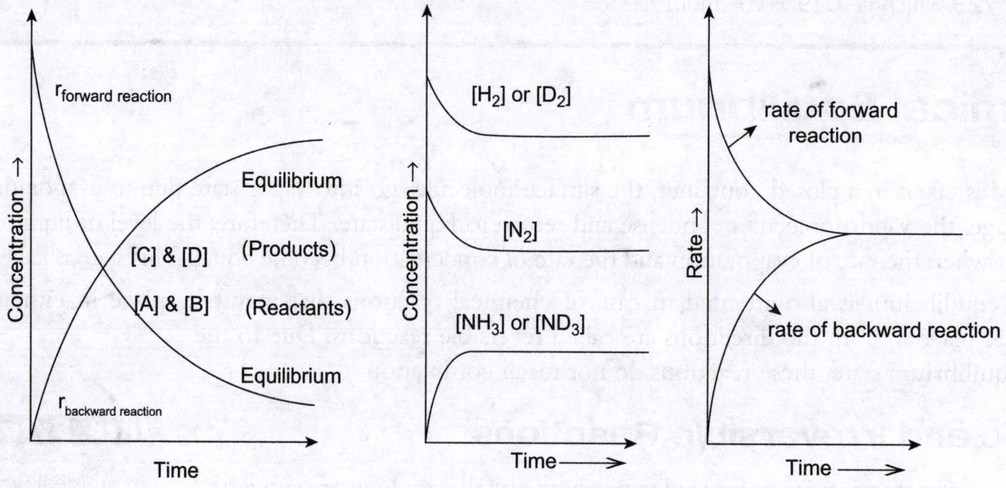

Figure 5.4 Dynamic equilibrium

Experiment to Show the Dynamic Nature of Chemical Equilibrium

Two reactions are conducted separately by taking known amounts of nitrogen and hydrogen in the first case and nitrogen and deuterium in the second case. The amount of ammonia, N_2 and H_2 in the first reaction and amount of ND_3, N_2 and D_2 in the second reaction is noted at regular intervals. After a certain time, the composition of reaction mixture is found to remain unaltered with time. This constancy in composition indicates the state of equilibrium. At this stage, the reaction mixtures of both the reactions are mixed together and left for some time. The analysis of the mixture showed not only the same concentration of ammonia but also existence of some deuterium-containing forms of ammonia in the reaction mixture. Thus, it can be concluded that the interchange of H and D atoms has taken place because the forward and backward reactions proceed even after equilibrium is attained.

Characteristics of Dynamic Equilibrium

1. The observable properties, such as concentration, density, color, pressure, etc., remain constant at constant temperature.
2. Equilibrium can be attained from either direction.
3. Usage of a catalyst does not alter the position of equilibrium.
4. Equilibrium state proceeds indefinitely unless it is disturbed by external factors.

Info Bytes!

The balance in dynamic equilibrium is delicate and can be tipped by changing conditions such as temperature or pressure.

Identification of Equilibrium

The equilibrium stage can be identified by constancy of some observable properties. Depending on the nature of various substances, a particular property is taken for observation.

Example:

$$CaCO_3(s) \rightleftharpoons CaO(s) + CO_2(g)$$

Since there is only one gaseous product in the above reaction, equilibrium can be identified by constancy of pressure exerted by CO_2:

$$NO_2(g) + CO(g) \rightleftharpoons NO(g) + CO_2(g)$$

Since NO_2 is a reddish brown gas, the equilibrium can be identified by constancy of colour.

Info Bytes!

Ever noticed a soda going flat? It's a real-time demonstration of reaching equilibrium. Carbon dioxide in the drink tries to reach equilibrium with the CO_2 in the air, leading to a loss of fizz.

Law of Chemical Equilibrium or Law of Mass Action

The **law of mass action** states that the rate of a reaction is proportional to the product of the molar concentrations of the reactants.

For a reversible reaction, $xA + yB \rightleftharpoons mC + nD$

$r_f \propto [A]^x [B]^y$, where r_f is the rate of forward reaction

$$r_f = K_f [A]^x [B]^y$$

$r_b \propto [C]^m [D]^n$, where r_b is rate of backward reaction

$$r_b = K_b [C]^m [D]^n$$

At equilibrium, $r_f = r_b$

$$K_f [A]^x [B]^y = K_b [C]^m [D]^n$$

$$\frac{K_f}{K_b} = K_c = \frac{[C]^m [D]^n}{[A]^x [B]^y}$$, where K_c is called equilibrium constant

Info Bytes!

Guldberg and Waage, in the late 19th century, established the Law of Mass Action, laying the foundation for understanding chemical equilibrium at a molecular level.

Application of Law of Mass Action to Various Equilibria

The chemical equilibria are basically of two types as discussed below.

1. **Homogeneous Equilibria:** In these equilibrium reactions, all the reactants and products are in one phase only. In these cases, when all the reactants and products are in gaseous phase, the molar concentrations of all the substances are taken into consideration for writing the equilibrium constant.

   Examples:

   - $H_2(g) + I_2(g) \rightleftharpoons 2HI(g)$

     $$K_c = \frac{[HI]^2}{[H_2][I_2]}$$

   - $N_2(g) + 3H_2(g) \rightleftharpoons 2NH_3(g)$

     $$K_c = \frac{[NH_3]^2}{[N_2][H_2]^3}$$

2. **Heterogeneous Equilibria:** In the reactions involving heterogeneous equilibria, the reactants and the products exist in different phases. In these cases, all the reactants and products are not taken into consideration for writing the equilibrium constant. The concentration of the reactants and the products existing in solid state or in pure liquid state are taken in unity since their concentration cannot be changed.

Example:

$$NH_4HS(s) \rightleftharpoons NH_3(g) + H_2S(g)$$

$$K_c = \frac{[NH_3][H_2S]}{[NH_4HS]}$$

Since $[NH_4HS] = 1$

$K_c = [NH_3][H_2S]$

Equilibrium Constant in Terms of Partial Pressure

The expression for equilibrium constant involves molar concentration of reactants and products and hence is called **equilibrium constant with respect to concentration** (K_c). However, in case of gas phase reactions, the concentration of reactants and products can be expressed preferably in terms of partial pressures of the gases in the expression. Therefore, it is called **equilibrium constant with respect to pressure**. In this case, K_c is denoted by K_p.

The ideal gas equation is PV = nRT

$$\Rightarrow P = \frac{n}{v}RT$$

But concentration in mol/L is $C = \frac{n}{v}$

$\therefore$ P = CRT

R is constant and at constant temperature $P \propto C_{gas}$.

Example: $H_2(g) + I_2(g) \rightleftharpoons 2HI(g)$

$$K_c = \frac{[HI]^2}{[H_2]\cdot[I_2]} \quad K_p = \frac{p_{HI}}{p_{H_2}\cdot p_{I_2}}$$

where, p_{HI} = partial pressure of H_I

p_{H_2} = partial pressure of H_2

p_{I_2} = partial pressure of I_2

Applications of Equilibrium Constant

1. On the basis of the value of the equilibrium constant, it is possible to predict the direction of a chemical reaction. The ratio of molar concentrations of the reactants to the products at any stage of the reaction is known as the **reaction quotient** (Q_c). Depending on the relative values of K_c and Q_c, it is possible to predict the direction of the equilibrium reaction.

   If $Q_c = K_c$, then the reaction is at equilibrium.

   If $Q_c > K_c$, then the reaction proceeds in the backward direction.

   If $Q_c < K_c$, then the reaction proceeds in the forward direction.

2. On the basis of the value of the equilibrium constant, the extent to which a chemical reaction takes place can be known. A greater value of K_c implies that the reaction mostly proceeds towards the products and the yield of the products will be more. A lower value of K_c indicates the lesser yield of products.
3. K_c values help in the calculation of the equilibrium concentrations of various substances in the reaction.

EXAMPLE 5.4 (i) When two moles of hydrogen are heated with two moles of iodine, 2.96 moles of hydrogen iodide are formed. Calculate K_c for the reaction of formation of hydrogen iodide.

(ii) Calculate Kp for the following reaction if partial pressures of NH_3, N_2 and H_2 are 0.4, 0.3 and 0.2 atm, respectively.

SOLUTION

	$H_2(g)$	+	$I_2(g)$	$\rightleftharpoons$	$2HI(g)$
(i) At equilibrium,	$2-x$		$2-x$		$2x$

$$2x = 2.96$$

$$x = \frac{2.96}{2} = 1.48$$

$$K_c = \frac{[HI]^2}{[H_2][I_2]} = \frac{(2x)^2}{(2-1.48)(2-1.48)} = \frac{4\times(1.48)^2}{0.52\times0.52} = 32.4$$

(ii)

$$K_p = \frac{p^3_{H_2}\cdot p_{N_2}}{P^2_{NH_3}}$$

$$K_p = \frac{(0.2)^3(0.3)(\text{atm})^4}{(0.4)^2(\text{atm})^2}$$

$$K_p = 0.015\ \text{atm}^2$$

EXAMPLE 5.5 If K_c for the formation of HI from H_2 and I_2 each is 64, then calculate K_c for the decomposition of 1 mole of HI.

SOLUTION

$H_2 + I_2 \rightleftharpoons 2HI$

$1/2\ H_2 + 1/2\ I_2 \rightleftharpoons HI$

$$\Rightarrow K_{c_1} = \frac{[HI]^2}{[H_2]^1[I_2]^1} \qquad \Rightarrow K_{c_2} = \frac{[HI]}{[H_2]^{1/2}[I_2]^{1/2}}$$

$$\therefore K_{c_2} = \frac{1}{\sqrt{K_{c_1}}} = \frac{1}{\sqrt{64}} = \frac{1}{8} = 0.125$$

EXAMPLE 5.6 In the reaction $N_2O_4 \rightleftharpoons 2NO_2$, the dissociation of N_2O_4 was found to be 40 per cent at equilibrium when the reaction is conducted in a 2 L container at 300 K. Find the equilibrium constant and the number of moles of reactants and products.

SOLUTION

	N_2O_4	$\rightleftharpoons$	$2NO_2$
Initial moles	1		0
Number of moles at equilibrium 1 – 0.4 =	0.6		0.8
Concentration at equilibrium 0.6/2 =	0.3		0.8/2 = 0.4

$$\therefore K_c = \frac{[NO_2]^2}{[N_2O_4]} = \frac{(0.4)^2}{0.3} = 0.533\ \text{mol/L}$$

Factors Affecting the Equilibrium

The different factors that affect the chemical equilibrium are the concentration of the reactants or products, temperature and pressure. The change in the behavior of the system at equilibrium due to the alteration of those factors was first enunciated by Le Chatelier.

Le Chatelier's principle has been proposed to explain the effect of various factors on the equilibrium.

Le Chatelier's Principle

According to this principle, when a system at equilibrium is subjected to a constraint or change, the position of the equilibrium shifts in a direction that opposes the constraints.

Effect of Concentration

When the concentration of any of the reactants or products in a reaction at equilibrium is changed, the composition of the equilibrium reaction mixture also changes in such a way as to compensate the effect of the concentration change.

Example:

$$H_2(g) + I_2(g) \rightleftharpoons 2HI(g)$$

Addition of hydrogen or iodine at equilibrium disturbs the equilibrium concentration of the reactants. Hence, the reaction proceeds in that direction in which large amounts of hydrogen or iodine are consumed. This means that the equilibrium shifts in the forward direction. The yield of HI increases. The same shift takes place by the removal of HI from the reaction mixture at equilibrium.

However, addition of HI at equilibrium results in the shift of equilibrium in the backward direction.

Example:

$$2K_2CrO_4 + 2HCl \rightleftharpoons K_2Cr_2O_7 + 2KCl + H_2O$$

Aqueous solution of potassium chromate that is yellow in color changes to orange-colored solution of potassium dichromate by the addition of the acid.

Addition of HCl to the reaction mixture at equilibrium shifts the reaction in the forward direction. This is indicated by the intensification of color of the reaction mixture. Addition of water to the equilibrium mixture shifts the reaction in the backward direction. This is marked by fading of orange color.

Effect of Pressure

According to Boyle's law, an increase in pressure leads to a decrease in volume at constant temperature.

When a system at equilibrium is subjected to increase in pressure, the reaction takes place in that direction, which is associated with decrease in volume. Similarly, decrease in pressure makes the reaction proceed in that direction, which is accompanied by increase in volume.

Avogadro's law states that under similar conditions of temperature and pressure, equal volumes of all gases contain equal number of moles. The reactions that proceed with a change in the number of moles involve a change in volume.

Therefore, the effect of pressure is applicable to only those reactions accompanied by change in the number of moles (change in volume). Pressure has no effect on those equilibria that do not involve a change in the number of moles.

> **Info Bytes!**
>
> Mountain climbers and deep-sea divers are, perhaps unknowingly, well-acquainted with the concept of partial pressures, as oxygen levels change with altitude and depth.

Example:

$$H_2(g) + I_2(g) \rightleftharpoons 2HI(g)$$

$$n_R = 2n_p = 2\Delta n = n_p - n_R = 0$$

where n_R and n_P represent the number of moles of the reactants and products, respectively. Since the number of moles of reactants is equal to the number of moles of products, change in pressure has no effect on the position of equilibrium.

Reactions Associated With a Change in the Number of Moles

Case I: Increase in the number of moles (volume)

Example: $PCl_5 \rightleftharpoons PCl_3 + Cl_2$ (change in volume $PCl_3 + Cl_2$)

$n_R = 1$ $n_P = 2$

$\Delta n = n_P - n_R = 2 - 1 = 1$

The forward reaction proceeds with an increase in the number of moles, which means that an increase in volume takes place during the reaction. Therefore, decrease in pressure favors the forward reaction and speeds up the dissociation process. Increase in the pressure shifts the equilibrium in the backward direction thereby suppressing the dissociation process.

Case II: Decrease in the number of moles (volume)

Example: $N_2(g) + 3H_2(g) \rightleftharpoons 2NH_3(g)$

$n_R = 4$ $n_P = 2$

$\Delta n = n_P - n_R = -2$

The forward reaction proceeds with decrease in the number of moles, that is, decrease in volume. Hence, increase in pressure favors the forward reaction and enhances the yield of ammonia. Obviously, decrease in pressure speeds up the dissociation of ammonia into nitrogen and hydrogen. Due to this reason only, high pressure (200 – 1000 atm) is maintained during the process of the synthesis of ammonia by Haber's process (a favourable condition for getting greater yield of the products).

Effect of Temperature

Most of the chemical reactions are associated with the absorption or evolution of heat. Hence, change in temperature changes the state of equilibrium. Increase in temperature makes the reaction proceed in that direction in which more heat is absorbed. Similarly, decrease in temperature allows the reaction to take place in a direction associated with the release of heat energy.

Case I: Absorption of heat energy

Example: $N_2 + O_2 \rightleftharpoons 2NO - \text{Heat}$

Since absorption of heat takes place in the forward reaction, increase in temperature shifts the equilibrium in the forward direction. It can be concluded that for all endothermic reactions, high temperature is the favorable condition for greater yield of products.

Case II: Evolution of heat energy

Example: $N_2 + 3H_2 \rightleftharpoons 2NH_3 + \text{Heat}$

Since the forward reaction is accompanied by release of heat energy, decrease in temperature favors the forward reaction, which means that for all exothermic reactions, low temperature is the most favorable condition.

EXAMPLE 5.7

(i) What is the effect of pressure on the equilibrium of the reaction between nitrogen and oxygen to give nitric oxide?

(ii) In a reversible reaction, some amount of heat energy is liberated in the forward reaction. Name the reaction. What change in temperature favours the forward reaction?

SOLUTION

(i) $N_2 + O_2 \rightleftharpoons 2NO$

As the total number of moles on reactants side and products side is same, there is no effect of pressure on the equilibrium.

(ii) In a reversible reaction, evolution of heat energy indicates that it is an exothermic.

reaction and ΔH = –ve.

For example, A+ B $\rightleftharpoons$ C + D + Energy

Hence, low temperature favours the formation of products.

EXAMPLE 5.8 A teacher, while revising, asked Raman and Bose to sketch a potential energy diagram for a reaction A + B $\rightleftharpoons$ C + D. ΔH for the reverse reaction is –10 kJ and E_a of the forward reaction is 40 kJ. The graphs drawn by both of them are X and Y, respectively. Between X and Y, which graph is correct and why? Also, explain why the other one is wrong.

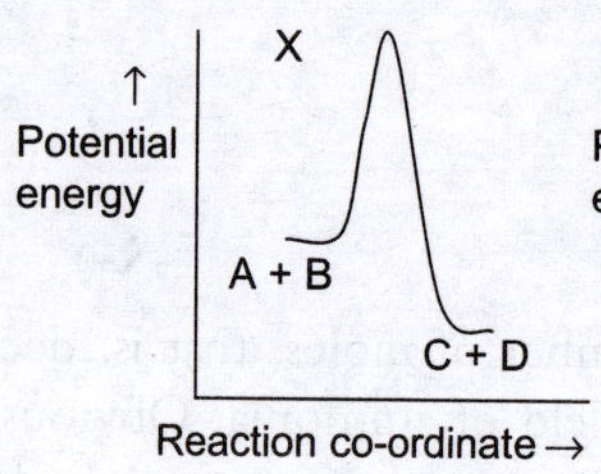

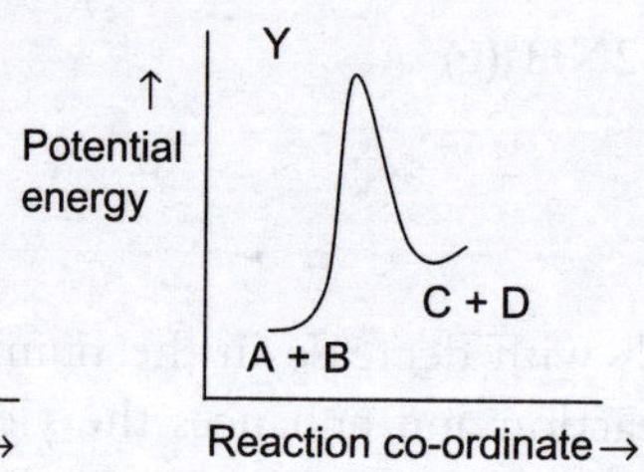

SOLUTION

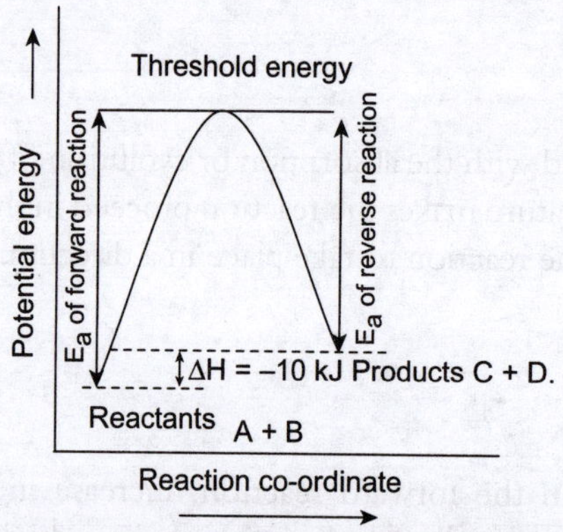

As the energy released in the backward reaction is 10 kJ, the backward reaction is exothermic indicating that the energy of reactants is less than the energy of products. Hence Y is correct. X is wrong because as the energy of C + D is less than A + B, on the reverse reaction would be endothermic (ΔH = +ve).

EXAMPLE 5.9 During the preparation of soap the addition of common salt allows the precipitation of soap. Explain the principle involved (Soap is the sodium salt of carboxylic acid).

SOLUTION

The addition of common salt results in the addition of Na^+ ions. Equilibrium exists between sodium stearate molecules and sodium and stearate ions. The addition of Na^+ ions shifts the equilibrium towards left thus sodium stearate precipitates.

$RCOO^-Na^+ \rightleftharpoons RCOO^- + Na^+$

POINTS TO REMEMBER

- ✔ A chemical reaction involves transformation of reactants into products.
- ✔ The reactions that reach completion within a fraction of a second are called instantaneous reactions.
- ✔ The chemical reactions that require time ranging from a few minutes to hours to reach completion are called moderate reactions.
- ✔ Some chemical reactions require longer time ranging from days to months, or even years for completion. Such reactions are called slow reactions.
- ✔ The change in concentration of the reactants or products with respect to time is known as the rate of reaction.
- ✔ The rate of reaction at the beginning of the reaction is proportional to the initial concentrations of the reactants is called the initial rate of reaction.
- ✔ The rate of reaction is always taken as the change in the concentration of reactants or products in a definite interval of time. This is called the average reaction rate.
- ✔ The rate of a reaction determined at a particular instant is called the instantaneous reaction rate.
- ✔ The reason behind different rates for different chemical reactions and factors influencing the rate of a reaction has been interpreted in terms of collision theory of gases.
- ✔ Rate law is an expression that gives a quantitative estimation of the change in the rate of reaction with the change in concentration of reactants.
- ✔ Order of a reaction can be defined as the sum of the powers to which the concentration terms are raised in the rate expression for that reaction.
- ✔ A catalyst increases the rate of reaction by providing an alternative path for the reaction.
- ✔ In most of the reactions, catalysts increase the rate of reactions. These types of catalysts are called positive catalysts.
- ✔ There are few reactions in which catalysts slow down the process. Such type of catalysts is called negative catalysts.
- ✔ Reactions in which the reactants are converted to products and the products are converted back to reactants are called reversible reactions.
- ✔ Reactions in which the reactants are converted into products but the products cannot be converted back to reactants are called irreversible reactions.
- ✔ The law of mass action states that the rate of a reaction is proportional to the product of the molar concentrations of the reactants.
- ✔ The expression for equilibrium constant involves molar concentration of reactants and products and hence is called equilibrium constant with respect to concentration (K_c).
- ✔ In case of gas phase reactions, the concentration of reactants and products can be expressed preferably in terms of partial pressures of the gases in the expression. Therefore, it is called equilibrium constant with respect to pressure.
- ✔ The ratio of molar concentrations of the reactants to the products at any stage of the reaction is known as the reaction quotient (Q_c).
- ✔ According to Le Chatelier's principle, when a system at equilibrium is subjected to a constraint or change, the position of the equilibrium shifts in a direction that opposes the constraints.

PRACTICE QUESTIONS CLASSROOM WING

Very Short Answer Type Questions

Direction for questions from 1 to 9:

Fill in the blanks.

1. Formation of nitric oxide is an _____ reaction with a _____ value for the heat of the reaction.
2. ________ enables any two systems to reach a state of equilibrium more quickly.
3. The rate of ________ reactions cannot be determined experimentally.
4. In the reaction $2NO(g) + 2H_2(g) \rightarrow N_2(g) + 2H_2O$, if initial concentration of hydrogen is kept constant and the concentration of NO is doubled, the rate of reaction increases by four times. This shows that rate is directly proportional to ______.
5. The equilibrium $H_2(g) + I_2(g) \rightleftharpoons 2HI(g)$ is not affected by the change in ________.
6. Active mass of a solid is taken as __________.
7. If K_c for the formation of HI from H_2 and I_2 is 48, then K_c for decomposition of 1 mole of HI is ______.
8. The magnitude of _________ decreases in the presence of a catalyst.
9. A chemical equilibrium is ________ in nature.

Direction for questions from 10 to 23:

Answer the following questions.

10. Identify the factor that affects the equilibrium position but does not affect the equilibrium constant.
11. Which among the factors: Temperature, Catalyst, Initial concentration and Pressure, affects neither equilibrium position nor equilibrium constant?
12. Give the general expression for a balanced chemical equation by applying the law of mass action.
13. How is the attainment of equilibrium recognized in case of following equilibria?
    (i) Dissociation of magnesium carbonate in a closed vessel
    (ii) Dissociation of N_2O_5 in a closed vessel
14. When the reaction of synthesis of ammonia is carried out with a mixture of hydrogen and deuterium, what are the products obtained at the end of the process?
15. Write the equilibrium constant for the dissociation of $CaCO_3$.
16. What are effective collisions?
17. Define a reversible reaction. Give an example.
18. What is meant by specific reaction rate?
19. The value of equilibrium constant for a reversible reaction is 3×10^{-2}. If the reaction quotient for the same reaction is 5×10^{-3}, predict the direction of equilibrium reaction.
20. What is the effect of a catalyst on the equilibrium?
21. Ammonia dissociates to give nitrogen and hydrogen. What happens if the pressure is increased on the system at equilibrium?
22. What are the units for the rate of the reaction $A \rightarrow B$?
23. Give the units of K_c for the formation of 1 mole of NH_3 from its constituents.

Short Answer Type Questions

24. Rate of a reaction with respect to B is 1/3dC/dt and half the rate with respect to A. Identify the stoichiometric equation corresponding to the abovementioned conditions.
25. The equilibrium constant for the decomposition of one mole of hydrogen iodide is 0.25. What is the equilibrium constant for the equilibrium reaction of the formation of HI from one mole of each of the reactants?
26. Rate of a reaction with respect to hydrogen is -3.9×10^{-4} mole L^{-1} s^{-1}. For the reaction corresponding to the formation of ammonia, what could be the rate of reaction with respect to ammonia?

27. Does the rate equation $r = k[A]^0\ [B]^0$, correspond to a reaction with rate constant having the same units as rate of reaction?

28. Discuss how the chemical equilibrium is dynamic by giving graphical representation.

29. Explain the effect of a catalyst on the rate of reaction on the basis of collision theory.

30. What are the characteristics of dynamic equilibrium?

31. How is it possible to make reversible reaction irreversible?

32. Apply the law of mass action to the following equilibria:
    (i) Formation of SO_3 from SO_2 and O_2
    (ii) Formation of NO_2 from nitric oxide and oxygen

33. How does a catalyst influence the equilibrium constant?

34. 'The quantitative estimation of change in the rate of reaction with change in concentration does not always follow stoichiometric equation.' Justify.

35. Predict the shift in equilibrium when the volume is decreased on the following equilibrium reactions:
    (i) $PCl_3(g) + Cl_2(g) \rightleftharpoons PCl_5(g)$
    (ii) $N_2(g) + O_2(g) \rightleftharpoons 2NO(g)$

36. What are the applications of equilibrium constant?

37. Calculate K_p if the partial pressures of reactants and products in the dissociation of 1 mole of phosphorous pentachloride are 0.3 atm, 0.4 atm, and 0.2, atm respectively.

38. One mole of PCl_5 is subjected to heating in a 1 L vessel. The number of moles of PCl_3 formed at equilibrium is 0.6. Calculate the equilibrium constant for the dissociation of PCl_5.

Essay Answer Type Questions

39. The value of the rate constant for a reaction is found to be 1.6 ″ 10^{-3} $mole^{-2}\ L^2\ s^{-1}$. Could $k[A]^2[B]^0$ be the probable rate equation for the reaction?

40. A reaction is second order with respect to 'A', first order with respect to 'B'. What happens to the rate of reaction, when we:
    (i) Double the concentration of 'A' alone.
    (ii) Double the concentration of 'B' alone.
    (iii) Double the concentration of both A and B at a time.

41. Two moles each of sulphur dioxide and oxygen are taken in a 2-L vessel and subjected to a chemical reaction. At equilibrium, 0.8 moles of sulphur trioxide were found. Find out K_c value.

42. State and explain the law of mass action. Apply it to the following equilibria:
    (i) $H_2(g) + F_2(g) \rightleftharpoons 2HF(g)$
    (ii) $NH_4HS(s) \rightleftharpoons NH_3(g) + H_2S(g)$
    (iii) $PCl_5(s) \rightleftharpoons PCl_3(\ell) + Cl_2(g)$

43. State Le Chatelier's principle and apply it to the following equilibria:
    (i) $2NO(g) \rightleftharpoons N_2(g) + O_2(g) + \text{Heat}$
    (ii) $N_2O_4(g) \rightleftharpoons 2NO_2(g) - \text{Heat}$

PRACTICE QUESTIONS COMPETITION WING

Level 1: Apply your Concepts

Direction for questions from 1 to 7:
State whether the following statements are true or false.

1. If the rate with respect to O_2, NO and NO_2 are, respectively
$$\frac{-\Delta[O_2]}{\Delta t}, \frac{-1}{2}\frac{\Delta[NO]}{\Delta t}, \frac{+1}{2}\frac{\Delta[NO_2]}{\Delta t}$$
then the corresponding chemical equation is $2NO + O_2 \rightarrow 2NO_2$.
2. The slope obtained by drawing a tangent at time 't' on the curve for the concentration of reactants vs time is equal to instantaneous rate.
3. In an equilibrium, the catalyst increases the rate of the forward reaction while decreases the rate of the backward reaction.
4. Threshold energy = Energy of normal molecules + Activation energy.
5. An increase in pressure increases the rate of reaction due to the increase in the number of collisions among the molecules.
6. In the reaction: $NO_2 + CO \rightleftharpoons NO + CO_2$, the equilibrium state may be recognised by the constancy of colour.
7. At equilibrium the reaction quotient is greater than equilibrium constant.

***Direction for questions from 8 to 19*:**
Fill in the blanks.

8. Addition of ammonium chloride shifts the equilibrium to the ______ in an equilibrium for the dissociation of ammonium hydroxide?
9. The equation that describes mathematically the dependence of the rate of reaction on the concentration terms of reactants is ______ or ______.
10. The reaction between Zn and H_2SO_4 is an example for ______ reaction.
11. For _________, The activation energy for an uncatalysed reaction is less than that for a catalysed reaction.
12. A ______ does not change the position of equilibrium but ______ the rate of backward as well as forward reaction.
13. Equilibrium constant has a definite value for every reaction at a given temperature. It is independent of __________ and __________.
14. The minimum energy that two molecules should possess so that their collisions result in a chemical reaction is called __________ energy.
15. Decomposition of phosphorous pentachloride is an example of ______ equilibria.
16. K_c changes with change in ______.
17. __________ in temperature favours an endothermic reaction.
18. The equilibrium constant of a reaction $A + B \rightleftharpoons 2C$ if the concentrations of A and B together is 0.8 moles L^{-1} and that of C is 0.6 mol L^{-1} is ______
19. If K_C for the formation of ammonia is 2 mol^{-2} L^2, K_c for decomposition of ammonia is ______.

***Direction for question 20*:**
Match the entries given in Column A with appropriate ones from Column B.

20.

Column A [Reaction (Gas Phase)]	Column B (Favourable Conditions
(i) $A + B \rightarrow 2C + Q$ kcal	(A) High temperature and low pressure
(ii) $2A \rightarrow X - Q$ kcal	(B) Low temperature and high pressure
(iii) $X + 3Y \rightarrow 2XY + Q$ kcal	(C) Low temperature and no effect of pressure
(iv) $X + Y \rightarrow 3Z - Q$ kcal	(D) High temperature and no effect of pressure
(v) $A_2 + B_2 \rightarrow 2AB - Q$ kcal	(E) High temperature and high pressure

Direction for questions from 21 to 43:
For each of the questions, four choices have been provided. Select the correct alternative.

21. **Assertion (A):** A reaction of the type $A + B \rightarrow 2C$ is invariably a second-order reaction.
Reason (R): Order of the reaction is the sum of the powers of concentration terms in the rate equation.
(a) Both A and R are true and R is the correct explanation of A.
(b) Both A and R are true, but R is not the correct explanation of A.
(c) A is true and R is false.
(d) A is false and R is true.

22. **Assertion (A):** Synthesis of hydrogen chloride is a zero-order reaction.
Reason (R): Rate of formation of HCl is dependent only on the intensity of light used.
(a) Both A and R are true and R is the correct explanation of A.
(b) Both A and R are true, but R is not the correct explanation of A.
(c) A is true and R is false.
(d) A is false and R is true.

23. **Assertion (A):** For the reaction of the formation of ammonia, K_C value decreases with an increase in temperature.
Reason (R): With the increase in temperature, the number of effective collisions increases.
(a) Both A and R are true and R is the correct explanation of A.
(b) Both A and R are true, but R is not the correct explanation of A.
(c) A is true and R is false.
(d) A is false and R is true.

24. **Assertion (A):** For the reaction of decomposition of PCl_5, K_C value increases with an increase in temperature.
Reason (R): Decomposition of PCl_5 is an exothermic reaction.
(a) Both A and R are true and R is the correct explanation of A.
(b) Both A and R are true, but R is not the correct explanation of A.
(c) A is true and R is false.
(d) A is false and R is true.

25. For a chemical reaction to occur:
(a) the reacting molecules must collide with each other
(b) reacting molecules should have sufficient energy at the time of collision
(c) reacting molecules must be properly oriented
(d) all of the above

26. If an activated complex is formed in chemical reactions according to the collision theory, which of the following is true with respect to its stability?
(a) It is highly stable because it has high energy.
(b) It is less stable because it has lower energy.
(c) It is less stable because it has high energy.
(d) None of the above.

27. The equilibrium constant for the reactions
$N_2(g) + O_2(g) \rightleftharpoons 2NO(g)$
and $NO(g) \rightleftharpoons \frac{1}{2}N_2(g) + \frac{1}{2}O_2(g)$ are k and k^1, respectively, the relation between k and k^1 is:
(a) $k = (k^1)^2$
(b) $k = \left(\frac{1}{k^1}\right)^2$
(c) $k^2 = k^1$
(d) $k^1 = \left(\frac{1}{k}\right)^2$

28. With respect to the equilibrium reaction $A \rightleftharpoons B$, which of the following graphs indicate the highest K_c value?

(a)
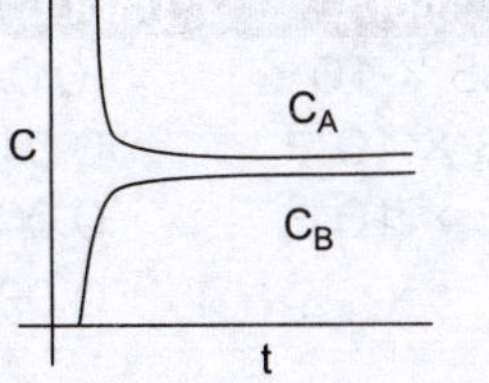

(b)
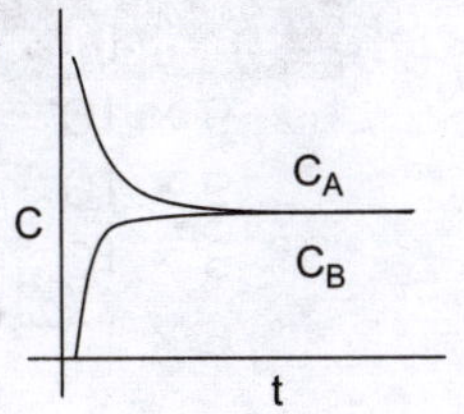

(c)
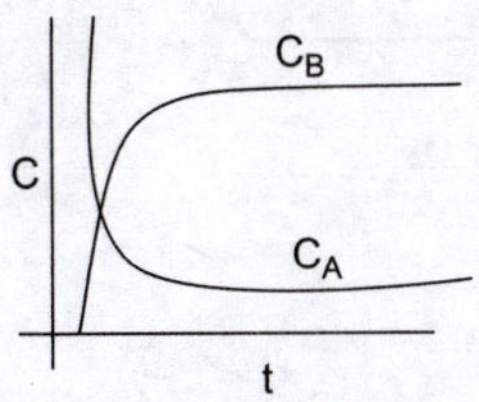

(d)
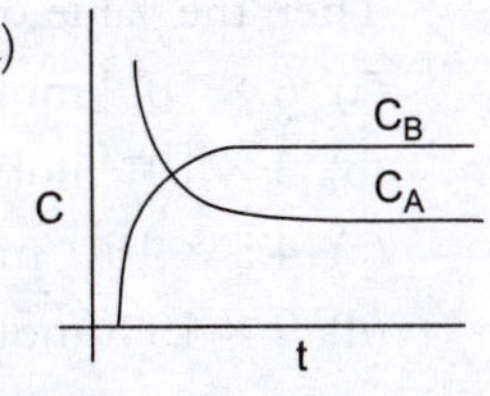

29. Equilibrium position of which of the following reactions is not affected by change in pressure?
(a) $I_2(s) + 5F_2(g) \rightarrow 2IF_5(g)$
(b) $FeO(s) + CO(g) \rightarrow Fe(s) + CO(g)$
(c) $2Cu(NO_3)_2(s) \rightarrow 2CuO(s) + 4NO_2(g) + O_2(g)$
(d) $N_2O_4(g) \rightarrow 2NO_2(g)$

30. The equilibrium constant K_c is 10^2 for the reaction $AB + C \rightleftharpoons AC + B$

The rate constant for the forward reaction K is 10^6, the rate constant of backward reaction is:

(a) 10^4 (b) 10^8

(c) 10^{-4} (d) $\frac{1}{100}$

31. Which among the following is the graphical representation of a reaction if the ΔH for the forward reaction is twice the activation energy of the I step and activation energy of the II step is half of the I step

(a)

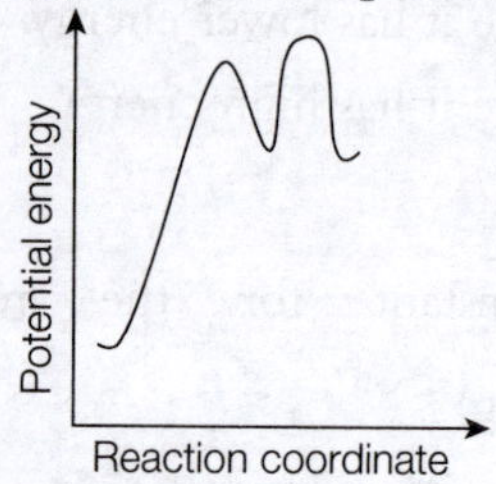

(b)

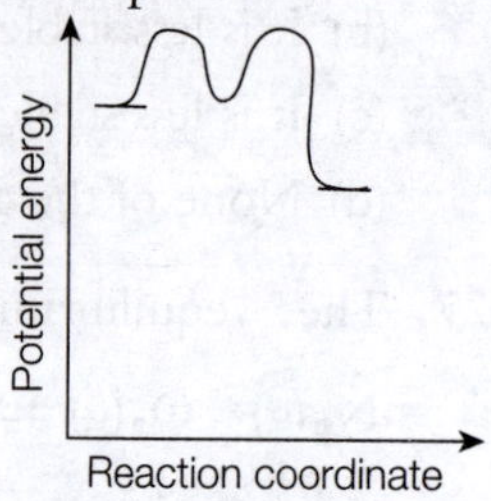

(c)

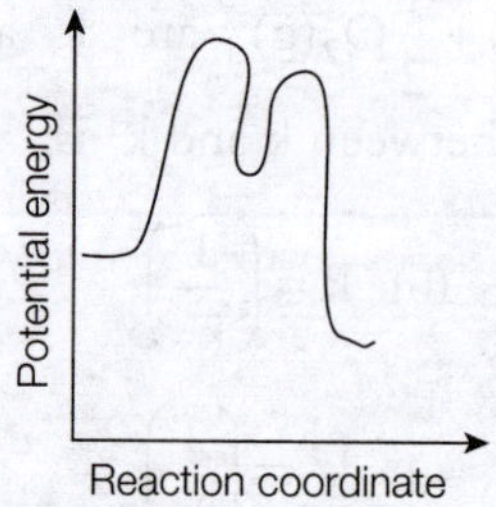

(d)

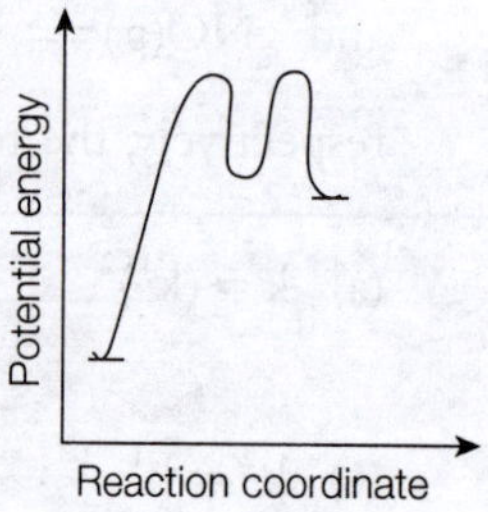

32. For a particular reaction, A + B → C was studied at 25°C. The following results are obtained:

[A] mol/L	[B] mol/L	Rate (mol L^{-1} s^{-1})
9×10^{-5}	1.5×10^{-2}	0.06
9×10^{-5}	3×10^{-3}	0.012
3×10^{-5}	3×10^{-3}	0.004
6×10^{-5}	x	0.024

Then the value of x is ________.

(a) 6×10^{-3} mol L^{-1}

(b) 3×10^{-3}mol L^{-1}

(c) 4.5×10^{-3} mol L^{-1}

(d) 9×10^{-3} mol L^{-1}

33. $2SO_2(g) + O_2(g) \rightleftharpoons 2SO_3(g) + Q$ kJ

In the above reaction, how can the yield of product be increased without increasing the pressure?

(a) by increasing temperature

(b) by decreasing temperature

(c) by increasing the volume of the reaction vessel

(d) by the addition of the catalyst

34. For a reaction 2A + B → 2AB, it is found that doubling the concentration of both the reactants increases the rate to eight times that of initial rate but doubling the concentration of B alone doubles the rate. Then the order of the reaction with respect to A and B is:

(a) 0, 3 (b) 0, 2

(c) 2, 1 (d) 2, 2

35. In the reaction $N_2O_4 \rightleftharpoons 2NO_2$, the degree of dissociation of N_2O_4 increases with the:

(a) increase in pressure (b) decrease in temperature

(c) increase in volume (d) presence of catalyst

36. Identify the correct sequence of steps in an experiment to show the effect of temperature on the rate of the reaction.

(1) Measuring the volumes of H_2 gas liberated in the two test tubes.

(2) Heating the test tube B by 10°C.

(3) Comparison of relative volumes of H_2 liberated in test tubes B and A.

(4) Addition of same concentration of HCl to the two test tubes.

(5) Taking equal masses of fine granules of zinc in two test tubes A and B.

(a) 3, 4, 5, 1, 2 (b) 5, 4, 2, 1, 3

(c) 2, 1, 3, 5, 4 (d) 5, 4, 2, 3, 1

37. The graph given below shows the change in concentration of 'B' with time for the reaction A → B. Identify the steps given below in sequence for determining instantaneous rate.

(1) Find the slope of the tangent $= \frac{y_2 - y_1}{x_2 - x_1}$.

(2) Change in the *y*-axis, that is, y_2–y_1 gives change in concentration of 'B,' whereas change in the. *x*-axis, that is, x_2–x_1 gives a small change in time interval.

(3) Slope of the tangent is equal to instantaneous rate.

(4) Draw the tangent on the curve at a particular instant of time 't.'

(a) 3, 1, 2, 4 (b) 1, 2, 3, 4

(c) 4, 2, 1, 3 (d) 4, 3, 1, 2

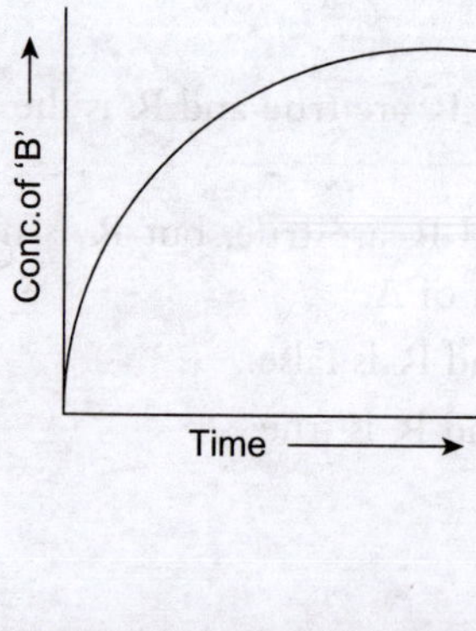

38. For the reaction A → B, identify the correct sequence of steps for the calculation of average rate of reaction.

(1) plotting a graph of concentration of 'A' at various time intervals

(2) identification of C_2 and C_1 at different time intervals t_2 and t_1, respectively, by reading the graph

(3) calculation of $\frac{C_2 - C_1}{t_2 - t_1}$

(4) finding out the experimental values of concentrations of 'A' at regular intervals

(a) 4, 2, 3, 1 (b) 4, 1, 2, 3

(c) 3, 2, 1, 4 (d) 1, 2, 3, 4

39. Initial number of moles of reactants taken in a closed reaction vessel is given. Percentage degree of dissociation is also given. Identify the correct sequence of steps to calculate K_c value.

(1) calculation of equilibrium concentrations of reactants and products

(2) calculation of equilibrium number of moles

(3) writing equilibrium constant expression for the reaction

(4) calculation of K_c value by using the equilibrium concentration

(a) 4, 2, 3, 1 (b) 2, 1, 3, 4

(c) 3, 2, 1, 4 (d) 2, 1, 4, 3

40. Which among the following reactions is an example of instantaneous reaction under normal conditions?

(a) $2H_2 + O_2 \rightarrow 2H_2O$

(b) $N_2 + O_2 \rightarrow 2NO$

(c) $NaOH + HCl \rightarrow NaCl + H_2O$

(d) $C_{12}H_{22}O_{11} + H_2O \rightarrow C_6H_{12}O_6 + C_6H_{12}O_6$

41. The rate for the reaction between ionic compounds cannot be determined because they are generally:

(a) immeasurably slow reactions

(b) moderately slow reactions

(c) instantaneous reactions

(d) not precipitation reactions

42. For a reaction A + B → C, the rate law is written as $r = k[A]^2[B]$. Doubling the concentration of 'A' without changing concentration of 'B' increases the rate of reaction by:

(a) 2 times (b) 4 times

(c) 8 times (d) 16 times

43. Identify the common property for a chemical reaction at dynamic equilibrium:

(a) The measurable properties like concentration, density, color, pressure, etc., remain constant at constant temperature.

(b) The forward and backward reactions take place with the same rate.

(c) It can be achieved from both directions.

(d) All of the above.

Level 2: Review your Concepts

44. For a gaseous reaction 2A + 3B → 2P, the equilibrium constant value is equal to 25 L^3 $mole^{-3}$. What would be the value of the equilibrium constant for the equilibrium of decomposition of 1 mole of P?

45. Arrange the given units of K_C in the order of the following equilibrium reactions. Consider room temperature conditions.

(i) Decomposition of NO

(ii) Dimerization of NO_2

(iii) Decomposition of NH_4HS

(iv) Synthesis of NH_3

(v) Decomposition of NO_2 to NO and O_2

(A) $mole^2\ L^{-2}$ (B) No units

(C) mole L^{-1} (D) $mole^{-1}$ L

(E) $mole^{-2}\ L^2$

46. The following are the certain criteria of four reversible two-step reactions. Arrange them in the order of the conclusions drawn regarding the nature of the reactions given.

(i) E_a(step I) > E_a (step II); Exothermic

(ii) E_a(step I) > E_a(step II); Endothermic

(iii) E_a(step II) > E_a (step I); Endothermic

(iv) E_a(step II) > E_a(step I); Exothermic

(A) Step II → Rate determining step; E_a(forward reaction) < E_a(backward reaction)

(B) Step I → Rate determining step; E_a(forward) > E_a(backward)

(C) Step II → Rate determining step; E_a(forward) > E_a (backward)

(D) Step I → Rate determining step; E_a(forward) < E_a(backward)

47. The following are the two energy profile diagrams for the same reaction under two different conditions. Identify the condition that was subjected to change.

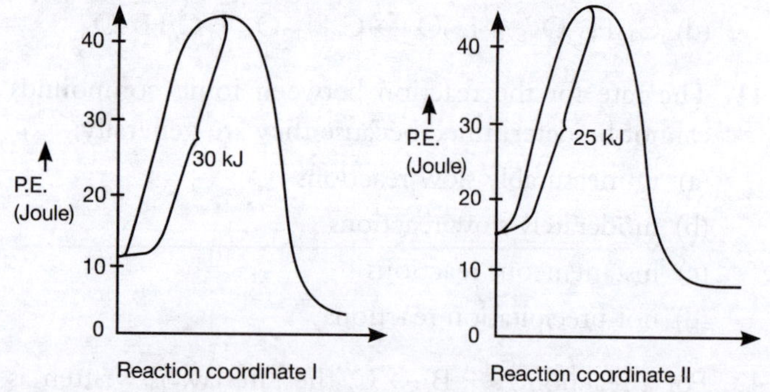

48. Energy profile diagram for a reversible chemical reaction is given. On the basis of the given diagram, explain the effect of temperature on the equilibrium.

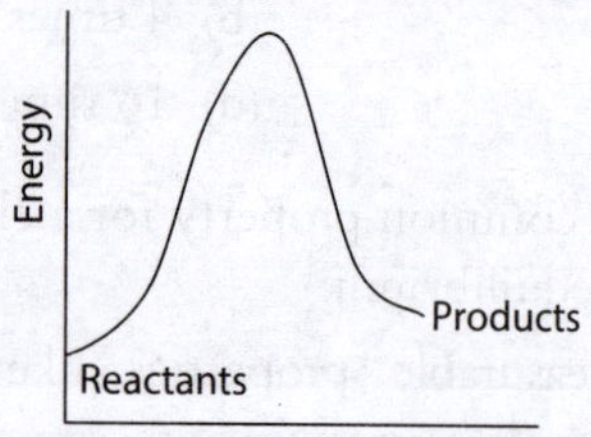

49. For a reversible reaction, the activation energy of a forward reaction is 85 kJ/mol. The net reaction is associated with the release of 15 kJ/mol. What is the activation energy of the backward reaction? Explain it on the basis of the collision theory.

50. On what factors do the equilibrium position and equilibrium constant depend? Explain by giving appropriate reasons.

51. In a gas phase reaction, the decomposition of PCl_5 takes place at 273°C and 1 atmospheric pressure. Its percentage degree of dissociation is 40 per cent. Assuming that all gases in the reaction behave ideally, calculate the density of the equilibrium mixture. [atomic weight of phosphorus = 3 and chlorine = 35.5]

52. Carbon monoxide and water vapor react to give CO_2 and H_2 in a vessel of 2 L capacity at 1090 K. Equilibrium is established and the number of moles of various components is found to be 0.8, 0.6, 0.4 and 1.2 mol, respectively. Calculate K_c value. If the concentration of CO has to be increased to 1.2 mol by increasing the concentration of CO_2 at the equilibrium, find the number of moles of CO_2 to be added to the reaction mixture at the same temperature.

53. For a gas phase reaction $Cl_2 + CHCl_3 \rightarrow HCl + CCl_4$, the rate law is given as $r = k[Cl_2]^{1/2}[CHCl_3]$. Explain how the rate of reaction varies when the concentration of chlorine is doubled. Give units of rate constant.

54. $BrO_3^- + 5Br^- + 6H^+ \rightarrow 3Br_2 + 3H_2O$. The order of reaction with respect to BrO_3^- is 2 and with respect to other reactants is one. Complete the following table.

	BrO_3	Br^-	H^+	Initial rates
I	0.1	0.1	0.1	?
II	0.2	0.1	0.1	1.6×10^{-3}
III		0.2	0.1	3.2×10^{-3}
IV	0.1	0.1	0.2	?

55. A reaction takes place in two steps. The rates of the two elementary steps are given. On the basis of these, predict the rate law and explain the trend of variation in the rates of reaction with changes in concentration. Also the given units of rate constant are

$2A(g) + B_2(g) \rightarrow 2AB(g) \rightarrow$ Overall reaction

in the first step,

$A + B_2 \rightarrow AB + B$, $r = 3.2 \times 10^4$ mol $L^{-1}s^{-1}$.

in the second step

$B + A \rightarrow AB$, $r = 1.9 \times 10^6$ mol $L^{-1}s^{-1}$.

Directions for questions from 56 to 65:
Application-Based Questions

56. A chemist was studying the reaction of type $2A(g) + 2B(g) \rightarrow C(g) + 2D(g)$ experimentally. He found out that the order of the reaction is 2. Complete the following table based on the experimental results given by him.

	[A]	[B]	Rates (mole L^{-1} s^{-1})
(i)	5×10^{-3} M	2.5×10^{-2} M	3.0×10^{-5}
(ii)	15×10^{-3} M	2.5×10^{-2} M	9.0×10^{-5}
(iii)	15×10^{-3} M	______ M	7.5×10^{-6}
(iv)	1.25×10^{-3} M	2.5×10^{-2} M	______

57. Energy profile diagrams for two hypothetical reactions $2A(g) + B(g) \rightarrow 2D(g)$ and $X_2(g) + Y_2(g) \rightarrow 2XY(g)$ are given below. Predict the slow and fast steps for these two reactions. Also identify the factors that favour the formation of reactants from products. Justify.

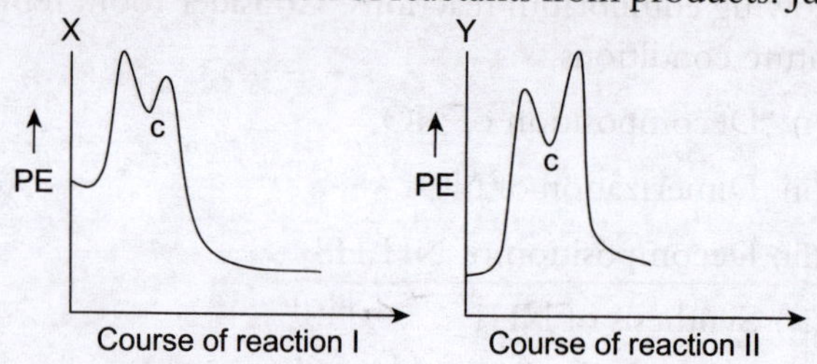

58. From the three energy profile diagrams A, B, and C, find out which of the above irreversible reactions gives maximum yield within a given period of time? Justify. Consider that the initial concentration of the reactants and temperature is same for all the reactions.

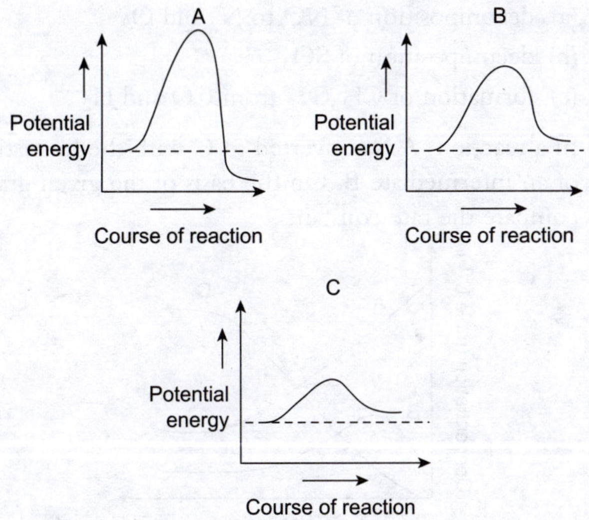

59. Why is the oxidation of SO_2 to SO_3 not rapid in clean and dry air?

60. Change in temperature results in change in equilibrium position. However, the addition of a catalyst results in no change in the equilibrium position. Justify.

61. $Ag_2S + 4NaCN \rightleftharpoons 2Na[Ag(CN)_2] + Na_2S$. Oxidation of sodium sulphide formed is the important step in the extraction of silver from its ore. Justify.

62. An absent-minded professor, Mr Waage, took elements A and B in a reaction vessel at room temperature, to study the reaction $A + 2B \rightleftharpoons 2C + D$. He took the concentration of B as 1.5 times the concentration of A. After the reaction reached equilibrium, he found that the concentrations of A and D were equal. However, he forgot to calculate K_c and removed one of the products from the mixture. Now, can you calculate K_c for the equilibrium attained in his experiment and help him out?

63. When 2.82 g of solid NH_4Cl is introduced into a 2 L flask at 30°C. 40 per cent of the solid NH_4Cl decomposes into two gaseous products, that is, NH_3 and HCl. Calculate the K_c. What would happen if more amount of NH_4Cl is introduced into the flask?

64. 0.5 moles of CO taken in a 2 L flask is maintained at 750 K in the presence of a catalyst so that the following reaction can take place: $CO + 2H_2 \rightleftharpoons CH_3OH$. When hydrogen is introduced, the pressure of the system is increased to 23.629 atm from 15.129 atm at equilibrium and 0.08 moles of gaseous product, methanol is formed. Calculate K_c.

65. A mixture of 0.75 mol of N_2 and 1.20 mol of H_2 is placed in a 3 L container. When the reaction

$$N_2 + 3H_2 \rightleftharpoons 2NH_3$$

reaches the equilibrium, the concentration of H_2 is 0.1M. Calculate the concentration of N_2 and NH_3 when the reaction is carried out with double the number of moles.

Level 3 : Assess Your Concepts

66. Energy profile diagrams for four hypothetical two-step reactions are given in the following diagram. Arrange the criteria of the given reactions in the order of the diagrams.

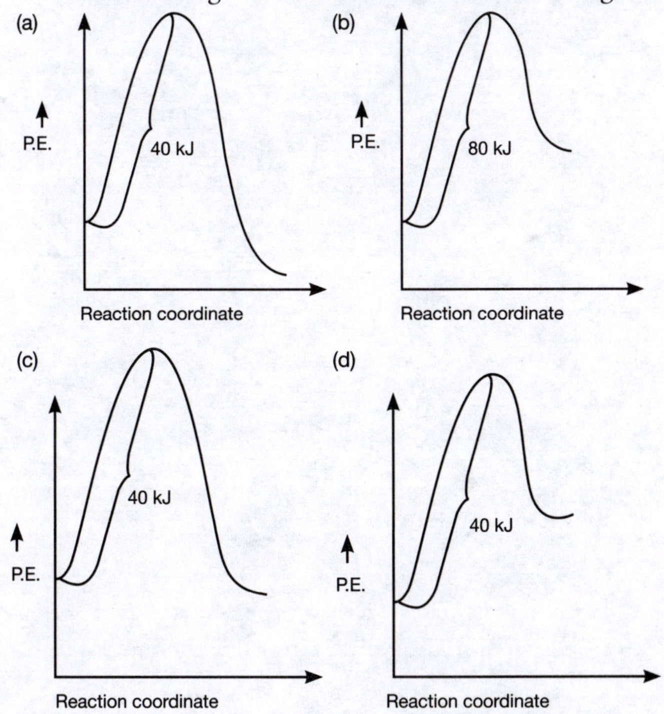

(A) H = –ve, $r_{step\ I} > r_{step\ II}$

(B) H = –ve, $r_{step\ I} < r_{step\ II}$

(C) H = +ve, $r_{step\ I} > r_{step\ II}$

(D) H = +ve, $r_{step\ I} < r_{step\ II}$

67. When the concentration of 'A' is halved, the rate of reaction is decreased by 8 times. Change in concentration of 'B' has no effect on the rate of the reaction. Predict the rate equation that complies with the above-mentioned experimental result.

68. Three moles of PCl_5 is taken in a 3-L vessel and subjected to decomposition in a closed system. If it undergoes 60% dissociation at equilibrium, then calculate K_c value for the reaction.

69. Energy profile diagram for a two-step reaction is given. On the basis of given diagram, predict the slow and fast steps in the reaction. Explain it on the basis of collision theory. Predict the factors that favor the formation of reactants from the products.

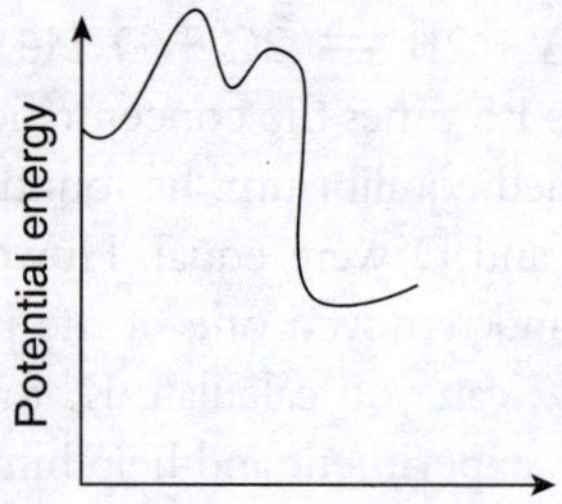

70. Explain the effect of addition of CO and O_2 and solid carbon to the equilibrium mixture separately. Also explain the effect of addition of all the three simultaneously. What happens to the equilibrium when the above changes are carried out in a container having less volume?

71. A 1 L reaction vessel contained 1 mole each of solid NH_4HS, NH_3 and H_2S at a temperature of 150°C. When the decomposition of NH_4HS was carried out, equilibrium is established. K_p value at that temperature is 100. Calculate the equilibrium partial pressures of the gases in the mixture. Also calculate the pressure at which 60 per cent dissociation of NH_4HS takes place at a lower temperature where K_p value is equal to 200 atm^2.

72. Under what conditions, addition of inert gas affects the equilibrium position in case of the following equilibria at constant temperature. Give a reason in support of your answer.

(a) decomposition of NO to N_2 and O_2
(b) decomposition of SO_3
(c) formation of CH_3OH from CO and H_2

73. In a reaction, A is converted to C with the formation of an intermediate B. On the basis of the given graph compare the rate constants.

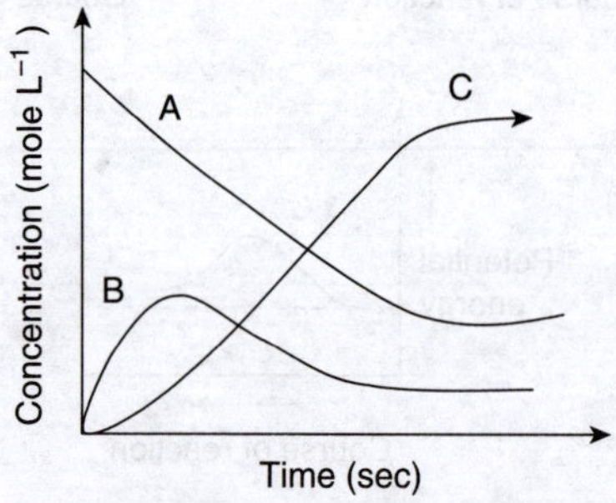

74. Nitric oxide can catalyze ozone formation in troposphere. Justify.

75. Carbon monoxide and water vapor react to give CO_2 and H_2 in a vessel of 2 L capacity at 1090 K. Equilibrium is established and the number of moles of various components is found to be 0.8, 0.6, 0.4 and 1.2, respectively. Calculate K_c value. If the concentration of CO has to be increased to 1.2 mol by increasing the concentration of CO_2 at the equilibrium, find the number of moles of CO_2 to be added to the reaction mixture at the same temperature.

AT

PRACTICE QUESTIONS JEE-NEET SPECIAL WING

Multiple-Answer Type Questions

Directions for questions 1 to 5:

Select one or more correct alternative(s) from the given choices.

1. Observe the given energy profile diagram of a reaction given below. Identify the statements which comply with the reaction.

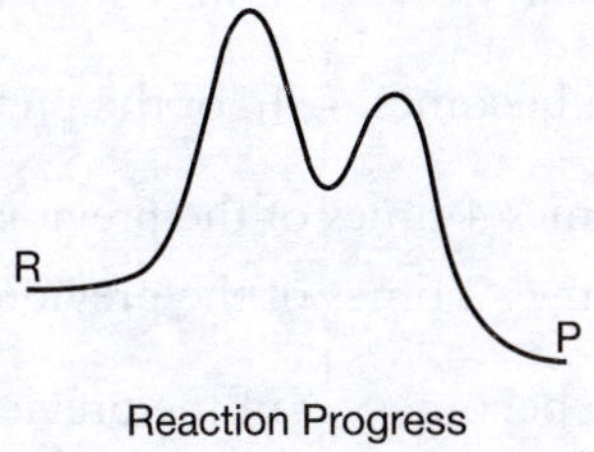

(a) The overall reaction is associated with the net release of heat.

(b) The activation energy of 1st step is greater than the activation energy of 2nd step.

(c) The order of the reaction is indicated by the stoichiometric equation for the reaction.

(d) Decrease in temperature favours the forward reaction there by increasing the yield of the product.

2. The rate equation for a chemical reaction represented by the stoichiometric equation:

$2A + 3B \rightarrow 2C$ is given by $r = k\,[A][B]^2$.

Identify the sets of values which comply with this reaction. The rate of reaction was found to be 6.4×10^{-4} mol L^{-1} s^{-1} when the concentrations of A and B are considered as 0.01 mol/L each at 25°C temperature.

	[A] in mol/L	[B] in mol/L	Rate of reaction
(a)	0.005	0.02	6.4×10^{-4}
(b)	0.02	0.01	1.28×10^{-3}
(c)	0.02	0.04	2×10^{-2}
(d)	0.01	0.005	1.6×10^{-4}

3. The value of rate constant for a particular reaction A + B → Products is 2.8×10^{-3} mol L^{-1} s^{-1}. Which among the following data suits for this reaction?

(a) The graph of concentration Vs time shows a straight line with negative slope which is the rate constant.

(b) The graph of rate of reaction Vs concentration shows a line parallel to concentration axis.

(c) The rate expression for the reaction can be given as $r = k[A][B]$

(d) The rate of reaction is independent of concentrations, temperature, and catalyst.

4. Consider a gas phase reaction of oxidation of nitric oxide to nitrogen dioxide. It is assumed to take place in a single step. Which among the following comply with the above reaction?

(a) The rate of reaction with respect to nitrogen dioxide will be same as that with respect to nitric oxide.

(b) The rate of disappearance of oxygen will be half of the rate of formation of NO_2

(c) The rate of reaction with respect to both the reactants would be same

(d) The reaction is second order with respect to nitric oxide and first order with respect to oxygen.

5. Observe the following graph and answer the question given below.

Which among the following statements regarding the kinetics of the reaction under consideration can be derived from the given graph?

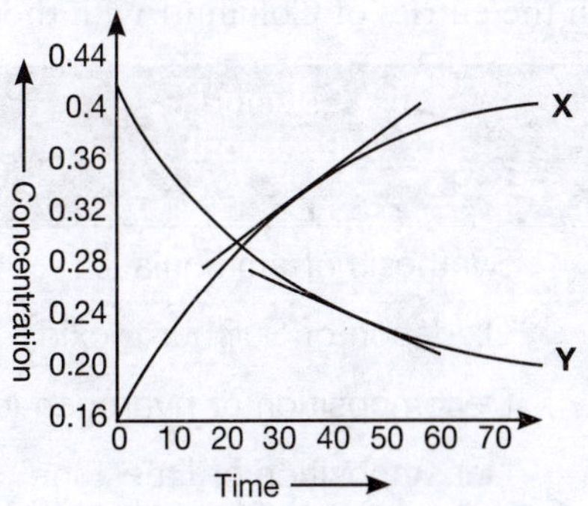

(a) The curve X and Y represent the rate of reaction with respect to reactant and product respectively.

(b) The instantaneous rate of reaction with respect to the product at 40th second as per the above graph comes out to be 4.13×10^{-1} mol L^{-1} s^{-1}

(c) The instantaneous rate of reaction with respect to the reactant at 40th second as per the above graph comes out to be 1.7×10^{-3} mol L^{-1} s^{-1}

(d) The rate of reaction between all the equal time intervals remains the same throughout the reaction.

Comprehension-Based Questions

Directions for questions 6 to 10:

Read the content in the following passage and answer the questions given below.

The synthesis of ammonia is an exothermic reaction. Nitrogen and hydrogen are taken in 1:2 molar ratio in a 1 litre vessel. The reaction is allowed to take place under suitable conditions.

6. Which among the following characteristics complies with this reaction?

(a) Increase in temperature increases the value of K_c

(b) The units of K_c are mole^2 litre^{-2}

(c) The value of K_p will be equal to the value of K_c

(d) Increase in pressure increases the value of K_c

7. Which of the following changes occur if the reaction is carried out in presence of platinum catalyst?

(a) Increase in activation energy.

(b) Decrease in activation energy.

(c) Change in equilibrium position.

(d) Increase in K_c value.

8. The reaction is allowed to take place with 1 mole nitrogen and 2 mole hydrogen as initial number of moles in a closed vessel of 1 litre volume. Assuming 50% dissociation of nitrogen at the equilibrium, find out the K_c value.

(a) 16 (b) 64

(c) 4 (d) 124

9. If the volume of the reaction vessel in the above case is reduced to half, how does the value of K_c change?

(a) K_c value becomes $\frac{1}{4}$th of the previous value

(b) K_c becomes 4 times of the previous value

(c) K_c becomes 2 times of the previous value

(d) K_c value becomes $\frac{1}{2}$ of the previous value

10. If the rate of disappearance of hydrogen is 'X' mol L^{-1} s^{-1}, what would be the rate of formation of ammonia? [Assume only numerical value and ignore the sign]

(a) $\frac{2X}{3}$ (b) $\frac{3X}{2}$

(c) $\frac{3X}{3}$ (d) 3X

Directions for question 11:

Read the content in the following passage and answer the questions given below.

The equilibrium constant with respect to concentration is denoted by K_c and the equilibrium constant with respect to pressure is denoted by K_p. K_c and K_p are related to each other by the expression $K_p = K_c \times (RT)^{\Delta n}$ where Δn is the difference between the number of moles of products and reactants.

11. Match the entries of Column I with those in Column II and Column III.

	Column-I (Reaction)		Column-II (Expression for relation between K_p and K_c)		Column-III (Units of K_c)
(a)	Synthesis of ammonia	(i)	$K_p = K_c \times (RT)^0$	(I)	mol L^{-1}
(b)	Oxidation of Sulphur trioxide	(ii)	$K_p = K_c \times (RT)^2$	(II)	mol^2 L^{-2}
(c)	Decomposition of hydrogen iodide	(iii)	$K_p = K_c \times (RT)^{-1}$	(III)	mol^{-1} L
(d)	Decomposition of limestone	(iv)	$K_p = K_c \times (RT)$	(IV)	mol^{-2} L
(e)	Decomposition of phosphorus pentachloride	(v)	$K_p = K_c \times (RT)^{-2}$	(V)	No units

Directions for questions 12 to 16:

Read the content in the following passage and answer the questions given below.

Any chemical reaction occurs due to the collisions between the reactant molecules which results in the formation of a high energy state such as transition state or activated complex. This is very short lived and gets converted to products. The energy of the activated complex is called threshold energy and the energy required for the reactants to reach this state is known as activation energy. All the collisions do not lead to a chemical reaction. Only those collisions which result in the formation of activated complex with sufficient energy become fruitful and are called effective collisions. Apart from the energy barrier, the effective collisions also should have proper orientation to result in the breakage of old bonds and formation of new bonds.

In case of a reversible reaction, the activation energy of forward and backward reactions might be different depending upon the energy levels of reactants and products. The overall reaction may involve net release or absorption of energy and is said to be exothermic or endothermic respectively. The net amount of energy released or absorbed is represented as ΔH. The value of ΔH is positive for endothermic reaction while it is negative for exothermic reaction.

Based on the following energy profile diagram for the reaction $CO + NO_2 \rightleftarrows CO_2 + NO$ given below, answer the following questions.

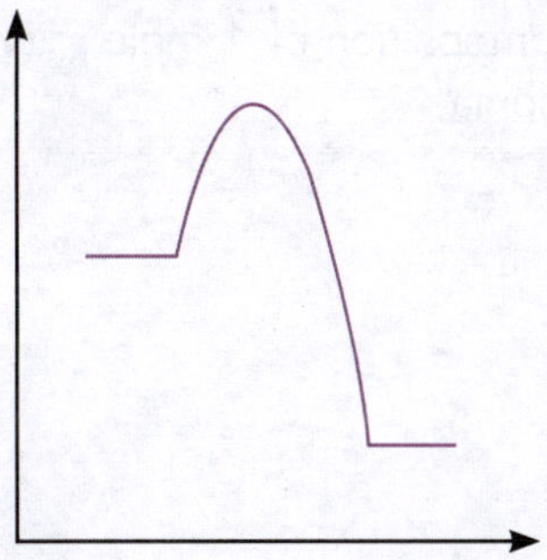

12. The reactants require 134 kJ energy to reach the threshold energy. If the reaction is considered in the reverse direction, the formation of transition state occurs with the absorption of 360 kJ energy. Identify the correct set of values for X, Y and Z for the reaction.

	X	Y	Z
(a)	134 kJ	360 kJ	226 kJ
(b)	360 kJ	134 kJ	–226 kJ
(c)	134 kJ	360 kJ	–226 kJ
(d)	360 kJ	134 kJ	226 kJ

13. Identify the effective collision among the following assuming that all of them have sufficient kinetic energy.

(a) 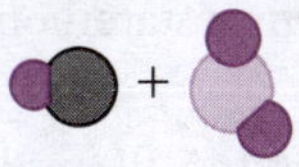

(b) 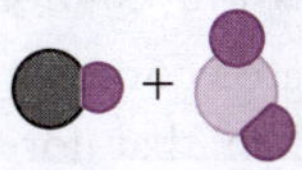

(c) 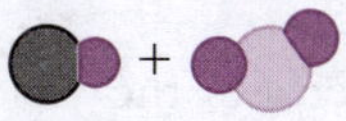

(d) 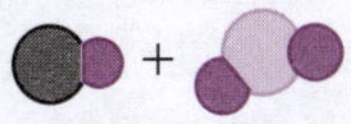

14. For just 10°C rise in temperature, the rate of reaction increases by 10 times. Identify the factor which justifies this.

(a) At higher temperature, the activated complex with lower threshold energy is formed.

(b) The activation energy of backward reaction decreases.

(c) Decrease in ΔH value for the reaction.

(d) Increase in number of effective collisions

15. The following energy profile diagram represents the decomposition of hydrogen peroxide. The continuous curve indicates the uncatalyzed reaction while the dotted curve indicates the reaction after the addition of small quantity of phosphoric acid.

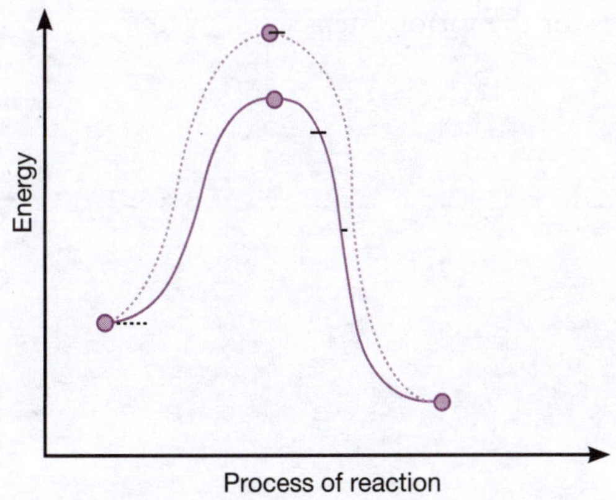

What inference (s) can you draw from the observation of the curve?

(a) The value for ΔH increases on the addition of a catalyst

(b) Phosphoric acid decreases the activation energy of the reaction

(c) The energy barrier is greater for the backward reaction than for forward reaction.

(d) None of these

16. For a certain reaction, the activation energy of forward reaction is 525 kJ/mol and that of backward reaction is 380 kJ/mol. Which of the following statements complies with the given reaction?
(a) ΔH for the reaction is given as 145 kJ/mol
(b) Threshold energy of the activated complex is lower for the backward reaction than that for forward reaction.
(c) Increase in temperature increases the yield of the product in unit time
(d) All of the above

Directions for question 17:

Read the content in the following passage and answer the questions given below.

The value of equilibrium constant depends on the direction of the reaction. If the direction of the reversible reaction is reversed, the reactants become the products and the products become the reactants. The value of equilibrium constant for this reaction would be the reciprocal of the equilibrium constant for the previous reaction. The value of equilibrium constant also changes with the change in the coefficients of the substances in the balanced chemical equation. If the coefficients are multiplied by 'n' times, the K_c value becomes K_c^n. If a reaction takes place in multiple steps, the overall reaction can be obtained by adding the equations for the various steps. The equilibrium constant for the overall reaction can be obtained by multiplying the K_c values for the various steps.

Synthesis of 2 mole ammonia $K_c = 6.25 \times 10^{10}$
Decomposition of 1 mole HI $K_c = 5\times10^{-2}$
Formation of 2 mole CO_2 from CO and O_2 $K_c = 4 \times 10^{92}$
Formation of 2 mole H_2O from the constituent elements $K_c = 25 \times 10^{80}$
Decomposition of 1 mole SO_3 to give SO_2 and oxygen $Kc= 2 \times 10^{-4}$
Formation of NO_2 from 3 mole NO and 1.5 mole O_2 $K_c = 64$

17. Based on the information given in the passage and the data given above, match the entries in column I with those in column II.

	Column-I		Column-II
(a)	$H_2O_{(g)} + CO_{(g)} \rightleftarrows CO_{2(g)} + H_{2(g)}$	(i)	4
(b)	Decomposition of SO_3 to form 2 mole SO_2 and 1 mole O_2	(ii)	4×10^{-6}
(c)	Synthesis of HI from one mole each of hydrogen and iodine	(iii)	4×10^{-8}
(d)	Formation of 1 mole NO_2 from NO and O_2	(iv)	4×10^{5}
(e)	Decomposition of 1 mole ammonia	(v)	400

ANSWER KEYS

Crossword

Across

6. Activated complex
8. Moderate reaction
9. Homogeneous equilibrium
11. Catalyst
12. Order of reaction
14. Reaction quotient
15. Activation energy
16. Rate determining step
17. Internal energy

Down

1. Instantaneous reaction rate
2. Fruitful collisions
3. Photochemical reaction
4. Zero order reaction
5. Common ion effect
7. Reversible reaction
10. Rate of reaction
13. Increases

Classroom Wing

Very Short Answer Type Questions

1. Endothermic; positive
2. Catalyst
3. Instantaneous
4. $[NO]^2$
5. Pressure
6. unity
7. $\frac{1}{\sqrt{48}} = 0.144$
8. energy barrier
9. Dynamic

Competition Wing

Level 1: Apply your Concepts

1. True
2. True
3. False
4. True
5. True
6. True
7. False
8. left
9. rate equation or rate law
10. irreversible
11. Negative catalyst
12. catalyst, increases
13. concentration, pressure
14. threshold
15. homogeneous
16. temperature
17. increase
18. 0.5625
19. 0.5 mol^2/L^2
20. (i) $\rightarrow$ (C); (ii) $\rightarrow$ (E); (iii) $\rightarrow$ (B); (iv) $\rightarrow$ (A); (v) $\rightarrow$ (D)
21. (d)
22. (a)
23. (b)
24. (c)
25. (d)
26. (c)
27. (b)
28. (c)
29. (b)
30. (a)
31. (c)
32. (d)
33. (a)
34. (c)
35. (b)
36. (b)
37. (c)
38. (b)
39. (b)
40. (c)
41. (c)
42. (b)
43. (d)

JEE-NEET Special Wing

Multiple-Answer Type Questions

1. (a; b; d)
2. (b; c; d)
3. (a; b)
4. (a; d)
5. (b; c)

Comprehension-Based Questions

6. (d)
7. (b)
8. (a)
9. (a)
10. (b)
11. (a) ↔ (v) ↔ (IV); (b) ↔ (iii) ↔(III); (c) ↔ (i) ↔ (V); (d) ↔ (ii) ↔ (II); (e) ↔ (iv) ↔ (I)
12. (b)
13. (a)
14. (d)
15. (c)
16. (d)
17. (a) ↔ (iv); (b) ↔ (iii); (c) ↔ (v); (d) ↔ (i) ; (e) ↔ (ii)

Hints and Explanations

Classroom Wing

Very Short Answer Type Questions

1. The formation of nitric oxide from N_2 and O_2 is an endothermic reaction with a positive value for the heat of the reaction.
2. Catalyst
3. Instantaneous
4. $[NO]^2$
5. Pressure
6. unity
7. $\frac{1}{\sqrt{48}} = 0.144$
8. energy barrier
9. Dynamic
10. A change in the concentration of the reactants at equilibrium changes the actual concentration of the reactants and products at equilibrium, which is known as the equilibrium position. However, the equilibrium constant remains unaltered as it is the ratio of the concentration of products to that of the reactants.
11. Usage of a catalyst does not change the concentration of reactants and products at equilibrium. Therefore, both the equilibrium position and equilibrium constant remain unaltered. Catalyst only changes the time taken for attaining the equilibrium

    5×10^{-4} mol L^{-1} sec^{-1}
12. $xA + yB \rightleftharpoons mC + nD$
13. (i) Constancy in pressure

    (ii) Constancy in color
14. $N_2 + 3D_2 \rightarrow 2ND_3$
15. $CaCO_3$ (s) $\rightarrow$ CaO (s) + CO_2 (g)

    $K_c = [CO_2]$
16. Collisions leading to the transformation of reactants to products.
17. The reaction in which reactants are converted into products and vice versa.

    (i) N_2

    (ii) H_2
18. Rate of reaction at unit concentration of reactants
19. $K_c > Q_c$; the reaction proceeds in forward direction
20. No effect on the position of equilibrium.
21. $2NH_3 \rightarrow N_2 + 3H_2$ (System shifts towards the product or the right side)
22. mol/L/s
23. litre $mole^{-1}$

Short Answer Type Questions

24. $rB = \frac{1}{3}rC; rB = \frac{1}{2}rA$

    2A + B $\rightarrow$ 3C should be the stoichiometric equation.

25. $HL \rightleftharpoons \frac{1}{2}H_2 + \frac{1}{2}L_2 \Rightarrow KC\frac{[H_2]^{1/2}[L_2]^{1/2}}{[HL]} = 0.25$

    $H_2 + L_2 \rightleftharpoons 2HL$

    $\therefore K_c^1 = \frac{[HL]^2}{[H_2][L_2]}$

    $\therefore Kc^1 = \left(\frac{1}{K_c}\right)^2 = \left(\frac{1}{0.25}\right)^2 = 16$

26. $N_2 + 3H_2 \rightarrow 2NH_3$

    $r_{H_2} = -3.9 \times 10^{-4}$ mol L^{-1} s^{-1}

    $r_{NH_3} = r_{H_2} \times 2/3 = +3.9 \times 10^{-4} \times 2/3$

    $= 2.6 \times 10^{-4}$ mol L^{-1} s^{-1}

27. Yes.

    Units of rate of reaction $\rightarrow$ mole L^{-1} s^{-1}

    Rate constant for zero order reaction also has same units.

    $r = k[A]^0 [B]^0$

    $k = \frac{r}{[A]^0[B]^0} = \frac{\text{mole } L^{-1}s^1}{\text{mole}^0 L^0} = \text{mole } L^{-1} s^{-1}$

28. Composition of reaction mixture at equilibrium

29. A catalyst increases the rate of reaction by providing an alternative path for the reaction.

30. (i) The observable properties, such as concentration, density, color, pressure, etc., remain constant at constant temperature.

(ii) Equilibrium can be attained from either direction.

(iii) Usage of a catalyst does not alter the position of equilibrium.

(iv) Equilibrium state proceeds indefinitely unless it is disturbed by external factors.

31. Removing the product we can make a reaction irreversible.

32. (i) Balancing the chemical equation

(ii) Rate of forward reaction and rate of backward reaction.

(iii) Equilibrium constant.

33. No change is observed if you add (or change) a catalyst.

34. Refer examples on page no. 5.9

35. If the volume of reactants is decreased, than the reaction will try to yield more of the reactants and the reaction will shift in backwards direction.

If the volume of products is decreased, than the reaction will try to yield more of the products and the reaction will shift in forward direction.

36. (i) It is possible to predict the direction of the equilibrium reaction.

(ii) the extent to which a chemical reaction takes place can be known.

(iii) calculation of the equilibrium concentrations of various substances in the reaction.

37. $K_p = 2$

38. Equation for dissociation;

$PCl_5 \rightarrow PCl_3 + Cl_2$

equilibrium concentrations are;

$PCl = 0.4$ M, $PCl_3 = 0.6$ M, $Cl_2 = 0.6$ M

So equillibrium constant is $= 0.6 \times 0.6/0.4$

$= 0.9$ mol/L

Essay Answer Type Questions

39. No, $r = k[A]^1[B]^2$ can be a probable rate equation for the reaction. The units of $mole^{-2}\ L^2\ s^{-1}$ for the rate constant corresponds to the rate equation $r = k[A]\ [B]^2$

40. $r = k\left[\frac{1}{2}\right]^n$; $n = 3$. The rate equation for the given reaction is $r = k[A]^2\ [B]^1$

$r = k[2]^2 \Rightarrow r = 4k \rightarrow$ Doubling concentration of 'A' alone increases the rate of the reaction by 4 times.

$r = k[2]^1 \Rightarrow r = 2k \rightarrow$ Doubling concentration of 'B' alone increases the rate of the reaction by 2 times.

$r = k[2]^2\ [2]^1 \Rightarrow r = 8k \rightarrow$ Doubling the concentration of both A and B increases the rate of the reaction by 8 times.

41.

	SO_2 +	$O_2 \rightleftharpoons$ 2	SO_2
Initial moles	2	2	
Equ. moles	2 – 0.8	2 – 0.4	0.8
	1.2	1.6	0.8
Equ. conc.	$\frac{1.2}{2} = 0.6$	$\frac{1.6}{2} = 0.8$	$\frac{0.8}{2} = 0.4$

$$K_c = \frac{[SO_3]^2}{[SO_2]^2[O_2]} = \frac{(0.4)^2}{(0.6)^2(0.8)} = 0.55\ mole^{-1}\ L$$

42. (i) $K = [HF]_2/[H_2]\ [F_2]$

(ii) $K = [NH_3][H_2S]\ /[NH_4\ HS]$

(iii) $K = [PCl_3][Cl_2]/[PCl_5]$

43. According to this principle, when a system at equilibrium is subjected to a constraint or change, the position of the equilibrium shifts in a direction that opposes the constraints.

Exothermic and endothermic reactions – effect of temperature. Hence, increasing temperature in the (i) reaction will move the reaction in forward direction whereas, in (ii) decreasing the temperature will move the reaction in backward reaction.

Competition Wing

Level 1: Apply your Concepts

8. Addition of ammonium chloride shifts the equilibrium to the left in an equilibrium for the dissociation of ammonium hydroxide. Ammonium hydroxide is a weak electrolyte. The addition of ammonium chloride, which is a strong electrolyte increases the rate of the back-ward reaction and suppresses the dissociation of ammonium hydroxide. This is due to the common ion effect.

20. (i) → (C); Exothermic → low temperature;
$\Delta n = 0$ → no effect of pressure
(ii) → (E); Endothermic → high temperature;
$\Delta n = -ve$ → high pressure
(iii) → (B); Exothermic → low temperature;
$\Delta n = -ve$ → high pressure
(iv) → (A); Endothermic → high temperature;
$\Delta n = +ve$ → low pressure
(v) → (D); Endothermic → high temperature;
$\Delta n = 0$ → no effect of pressure.
Hence, the answer is (i) → (C); (ii) → (E); (iii) → (B); (iv) → (A); (v) → (D).

21. The stoichiometry of the reaction does not always indicate the order of the reaction. Order is equal to the sum of the powers of the concentration terms in the rate equation written on the basis of experimental results.

Hence, the correct option is (d).

22. The formation of hydrogen chloride is a photochemical combination of hydrogen and chlorine. The rate of this reaction does not depend on the concentration of H_2 or Cl_2. It only depends on the intensity of light used. Hence, it is a zero-order reaction.

Hence, the correct option is (a).

23. Formation of ammonia is an exothermic reaction. The increase in temperature shifts the equilibrium to the left, thereby increasing the concentration of the reactants. Therefore, the K_c value decreases. Increase in temperature increases the number of effective collisions and hence increases the rate of the reaction. However, in this case, the rate of the backward reaction increases more than the rate of the forward reaction. Hence, the Kc value decreases.

Hence, the correct option is (b).

24. Decomposition of PCl_5 is an endothermic reaction. Increase in temperature shifts equilibrium towards the right, thereby increasing the K_c value.

Hence, the correct option is (c).

36. 5 taking equal masses of fine granules of zinc in two test tubes A and B.
4 addition of same concentration of HCl to the two test tubes.
2 heating the test tube B by 10°C
1 measuring the volumes of H_2 gas liberated in the two test tubes.
3 observation of volumes of H_2 liberated in test tubes B and A.

Hence, the correct answer is (b).

37. 4 Draw the tangent on the curve at a particular instant of time 't.'
2 Change in y-axis, that is, $y_2 - y_1$ gives change in concentration of 'B,' whereas change in x-axis, that is, $x_2 - x_1$ gives change in time interval.
1 find the slope of the tangent $\frac{y_2 - y_1}{x_2 - x_1}$.
3 slope of the tangent is equal to instantaneous rate.

Hence, the correct answer is (c).

38. 4 finding out the experimental values of the concentrations of A at regular intervals
1 plotting a graph of concentration of A at various times
2 identification of C_2 and C_1 at different time intervals t_2 and t_1 by reading the graph
3 calculation of $\frac{C_2 - C_1}{t_2 - t_1}$.

Hence, the correct answer is (b).

39. 2 calculation of equilibrium number of moles
1 calculation of equilibrium concentrations of reactants and products
3 writing equilibrium expression for the reaction
4 calculation of K_c value by using the equilibrium concentration

Hence, the correct answer is (b).

40. $NaOH + HCl \rightarrow NaCl + H_2O$ is a neutralization reaction between strong acid and strong base. Hence, it is an example of an instantaneous reaction.

Hence, the correct answer is (c).

41. The rate for the reaction between ionic compounds cannot be determined because they are generally instantaneous reactions.

Hence, the correct answer is (c).

42. Since the reaction is of 2nd order with respect to A, doubling the concentration of 'A' increases the rate of reaction by $2^2 = 4$ times.

Hence, the correct answer is (b).

43. (1) The measurable properties like concentration, density, color, pressure, etc., remain constant at constant temperature.

(2) The forward and backward reactions take place with same rate.

(3) It can be achieved from either direction.

Hence, the correct answer is (d).

Level 2: Review Your Concepts

44. $2A + 3B \rightleftharpoons 2P$

$$K_C = 25 = \frac{[P]^2[B]^2}{[H]^2}$$

$$P \rightleftharpoons A + \frac{3}{2}B$$

$$K_C{}^1 = \frac{[A][B]^{3/2}}{[P]}$$

$$K_C{}^1 = \sqrt{\frac{1}{25}} = 0.2$$

45. (B) $2NO_{(g)} \rightleftharpoons N_{2(g)} + O_{2(g)} \Rightarrow K_C = \frac{[N_2][O_2]}{[NO]^2}$ No units

(D) $2NO_{2(g)} \rightleftharpoons N_2O_{4(g)} \Rightarrow K_C = \frac{[N_2O_4]}{[NO_2]^2}\, mole^{-1}L$

(A) $2NO_2 \rightarrow 2NO + O_2 \Rightarrow K_C = \frac{[NO]^2[O_2]}{[NO]^2}\, mole^{-2}L^{-1}$

(E) $N_{2(g)} + 3H_{2(g)} \rightleftharpoons 2NH_3 \Rightarrow K_C = \frac{[NH_3]^2}{[N_2][H_2]^3}\, mole^{-2}L^2$

(C) $NH_4HS_{(s)} \rightleftharpoons NH_3 + H_2S \Rightarrow K_C = \frac{[NH_3[H_2S]]}{[NH_4HS]}\, mole^2L^{-2}$

Hence, the correct order is BDAEC.

46. (D) *Ea* (step I) > *Ea* (step II) $r_{\text{step II}} < r_{\text{step I}}$ step I → rate determining step

Ea (forward) < *Ea* (backward) → Exothermic (ΔH = -ve)

(B) Step II → rate determining step → *Ea(f)* < *Ea (b)* Endothermic reaction (ΔH = +ve)

(C) *Ea* (Step II) > *Ea* (Step I) Step II → rate determining step

Ea(f) > *Ea(b)*→ Endothermic (ΔH = +ve)

(A) *Ea* (Step II) > *Ea* (Step I) Step II → Rate determining step

Ea (b) > *Ea(f)* → Exothermic (ΔH = -ve).

Hence, the correct order is DBCA.

47. The difference between condition I and II is that in condition II, the activation energy of the reaction is decreased. However, the figure corresponding to condition II shows that the threshold energy remains the same and aver- age energy of reactant molecules is increased. That means, Condition II represents the reaction carried out at a higher temperature.

48. Increase in temperature makes the reaction proceed in that direction in which more heat is absorbed.

49. (i) relation between activation energy and effective collisions

(ii) calculation of E_a of backward reaction

(iii) comparing E_a of backward and forward reactions and its effect on effective collisions

50. Refer text for detailed answer.

51. (i) determination of total number of moles (reactants–products) at equilibrium

(ii) 3.08 g/L

(iii) calculation of the number of moles of the reactants and products present in the equilibrium mixture

(iv) calculation of weight of mixture

(v) calculation of volume of the mixture at STP

(vi) calculation of volume of equilibrium mixture at the given temperature and pressure

(vii) calculation of density

52. (i) expression for equilibrium constant

(ii) 1.5.

(iii) balanced chemical reaction

(iv) calculation of equilibrium constant

(v) calculation of composition of equilibrium mixture with change in concentration of CO.

53. (ii) equation for rate constant

(iii) equation for rate constant with double the concentration of Cl_2

(iv) comparison of both the equations

(v) unit = 1/sec

54. (ii) calculation of initial rate of reaction in experiment I on the change of concentration of BrO^{-3} in experiment II and the order of reaction with respect to BrO_3^-

(iii) calculation of concentration of BrO^{3-} in experiment III based on the change of initial rate in experiment III, change of concentration of other reactants and the order of reaction with respect to Br^- and H^+

(iv) calculation of initial rate in experiment IV on the basis of change of concentration of all the reaction

55. (i) rate-determining step of a reaction

(ii) determination of rate law on the basis of stoichiometry of the rate-determining step

(iii) determination of change in rate of reaction with the change of concentration of the reactions from rate law

(iv) determination of the unit of rate constant from rate law

56. Let us first find out order with respect A and B. We know r = k [A]x [B]y, x and y are orders with respect to A and B, respectively.

(i) $\frac{r_1}{r_2} = \left[\frac{[A_1]}{[A_2]}\right]^x \Rightarrow \frac{3.0\times10^{-5}}{9.0\times10^{-5}}$

$$= \left(\frac{(5\times10^{-3})}{(15\times10^{-3})}\right)^x$$

$$3 = (3)^x$$

$$x = 1$$

∴ Order with respect to A is 1

∴ Order with respect to B = 2 – 1 = 1

(ii) $r_1 = k\,[A]\,[B]$

$3 \times 10^{-5} = k \cdot (5 \times 10^{-3}) \times (2.5 \times 10^{-2})$

$$k = \frac{3\times10^{-5}}{12.5\times10^{-5}} = 0.24\ \text{mol}^{-1}\ \text{L}\ \text{s}^{-1}$$

(iii) $r = k\,[A_3] \cdot [B_3]$

$7.5 \times 10^{-6} = 0.24 \times 15 \times 10^{-3} \times [B_3]$

$$[B_3] = \frac{7.5\times10^{-6}}{0.24\times15\times10^{-3}}$$

$$= 2.08\times10^{-3}\ \text{mol L}^{-1}\ \text{s}$$

(iv) From ii and iv, $\frac{[A_2]}{[A_4]} = \frac{r_2}{r_4}$

$$\Rightarrow \frac{15\times10^{-3}}{1.25\times10^{-3}} = \frac{9.0\times10^{-5}}{r_4}$$

$$\Rightarrow r_4 = 7.5\times10^{-6}\ \text{mol L}^{-1}\ \text{s}^{-1}$$

[A]	[B] (mol L⁻¹ s⁻¹)	Rate
(i) 5×10^{-3} M	2.5×10^{-2} M	3.0×10^{-5}
(ii) 15×10^{-3} M	2.5×10^{-2} M	9.0×10^{-5}
(iii) 15×10^{-3} M	2.08×10^{-3} M	7.5×10^{-6}
(iv) 1.25×10^{-3} M	2.5×10^{-2} M	7.5×10^{-6}

57. Reaction I is exothermic reaction. The first step from A to C (intermediate) is associated with higher activation energy and hence is slow. Therefore, it is the rate-determining step. Formation of reactants from products is a backward reaction that is endothermic and is associated with increase in volume. Therefore, high temperature and low pressure are the favourable conditions.

Reaction II is an endothermic reaction. The backward reaction being exothermic is favoured by low temperature. Since the reaction takes place with no change in volume, there is no effect of pressure on the equilibrium.

58. From the graphs of A, B, and C, we can compare the activation energy and the energy of respective products. The product formed in graph A has the least energy and is most stable while the activation energy of the reaction in graph C is the least. The yield of the product is more for that reaction that involves least activation energy as most of the reacting molecules undergo effective collisions and hence form a product. Thus it can be concluded that the yield of product in graph C is maximum.

59. The conversion or oxidation of SO_2 to SO_3 takes place in the presence of a catalyst. Water droplets associated with dust particles act as the catalyst for this reaction. The dust particles can adsorb the SO_2 on their surface where it can be oxidized to SO_3. Hence, oxidation of SO_2 to SO_3 is not rapid in clean and dry air.

60. When the temperature is changed, the rate of forward reaction and backward reaction varies differently. If the forward reaction is exothermic, increase in temperature decreases the rate of forward reaction thereby decreasing the concentration of products. If the forward reaction is endothermic, an increase in temperature favors forward reaction and increases the concentration of products. Therefore, the composition of reaction mixture at equilibrium changes. When a catalyst is added, the rate of forward reaction increases due to decrease in activation energy of the forward reaction. Since the reaction takes an alternative path, the activation energy of backward reaction also is reduced. Activated complex is formed at a lower energy state in a catalyzed reaction. As both the rate of forward reaction and that of the backward reaction change to the same extent, the composition of equilibrium mixture remains constant. Therefore, the equilibrium position remains same for both catalyzed and uncatalysed reactions.

61. In the extraction of silver from its ore, one of the important steps is the formation of sodium argentocyanide and sodium sulphide that is a reversible reaction. To prevent the reversibility of the reaction sodium sulphide should be subjected to oxidation. Because according to Le Chatelier's principle, with the removal of one of the products, the reaction shifts in the forward direction.

62.

	A	2B	⇌ 2C	+ D
Initial concentration	a	1.5a	0	0
Equilibrium concentration	a − x	1.5a − 2x	2x	x

At equilibrium, the concentration of A and that of D are equal

$\therefore$ a − x = x ⇒ a = 2x or x = a/2

$$K_c = \frac{(2x)^2 x}{(a-x)(15a-2x)^2} \text{ as } a = 2x,$$

$$\Rightarrow \frac{4x^2 \cdot x}{x \times (x)^2} \Rightarrow K_c = 4.$$

63. $NH_4Cl(s) \rightleftharpoons NH_3(g) + HCl(g)$

2.82 g of NH_4Cl is subjected to decomposition.

Molecular weight of NH_4Cl = 14 + 4 + 35.5 = 53.5

$$\Rightarrow \text{No. of moles of } NH_4Cl = \frac{2.82}{53.5} = 0.0527$$

Given that per cent dissociation of NH_4Cl is 40 per cent 0.0527 moles decomposition corresponds to 100 per cent

? moles decomposition corresponds to 40 per cent

$$= \frac{40 \times 0.0527}{100} = 0.0210$$

	NH_4Cl ⇌	NH_3	HCl
Initial number of moles	0.0527	0	0
Number of moles at equilibrium	0.0527 − 0.0210 = 0.0317	0.0210	0.0210

$$\therefore K_c = [NH_3][HCl] = \frac{0.0210}{2} \times \frac{0.0210}{2}$$

$$= \frac{0.0210 \times 0.0210}{4} = 1.1 \times 10^{-4}\ \text{mol}^2/\text{L}^2$$

Addition of a solid or liquid reactant at equilibrium does not affect the equilibrium. So addition of solid NH4Cl does not affect the equilibrium.

64.

	CO +	$2H_2$ ⇌	CH_3OH
Initial moles	0.5	a	0
At equilibrium	0.5 − x	a − 2x	x

Given that x = 0.08

Moles of CO = 0.5 − 0.08 = 0.42

Moles of H_2 = a − 0.16

Moles of CH_3OH = 0.08

No. of moles of H_2 can be calculated by using PV = nRT

Pressure of hydrogen = 23.629 – 15.129 = 8.5 atm

$$n = \frac{PV}{RT} = \frac{8.5 \times 2}{0.082 \times 750} = 0.276\,(a)$$

$\therefore$ Number of moles of H_2 at equilibrium = 0.276 − 0.16 = 0.116

$$K_c = \frac{0.08/2}{\left(\frac{0.116}{2}\right)^2 \times \frac{0.42}{2}} = 56.66\ L^2\ mol^{-2}$$

65. $N_2 + 3H_2 \rightleftharpoons 2NH_3$

Concentration of N_2 = 0.75/3 = 0.25 mol L^{-1}

Concentration of H_2 = 1.20/3 = 0.4 mol L^{-1}

	N_2 +	$3H_2$ ⇌	$2NH_3$
Initial concentration	0.25	0.4	0
At equilibrium	0.25 − x	0.4 − 3x	2x

Concentration of H_2 at equilibrium is given as = 0.1

$\therefore$ 0.4 − 3x = 0.1 ⇒ x = 0.1

Concentration of N_2 at equilibrium = 0.25 − 0.1 = 0.15

Concentration of NH_3 at equilibrium = 0.1 × 2 = 0.2

When the reaction is carried with double the number of moles,

concentration of N_2 = 0.15 × 2 = 0.3 mol L^{-1} and

concentration of NH_3 = 0.2 × 2 = 0.4 mol L^{-1}.

Level 3: Assess Your Concepts

66. (D) ΔH = +ve; E_a (step I) > E_b (step II) $r_{step\ I} < r_{step\ II}$ (Endothermic).

(A) ΔH = −ve; E_a (step I) < E_a (step II) $r_{step\ II} < r_{step\ II}$ (Exothermic)

(B) ΔH = +ve; E_a (step I) > E_a (step II) $r_{step\ II} < r_{step\ I}$ (Endothermic)

(C) ΔH = −ve; E_a (step II) > E_a (step I) $r_{step\ I} < r_{step\ II}$ (Exothermic)

Hence, the correct order is DABC.

67. As rate of reaction is not dependent on the concentration of 'B', the reaction is zero order with respect to B.

Rate equation corresponding to the abovementioned results is $r: k[A]^3\ [B]^0$.

68.

	$PCl_5 \rightarrow$	$PCl_3 +$	Cl_2
Initial moles	3	0	0
Equ. moles	3 − 1.8	1.8	1.8
	1.2	1.8	1.8
Equ. conc.	$\frac{1.2}{3} = 0.4$	$\frac{1.8}{3} = 0.6$	$\frac{1.8}{3} = 0.6$

$$K_C = \frac{[PC_3][Cl_2]}{[PCl_5]} = \frac{0.6 \times 0.6}{0.4} = 0.9\ mole\ L^{-1}$$

69. (i) prediction of slow and fast steps on the basis of activation energies of the two steps

(ii) prediction of slow and fast steps on the basis of activation energies of the two steps

(iii) prediction of nature of reaction with respect to energy changes

(iv) prediction of energy changes in the net reaction

70. (i) According to Le Chatelier's principle addition of CO and O_2 to the overall reaction, the reaction will increase the rate forward reaction.

(ii) Adding Solid carbon will have no change on the reaction as adding solid do not change the concentration of the reactants.

71. $NH_4HS(s) \rightleftharpoons NH_3(g) + H_2S(g)$

$1 - x \qquad 1 + x \qquad 1 + x$

$$K_p = p_{NH_3} \times p_{H_2S}$$

Total no. of moles at equilibrium = (1 + x) + (1 + x) = 2x + 2

Partial pressure = Mole fraction × P

$$\text{Mole fraction of } NH_3 = \frac{1+x}{2x+2}$$

$$\therefore \text{Partial pressure of } NH_3 = \frac{1+x}{2x+2} \times P$$

$$\text{Mole fraction of } H_2S = \frac{1+x}{2x+2}$$

$$\therefore \text{Partial pressure of } H_2S = \frac{1+x}{2x+2} \times P$$

$$K_p = \left(\frac{1+x}{2x+2} \times P\right)\left(\frac{1+x}{2x+2} \times P\right)$$

$$K_p = \frac{(1+x)^2}{(2x+2)^2} = 100$$

$$\frac{(1+x)^2 P^2}{4(x+1)^2} = 100$$

$$\frac{(1+x)^2 P^2}{4(1+x)^2} = 100 \Rightarrow P^2 = 100 \times 4$$

$$P = \sqrt{400} = 20\ \text{atm}$$

$$p_{H_2S} = \frac{(1+x)20}{2(x+1)} = 10\ \text{atm}$$

$$p_{NH_3} = 10\ \text{atm}$$

60 per cent dissociation of NH_3 and H_2S corresponds to moles each of NH_3 and H_2S.

$$K_p = p_{NH_3} \times p_{H_2S}$$

$$p_{NH_3} = \frac{1.6}{3.2} \times P, p_{H_2S} = \frac{1.6}{3.2} \times P$$

$$K_p = \frac{(1.6)^2 \times P^2}{(3.2)^2} = 200$$

$$P^2 = \frac{200 \times (3.2)^2}{(1.6)^2} = 400$$

$$P = \sqrt{400} = 20\ \text{atm}$$

72. (a) $2NO \rightleftharpoons N_2 + O_2$

The above equilibrium is associated with no change in volume. Therefore addition of inert gas has no effect on the equilibrium under any conditions.

(b) $2SO_3 \rightleftharpoons 2SO_2 + O_2$

The above equilibrium is associated with increase in volume. Addition of an inert gas has no effect at constant volume. At constant pressure, addition of inert gas favours the forward reaction since increase in volume takes place.

(c) $CO(g) + 2H_2(g) \rightleftharpoons CH_3OH(g)$

The above equilibrium is associated with decrease in volume. Addition of the inert gas has no effect at constant volume. At constant pressure, addition of the inert gas favors backward reaction since increase in volume takes place.

73. From the given graph we can know that

$$A \xrightarrow{K_1} B \text{ (intermediate)}$$

$$B \xrightarrow{K_2} C$$

That is, A is converted to C with an intermediate B.

The concentration of B first increases with time and then starts decreasing showing that after time t it acts as a reactant. The concentration of C on the other hand increases continuously with time.

So, the rate constant $k_1 \neq k_2$.

The first step is the slow step or the rate-determining step while the second step is the fast step.

Hence, $k_1 < k_2$.

74. Nitric oxide (NO) in the troposphere reacts with the oxygen forming nitrogen dioxide:

$$2NO + O_2 \rightarrow 2NO_2$$

Nitrogen dioxide, in the presence of light, decomposes to NO and nascent oxygen:

$$NO_2 \xrightarrow{\text{light}} NO + [O]$$

The nascent oxygen produced is highly reactive and oxidizes oxygen to ozone:

$$O_2 + [O] \rightarrow O_3$$

75. $$CO + H_2O \rightleftharpoons CO_2 + H_2$$

$$0.8 \quad 0.6 \qquad 0.4 \quad 1.2$$

$$K_c = \frac{0.4 \times 1.2}{0.8 \times 0.6} = 1$$

but 'a' moles of CO_2 is added at equilibrium. The new number of moles of CO is 1.2 showing an increase by 0.4 mol.

After the addition of 'a' moles of CO_2, balanced reaction takes place:

$$CO + H_2O \rightleftharpoons CO_2 + H_2$$

$$(0.8+0.4)(0.6+0.4) \qquad (0.4+a-0.4)\ (1.2-0.4)$$

$$1.2 \qquad 1.0 \qquad a \qquad 0.8$$

$$K_c = \frac{(0.6+0.4)(0.8+0.4)}{(0.4+a-0.4)(1.2-0.4)} = \frac{1 \times 1.2}{a \times 0.8} = 1$$

$$\Rightarrow a = \frac{1.2}{0.8} = 1.5$$

JEE-NEET Special wing

Multiple-Answer Type Questions

1. Since the products are at a lower energy state than the reactants, the overall reaction is exothermic. It is associated with the release of heat. The activation energy of 1st step is greater than the activation energy of 2nd step. The order of the reaction cannot be determined by the stoichiometric expression of the reaction as the reaction takes place in multiple steps. Since the reaction is exothermic, it is favoured by lowering the temperature.

2. The change in rate of reaction with the change in concentration of the reactants depends on the order of the reaction with respect to the respective reactants. Since the reaction is 1st order with respect to the reactant 'A', increase in concentration by '*n*' times increases the rate of reaction by '*n*' times. The reaction being 2nd order wrt 'B', increase in concentration of B by 'n' times increases the rate of reaction by '2*n*' times. The correct choices are given in the table below.

	[A] in mol/L	[B] in mol/L	Rate of reaction
(b)	0.02	0.01	1.28×10^{-3}
(c)	0.02	0.04	2×10^{-2}
(d)	0.01	0.005	1.6×10^{-4}

3. The units of rate constant are same as the units of rate of reaction. This is possible only in case of zero order reactions. For a zero-order reaction, the graph of rate of reaction Vs concentration shows a line parallel to concentration axis. The graph of concentration Vs time shows a straight line with negative slope which is the rate constant.

4. The stoichiometric equation for the reaction is:
$2NO + O_2 \rightarrow 2NO_2$
The rate of reaction with respect to nitrogen dioxide will be same as that with respect to nitric oxide. The reaction is second order with respect to nitric oxide and first order with respect to oxygen. For a single step reaction, the rate equation follows the stoichiometry of the reaction.

$$r = \frac{-1}{2}\frac{d[NO]}{dt} = \frac{-d[O_2]}{dt} = \frac{+1}{2}\frac{d[NO_2]}{dt}$$

$r = k[NO]^2[O_2]$

5. The curve X represents the graph of rate of reaction with respect to the product while the curve Y represents the graph of rate of reaction with respect to the product the reactant. The instantaneous rate of reaction with respect to the product at 40th second as per the above graph comes out to be 4.13×10^{-1}mole L^{-1} s^{-1} The instantaneous rate of reaction with respect to the reactant at 40th second as per the above graph comes out to be 1.7×10^{-3}mole L^{-1} s^{-1} The rate of reaction changes continuously and hence it will not be same between all the equal time intervals.

Comprehension-Based Questions

6. The reaction being exothermic, increase in temperature favours the backward reaction and hence decreases the K_c value. The units of K_c are $mol^{-2}\,L^2$. Increase in pressure favours the forward reaction as the reaction is associated with the decrease in number of moles or volume. Therefore, increase in pressure increases the value of K_c.

7. Platinum acts as a positive catalyst for the reaction of synthesis of ammonia. The catalyst alters the rate of reaction by making the reaction proceed in an alternative pathway. The positive catalyst increases the rate of reaction as it allows the reaction to proceed in a path with lower activation energy.

8. The stoichiometric reaction is

	$N_2(g)$ +	$3H_2(g)$ ⇄	$2NH_3(g)$	
Initial	1 mol	2 mol	0 mol	
Equilibrium	$1-x$	$2-3x$	$2x$	$(x=0.5)$

$$K_c = \frac{(2\times0.5)^2}{(1-0.5)(2-1.5)^3} = \frac{1}{(0.5)^4} = 16$$

9. K_c value becomes 1/4th of the previous value.

$K_c = (2\times0.5/0.5)^2/[(1\text{-}0.5)/0.5]\,(2\text{-}1.5/0.5)^3] = 4$

10. The relation between rate of reaction with respect to different substances in the reaction can be given as follows:

$$r_{N_2} = \frac{-1}{2}\frac{d[N_2]}{dt} \qquad r_{H_2} = \frac{-1}{3}\frac{d[H_2]}{dt}$$

$$r_{NH_3} = \frac{1}{2}\frac{d[NH3]}{dt}$$

$$r_{NH_3} = \left(\frac{3}{2}\right) r_{H_2} = \frac{3x}{2}$$

11.

	Column-I (Reaction)		Column-II (Expression for relation between K_p and K_c)		Column-III (Units of K_c)
(a)	Synthesis of ammonia	(v)	$K_p = K_c \times (RT)^{-2}$	(IV)	$mol^{-2}L^2$
(b)	Oxidation of Sulphur trioxide	(iii)	$K_p = K_c \times (RT)^{-1}$	(III)	$mol^{-1}L$
(c)	Decomposition of hydrogen iodide	(i)	$K_p = K_c \times (RT)^0$	(V)	No units
(d)	Decomposition of limestone	(ii)	$K_p = K_c \times (RT)^2$	(II)	$mol^2 L^{-2}$
(e)	Decomposition of phosphorus pentachloride	(iv)	$K_p = K_c \times (RT)$	(I)	$mol\ L^{-1}$

12.

X	Y	Z
360 KJ	134 KJ	-226 KJ

13. The orientation of the collision should be such that the atoms undergoing the bond breakage should face each other.

14. With the increase in temperature, the average kinetic energy of the molecules increases and hence activation energy decreases. As a result, the number of effective collisions increases leading to drastic increase in the rate of reaction.

15. Since the reaction is exothermic, the energy barrier (activation energy) is greater for the backward reaction than for the forward reaction.

16. All the statements are correct since the reaction is endothermic.

17.

	Column-I		Column-II
(a)	$H_2O_{(g)} + CO_{(g)} \rightleftarrows CO_{2(g)} + H_{2(g)}$	(iv)	4×10^5
(b)	Decomposition of SO_3 to form 2 mole SO_2 and 1 mole O_2	(iii)	4×10^{-8}
(c)	Synthesis of HI from one mole each of hydrogen and iodine	(v)	400
(d)	Formation of 1 mole NO_2 from NO and O_2	(i)	4
(e)	Decomposition of 1 mole ammonia	(ii)	4×10^{-6}

Unit II

Inorganic Chemistry

In this Unit

CHAPTER

6

Periodic Classification of Elements

Remember

Before beginning this chapter, you should be able to:

- review the basic concepts of physical and chemical properties of matter.
- understand classification of matter.

Key Ideas

After completing this chapter, you should be able to:

- describe earlier versions of classification of elements, like, Newland's law of octaves and Dobereiner's Triads with emphasis on Mendeleev's periodic table.
- understand the placement of elements on modern periodic table—its merits and defects.
- explain about the similarities and gradual changes in the properties, such as, atomic size, ionization energy, electron affinity, electropositivity, oxidizing, reducing property, etc.

Scientific Crypt

A Tribute to Dmitri Ivanovich Mendeleev (1834–1906)

The need for systematic classification of elements was realized long back and many scientists like Antoine Lavoisier, Dobereiner and Newland made considerable contributions in the field of classification of elements. Dmitri Mendeleev is considered as the creator of the first version of the Periodic Table.

Dmitri Ivanovich Mendeleev was born on February 8, 1834, in Tobolsk, Russia. At the age of 13, his father passed away. Even in extreme poverty, his mother did not give up her dreams for her son. In 1863 he became a professor of Chemistry at St. Petersburg State University.

In the late 1860's Mendeleeff started working on the classification of the elements. His work is considered to be great as he arranged then-known 63 elements in the increasing order of their atomic weights and grouped them based on their similarities in properties. He left a few positions blank in the periodic table in order to maintain the similarities in properties. His systematic classification of elements was carried forward by the scientist, Moseley who constructed the periodic table for the arrangements of elements on the basis of atomic number.

Dmitri Mendeleef, the educator and the scientist suffered from influenza and then passed away at the age of 72 in St. Petersburg. His death was a great loss to the scientific world. The radioactive element, Mendelevium (atomic number 101) in the periodic table is named after him.

FUN TIME

CROSSWORD

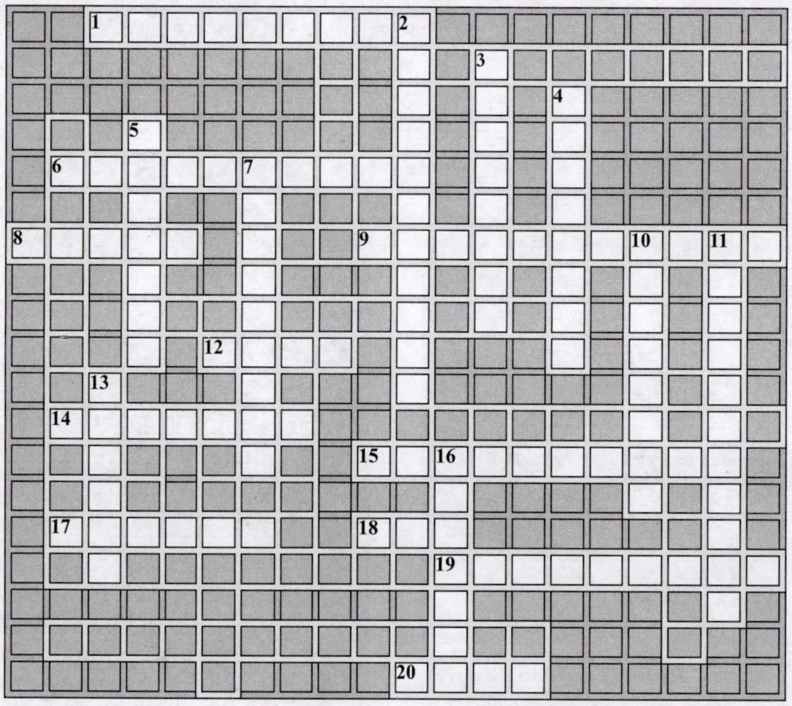

Across

1. On moving down the group ionisation energy ______.
6. ______elements are present from III B group to II B group in the periodic table.
8. Very short period in the periodic table is the ______ period.
9. Regular gradation in the property of elements and their repetition at regular intervals is called ______.
12. Elements belonging to same group possess______ number of valence electrons.
14. Modern periodic law was proposed by______.
15. Law of triads was proposed by______.
17. Noble gas having a duplet configuration
18. Valency of elements present in II A (2) group is ______.
19. Arsenic is a ______.
20. Electron affinity of noble gases is ______.

Down

2. Chlorine is present in this group.
3. Most electronegative elements in the periodic table
4. Modern name for eka boron
5. This metal is present in the sixth period and is used in making solar cells.
7. On moving down the group atomic size generally ______.
10. The element which has the highest electron affinity
11. Elements after uranium are called ______ elements.
13. The name of the element with atomic number 29 is______.
16. The liquid non-metal at room temperature

INTRODUCTION

Since antiquity, elements such as gold, silver, tin, copper, lead, and mercury have been known. The first scientific discovery of element was done by Hennig Brand in 1649 and he discovered phosphorus.. The discovery of elements then continued and the scientists started recognizing the similarities and dissimilarities among the elements in order to make the study of the elements easy and systematic.

A series of efforts for the classification of elements depending on the pattern of their properties eventually led to the construction of the periodic table, presently comprising of 118 elements. The periodic table is a tabular arrangement of elements, which depicts the trend of their physical behaviour and chemical properties.

Why Do We Need to Classify Elements?

Our universe is full of different materials, and these are made up of unique elements. As we learned more about the world around us, we found many different elements. But with so many elements, it became a bit confusing. So, to make things easier, scientists decided to group or classify these elements by what they had in common. This helped them see patterns and guess how certain elements might behave. In simple words, by grouping elements, scientists could better understand and study the huge variety of elements in our universe.

Döbereiner's Triads

The German Chemist, Johann Dobereiner made the first significant effort in the development of the periodic table. In the year 1817, Johann Wolfgang Döbereiner, a German chemist, tried to arrange the elements with similar properties into groups. He identified some groups having three elements each. So he called these groups **'triads'**. Döbereiner showed that when the three elements in a triad were written in the order of increasing atomic masses, the atomic mass of the middle element was roughly the average of the atomic masses of the other two elements. he noticed that a group of three elements (like, Ca, Sr, and Ba) showed similar chemical properties and there was a regular trend in their physical properties when these elements are arranged in an increasing order of atomic weight. The atomic weight of strontium is approximately equal to the average of the atomic weights of calcium and barium.

Element	At. Wt.	Property
Lithium (Li)	6.94	Alkali metal, reacts with water
Sodium (Na)	22.99	Alkali metal, reacts vigorously with water
Potassium (K)	39.10	Alkali metal, reacts explosively with water

In the above triad:

- Sodium's atomic weight is roughly the average of the atomic weights of Lithium and Potassium.
- All three elements are alkali metals and react with water, but the intensity increases from Lithium to Potassium.

Later on, in 1829, he discovered the halogen triad and alkali metal triad consisting of Cl, Br, and I and Li, Na, and K and proposed that a triads of elements with similar chemical properties and the atomic weight of the second element of the triad is the average of the other two.

Döbereiner's Triads: Merits and Demerits

Merits

Foundational: Laid the groundwork for future element classification.

Simple Approach: Grouped elements easily in sets of three based on weight.

Predicted Trends: Successfully grouped several elements with similar properties.

Highlighted Periodicity: Pointed to recurring patterns among elements.

Demerits

Not All-Inclusive: Worked for only a few known elements.

Exceptions Existed: Weight patterns sometimes didn't align with property similarities.

Lacked Flexibility: Couldn't accommodate growing list of elements.

Over-reliance on Weight: Ignored other critical elemental attributes.

Despite its limitations, Döbereiner's idea of triads was a stepping stone toward the development of more comprehensive and accurate classification systems, like the Periodic Table. It showed that there were patterns in elemental properties waiting to be discovered and understood.

Newland's Arrangement of Elements in Octaves

In 1864, the English Chemist, John Newland arranged the then known 56 elements in an increasing order of their atomic weights. He noticed that atomic weights of many pairs of elements which differed by eight or a multiple of eight exhibited similarities in their chemical properties. Based on this observation, he proposed the **law of octaves**.

The law states that the eighth element starting from a given one is a kind of repetition of the first like the eighth note of an octave of music. Newland's system of classification failed to explain similarities in higher elements.

Table 6.1 Newland's arrangement of elements

H	F	Cl	Co/Ni	Br	Pd	I	Pt/Ir
Li	Na	K	Cu	Rb	Ag	Cs	Tl
Be	Mg	Ca	Zn	Sr	Cd	Ba/V	Pb
B	Al	Cr	Y	Ce/La	U	Ta	Th
C	Si	Ti	In	Zr	Sn	W	Hg
N	P	Mn	As	Di/Mo	Sb	Nb	Bi
O	S	Fe	Se	Ro/Ru	Te	Au	Os

Info Bytes!

- Newlands' arrangement only worked accurately for elements up to calcium. Beyond that, the law broke down and couldn't accommodate all known elements of the time.

Limitations of Newland's Law of Octaves

Limited Range: Worked mainly for elements up to calcium; failed for heavier elements.

Grouping Issues: Mixed elements with different properties, like cobalt and nickel.

Exclusions: Disregarded certain known elements and left no room for undiscovered ones.

Ordering Errors: Elements with similar properties, like iron and nickel, were separated.

Noble Gas Challenge: Couldn't fit the newly discovered noble gases without disrupting the order.

Overemphasis on Analogy: The musical "octave" concept was catchy but not deeply scientific.

Despite its flaws, Newland's effort marked a significant step towards understanding elemental periodicity.

Mendeleev's Periodic Table

Dobereiner, Newland and many other scientists contributed significantly to the systematic classification of elements. Their efforts ultimately enabled the Russian chemist Mendeleev to construct his periodic table in 1869.

He stated in his famous periodic law that 'physical and chemical properties of elements are periodic functions of their atomic weights.'

Like Newland, he also arranged the then known 63 elements in the increasing order of their atomic weights in his periodic table in 8 vertical columns and 7 horizontal rows called **groups** and **periods**, respectively.

Konnect

- Mendeleev's original table had the elements arranged on cards which he shuffled like a deck of playing cards to find the best arrangement.

After the discovery of noble gases and radioactive elements another research of Mendeleev's periodic table was published in 1905. In this version '0' group was added to accommodate the noble gases and the seventh period for the radioactive elements of the elements known at that time.

Merits of Mendeleev's Periodic Table

1. Mendeleev left some gaps in his periodic table for some of the then unknown elements based on the properties of the other elements present in the same group. He named these missing elements as Eka boron, Eka aluminium and Eka silicon. Later on, these elements were discovered and named as scandium, gallium and germanium, respectively.
2. Mendeleev corrected the doubtful atomic weights of some elements. For example, the atomic weight of indium, i.e., 76 was based on the assumption that indium oxide had the formula InO. This atomic weight placed indium, which has metallic properties, among the non-metals. Mendeleev corrected the formula of indium oxide from InO to In_2O_3. Based on this corrected formula, the atomic weight of indium is 113. He also corrected the atomic weights of the elements beryllium and uranium.

Limitations of Mendeleev's Periodic Table

1. **Anomalous Pairs:** In Mendeleev's periodic table, there are some pairs of elements in which the element with a higher atomic weight is placed before that of the lower atomic weight element in order to maintain the similarity in chemical properties of the elements belonging to the same group.

   The pairs are: (i) Co 58.9, Ni 58.6 (ii) Te 127.6, I 126.9 (iii) Ar 39.94, K 39.10

2. **Position of Hydrogen:** The position of hydrogen was not justified.
3. **Positions of Isotopes:** The isotopes of an element have different atomic weights. But there was no position for the isotopes in Mendeleev's periodic table.
4. **Position of Lanthanides and Actinides:** Two sets of 14 elements each (lanthanides and actinides, respectively), which follow lanthanum and actinium in the order of atomic weights, have not been provided regular or separate places in the periodic table. They have just been put together along with lanthanum and actinium, respectively.
5. **Position of Elements of Group VIII:** Three triads of the transition elements are placed in group VIII of the periodic table. They should have been given separate positions.
6. **Anomalous Placement of the Transition and Coinage Metals:**
   (a) Transition elements were placed along with typical elements under the same group.
   (b) Coinage metals were placed with alkali metals.
7. **Position of Noble Gases**

   When Mendeleev created his periodic table, the noble gases (like Helium, Neon, and Argon) hadn't been discovered yet. After their discovery by scientists like Sir William Ramsay in the late 19th and early 20th centuries, there was a dilemma about where to place them in the periodic table. Because of their unique properties, primarily their inertness, they couldn't be fit into any of the existing groups in Mendeleev's table.

   However, in the modern periodic table, these elements found their place in a new group, known as the Noble Gases or Group 18. This addition showcased one of Mendeleev's genius predictions: he had left gaps in his table for undiscovered elements, showing the adaptability of his design, even though he hadn't specifically predicted the noble gases.

Info Bytes!

- Mendeleev's Periodic Table, despite its limitations, became the foundation for the modern periodic table we use today.

Owing to these limitations and the later discovery of atomic structure, Mendeleev's periodic table has no practical significance at present. Nevertheless, its significance lies in the fact that the concept of periodicity in properties and the resultant arrangement of elements in a periodic table originated from Mendeleev's classification of elements.

Table 6.2 Mendeleev's periodic table

SERIES	GROUPS OF ELEMENTS											
S	O	I	II	III	IV	V	VI	VII	VIII			
1	—	Hydrogen	—	—	—	—	—	—				
		H 1.008										
2	Helium	Lithium	Beryllium	Boron	Carbon	Nitrogen	Oxygen	Fluorine				
	He 4	Li 7.03	Be 9.1	B 11.0	C 12.0	N 14.04	O 16.00	F 19.0				
3	Neon	Sodium	Magnesium	Aluminium	Silicon	Phosphorus	Sulphur	Chlorine				
	Ne 19.9	Na 23.05	Mg 24.3	Al 27.0	Si 28.4	P 31.0	S 32.06	Cl 35.45				
4	Argon	Potassium	Calcium	Scandium	Titanium	Vanadium	Chromium	Manganese	Iron	Cobalt	Nickel	(Cu)
	Ar 38	K 39.1	Ca 40.1	Sc 44.1	Ti 48.1	V 51.4	Cr 52.1	Mn 55.0	Fe 55.9	Co 58.93	Ni 58.69	
5		Copper	Zinc	Gallium	Germanium	Arsenic	Selenium	Bromine				
		Cu 63.6	Zn 65.4	Ga 70.0	Ge 72.3	As 75	Se 79	Br 79.95				
6	Krypton	Rubidium	Strontium	Yttrium	Zirconium	Niobium	Molybdenum	—	Ruthenium	Rhodium	Palladium	(Ag)
	Kr 81.8	Rb 85.4	Sr 87.6	Y 89.0	Zr 90.6	Nb 94.0	Mo 96.0		Ru 101.7	Rh 103.0	Pd 106.5	
7	Silver	Cadmium	Indium	Tin	Antimony	Tellurium	Iodine					
	Ag 107.9	Cd 112.4	In 114.0	Sn 119.0	Sb 120.0	Te 127	I 127					
8	Xenon	Caesium	Barium	Lanthanum	Cerium	—	—	—	—	—	—	
	Xe 128	Cs 132.9	Ba 137.4	La 139	Ce 140							
9		—	—	—	—	—	—	—	—			
10	—	—	—	Ytterbium	—	Tantalum	Tungsten	—	Osmium	Iridium	Platinum	(Au)
				Yb 173		Ta 183	W 184		Os 191	Ir 193	Pt 194.9	
11			Gold	Mercury	Thallium	Lead	Bismuth	—	—			
			Au 197.2	Hgf 200.0	Tl 204.1	Pb 206.9	Bi 208					
12	—	—	Radium	—	Thorium	—	Uranium					
			Rd 224		Th 232		U 239					
HIGHER SALINE OXIDES												
	R	R_2O	RO	R_2O_3	RO_2	R_2O_5	RO_3	R_2O_7			RO_4	
HIGHER GASEOUS HYDROGEN COMPOUNDS												
					RH_4	RH_3	RH_2	RH				

EXAMPLE 6.1 Is Dobereiner's law of triads applicable to lithium, sodium, and potassium? Explain.

SOLUTION

Yes, Li, Na, and K also follow Dobereiner's law of triad:

Atomic weight of Li = 6.94
Atomic weight of Na = 22.99 $= \frac{6.94 + 39.10}{2} = 23.02 \approx 22.$
Atomic weight of K = 39.10

(Note: The atomic weights used here are rounded values.)

EXAMPLE 6.2 Consider a Dobereiner's triad with elements A, B, and C. The sum of atomic weights of extreme elements, A and C is 80 and the difference of atomic weights of C and B is two times the atomic number of nitrogen. Identify A, B, and C.

SOLUTION

Given, A + C = 80 ... (1)

C − B = 14 ... (2)

As $\frac{A+C}{2} = B$, (Dobereiner's law of triads).

$\therefore$ B = $\frac{80}{2}$ = 40 ... (3)

From equation (2) and (3),

C − 40 = 14

⇒ C = 54

From equation (1),

A + C = 80

⇒ A + 54 = 80

⇒ A = 26

So, A, B, and C are Fe, Zn, and Xe, respectively.

Note: The elements mentioned in the solution may not actually fit Dobereiner's triad in real chemistry, and the atomic weights are fictional. This is just for conceptual exercise purposes.

Modern Periodic Table—The Long Form of the Periodic Table

In 1913, H.G.J. Moseley worked on X-ray spectra of elements and established that the atomic number is equal to the total nuclear charge and it is a more fundamental characteristic of an element than atomic weight.

Moreover, it was found that some of the major defects of Mendeleev's periodic table like the anomalous position of some pairs of elements (Co–Ni, Te–I, Ar–K), placements of isotopes, etc., would automatically disappear, if atomic number, i.e., the total nuclear charge is used as the basis of the compilation of the periodic table instead of the atomic weight. Based on these observations, Moseley proposed the modern periodic law which states that 'the physical and chemical properties of elements are the periodic functions of their atomic numbers.'

Info Bytes!

The concept of 'periodicity', the repetition of properties, is so consistent that scientists have used the periodic table to predict the properties of elements even before they were discovered.

Thus, according to the modern periodic law, if the elements are arranged in the order of their increasing atomic numbers, the elements with similar properties are repeated after certain regular intervals.

The long form of the periodic table (also called **Bohr's table**) consists of horizontal rows called **periods** and vertical columns called **groups** or **families**.

There are 7 periods and 18 groups in the periodic table. The groups from I to VII are divided into subgroups 'A' and 'B.' VIII group consists of 3 vertical columns. All noble gases are kept in the zero group.

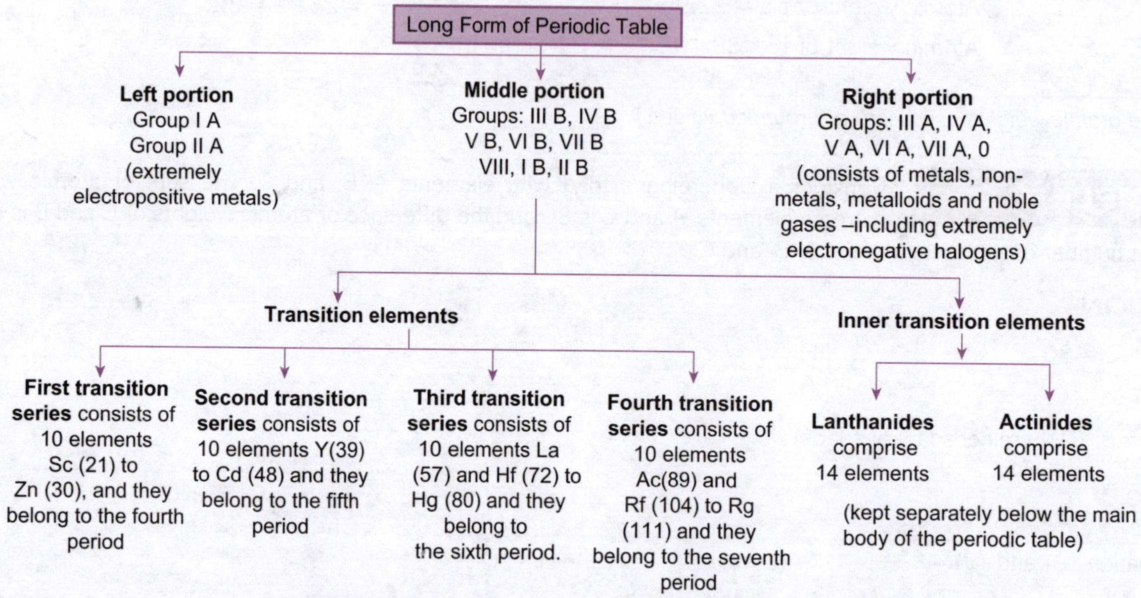

Figure 6.1 Division of periodic table into different portions

Periods Some Characteristics of Periods are Tabulated Below

Table 6.3 Periods and their characteristics

Periods	Characteristics
First	This period has only two elements, hydrogen and helium which have only one energy level or shell. This period is called **very-short period**.
Second	It has 8 elements: Li 3 to Ne 10. Elements have two shells. The elements of this period are called **bridge elements**.
Third	This period also has 8 elements: Na 11 to Ar 18. The second and third periods are called **short periods**. These elements have 3 shells. The elements of this period are called **typical elements**.
Fourth	This period has 18 elements: K 19 to Kr 36. They have 4 energy levels or 4 shells.
Fifth	This period also has 18 elements: Rb 37 to Xe 54. They have 5 energy levels or 5 shells.
Sixth	This period has 32 elements: Cs 55 to Rn 86. They have six energy levels or 6 shells. The fourth, fifth and sixth periods are called **long periods**.
Seventh	This period has 32 elements. All these elements are radioactive. Out of these, the naturally occurring radioactive elements are Fr 87, Ra 88, Ac 89 Th 90, Pa 91, and U 92 while the remaining elements after uranium, i.e., Np 93 to Db 105 are artificially prepared radioactive elements and these are called **transuranic elements**. Atoms of these elements have 7 energy levels or 7 shells.

Groups

1. Groups IA, IIA, IIIA, IVA, VA, VIA, VIIA contain metals, non-metals and metalloids. These elements are called **representative elements** because their valence electrons represent their group numbers.

2. Groups IB, IIB, IIIB (only Sc, Y, La and Ac), IV B, V B, VI B, VII B and VIII contain only transition metals.
3. In group III B except Sc, Y, La and Ac, the other elements are called **inner-transition metals** and are placed separately in two rows under the periodic table. They belong to the sixth period (Ce to Lu) and seventh period (Th to Lr).
4. The zero group contains noble gases.

Merits of the Long Form of the Periodic Table

1. The classification is based on the atomic number of elements, which is more fundamental than the atomic weight.
2. In this periodic table, the position of an element is related to the electronic configuration of the atom. Elements belonging to the same group possess same number of electrons in their valence shells and show similar chemical characteristics.

Table 6.4 Elements of the same group and their electronic configurations

	Element	Atomic Numbers	No. of Shells	Electronic Configurations	No. of Electrons in Valence Shell
Alkali metals	Li	3	2	2, 1	1
	Na	11	3	2, 8, 1	1
	K	19	4	2, 8, 8, 1	1
	Rb	37	5	2, 8, 18, 8, 1	1
	Cs	55	6	2, 8, 18, 18, 8, 1	1
	Fr	87	7	2, 8, 18, 32, 18, 8, 1	1
Halogens	F	9	2	2, 7	7
	Cl	17	3	2, 8, 7	7
	Br	35	4	2, 8, 18, 7	7
	I	53	5	2, 8, 18, 18, 7	7
	At	85	6	2, 8, 18, 32, 18, 7	7

3. Variation of chemical properties along a period is correlated with gradual filling of electrons in a particular shell in the period.
4. In this table, inert gases are placed at the end of each period which is very logical because valence shells have an octet configuration. So, their inertness can also be explained in terms of the electronic configuration.
5. Due to the separation of the two subgroups, dissimilar elements (e.g., alkali and coinage metals) do not fall together.
6. Different types of elements, such as, (a) active metals, (b) transition metals, (c) non-metals and metalloids (d) noble gases, and (e) inner transition elements (lanthanides and actinides) have their separate locations in this periodic table.

Defects of the Long Form of the Periodic Table

1. Even after the compilation of the modern periodic table, the position of hydrogen remained controversial. This is because hydrogen with one electron in its valence shell shows similarities with both alkali metals and halogens. Therefore, placing hydrogen in IA group is not completely justifiable.
2. The elements lanthanides and actinides could not be placed in the main body of the modern periodic table.
3. This periodic table does not reflect the exact distribution of electrons of some of the transition and inner transition elements.

Table 6.5 Modern periodic table

Key: 1 — Atomic number, Z; H — Element symbol; 1.008 — Relative atomic mass, A

1	2	3	4	5	6	7	8	9	10	11	12	13	14	15	16	17	18
1 **H** 1.008																	2 **He** 4.00
3 **Li** 6.94	4 **Be** 9.01											5 **B** 10.81	6 **C** 12.01	7 **N** 14.01	8 **O** 16.00	9 **F** 19.00	10 **Ne** 20.18
11 **Na** 22.99	12 **Mg** 24.31											13 **Al** 26.98	14 **Si** 28.09	15 **P** 30.97	16 **S** 32.06	17 **Cl** 35.45	18 **Ar** 39.95
19 **K** 39.10	20 **Ca** 40.08	21 **Sc** 44.96	22 **Ti** 47.90	23 **V** 50.94	24 **Cr** 52.01	25 **Mn** 54.94	26 **Fe** 55.85	27 **Co** 58.93	28 **Ni** 58.69	29 **Cu** 63.54	30 **Zn** 65.41	31 **Ga** 69.72	32 **Ge** 72.59	33 **As** 74.92	34 **Se** 78.96	35 **Br** 79.91	36 **Kr** 83.80
37 **Rb** 85.47	38 **Sr** 87.62	39 **Y** 88.91	40 **Zr** 91.22	41 **Nb** 92.91	42 **Mo** 95.94	43 **Tc** 98.91	44 **Ru** 101.07	45 **Rh** 102.91	46 **Pd** 106.42	47 **Ag** 107.87	48 **Cd** 112.40	49 **In** 114.82	50 **Sn** 118.71	51 **Sb** 121.75	52 **Te** 127.60	53 **I** 126.90	54 **Xe** 131.30
55 **Cs** 132.91	56 **Ba** 137.34	**La–Lu**	72 **Hf** 178.49	73 **Ta** 180.95	74 **W** 183.85	75 **Re** 186.21	76 **Os** 190.23	77 **Ir** 192.22	78 **Pt** 195.08	79 **Au** 196.97	80 **Hg** 200.59	81 **Tl** 204.37	82 **Pb** 207.19	83 **Bi** 208.98	84 **Po** 210	85 **At** 210	86 **Rn** 222
87 **Fr** 223	88 **Ra** 226.03	**Ac–Lr**	104 **Rf** [261]	105 **Db** [262]	106 **Sg** [266]	107 **Bh** [264]	108 **Hs** [277]	109 **Mt** [268]	110 **Ds** [271]	111 **Rg** [272]	112 **Cn** [285]	113 **Nh** [286]	114 **Fl** [289]	115 **Mc** [286]	116 **Lv** [293]	117 **Ts** [294]	118 **Og** [294]

Lanthanoids	57 **La** 138.91	58 **Ce** 140.12	59 **Pr** 140.91	60 **Nd** 144.24	61 **Pm** 146.92	62 **Sm** 150.36	63 **Eu** 151.96	64 **Gd** 157.25	65 **Tb** 158.92	66 **Dy** 162.50	67 **Ho** 164.93	68 **Er** 167.26	69 **Tm** 168.93	70 **Yb** 173.04	71 **Lu** 174.97
Actinoids	89 **Ac** 227.03	90 **Th** 232.04	91 **Pa** 231.04	92 **U** 238.03	93 **Np** 237.05	94 **Pu** 239.05	95 **Am** 241.06	96 **Cm** 244.07	97 **Bk** 249.08	98 **Cf** 252.08	99 **Es** 252.09	100 **Fm** 257.10	101 **Md** 258.10	102 **No** 259	103 **Lr** 262

EXAMPLE 6.3 Why is the atomic number pivotal in determining the position of an element in the periodic table, rather than its atomic weight?

SOLUTION

The position of an element in the periodic table is primarily determined by its electron configuration, which dictates its chemical behaviour. The number of electrons in an atom corresponds to the number of protons, and this count of protons is referred to as the atomic number. Since each element has a unique atomic number, it holds a specific place in the periodic table based on this value. Conversely, atomic weights can be very close between different elements. For instance, potassium and argon have atomic weights of 39.1 and 39.9, respectively. Despite their similar atomic weights, their properties and positions in the periodic table are distinctly different.

EXAMPLE 6.4 Helium's placement in the modern periodic table often raises questions since it behaves anomalously. Why?

SOLUTION

Helium has two electrons in its outermost shell, making it a completely filled s-shell like the noble gases. However, unlike other noble gases that have p-orbitals, helium lacks them, aligning more with the s-block elements. This gives it characteristics similar to both the noble gases and the s-block elements. Because of its unique behaviour and properties that resonate with both groups, its exact placement in the modern periodic table becomes a topic of debate, leading some to refer to it as an anomaly.

Periodicity

The regular gradation in the properties of elements and their repetition at regular intervals is called **periodicity**. The properties which show such regular trends are called **periodic properties**. Some of the periodic properties include the following:

1. atomic size
2. ionization potential
3. electron affinity
4. electronegativity
5. electropositive character
6. oxidizing/reducing capacity
7. metallic/non-metallic character

Info Bytes!

Factors like atomic size, ionization energy, and electronegativity play a critical role in determining the properties of elements, influencing everything from an element's reactivity to its conductivity.

Atomic Size

The size of an atom depends on the distance between the valence shell and the nucleus, i.e., the atomic radius.

Variation of Atomic Size Along a Period and a Group in the Periodic Table

Period: The atomic radii generally decrease from left to right across a period. When we proceed along a period, electrons are added to the subshells of the same main energy level. With the addition of each electron, the nuclear charge increases by 1. Hence, the increased nuclear charge attracts the electrons more strongly and the size of the atom decreases.

Group: On moving down a group, the atomic radii of the elements increase with an increase in the atomic number. On proceeding downward in a group, the electrons are added to the next main energy level which are farther from the nucleus. This effect decreases the electrostatic force of attraction between the nucleus and the valence shell electrons. Consequently, the atomic radii of the atoms of the elements increase along a group from top to bottom.

Ionization Energy

Ionization energy of an element is the minimum amount of energy required to remove the most loosely held electron from the outermost shell of an isolated neutral gaseous atom of that element in its lowest-energy state to produce a cation.

Successive Ionization Potentials

The amount of energy required to remove the first electron from a neutral atom is called **first ionization energy**.

The energy required to remove the electron from a unipositive charged ion is called **second ionization energy**.

Similarly, the third and the fourth ionization energy or ionization potentials can be defined in the same way.

If the first ionization energy is considered as I_1 and the second is I_2 and so on, then $I_1 < I_2 < I_3 < I_4 < \ldots\ldots$

The successive increase in these values is due to the fact that it is relatively more difficult to remove an electron from a cation having higher positive charge than from a cation having lower positive charge than from a neutral atom.

Variation of Ionization Potential Along a Period and a Group in the Periodic Table

Period: Ionization energy generally increases from left to right along a period because the atomic size of the elements gradually decreases due to the increase in the atomic number.

Group: Ionization energy decreases from top to bottom in a group because of the increase in the atomic radius which is due to the increase in the number of shells.

Electron Affinity

The amount of energy released when an electron is added to an isolated neutral gaseous atom in its lowest-energy state to produce an anion is called its **electron affinity.**

Factors influencing the magnitude of electron affinity are the following:

1. atomic size **2.** effective nuclear charge.

Variation of Electron Affinity Along a Period and Along a Group of the Periodic Table

Period: Electron affinity values generally increase on moving from left to right along a period due to the decrease in the atomic size and the increase in its effective nuclear charge.

Group: Electron affinity gradually decreases from top to bottom in a group. This is due to the steady increase in the atomic radius and the decrease in the effective nuclear charge of the elements.

Electronegativity

Electronegativity of an element is defined as the relative tendency or ability of the atom of an element present in a molecule to attract the shared electron pair towards itself.

Variation of Electronegativity Along a Group and a Period of the Periodic Table

Period: Electronegativity increases on moving along a period from left to right. This is due to the increase in nuclear charge and decrease in atomic size, as a result of which shared electron pair can be attracted more towards itself.

Group: Electronegativity decreases from top to bottom in a group due to an increase in the atomic size, as a result of which the shared electron pair is less attracted towards itself.

Electropositive Character

Electropositive character of an element is its ability to lose one or more electrons to form a positively charged ion.

Variation of Electropositivity Along a Period and a Group in a Periodic Table

Period: Electropositive character decreases from left to right along a period due to the increase in ionization potential.

Group: Electropositive character increases from top to bottom along a group due to the decrease in ionization potential.

Oxidizing and Reducing Property

The higher the value of electron affinity of the element, the greater would be its capacity to accept an electron, i.e., the element behaves as a strong oxidizing agent.

The lower the value of the ionization potential of an element, the greater would be its capacity to lose electrons, i.e., the element behaves as a strong reducing agent.

Variation of Oxidizing and Reducing Property Along a Period and a Group in a Periodic Table

Period: Due to the increase in electron affinity from left to right of a period, the oxidizing capacity of the elements increases and the reducing capacity decreases from left to right along a period.

Group: Due to the decrease in ionization potential as well as electron affinity from top to bottom of a group, oxidizing capacity of the element decreases, whereas its reducing capacity increases on descending a group.

Metallic and Non-metallic Property

Non-metals generally have high electronegativity and metals have low electronegativity.

Variation of Metallic and Non-metallic Character Along a Period and a Group of the Periodic Table

Period: Electronegativity increases from left to right along a period in the periodic table. Consequently, the metallic character along a period decreases from left to right and the non-metallic character increases.

Group: Since electronegativity decreases from top to bottom along a group in the periodic table, the metallic character of an element increases on descending a group and non-metallic character decreases.

This trend is very much prominent in the case of elements of IVA and VA groups. These groups begin with non-metals C and N, respectively, and end with metals Pb and Bi, respectively.

EXAMPLE 6.5 Why do the chemical properties along a period vary?

SOLUTION

Chemical property of an element is due to electrons present in the valence shell. Elements of the same period possess different number of valence electrons. Hence, their chemical properties vary along a period.

EXAMPLE 6.6 How does the magnitude of effective nuclear charge influence the electron affinity of an element?

SOLUTION

The nucleus has positive charge, and hence, it attracts the electrons present in the atom. As the distance of electrons from the nucleus increases, the attraction experienced by electrons because of nuclear charge decreases. The net nuclear force of attraction experienced by the electron is called **effective nuclear charge**. The greater the effective nuclear charge, the higher is the electron affinity of an atom.

EXAMPLE 6.7 Predict the position and properties like metallic/non-metallic character and oxidizing/reducing capacity of an element with atomic number 35 in the periodic table.

SOLUTION

Element with atomic number 35 is bromine and its electronic configuration is 2, 8, 18, 7. Bromine belongs to VIIA (17) group (halogens). Due to this electronic configuration, bromine has strong electron affinity. Hence, it is a reducing agent. Since bromine has seven valence electrons, it is a non-metal.

EXAMPLE 6.8 Write the electronic configuration of the most stable cation of the fourth period element which has the lowest ionization potential value. Justify your answer.

SOLUTION

The elements belonging to group IA or 1 have the least ionization potential value in a period. Since it has only one valence electron, the monopositive cation is the most stable cation. The element belongs to fourth period, hence, the electronic configuration of the cation is 2, 8, 8.

EXAMPLE 6.9 How is electropositive character related to reducing property of an element? How does it vary in the group?

SOLUTION

Electropositive character is defined as the tendency of the element to lose electrons. Reducing property of an element is its ability to give up electron(s) and by virtue of this ability, it reduces the other element. The greater the electropositive character, the more is its reducing property. In a group, reducing property increases from top to bottom as electropositive character increases from top to bottom.

POINTS TO REMEMBER

- ✔ Mendeleev stated in his famous periodic law that physical and chemical properties of elements are periodic functions of their atomic weights.
- ✔ Mendeleev arranged the then known 63 elements in the increasing order of their atomic weights in his periodic table in 8 vertical columns and 7 horizontal rows called groups and periods, respectively.
- ✔ Moseley proposed the modern periodic law which states that 'the physical and chemical properties of elements are the periodic functions of their atomic numbers.'
- ✔ The long form of the periodic table (also called Bohr's table) consists of horizontal rows called periods and vertical columns called groups or families.
- ✔ Ionization energy of an element is the minimum amount of energy required to remove the most loosely held electron from the outermost shell of an isolated neutral gaseous atom of that element in its lowest-energy state to produce a cation.
- ✔ The amount of energy released when an electron is added to an isolated neutral gaseous atom in its lowest-energy state to produce an anion is called its electron affinity.
- ✔ Electronegativity of an element is defined as the relative tendency or ability of the atom of an element present in a molecule to attract the shared electron pair towards itself.
- ✔ Electropositive character of an element is its ability to lose one or more electrons to form a positively charged ion.
- ✔ The higher the value of electron affinity of the element, the greater would be its capacity to accept an electron, i.e., the element behaves as a strong oxidizing agent.
- ✔ The lower the value of the ionization potential of an element, the greater would be its capacity to lose electrons, i.e., the element behaves as a strong reducing agent.

PRACTICE QUESTIONS CLASSROOM WING

Very Short Answer Type Questions

Direction for questions from 1 to 5:
Fill in the blanks.

1. The reducing property is maximum for ________.
2. Lanthanides and actinides are called ________ elements.
3. The elements in the very-short period are __________ and __________.
4. An increase in atomic radius results in ________ in the electron affinity of an element.
5. ________ group elements have a greater tendency to form cations.

Direction for questions from 6 to 25:
Answer the following questions

6. Identify the best oxidizing agent among the elements: K, O, F and N.
7. Give an example of the set of three elements which can obey the Law of triads.
8. Element 'X' undergoes sublimation on heating. Identify the group to which X belongs.
9. Does the set of atomic numbers: 5, 13, 31 obey the Döbereiner's Law of triads?
10. Which group contains the inner transition elements?
11. What is the modern periodic law?
12. What is the basis of the modern periodic table?
13. Which periods are called short periods and which periods are called long periods? Why?
14. What do you mean by representative elements? Give example.
15. Where are the extremely electropositive metals positioned in the periodic table?
16. What type of elements does the right portion of the periodic table contain?
17. What is meant by atomic radius?
18. Which group contains the noble gases and what are the special characteristics of these gases?
19. Which elements are called transuranic elements?
20. Define ionization potential.
21. Describe the trend of the metallic and non-metallic character of the elements in a group.
22. Define electronegativity. What are its units?
23. Give the number of valence electrons of
    (a) alkali elements and
    (b) halogens.
24. The electronic configuration of element 'X' is 2, 8 and 7 and belongs to which group and period?
25. Two metals 'A' and 'B' showed a drastic increase in 2nd and 4th I.P. values, respectively. Identify the atomic numbers of A and B.

Short Answer Type Questions

26. Atoms of two elements 'A' and 'B' have 56 and 37 protons, respectively. What is the relation between the I.P. of A and B?
27. Give some examples of Dobereiner's triads. Explain how they are grouped as triads.
28. What are the achievements and the limitations of Newland's classification?
29. Give the limitations of Dobereiner's classification.
30. Give brief description of Mendeleev 's periodic table.
31. (a) What is the basic difference between Mendeleev's periodic table and the modern periodic table?
    (b) The atomic numbers of three elements A, B, and C are 12, 33 and 19 respectively. Predict the positions of A, B, and C in the modern periodic table.
    Elements belonging to the same group show same chemical properties. Give reason.

32. Why are the lanthanides and the actinides given a separate position in the modern periodic table?

33. Why is there an increase in successive IP values?

34. Why do the elements of the same group show identical property? Explain.

35. How does electronegativity vary along a group and along a period? Give reasons and explain with examples.

36. How does the atomic size vary along a group and a period? Give reasons and explain with the help of an example.

37. What is the difference between electronegativity and electropositivity?

38. Why is the modern periodic table also referred to as Bohr's table?

39. How do the oxidizing and reducing capacity of an element depend on the ionization potential and electron affinity?

Essay Answer Type Questions

40. Arrange the elements mentioned below in the order of maximum:

(A) Metallic character (B) Electronegativity

(C) Ionization energy (D) Electron affinity

(i) A belongs to the first period and the 18th group.

(ii) B belongs to the sixth period and the first group.

(iii) C belongs to the third period and the 17th group.

(iv) D belongs to the second period and 17th group.

41. 'A', 'B', 'C' and 'D' are four elements belonging to the third period. A and B can form monovalent and divalent cations, respectively. C and D can form monovalent and divalent anions, respectively. Arrange the corresponding elements in the increasing order of sizes of the respective ions.

42. What is meant by periodicity? What are the various periodic properties? Explain how and why atomic radius varies in a group and period. Give an example.

43. What are the merits and limitations of the long form of periodic table?

44. How does ionization potential, electron affinity, electropositivity, oxidizing and reducing capacity vary along a group and a period? Give reasons.

45. Given is the periodic table showing only the main groups. The letters A to G do not represent their actual symbols. Using only these letters, answer the questions given.

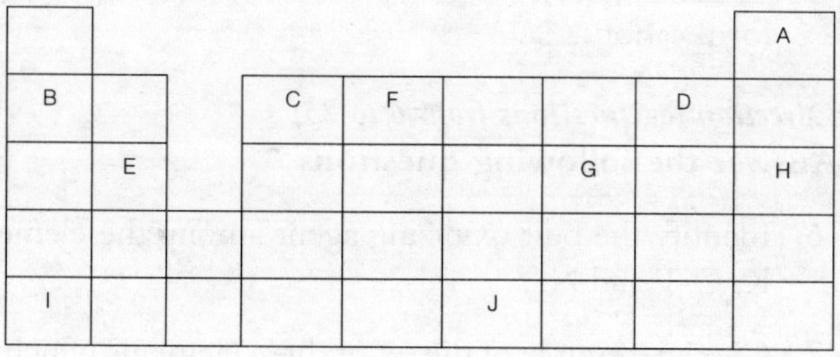

(a) Which of these elements is (i) a halogen and (ii) an alkaline earth metal?

(b) What is the electronic configuration of G?

(c) Which element has an octet configuration in its outermost orbit?

(d) Identify the element with the largest atomic radius.

PRACTICE QUESTIONS COMPETITION WING

Level 1: Apply your Concepts

Direction for questions from 1 to 8:
State whether the following statements are true or false.

1. In Dobereiner's classification, the atomic weight and the properties of the first element are almost equal to the average of those of the 2nd and 3rd elements of a triad.
2. Atomic numbers of the isotopes of an element are different.
3. Differentiating electrons enter anti-penultimate shell in transition elements.
4. Along a period, atomic volume of the elements gradually increases from left to right due to an increase in the number of valence electrons.
5. The element with atomic number 17 has the least size among all the elements of that period.
6. The lower is the value of ionization potential of an element, the greater is its reducing power.
7. Among all the groups, the maximum number of elements is found in IIIB group.
8. We classified elements for easy and systematic study.

Direction for questions from 9 to 19:
Fill in the blanks.

9. The element in between lithium and potassium in Dobereiner's classification is ______.
10. ______________ was the basis of Dobereiner's classification of the elements.
11. In Newland's classification, elements are arranged in an increasing order of their ______.
12. Mendeleev placed coinage metals with ________ metals.
13. In the modified Mendeleev's periodic table, ________ groups and ________ periods are present, whereas in modern periodic table, _____ groups and _____ periods are present.
14. If three elements X, Y, and Z form a triad and atomic weights of X and Z are 9 and 40, respectively, then the atomic weight of an element Y is _____.
15. Mendeleev named certain undiscovered elements as eka boron and eka aluminium which when later discovered were called ______and______.
16. According to Newland's classification, the properties of the 3rd element will find similarity with those of the______ element.
17. Extremely electropositive metals are present in ________ and ________ groups.
18. The atomic number of an element that belongs to the IVA group and 4th period is __________.
19. Good reducing agents are found in _____ and _____ groups.

Direction for question 20:
Match the entries given in Column A with appropriate ones in Column B.

20. Match the statements of Column A with those of Column B.

Column A	Column B
(i) Caesium	(A) Second long period
(ii) Xenon	(B) Very long period
(iii) Potassium	(C) Incomplete period
(iv) Radium	(D) Long period

Direction for questions from 21 to 42:
For each of the questions, four choices have been provided. Select the correct alternative.

21. **Assertion (A):** The order of the first ionization potential (I.P.) values is Mg > Al > Na.

    Reason (R): Across the period, I.P. values generally increase.

    (a) Both A and R are true and R is the correct explanation of A.

    (b) Both A and R are true, but R is not the correct explanation of A.

    (c) A is true and R is false.

    (d) A is false and R is true.

22. **Assertion (A):** In a given period, halogens possess the highest electron affinity (E.A.) values.

Reason (R): Across the period, nuclear charge increases and hence, atomic size decreases.

(a) Both A and R are true and R is the correct explanation of A.

(b) Both A and R are true, but R is not the correct explanation of A.

(c) A is true and R is false.

(d) A is false and R is true.

23. Which of the following belong to the same group?

A^{3+} (number of electrons = 10)

B^{2+} (number of electrons = 10)

C (number of electrons = 5)

D (number of electrons = 31)

(a) ABC (b) BCD

(c) ACD (d) ADB

24. **Assertion (A):** The second I.P. of Na is greater than that of Mg.

Reason (R): Na^+ ion has a stable octet configuration.

(a) Both A and R are true and R is the correct explanation of A.

(b) Both A and R are true, but R is not the correct explanation of A.

(c) A is true and R is false.

(d) A is false and R is true.

25. **Assertion (A):** Formation of F^- is an exothermic process and that of F^{-2} is an endothermic process.

Reason (R): Repulsive force is directly proportional to the number of electrons in the species.

(a) Both A and R are true and R is the correct explanation of A.

(b) Both A and R are true, but R is not the correct explanation of A.

(c) A is true and R is false.

(d) A is false and R is true.

26. Why is the ionization energy of sulphur less than that of phosphorous, though sulphur is next to phosphorous in the period?

(a) Atomic radius of sulphur is greater than that of phosphorous.

(b) Sulphur has half-filled electronic configuration.

(c) Phosphorus has half-filled electronic configuration.

(d) In the third period the ionization energy decreases along the period.

27. The element which accepts electrons readily to form anion belongs to

(a) VII A group and second period

(b) VII A group and third period

(c) 0 group and third period

(d) VIA group and third period

28. Identify the oxide which forms the strongest base.

(a) MgO (b) Al_2O_3

(c) Na_2O (d) CaO

29. The formula of the oxide of an element M is M_2O_3. The first four ionization energies of the element M can be in the order:

(a) 120 kcal, 270 kcal, 400 kcal, and 5098 kcal

(b) 210 kcal, 150 kcal, 370 kcal, and 590 kcal

(c) 70 kcal, 100 kcal, 105 kcal, and 120 kcal

(d) 560 kcal, 410 kcal, 320 kcal, and 290 kcal

30. The chemistry of alkali metals is essentially the chemistry of unipositive ions because

(a) they have low ionization energy values

(b) they have strong tendency to lose single valence electron

(c) second ionization energy values are very high

(d) all the above

31. Na^+, F^- and Mg^{2+} ions have the same

(a) size

(b) electronic configuration

(c) ionization energy

(d) nuclear charge

32. Gallium is more electronegative than aluminium even though electronegativity of the elements decreases down the group. It is due to ______.

(a) increase in the atomic size

(b) increase in the ionization energy

(c) increase of effective nuclear charge

(d) all the above

33. The total number of inner transition elements is:

(a) 14 (b) 28

(c) 20 (d) 15

34. Which one of the following doesn't come under zero group?
(a) He (b) K
(c) Ne (d) Ar

35. The atomic numbers of 4 elements A, B, C and D are 8, 9, 10, and 11, respectively. The order of their atomic volume is
(a) $A > B > C < D$ (b) $A < B < C > D$
(c) $A > B < C < D$ (d) $A < B > C > D$

36. Arrange the following statements in chronological order:
(1) Some elements be grouped in sets of three elements in the increasing order of their atomic weights in which the atomic weight of the middle element was found to be the arithmetic mean of the atomic weights of the other two elements.
(2) The physical and chemical properties of elements are periodic functions of their atomic numbers.
(3) The physical and chemical properties of elements are periodic functions of their atomic weights.
(4) When elements are arranged in the increasing order of their atomic weights, the eighth element resembles the first in physical and chemical properties just as the eighth note on a musical scale resembles the first one.
(a) 1432 (b) 1342
(c) 4213 (d) 2431

37. The electron affinity increases on moving from left to right along a period. Arrange the reasons in a proper sequence.
(1) The amount of energy released during the addition of an electron increases from left to right along a period.
(2) Effective nuclear charge of the elements increases from left to right.
(3) The atomic size of the elements decreases from left to right.
(4) The tendency to gain electrons and form anion increases from left to right.
(a) 1324 (b) 3241
(c) 3142 (d) 4321

38. X belongs to IA or first group and fifth period and Y succeeds X in the group. Z succeeds Y in the period. Arrange the suitable statements in the correct sequence in order to arrange X, Y and Z in the increasing order of their atomic sizes.
(A) effect of number of valence electrons and number of shells on the atomic size
(B) identification of the elements X, Y and Z
(C) determination of the number of shells and the number of valence electrons present in X, Y and Z
(D) determination of the positions of Y and Z in the periodic table based on the position of X
(a) DBCA (b) BDCA
(c) CAD (d) DCA

39. Among third period elements halogen and alkaline earth metals are, respectively.
(a) Cl, Na (b) S, Na
(c) S, Mg (d) Cl, Mg

40. Which among the following pairs of elements have maximum and minimum electron affinity values, respectively?
(a) Be, Cl (b) He, K
(c) Be, S (d) Cl, Cs

41. Which of these triads could not be justified as Dobereiner's triad?
(a) Li, Na, K (b) Cl, Br, I
(c) C, N, O (d) Ca, Sr, Ba

42. An element belongs to IIIA group and forth period in the modern periodic table. What could be the probable atomic number of that element?
(a) 23 (b) 49
(c) 31 (d) 13

Level 2: Review your Concepts

43. The atomic numbers of five elements 'A', 'B', 'C', 'D' and 'E' are 19, 16, 11, 7 and 38, respectively. Arrange them in decreasing order of their atomic volume

44. The order of the first I.P. values of three elements 'X', 'Y' and 'Z' is $Y > Z > X$. Give an example of the elements X, Y and Z, from the atomic numbers 1 to 10.

45. Identify the correct order of sizes of neutral atoms and their corresponding ions.

46. The electronic configuration of element 'X' is 2, 8 and 6. X is surrounded by four elements as shown in the figure. Identify the element with the least non-metallic character.

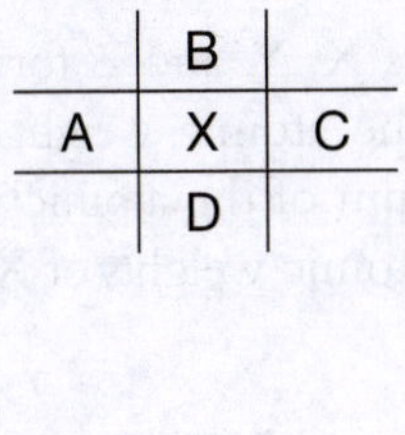

47. If the atomic numbers of some elements in the modern periodic table are 8, 7, 11, 12, 13, and 9, what type of ions do they form? Arrange the ions in the increasing order of their size and justify.

48. (a) 'The densities of transition metals are greater than those of the alkali and alkaline earth metals.' Justify.

(b) The order of ionization energies of an element X is $I.P_4 > I.P_3 >>>> I.P_2 > I.P_1$

(a) Which of the elements could X be

(i) Na (ii) Ca

(iii) Al

(b) Mention the type of ion formed by X.

49. An element R belongs to IVA group and third period in the periodic table. Arrange the elements that are placed below R and towards right in the periodic table in increasing order of atomic size and ionization potential.

50. Predict the position of the elements which form the largest cation and the smallest anion in the modern periodic table.

51. Why do transition metals show catalytic behaviour?

52. Elements with more non-metallic character are good oxidizing agents and those with more electropositive character are good reducing agents. Explain.

53. An element X belongs to group II A and fourth period in the periodic table. Find out the atomic number of X and the element which is placed just below X in the periodic table.

54. Explain why the addition of an electron to a neutral atom is associated with release of energy.

55. The first four ionization energies of an element R are 580, 640, 1000, and 2700 kcal/mole, respectively. Find the group number of R and write formulae of its chloride and oxide.

56. B and Al belong to the same group, but the nature of oxides formed by them are different, whereas Be, Al form same type of oxides although they belong to different groups. Comment.

Directions for questions from 57 to 66:

Application-Based Questions

57. Chlorine, Y and iodine form a Dobereiner's triad. Identify the atomic weight of Y.

58. Three elements X, Y, and Z form a Dobereiner triad. The ratio of the atomic weight of X to that of Z is 7 : 25. If the sum of the atomic weights of X and Z is 160, find the atomic weights of X, Y, and Z.

59. The total number of electrons present in the first two and the last two shells is the same for an atom of an element X. The sum of the electrons present in second, fourth and fifth shells is equal to the number of electrons present in the third shell and the fifth shell is the valence shell. Identify X and predict its position in the periodic table.

60. The atomic number of elements X, Y and Z are (A – 2), A and (A + 2), respectively. Y is a noble gas (not helium) then

(a) predict the group to which X, Y and Z belong

(b) predict the formula of a molecule formed by X and Z

61. Consider the isotopes of carbon, i.e., C – 12, C – 13, C – 14, would you place them in same or different slots in the periodic table? Give reason.

62. Given below is the graph representing the ionization energies of a few elements, A to H with successive atomic numbers.

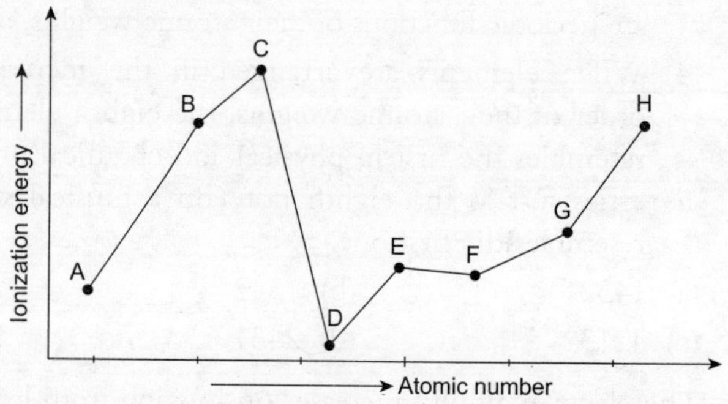

(a) Identity the noble gas.

(b) Which of the following elements could D be?

(i) Ne (ii) Ca

(iii) Na

(c) Which element has the highest electron affinity?

(d) Which element has the strongest metallic character?

(e) Write the unit of ionization energy.

63. A physical science teacher said that work is directly proportional to force and displacement. One of the students who attended the 'TIME IIT' foundation course said that work done in removing an electron from a cation is directly proportional to the charge on it. The teacher appreciated the student and explained the above concept. What was her explanation?

64. Elements A, B, and C with atomic numbers z, $z + 1$ and $z + 2$, respectively, form positive ions having equal number of electrons. Compare and contrast the sizes of the respective ions.

65. Elements with higher electronegativity are good oxidizing agents. Give reasons.

66. ${}^{40}_{20}X$, ${}^{39}_{19}Y$ ${}^{24}_{12}Z$, ${}^{132}_{55}A$. From the given elements

(a) Identify the elements which belong to same group.

(b) Arrange the elements in the increasing order of electropositive character.

Level 3: Assess Your Concepts

67. The electron structures of four elements are given below.

(i) A → 2, 8, 1 (ii) B → 2, 8, 8

(iii) C → 2, 8, 7 (iv) D → 2, 8, 18, 8, 1

Arrange the above elements in the order of elements with:

(A) zero electron affinity.

(B) minimum ionization energy.

(C) good oxidizing agent.

(D) best reducing agent in the third period.

68. Study the following statements:

(A) Element 'A' requires the least energy to form a cation.

(B) Element 'B' requires more energy to form a stable cation.

(C) Element 'C' gives out more energy during the formation of anion.

(D) Element 'D' gives out less energy during the formation of anion.

The given elements belong to the same period. Arrange the elements in the increasing order of their atomic sizes.

69. Why do alkali metals tarnish on exposure to air?

70. Electron affinity values of noble gases are zero, whereas they are negative for alkaline earth metals. How do you account for this?

71. Explain how the density changes across a period from K to Ni and compare it with the change down the group from K to Cs, respectively.

Directions for questions from 72 to 77:
Application-Based Questions

72. Which elements can be used in solar cells and why?

73. Explain the energy changes involved in the formation of F^- and O^{2-} from their respective atoms.

74. 'Addition of an electron to a uninegative ion (except to VIA group elements) is an endothermic process, whereas the formation of uninegative ion from its neutral atom is an exothermic process.' Comment.

75. A, B, C, and D are four 9th class students. Their chemistry teacher conducted a role play in the class which is as given below. She assumed that A is a metal and B is a non-metal. C and D need to carry out two separate experiments. For this purpose, C needs an oxidizing agent and D needs a reducing agent. Accordingly they have to form two groups consisting of two students each. How will they form the group? Explain this with appropriate reasons.

76. Three elements A, B, and C have successive atomic numbers in increasing order. A attains stability when an electron is added to the third shell which is the valence shell. Identify A, B and C and predict the respective elements possessing the maximum ionization energy, oxidizing power, reducing power, electron affinity, and atomic size.

77. Electron affinity values (in eV) of same period elements are given below and consider that the elements are not in the same order as in periodic table.

Element	A	B	C	D	E	F	G	H
Electron Affinity (eV)	−2.4	−1.4	0	0.3	0.6	1.2	1.4	3.4

Answer the following questions.

(a) Identify the noble gas

(b) Identify VIIA group element.

(c) Which element could be the best oxidizing agent?

AT

PRACTICE QUESTIONS JEE-NEET SPECIAL WING

Multiple-Answer Type Questions

Directions for questions 1 to 5:

Select one or more correct alternative(s) from the given choices.

1. Identify the atomic numbers of elements which belong to 5th period and possess incomplete d subshell.
   (a) 40 (b) 49
   (c) 76 (d) 47

2. The elements A, B, C and D are given along with their group numbers and period numbers in the table given below. The descriptions are given in the choices. Identify the correct descriptions for the respective elements.

Element	Period	Group
A	4	11
B	5	16
C	6	1
D	2	17

   (a) A-One of the coinage metals
   (b) B-Metalloid element of that group
   (c) C-The element with highest ionisation potential value
   (d) D-The most electronegative element

3. An atom of an element has 3 electrons in the M shell. The stable ion of the element has the radius equal to 0.54 A. The period and group to which the elements belong are given below. The stable ions of which among the following elements have radius greater than 0.54 A?
   (a) The element belonging to 2nd period and 16th group.
   (b) The element belonging to 3rd period and 1st group.
   (c) The element belonging to 2rd period and 15th group.
   (d) The element belonging to 3rd period and 2nd group.

4. Observe the values of successive ionisation potentials and identify the sets which comply with the element which forms the oxide of the formula M_2O_3

	1st IP	2nd IP	3rd IP	4th IP
(a)	380	415	1753	2045
(b)	157	348	589	2169
(c)	276	3449	4297	5583
(d)	558	1274	2489	5976

5. Identify the correctly matched sets among the following.

	Elements in Sequential order	Periodic property
(a)	Cl > F > Br	Electron affinity
(b)	Ne < F < O	Atomic radius
(c)	K < Rb < Cs	Reducing capacity
(d)	Cl < Ar > K	Ionisation potential

Comprehension-Based Questions

Directions for Questions 6–10:

Read the content given in the following passage and answer the questions given below.

Observe the Ionisation Potential curve for the elements of first 3 periods. The elements are indicated by alphabets. The alphabets are not in the sequential order of atomic numbers of the elements. Based on the concept of factors affecting the ionisation potential values, answer the questions given below.

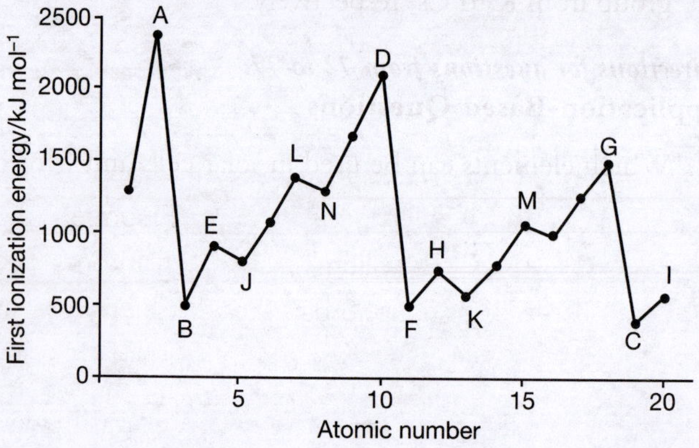

6. Identify the middle element between J and L in the curve.
(a) Carbon (b) Boron
(c) Nitrogen (d) Beryllium

7. Predict the set of elements indicated by F;H;K.
(a) Mg;Al;Si (b) Al;Si;P
(c) Na;Mg;Al (d) Si;P;S

8. Which of the following placements in the curve is correct as per the trend of IP values?
(a) Nitrogen between J and L
(b) Fluorine between N and D
(c) Phosphorus between K and M
(d) Aluminium between F and K

9. Identify the reason for the decrease in IP value from H to K.
(a) Increase in nuclear charge with increase in atomic number
(b) Presence of paired electrons in H
(c) Valence electrons belong to different shells in H and K
(d) Increase in number of valence electrons from H to K

10. Identify the true statement which complies with the IP values in the given curve.
(a) Increase in IP value from F to H is as per the regular periodic trend.
(b) C is the element which can form the cation most easily among the given elements
(c) 'A' indicates the element with the highest IP value in the periodic table.
(d) All of these

Directions for Questions 11–15:

Read the content given in the following passage and interpret the data given in the tables to answer the questions given below.

In the tables given below, some elements are given starting from A to F and P to U. The preceding and succeeding elements of these elements are given in another column. Based on these, identify the given elements and answer the questions that follow.

Element	Preceding element	Succeeding element
A	Sulphur	Argon
B	Nitrogen	Fluorine
C	Beryllium	Carbon
D	Phosphorus	Chlorine
E	Oxygen	Neon
F	Chromium	Iron

Element	Preceding element	Succeeding element
P	Lithium	Boron
Q	Argon	Calcium
R	Boron	Nitrogen
S	Silicon	Sulphur
T	Carbon	Oxygen
U	Potassium	Scandium

11. Identify the correct statements corresponding to the elements given in the table.
(a) The element below A in the periodic table has atomic number 35.
(b) The element 'F' forms coloured compounds
(c) The succeeding element of Q forms ion isoelectronic with the ion of S having same valency
(d) E>B>T represents the correct order of electronegativity of these elements

12.

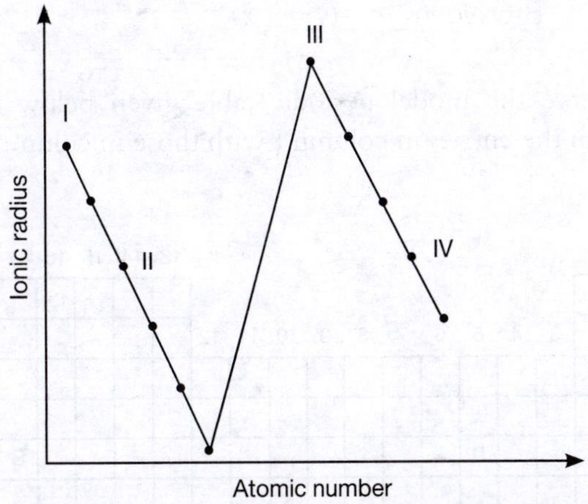

The given graph represents two sets of isoelectronic ions of some elements given in the above table. Identify the option which indicates the correct set of ions.

	I	II	III	IV
(a)	D^{-2}	Q^{+}	A^{-}	F^{+2}
(b)	B^{-2}	F^{+2}	T^{-3}	R^{-4}
(c)	E^{-}	S^{-3}	Q^{+}	A^{-}
(d)	T^{-3}	E^{-}	S^{-3}	U^{+2}

13. Identify the set of elements representing the correct trend of IP values.
(a) C<P<R (b) D<B<A
(c) D<B>A (d) P<C>R

14. **Assertion (A):** The second electron affinity of the element D is negative

Reason (R): The uninegative ion of D would be highly stable

(a) Both A and R are correct and R is the correct explanation of A

(b) Both A and R are correct and R is not the correct explanation of A

(c) A is correct and R is wrong

(d) R is correct and A is wrong

15. Arrange the elements C, P, Q and F in the correct order of Electropositivity.

(a) $C > P > F > Q$ (b) $C < P < F < Q$

(c) $C > P < F > Q$ (d) $C < P > F < Q$

Match The Column

16. The elements and their corresponding values of EA in terms of '*x*' are given in column I and column II. Match the entries in column I with those in column II.

	Element		EA value
(a)	T-nitrogen	(i)	50*x*
(b)	A-Chlorine	(ii)	20*x*
(c)	D-Sulphur	(iii)	47*x*
(d)	E-Fluorine	(iv)	29*x*
(e)	B-Oxygen	(v)	*x*

17. Observe the model periodic table given below and match the entries in column I with those in column II.

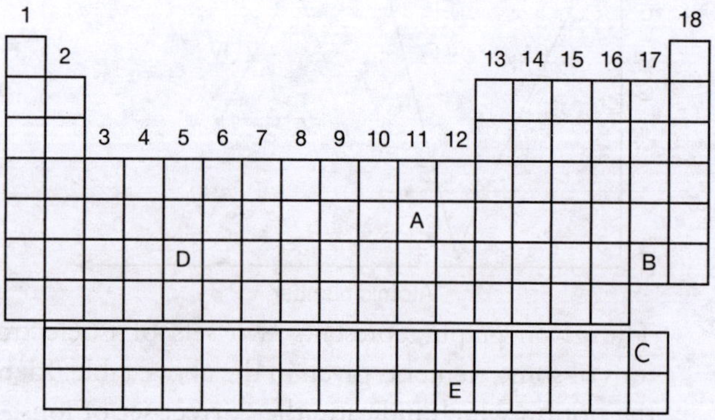

	Column I		Column II
(a)	A	(i)	Post lanthanide element
(b)	B	(ii)	Last element of transition series
(c)	C	(iii)	Coinage metal
(d)	D	(iv)	Radioactive element
(e)	E	(v)	Last element of lanthanide series
		(vi)	Transuranic element
		(vii)	Noble gas element

ANSWER KEYS

Crossword

Across

1. Decreases
6. Transition
8. First
9. Periodicity
12. Same
14. Moseley
15. Dobereiner
17. Helium
18. Two
19. Metalloid
20. Zero

Down

2. Seventeenth
3. Fluorine
4. Scandium
5. Caesium
7. Increases
10. Chlorine
11. Transuranic
13. Copper
16. Bromine

Classroom Wing

Very Short Answer Type Question

1. Caesium
2. inner transition elements
3. Hydrogen, helium
4. decrease
5. IA

Competition Wing

Level 1: Apply your Concepts

1. False
2. False
3. False
4. False
5. True
6. True
7. True
8. True
9. Sodium
10. Atomic weight
11. Atomic weights
12. alkali
13. 8, 7, 18, 7
14. 24.5
15. scandium, gallium
16. 10th
17. IA and IIA
18. 32
19. IA, IIA
20. (i) → (B); (ii) → (A); (iii) → (D); (iv) → (C)
21. (b)
22. (a)
23. (c)
24. (a)
25. (a)
26. (c)
27. (b)
28. (c)
29. (a)
30. (d)
31. (b)
32. (c)
33. (b)
34. (b)
35. (c)
36. (a)
37. (b)
38. (d)
39. (d)
40. (d)
41. (c)
42. (c)

JEE-NEET Special Wing

Multiple-Answer Type Questions

1. (a; d)
2. (a; b; d)
3. (a; b; c; d)
4. (b; d)
5. (a; c; d)

Comprehension-Based Questions

6. (a)
7. (c)
8. (b)
9. (b)
10. (d)
11. (a; b; c; d)
12. (d)
13. (d)
14. (c)
15. (a)

Match The Column

16. (a) ↔ (ii); (b) ↔ (i); (c) ↔ (v); (d) ↔ (iii) ; (e) ↔ (iv)
17. (a) ↔ (iii); (b) ↔ (iv); (c) ↔ (v); (d) ↔ (i) ; (e) ↔ (vi)

Hints and Explanations

Classroom Wing

Very Short Answer Type Question

1. Reducing property is the maximum for caesium.
2. inner transition elements
3. Hydrogen, helium
4. decrease
5. IA
6. Oxidizing property is directly proportional to electro negativity and electron affinity. Therefore, fluorine is a good oxidizing agent.
7. Be, Mg, Ca. According to the law of triads, the average atomic weight of Be and Ca is equal to the atomic weight of Mg.
8. X is iodine and it belongs to the VII-A group.
9. No, the set of atomic numbers: 5, 13, 31, does not obey Dobereiner's Law of Triads.
10. III B
11. Periodic function of their atomic number
12. Groups IA, IIA, IIIA, IVA, VA, VIA and VIIA contain metals, non-metals and metalloids. These elements are called representative elements because their valence electrons represent their group numbers.
13. 2nd and 3rd, 4th and 5th
14. Modern periodic law states that the physical and chemical properties of elements are the periodic functions of their atomic numbers.
15. IA group has most electropositve elements.
16. Right portion of Long Form of Periodic Table consists of metals, non-metals, metalloids and noble gases including extremely electronegative halogens.
17. Distance from centre of nucleus to the outermost orbit
18. Noble gases have very low chemical reactivity. They are contained in group 18.
19. Artificially prepared radioactive elements
20. Minimum energy required for removal of valence electron
21. Down a group–metallic character increases and non-metallic character decreases.
22. Tendency to attract the shared pair of electrons, it is a relative property. It has no units.
23. 1, 7
24. Element X belongs to the VII-A group and third period. Third-period elements are called typical elements.
25. Drastic increase in the second and fourth I.P. values indicate the two elements A and B belong to the I-A and III-A groups, respectively.

Short Answer Type Questions

26. Element A is Ba and B is Rb. I.P. of Ba is less than that of Rb.
27. (i) Ca, Sr, Ba
    (ii) Cl, Br, I
    (iii) Li, Na, K.
    Similar chemical properties.
28. Newland arranged the then known 56 elements in an increasing order of their atomic weights but this system of classification failed to explain similarities in higher elements.
29. Dobereiner could find only three triads and could not not classify most of the other elements.
30. (i) Mendeleev's Periodic Table represents the relationship in the entire network, i.e., in vertical columns and in horizontal rows.
    (ii) Mendeleev left some gaps in his periodic table for some of the then unknown elements based on the properties of the other elements present in the same group. He named these missing elements as Eka boron, Eka aluminium and Eka silicon. Later on, these elements were discovered and named as scandium, gallium and germanium, respectively.

(iii) Mendeleev corrected the doubtful atomic weights of some elements. For example, the atomic weight of indium, i.e., 76 was based on the assumption that indium oxide had the formula InO. This atomic weight placed indium, which has metallic properties, among the non-metals. Mendeleev corrected the formula of indium oxide from InO to In_2O_3. Based on this corrected formula, the atomic weight of indium is 113. He also corrected the atomic weights of the elements beryllium and uranium.

31. (a) (i) Mendeleev's periodic table–Atomic weight.

(ii) Modern periodic table–Atomic number.

(b) A(12) $\rightarrow$ 2, 8, 2 $\Rightarrow$ IIA group and 3rd period

B(33) $\rightarrow$ 2, 8, 18, 5 $\Rightarrow$ VA group and 4th period

C(19) $\rightarrow$ 2, 8, 8, 1 $\Rightarrow$ IA group and 4th period

The chemical properties of elements belonging to same group are similar because they have same number of valence electrons and these electrons only participate in the chemical reactions.

32. Due to their electronic configurations and convenience for keeping Periodic Table organized.

33. Effective nuclear charge increases.

34. Due to same number of valence electrons.

35. (i) Along a period—atomic radius decreases.

(ii) Along a group—atomic radius increases.

36. (i) Group—Number of shells change

(ii) Period—Number of electrons in the valence shell change

37. (i) Tendency of an atom of an element present in a molecule to attract shared electron pair more towards itself is called electronegativity.

(ii) Tendency of an atom of an element to lose one or more electrons to form a positively charged ion is called electropositivity.

38. Modern Periodic table is also referred to as Bohr's table because it follows Bohr's model of the arrangement of elements into four types based on their electronic configuration.

39. (i) Effect of ionization potential and electron affinity on losing and gaining electrons.

(ii) Effect of losing and gaining electrons on oxidizing and reducing nature.

Essay Answer Type Questions

40. A $\rightarrow$ He, B $\rightarrow$ Cs, C $\rightarrow$ Cl, D $\rightarrow$ F

Maximum metallic character is Cs.

Maximum electronegativity is F.

Maximum electron affinity is Cl.

Maximum ionization energy is He.

Hence, the correct order is BDAC.

41. A $\rightarrow$ I-A group and cation formed is A^{+1} (Na^{+1}).

B $\rightarrow$ II-A group and cation formed is B^{+2} (Mg^{+2}).

C $\rightarrow$ VII-A group and anion formed is C^{-1} ($\overline{Cl}$).

D $\rightarrow$ VI-A group and anion formed is D^{-2} (S^{-2}).

$\therefore$ Increasing order of sizes is CDBA.

42. (i) The regular gradation in the properties of elements and their repetition at regular intervals is called periodicity. Some periodic properties are: atomic size, ionization potential, electron affinity, electronegativity, metallic/non-metallic character, electropositive character, etc.

(ii) In a period : atomic radii change as electrons are added to the same energy levels, nuclear charge increases.

(iii) In a group: Addition of an extra shell.

43. Merits

(i) The classification is based on the atomic number of elements, which is more fundamental than the atomic weight.

(ii) In this periodic table, the position of an element is related to the electronic configuration of the atom. Elements belonging to the same group possess same number of electrons in their valence shells and show similar chemical characteristics.

(iii) Variation of chemical properties along a period is correlated with gradual filling of electrons in a particular shell in the period.

(iv) In this table, inert gases are placed at the end of each period which is very logical because valence shells have an octet configuration. So, their inertness can also be explained in terms of the electronic configuration.

(v) Due to the separation of the two subgroups, dissimilar elements (e.g., alkali and coinage metals) do not fall together.

(vi) Different types of elements, such as, (a) active metals, (b) transition metals, (c) non-metals and metalloids (d) noble gases and (e) inner transition elements (lanthanides and actinides) have their separate locations in this periodic table.

Defects

(i) Even after the compilation of the modern periodic table, the position of hydrogen remained controversial. This is because hydrogen with one electron in its valence shell shows similarities with both alkali metals and halogens. Therefore, placing hydrogen in IA group is not completely justifiable.

(ii) The elements lanthanides and actinides could not be placed in the main body of the modern periodic table.

(iii) This periodic table does not reflect the exact distribution of electrons of some of the transition and inner transition elements.

44. Along a period – Electron affinity, Ionization potential, oxidizing capacity increases, reducing capacity decreases

Along a group – Electron affinity, oxidizing capacity, ionization potential decreases, reducing capacity increases.

45. (a) (i) D is a halogen.

(ii) E is an alkali earth metal.

(b) The electronic configuration of G is 2, 8, 6.

(c) H is the element which has octet configuration in its outermost orbit.

(d) I is the element which has the largest atomic radius.

Competition Wing

Level 1: Apply your Concepts

20. Caesium belongs to a very long period.

Xeon belongs to the second long period.

Potassium belongs to a long period.

Radium belongs to an incomplete period.

Hence, the correct answer is: (i) → (B); (ii) → (A); (iii) → (D); (iv) → (C)

21. Across the period, ionization energy increases due to a decrease in atomic size. Due to the stable valence electronic configuration of II-A group elements, they possess higher I.P values than corresponding III-A group elements.

Hence, the correct option is (b).

22. Across the period, electron affinity increases due to a decrease in atomic size. The 18th group elements possess zero electron affinity values due to stable octet configuration.

Hence, the correct option is (a).

24. Na^+ ion possesses a stable octet configuration. Hence, the second I.P. of Na^{+1} is greater than that of Mg^{+1}.

Hence, the correct option is (a).

25. With an increase in the number of electrons in the species, the repulsive force increases. Hence, the energy absorbed is more than the energy released during the addition of a second electron.

Hence, the correct option is (a).

36. 1 Some elements be grouped in sets of three elements in the increasing order of their atomic weights in which the atomic weight of the middle element was found to be the arithmetic mean of the atomic weights of the other two elements.

4 When the elements are arranged in the increasing order of their atomic weights, the eighth element resembles the first in physical and chemical properties just as the eighth note on a musical scale resembles the first one.

3 The physical and chemical properties of elements are periodic functions of their atomic weights.

2 The physical and chemical properties of elements are periodic functions of their atomic numbers.

Hence, the correct answer is (a).

37. 3 The atomic size of the elements decreases from left to right.

2 Effective nuclear charge of the elements increases from left to right.

4 The tendency to gain electrons and form anions increases from left to right.

1 The amount of energy released during the addition of an electron increases from left to right along periods.

Hence, the correct answer is (b).

38. D Determination of the positions of Y and Z in the periodic table based on the position of X.

C Determination of the number of shells and the number of valence electrons present in X, Y and Z.

A Effect of the number of valence electrons and number of shells on atomic size.

Hence, the correct answer is (d).

39. Among the third period elements halogen and alkaline earth metal are chlorine and magnesium, respectively.

Hence, the correct answer is (d).

40. Inert gases have zero electron affinity due to their stable octet configuration, whereas IA group elements have minimum electron affinity value due to large atomic size. Halogens have high electron affinity due to small atomic size. Hence, Cl and Cs have maximum and minimum electron affinity values, respectively.

Hence, the correct answer is (d).

41. According to Dobereiner's classification, the elements of the triads (Li, Na, K; Cl, Br, I; Ca, Sr, Ba) have similar chemical properties. Elements C, N and O do not show similar properties.

Hence, the correct answer is (c).

42. Elements in IIIA group are B, Al, Ga, In, Tl and in this B belongs to the second period.

∴ The element in IIIA group and fourth period is Ga (gallium), whose atomic number is 31.

Hence, the correct answer is (c).

Level 2: Review your Concepts

43. A → 2, 8, 8, 1 ⇒ 4th period and I-A group
B → 2, 8, 6 ⇒ 3rd period VI-A group
C → 2, 8, 1 ⇒ 3rd period I-A group
D → 2, 5 ⇒ 2nd period and V-A group
E → 2, 8, 18, 8, 2 ⇒ 5th period II-A group
The correct order of atomic sizes is E > A > C > B > D.

44. Due to the stable electronic configuration of N, it possesses a higher I.P. value than that of C.
∴ X → C
Y → N
Z → O

45. A > A^{+1}, B^{-2} > B. In the case of cation, the effective nuclear charge is more as against the corresponding neutral atom. Hence, the size of the atom is greater than the cation. It is the reverse in the case of anions.

46. X → S, B → O, D → Se
A → P, C → Cl
Selenium is the least non-metallic in nature.

47. The elements with atomic numbers 8, 7, 11, 12, 13 and 9 are oxygen, nitrogen, sodium, magnesium, aluminium, and fluorine, respectively. These elements belong to VIA (16), VA (15), IA (1), IIA (2), IIIA (13) and VIIA (17) groups. Generally, these elements form O^{-2}, N^{-3}, Na^+, Mg^{+2}, Al^{3+} and F^- ions. The order of ionic size is

$N^{-3} > O^{-2} > F^- > Na^+ > Mg^{+2} > Al^{3+}$.

48. (a) (i) Transition metals come to the right of the respective alkali and alkaline earth metals in the period.
(ii) Factors that affect density such as atomic mass, atomic radius varies from left to right.
(iii) atomic radius decreases from left to right.
(iv) atomic mass increases from lest to right. hence the density (mass per area) of transitions metal is greater than alkali and alkaline metals.
(b) (A) Since $I.P_3$ increases drastically, X belongs to IIA group and X could be Ca.
(B) Ca can form dipositive ion.

49. (i) R element is Si.
(ii) The atomic radius of atoms generally decreases across a period and increases across the group.
(iii) ionisation energies increases across the period and decreases across the group.

50. (i) Cations are smaller than their corresponding atoms and anions are larger than their corresponding atoms
(ii) trend of atomic size along a period and down a group
(iii) position of the largest atom which can form cation
(iv) position of the smallest atom which can form anion

51. (i) Transition metals shows catalytic behavior as they easily give and take electrons from other molecules. They have a valency of 2.
(ii) relation between electronic configuration and bonding

52. An oxidizing agent undergoes reduction and gain electrons and elements with non-metallic character readily gain electron and are good oxidizing agent.
A reducing agent undergoes oxidization and loses electron and more electropositive elements readily donate and lose electron and are good reducing agent.

53. (i) the element X is Ca
(ii) electronic configuration of X
(iii) atomic number of X based on periodic arrangement of elements
(iv) electronic configuration of element below X
(v) atomic number of element below X

54. Electrons addition to an atom makes the increased negative charge puts stress on the electrons already there, causing energy to be released

55. (i) Valance shell electron configuration -4 as the fourth ionization energy is the highest
(ii) identification of respective group number from the valence electrons
(iii) writing the formulae of its chloride and oxide

56. (i) position of B, Be, Al in the periodic table
(ii) comparison of size and ionization potential of B, Be and Al
(iii) relation between size, IP and nature of the oxides formed

57. Triad of chlorine, Y and iodine
Atomic weights 35.5 – 127

$$\text{Mean atomic wt} = \frac{35.5 + 127}{2} \Rightarrow 81.25$$

∴ atomic weight of Y = 81.25

58. Let the atomic weights of X, Y and Z be Z_x, Z_y and Z_z, respectively.

$$\therefore \frac{Z_x}{Z_z} = \frac{7}{25} \Rightarrow Z_x = \frac{7}{25}.Z_z \rightarrow (1)$$

Given that $Z_x + Z_z = 160$

$$\therefore \frac{7}{25}.Z_z + Z_z = 160 \Rightarrow Z_z = 125$$

From equation (1)

$$Z_x = \frac{7}{25}.125 = 35$$

Atomic weight of Y is $Z_y = \dfrac{35+125}{2} = 80$.

[$\therefore$ X, Y and Z form Dobereiner triad]

59. Electronic configuration of element X is

K	L	M	N	O
2	8	18	8	2

The element X is strontium with atomic number 38. It belongs to the fifth period and 2nd group (IIA) or group 2.

60. (a) As Y is a noble gas, the group of Y is 18th group or zero group.

X = A – 2; group of X is 16th group or VI A.

Z = A + 2; group of Y is 2nd group or II A

(b) X $\Rightarrow$ Valency = 2 (electronegative)

Z $\Rightarrow$ Valency = 2 (electropositive)

Hence, the formula is ZX.

61. They should be placed in the same slot, i.e., they belong to IVA or 14 group and 2nd period as they have same atomic number.

62. (a) The noble gas is C.
(b) D is an alkali metal, i.e., Na.
(c) B has the highest-electron affinity.
(d) D has the strongest-metallic character.
(e) The unit of ionization energy is kJ/mole.

63. As the positive charge increases, the effective nuclear charge on the outermost electron increases. So, work done for removing an electron increases with the increase of charge on the cation.

64. As the positive ions have equal number of electrons, A, B and C must be isoelectronic and form unipositive, dipositive and tripositive ions. With the increase in nuclear charge, the effective nuclear force of attraction on the outermost electrons increases. Therefore, the ionic size decreases from A^+, B^{2+}, and C^{3+}.

65. Elements with higher electronegativity have greater tendency to attract the shared pair of electrons present in a compound. An atom which undergoes reduction is an oxidizing agent. The greater the electronegativity value, the more is its tendency to undergo reduction. So, it acts as a good oxidizing agent.

66. X $\rightarrow$ 2, 8, 8, 2; Z $\rightarrow$ 2, 8, 2

Y $\rightarrow$ 2, 8, 8, 1; A $\rightarrow$ 2, 8, 18, 18, 8, 1

(a) Since X and Z; Y and A possess same number of valence electrons and they belong to the same group.

Level 3: Assess Your Concepts

67. A $\rightarrow$ Na; Na has less tendency to form cations.

B $\rightarrow$ Ar; Ar has zero electron affinity.

C $\rightarrow$ Cl; Cl has good oxidizing property.

D $\rightarrow$ Rb; Rb has minimum ionization energy.

Hence, the correct order is BDCA.

68. A belongs to IA group.

B belongs to II-A group.

C belongs to VII-A group.

D belongs to VI-A/IV-A/V-A groups.

$\therefore$ The correct order of atomic sizes is CDBA.

69. (i) Alkali metal are highly reactive metals

(ii) electronic configuration of alkali metals

(iii) ionization potential of alkali metals

(iv) effect of ionization potential on reactivity

(v) relating reactivity and tarnishing

70. (i) Noble gases have 8 valance electron whereas alkali earth metals have 2+ configuration, i.e., they can give up 2 electrons.

(ii) relation between valence shell electronic configuration and stability in both the cases

(iii) types of forces existing between an electron going to be added to a noble gas

(iv) energy change involved when an electron is added to a noble gas element

71. (i) comparison between different electrons entering different shells

(ii) variation of nuclear charge on the size of the elements from K to Ni

(iii) variation of the nuclear charge on elements K to Cs down the group

(iv) effect of nuclear charge on size

(v) relation between mass, size and density

72. The metals which belong to alkali metal groups, such as, K, Cs and Rb can be used in solar cells. The reason is that these metals have very low first ionization energy. Hence, they can lose electron easily when exposed to sunlight.

73. Though F^- and O^{2-} are isoelectronic species, the formation of F^- is exothermic while O^{2-} is endothermic. Elements (or) ions having inert gas configuration are highly stable. For attaining the nearest inert gas configuration fluorine has one electron less. So, it readily accepts electrons and the formation of F^- takes place. In this process, a large amount of energy is released. But in the case of the formation of O^{2-} repulsions exist between the added electron and already existing O^{1-} ion. So, this process requires supply of energy to overcome this repulsion. Hence, the formation of O^{2-} is an endothermic process.

74. Addition of an electron to uninegative ion involves repulsion between the electron and negatively-charged ion. So, energy is required to add an electron to a uninegative ion. Hence, it is endothermic process. When an electron is added to a neutral atom, it works towards the force of attraction exerted by the nucleus of the neutral atom, and hence, energy is released during this process.

75. Oxidizing agent is the substance which not only oxidizes other substances but also undergoes reduction by itself, i.e., it accepts electrons from the others. The more the non-metallic character of an element, the more is its tendency to accept electrons, and thus acting as a good oxidizing agent.

Reducing agent is the substance which reduces the other substances but itself undergoes oxidation. That means it gives up its own electrons.

The more the metallic character, the more is the tendency of losing electrons. Hence, metals are good reducing agents. The pairing should be A and D and B and C.

76. As A attains stability by gaining an electron, it must form a uninegative ion. The third shell being the valence shell of A, the electronic configuration of A is 2, 8, 7. So the atomic number is 17. A, B, and C have successive atomic numbers. So the atomic number of B is 18 and that of C is 19. A, B, and C are chlorine, argon, and potassium, respectively.

Group	VIIA(17)	0(18)	IA(1)
	A	B	C
	Cl	Ar	K
Z	17	18	19
Electronic configuration	2, 8, 7	2, 8, 8	2, 8, 8,

Since Cl has the highest-electron affinity, it gains an electron and attains stability, thus, it has greater oxidizing power. K which belongs to the IA(1) group and 4th period possesses greater atomic size, lower ionization potential and greater reducing power. Atomic size gradually increases from Cl to K. Ar which belongs to the 18th group possesses maximum ionization potential due to a stable octet configuration.

77. (a) Due to stable octet configuration, noble gas has zero electron affinity. Hence, noble gas is C.

(b) Generally, VIIA group elements possess the highest electron affinity value in a given period. Therefore, VIIA group element is H.

(c) Elements with the high electron affinity values are good oxidizing agents. Hence, H is the strongest oxidizing agent.

JEE-NEET Special Wing

Multiple-Answer Type Questions

1. Z = 40[Zirconium]; Z=47 [Silver] These are the 5th period elements belonging to 2nd transition series and possess two incomplete shells.

2.

Element	Period	Group	Element	Description
A	4	11	Silver	Coinage metal
B	5	16	Tellurium	Metalloid element of that group
D	2	17	Fluorine	The most electronegative element

3. All the given ions are isoelectronic species. The ionic radius increases with decrease in atomic number. Nitrogen, oxygen, sodium and magnesium possess lesser nuclear charge and hence can form stable ions with larger ionic radii.

2nd period and 16th group	Oxygen [2, 6]	O^{-2}[8p;10e⁻]
3rd period and 1st group	Sodium	Na^{+}[11p;10e⁻]
2rd period and 15th group	Nitrogen	N^{-3} [7p;10e⁻]
3rd period and 2nd group	Magnesium [2,8,2]	Mg^{+2}[12p;10e⁻]

4.

	1st IP	2nd IP	3rd IP	4th IP	Formula of oxide
(d)	380	415	1753	2045	MO
(e)	157	348	589	2169	M_2O_3
(f)	276	3449	4297	5583	M_2O
(d)	558	1274	2489	5976	M_2O_3

5.

	Elements in Sequential order	Periodic property
(a)	Cl > F > Br	Electron affinity
(c)	K < Rb < Cs	Reducing capacity
(d)	Cl < Ar > K	Ionisation potential

Comprehension-Based Questions

6. Carbon. J represents boron and L represents nitrogen.

7. Na;Mg;Al

8. N and D represent oxygen and neon. The middle element would be fluorine.

9. H indicates magnesium while K indicates aluminium. The presence of paired electrons in magnesium makes it difficult to remove the electron from valence shell. Hence IP value of magnesium is higher than the IP value of aluminium.

10. F and H: Sodium and Magnesium. Successive elements of the same period. Increase in IP value is as per the regular periodic trend.
C indicates potassium which has the least IP value among the given elements in the curve. Therefore, it forms the cation most easily.
A is helium which has the highest IP value in the periodic table.

Common Solutions for questions 11 to 15:
The elements indicated in the table can be identified as below.

Element	Name of the actual element
A	Chlorine
B	Oxygen
C	Boron
D	Sulphur
E	Fluorine
F	Manganese

Element	Name of the actual element
P	Beryllium
Q	Potassium
R	Carbon
S	Phosphorus
T	Nitrogen
U	Calcium

11. The element below chlorine in the periodic table is bromine with atomic number 35. Manganese is a transition element and forms pale pink coloured compounds. The succeeding element of potassium is calcium. It forms Ca^{+2} ion with electronic configuration 2,8,8. The stable ion of phosphorus is P^{-3} with the electronic configuration 2, 8, 8. These two are isoelectronic ions. F>O>N represents the correct order of electronegativity. All the statements are correct.

12.

	I	II	III	IV
(d)	T^{-3}	E^{-}	S^{-3}	U^{+2}

13. Beryllium > Boron < Carbon is the correct order of IP values. They are indicated by the alphabets P; C; R in the given table. Hence, the correct order is P>C<R.

14. D is sulphur. It forms stable S^{-2} ion and its 2nd EA value is negative and involves release of energy. So, assertion is correct but reason R is a wrong or incorrect statement.

15. Boron > Beryllium > Manganese> Potassium is the correct order of electropositivity

Match The Column

16.

	Element		EA value
(a)	T-nitrogen	(ii)	20*x*
(b)	A-Chlorine	(i)	50*x*
(c)	D-Sulphur	(v)	*x*
(d)	E-Fluorine	(iii)	47*x*
(e)	B-Oxygen	(iv)	29*x*

17.

	Column I		Column II
(a)	A	(iii)	Coinage metal
(b)	B	(iv)	Radioactive element
(c)	C	(v)	Last element of lanthanide series
(d)	D	(i)	Post lanthanide element
(e)	E	(vi)	Transuranic element

CHAPTER

7

Chemical Bonding

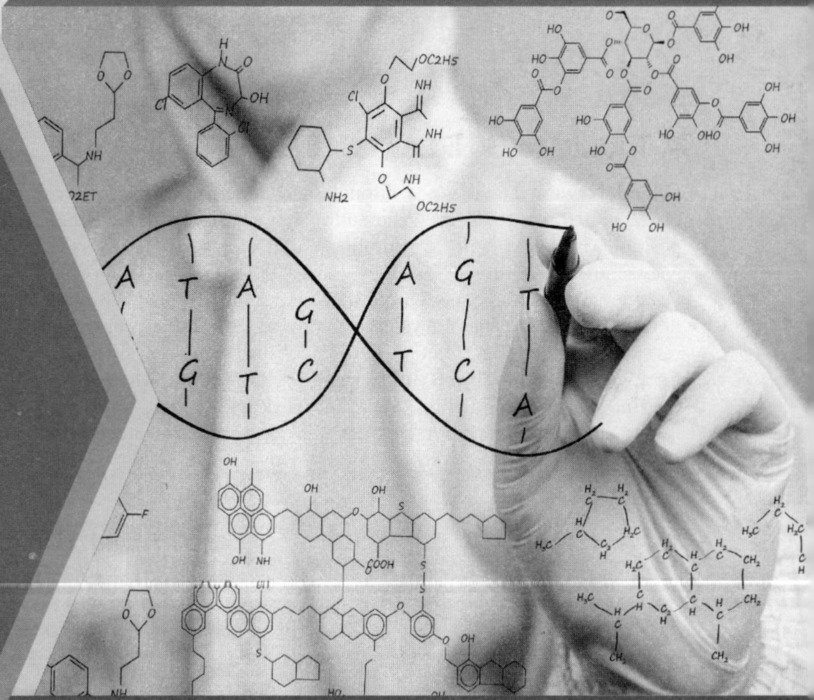

Remember

Before beginning this chapter, you should be able to:

- know concepts of atom and subatomic particles.
- understand structure of atom and related theories.
- express chemical reactions.

Key Ideas

After completing this chapter, you should be able to:

- **understand** the relation between electronic configuration and bond formation.
- describe the mode of formation of ionic and covalent bonds along with representation by Lewis dot structures and properties of ionic and covalent compounds
- explain the mode of formation of coordinate, covalent and metallic bonds, and to correlate with the properties of metals.
- compare the different intermolecular forces and their relation with properties of substances.
- understand the electronic concept of oxidation and reduction.

Scientific Crypt

A Tribute to G.N. Lewis (1875–1946)

Gilbert Newton Lewis was a distinguished American scientist born on 25th October 1875, in Weymouth, Massachusetts. He held high positions in world-famous institutions such as Harvard University, Massachusetts Institute of Technology and the University of California, Berkeley was where he spent most of his career and acquired the credit of transforming the chemistry department into a world-class centre for research and teaching. Though Lewis published a number of papers on a wide range of subjects, his paper '*The Atom and the Molecule*' was the one which contained his significant work on covalent bonds and its visualization of Lewis dot structure. His other studies included acids and bases, chemical thermodynamics, heavy water, phosphorescence etc. For such commendable contributions, he became the recipient of a large number of prestigious awards in science. But it is unfortunate and rather astonishing to realize that he was not on the list of Nobel laureates. Many scientists of his time also believed that he deserved to have acquired it as he was nominated for it as many as 35 times. However, the fact that many of his students became Nobel laureates either while working under him or in later years bears testimony to his excellence and in fact, this is a greater reward than he himself achieving it. Eventually, he took his last breath on 23rd March 1946 while working with liquid hydrogen cyanide in the laboratory.

FUN TIME

CROSSWORD

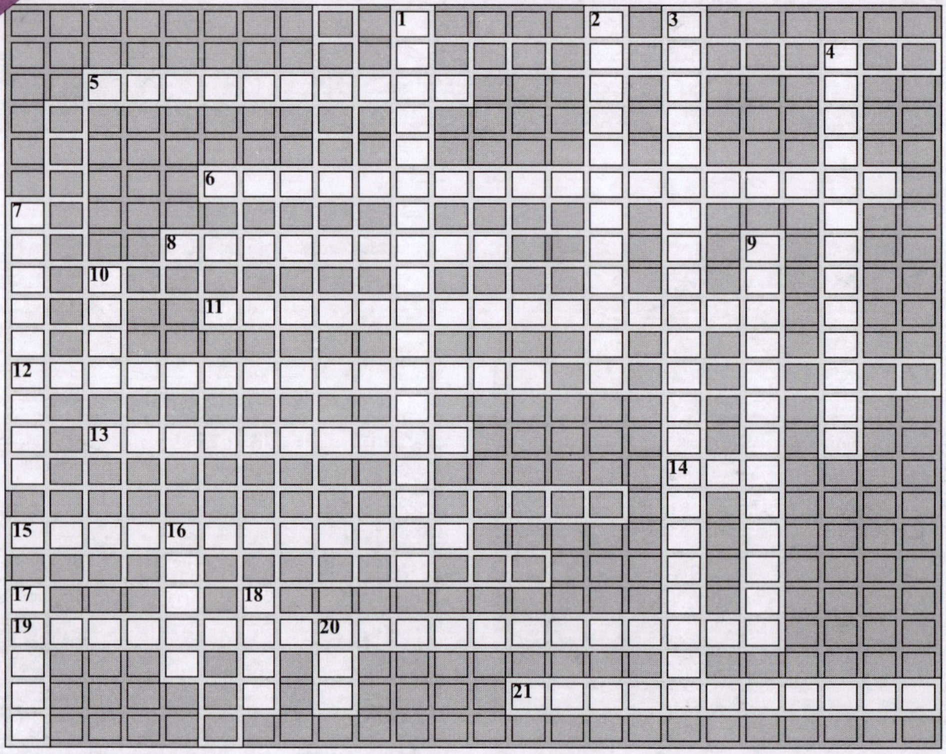

Across

5. Bond formed between ammonia and H^+
6. Bond formed between two oxygen atoms
8. Strong electrostatic force of attraction
11. The name given to the octet around the central atom in boron trichloride
12. Number of electrons lost or gained by an atom
13. The internuclear distance corresponding to the minimum energy state
14. Electrovalence of chlorine in magnesium chloride
15. Stronger dipole-dipole attraction due to high electronegativity difference
19. Condition favourable for the formation of anion
21. Metal ion in metal lattice

Down

1. Bond formed between carbon and hydrogen
2. Force of attraction which binds metal kernels in a metallic lattice
3. Condition favourable for the formation of cation
4. The name given to the octet around the central atom in sulphur hexafluoride
7. Number of electrons contributed for sharing
9. Energy associated with the formation of ionic crystal
10. Number of bond pairs in acetylene molecule
16. Presence of eight electron configuration in the valence shell
17. Covalency of nitrogen in ammonia
18. The gas with van der Waal's forces of attraction
20. Number of lone pairs in a water molecule

INTRODUCTION

There are numerous chemical reactions taking place in the nature. A chemical reaction involves change in molecular composition of a substance. It has been established that atom is the smallest particle of matter which takes part in a chemical reaction. Molecule is the smallest constituent particle of matter which has an independent existence and which represents the properties of the respective elements or compounds. Most of the elements in nature have been found to exist in a combined state. However, there are some atoms which have independent existence and are considered to be highly stable atoms. Except those of a few elements, atoms of most of the elements have an inherent tendency to combine and form molecules. The combining atoms may belong to the same element or different elements. Within the molecules, the atoms are held together by attractive forces. Study of the types of bonds, the conditions required for bond formation, and the energy changes involved in chemical bond formation are some aspects of study of chemical bonding.

Chemical Bond

Noble gases are monoatomic. They do not combine either with their own atoms or atoms of other substances. These are the unique gases having eight electrons (except helium) in their respective valence shells and their configuration is called an **octet configuration**. Helium has only two electrons as it has only one main energy level. This is called a **duplet configuration**.

Except noble gases, atoms of all other elements have 1–7 electrons in their valence shells. The octet of the noble gases and the pair of electrons in helium are so stable that atoms of other elements also strive to attain the same electronic configuration to become stable.

In order to attain stability, atoms unite to form molecules, their electrons get rearranged and a bond is said to be formed.

> **Konnect**
>
> The idea of a 'chemical bond' was first introduced by the American chemist G.N. Lewis in 1916. Before this, there was no concrete understanding of how atoms stuck together.

Types of Chemical Bonds

The various types of bonds are listed as follows:

1. Ionic bond
2. Covalent bond
3. Coordinate bond
4. Metallic bond

These bonds are discussed in length in the following chapter.

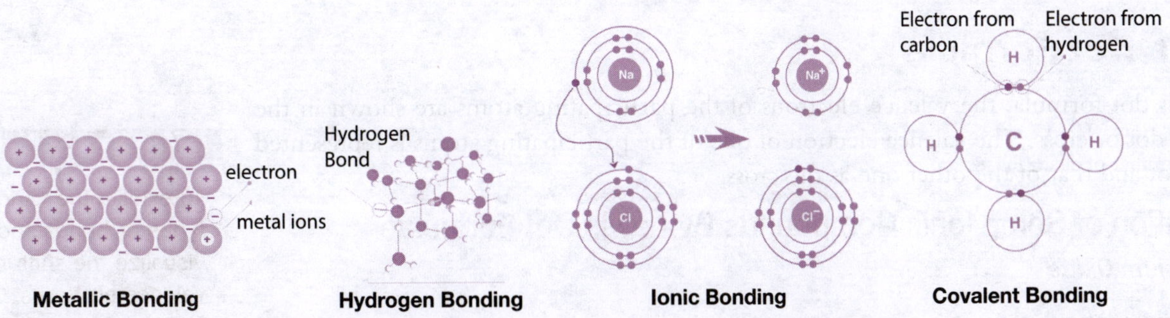

Figure 7.1 Different types of chemical bonds

Ionic Bond

A chemical bond is formed between two atoms by complete transfer of one or more electrons from one atom to the other as a result of which the atoms attain their nearest inert gas configuration. The electrostatic force of attraction which holds the two oppositely charged ions together is called **ionic bond**.

During the formation of an ionic bond, one atom loses electron(s) forming positively charged ion called **cation** while the other atom gains electron(s) forming negatively-charged ion called **anion**. The cation and anion are held together by strong electrostatic forces of attraction. The resulting compounds formed are called **ionic compounds**.

> **Info Bytes!**
>
> Ionic bonds form when one atom donates an electron (or electrons) to another. This transfer results in the formation of oppositely charged ions which attract each other.

Formation of Potassium Chloride

Electronic configuration of

Potassium (19) is 2, 8, 8, 1

Chlorine (17) is 2, 8, 7

Potassium has a tendency to lose its one valence electron to attain the nearest inert gas configuration of argon.

$$K - e^- \rightarrow K^+$$

Chlorine has a tendency to accept an electron from potassium to attain the electronic configuration of argon.

$$Cl + e^- \rightarrow Cl^-$$

$$K^+ + Cl^- \rightarrow KCl$$

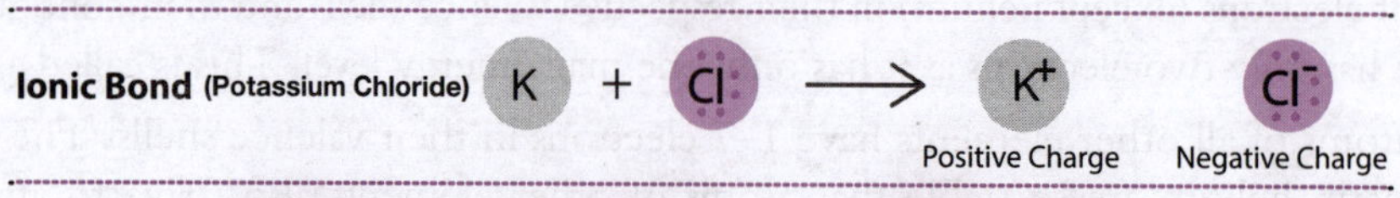

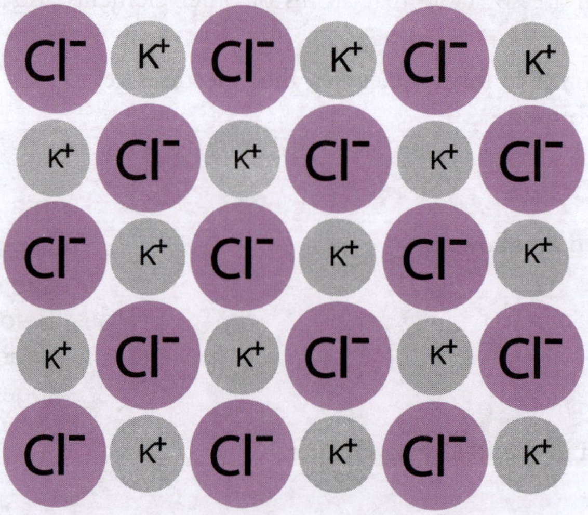

Figure 7.2 Formation of bonds in KCl

Lewis Dot Formula

In Lewis dot formula, the valence electrons of the participating atoms are shown in the form of dot or cross. The valence electron of one of the participating atoms is represented as the dot and that of the other one as the cross.

> **Info Bytes!**
>
> To explain the various types of bonds and to visualize the shift in the valence electrons, G. N. Lewis proposed the **Lewis dot formula**.

Formation of Some Ionic Compounds By Lewis Dot Formulae

Magnesium Oxide

Electronic configuration of

Magnesium (12) is 2, 8, 2

Oxygen (8) is 2, 6

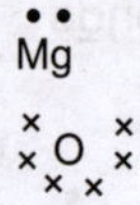

Magnesium loses two electrons from its valence shell while oxygen gains these two electrons such that both the elements attain the nearest inert gas configuration of neon.

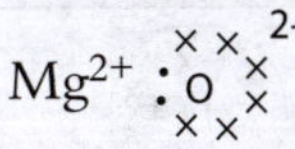

Formula: MgO

Calcium Fluoride

Electronic configuration of

Calcium (20) is 2, 8, 8, 2

Fluorine (9) is 2, 7

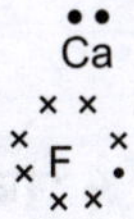

Calcium loses two electrons from its valence shell while fluorine can gain only one electron to attain its nearest inert gas configuration. Hence, the two electrons are lost by one calcium atom and one electron each is accepted by two fluorine atoms.

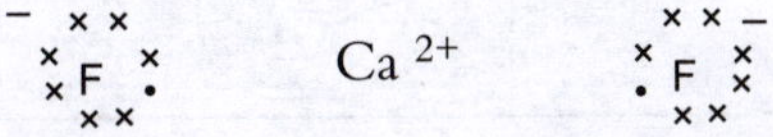

Formula: CaF_2

Covalent Bond

Covalent bond is a bond formed when two atoms share one or more electron pairs. Each atom contributes equal number of electron(s) towards the bond formation.

Formation of Hydrogen Molecule

Hydrogen has one electron. It shares this electron with another atom of hydrogen, attaining the duplet configuration. Hence, the two hydrogen atoms share the electron pair and thereby a covalent bond is formed between the two hydrogen atoms.

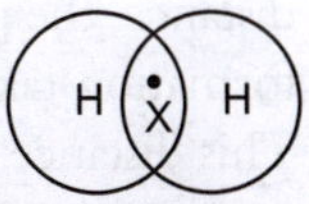

Formation of Hydrogen Chloride

Electronic configuration of

H (Z = 1) is 1

Cl (Z = 17) is 2, 8, 7

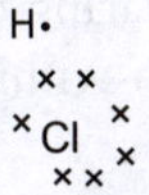

> **Info Bytes!**
>
> The strongest type of bond is the covalent bond, found in diamonds - making it the hardest known natural material on Earth.

The pair of electrons (one is contributed by hydrogen and another one by chlorine) is shared by both hydrogen and chlorine atoms. Thus, hydrogen attains its stable duplet configuration and chlorine attains its stable octet configuration.

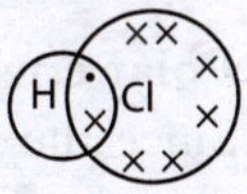

Some examples of covalent molecules using Lewis dot symbols are provided in the following:

Table 7.1 Covalent bonding using Lewis dot symbols

Molecules	No. of valence electrons	Structures
Hydrogen (H_2)	1	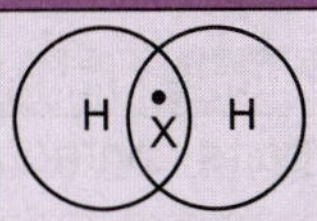 1 shared pair
Oxygen (O_2)	6	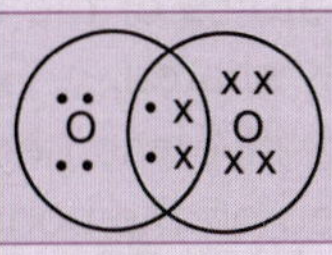 2 shared pairs
Nitrogen (N_2)	5	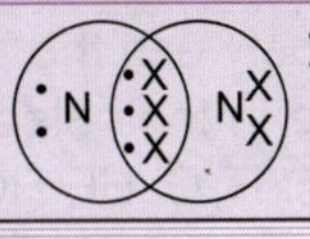 3 shared pairs

(Continued)

Table 7.1 Continued

Molecules	No. of valence electrons	Structures
Chlorine (Cl_2)	7	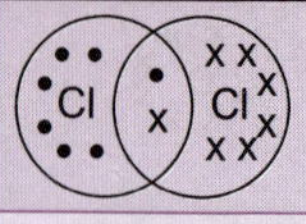 1 shared pair
Water (H_2O)	$H \rightarrow 1, O \rightarrow 6$	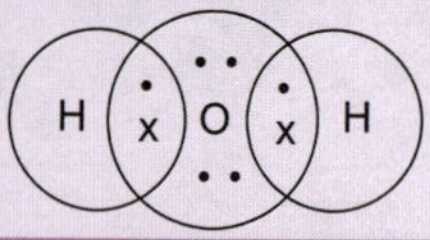 2 shared pairs
Methane (CH_4)	$C \rightarrow 4, H \rightarrow 1$	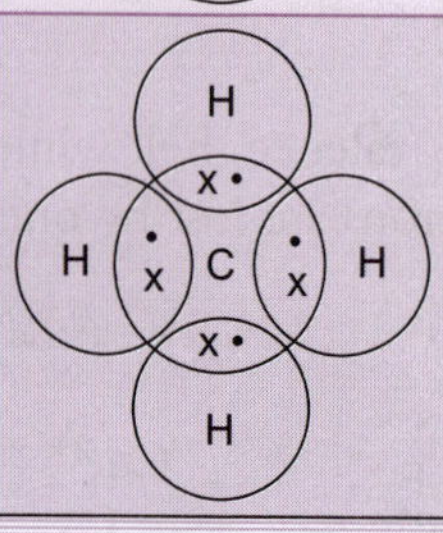 4 shared pairs

Energy Changes During Covalent Bond Formation

Consider the formation of hydrogen molecule, when two hydrogen atoms approach each other, attractive forces develop between the electrons of one atom and the nucleus of the other atom. At the same time, repulsive forces also exist between the nuclei of the two atoms and the electrons of the two atoms. As the two atoms are brought closer to each other, at some distance, the proton–electron attraction just balances the electron–electron repulsion and proton–proton repulsion. The bond formation takes place at this distance which corresponds to minimum possible energy state and the system becomes stable. This distance between the two nuclei is called **bond length**.

Non-Polar Covalent Bonds

In the hydrogen molecule, the electrons reside in the space between the two nuclei where they are attracted simultaneously by the protons present in both the nuclei of the two hydrogen atoms.

Since the bonding between two hydrogen atoms is associated with equitable sharing of electrons between the bonded atoms, this does not result in any charge separation within the molecule. These types of bonds are called **non-polar covalent bonds.**

Info Bytes!

Energy is always released when a covalent bond is formed. This is because the system becomes more stable as the atoms bond together.

Polar Covalent Bond

Polar covalent bond is a type of covalent bond formed between two non-identical atoms. Since the two atoms differ in their capacity to attract the shared electron pair, unequal sharing of electrons results. Due to the unequal sharing of electrons, partial positive and negative charges are developed on the bonded atoms and the bond is said to be polar.

Table 7.2 Comparative study between polar and non-polar covalent bonds

Parameters	Polar covalent compounds	Non-polar covalent compounds
Sharing of electrons	Electron pairs contributed by both the bonded atoms of the molecule are unequally shared.	Electron pairs contributed by both the bonded atoms forming the covalent molecule are equally shared.
Development of charge	Slight positive and negative charges are developed on the bonded atoms.	No charge is developed due to equal sharing of electrons.
Constituent atoms	Formed between the atoms having difference in their electronegativities. Examples: H_2O, HF, HCl, NH_3, etc.	Formed by identical atoms. Examples: Cl_2, O_2, N_2, etc.

Table 7.3 Properties responsible for the formation of ionic and covalent bond

Properties	Ionic bond	Covalent bond
Ionization energy	The lower the value of ionization potential of the element, the higher is the probability of cation formation. Likewise, higher ionization potential values lead to anion formation. Hence, if the difference of ionization potential between the two atoms is more, ionic compounds are formed.	Atoms with higher ionization potential are unable to lose their valence electrons and hence, prefer to form covalent bonds by sharing of electrons.
Electron affinity	Atoms with very low electron affinity form ionic bond with the atoms of higher electron affinity.	The formation of a covalent bond is favored when the combining atoms have almost equal electron affinity.
Electronegativity	The greater is the difference in electronegativities between the two combining atoms, the greater are the chances of transfer of electron(s) from one atom to another. Hence, greater electronegativity difference between the two combining atoms leads to the formation of an ionic bond.	If the electronegativities of the combining atoms do not differ much, then the bond formed between them is likely to be covalent.
Metallic and Non-metallic character	If one of the atoms is metallic and the other one is non-metallic, then the difference in ionization potential, electron affinity and electronegativity becomes more which leads to the formation of an ionic bond.	If both the atoms are non-metallic, then the difference in ionization potential, electron affinity and electronegativity is very less, and this leads to the formation of a covalent bond.

Table 7.4 Comparative study of the properties of ionic and covalent compounds

		Covalent compounds	
Properties	**Ionic compounds**	**Polar**	**Non-polar**
Physical state	Most of the ionic compounds are crystalline solids. X-ray studies of the ionic compound have revealed that the constituent particles of the crystals are ions, not molecules. The cations and anions are held together very strongly by electrostatic force of attraction. Hence, the ions cannot be displaced from their position, and thus, the ionic compounds are generally hard solids.	Generally liquids or gases. This is because kinetic energy of the molecules easily overcomes the weak intermolecular (electrostatic) forces between the polar covalent molecules.	Generally a liquid or a gas. This is because kinetic energy of the molecules easily overcomes the weak van der Waal's forces acting between the non-polar covalent molecules.
Melting and boiling points	Have high melting and boiling points. Considerable heat energy is required to overcome the electrostatic force of attraction between the ions of an electrovalent compound and make the ions mobile. Hence, they have high melting and boiling points.	Have low melting and boiling points because a small amount of energy is sufficient to overcome the weak electrostatic force of attraction or the H-bonding between the polar covalent molecules.	Have low melting and boiling points because a small amount of energy is sufficient to overcome the weak van der Waal's forces acting between the molecules.

(Continued)

Table 7.4 Continued

Properties	Ionic compounds	Covalent compounds: Polar	Covalent compounds: Non-polar
Solubility	Generally soluble in polar solvents like water, but insoluble in non-polar organic solvents. Molecules of the polar solvent like water can overcome the force of attraction between the ions in the crystal of the ionic solute. As a result, the ions become mobile and disperse in all directions in the polar solvent. Non-polar organic solvents cannot overcome the force of attraction between the ions of the ionic compound. Hence, ionic compounds do not dissolve in non-polar organic solvents.	Soluble in polar solvents due to the presence of partial charges. Also soluble in non-polar covalent liquids, due to similar forces between the molecules.	Insoluble in polar solvents like water because they do not ionize, but soluble in non-polar covalent liquids like benzene, carbon tetrachloride, due to similar forces.
Density	The oppositely charged ions in an ionic compound are held closely by electrostatic force of attraction. Hence, the number of ions per unit volume in an ionic compound is more and thereby its density is high.	Generally, they exist in the form of liquid or in gaseous states due to weak intermolecular forces. Hence, the number of molecules per unit volume is less, thereby leading to low density.	Generally, they exist in liquid or gaseous states due to weak intermolecular forces. Hence, the number of molecules per unit volume is less, thereby leading to low density.
Electrical conductivity	Electrovalent compounds conduct electricity either in the fused state or in their aqueous solutions, due to the presence of mobile ions. Since the ions are charged particles, they move towards the respective electrodes under the influence of an electric field and conduct electricity.	These compounds ionize in water and the ions help in conducting electricity.	These compounds do not ionize, and hence, do not conduct electricity.

EXAMPLE 7.1

(i) Why do atoms combine to form molecules instead of existing independently?

(ii) How do differences in electronegativity between atoms influence the polarity of a covalent bond?

(iii) Why are non-polar covalent compounds generally insoluble in water?

SOLUTION

(i) Atoms combine to form molecules because it allows them to achieve a more stable electronic configuration, often resembling the electron configuration of noble gases.

(ii) When there's a significant difference in electronegativity between two bonded atoms, the more electronegative atom pulls the shared electrons closer to itself, creating a partial negative charge on it and a partial positive charge on the other atom, leading to a polar covalent bond.

(iii) Non-polar covalent compounds lack the partial charges necessary for interactions with polar water molecules, making them generally insoluble in water.

EXAMPLE 7.2

Between MgO and Na_2O, which has a stronger ionic bond? Why?

SOLUTION

Mg^{2+} ion is smaller than Na^+ ion since the greater is the charge on the cation, the greater is the effective nuclear charge and the smaller is the size. Due to the smaller size of Mg^{2+}, MgO has a stronger ionic bond than Na2O.

EXAMPLE 7.3 Between lithium and aluminium, which can form oxides more easily and why?

SOLUTION

Lithium has a lower ionization potential value than aluminium. Therefore, lithium has a greater tendency to lose one electron and form Li^+ ion than aluminium which has to lose three electrons to form Al^{3+} ion. As a result, lithium can form oxides more easily than aluminium.

EXAMPLE 7.4 Silicon is a semiconductor whereas quartz (SiO_2) does not conduct electricity well. Explain.

SOLUTION

Silicon has a valency of four. In its crystalline form, silicon has a structure where each atom is covalently bonded to four other silicon atoms. When doped with certain elements, free charge carriers (either electrons or holes) are introduced, allowing it to conduct electricity. This is the basis for its use as a semiconductor in electronics. On the other hand, quartz is a compound made of silicon and oxygen (SiO_2). In quartz, each silicon atom is bonded to four oxygen atoms, forming a tetrahedral structure. This structure does not have free or loosely bound electrons, which inhibits the movement of electric charge. Thus, quartz does not conduct electricity well.

Coordinate Bond

Coordinate bonds are those covalent bonds where the electron pair is provided by only one of the bonded atoms but shared by both the atoms.

This atom which donates the electron pair is called **donor** and the other atom which accommodates the shared pair of electrons is called **acceptor**.

The coordinate bond is represented by a one-sided arrow '→' where the arrow head points towards the acceptor and the tail towards the donor.

Example:

1. **Formation of Ammonium Ion**

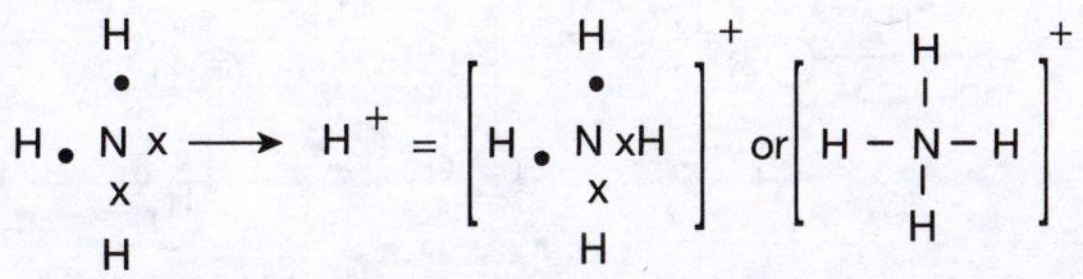

The lone pair of electrons is donated by N-atom of ammonia and it is accepted by H^+. Hence, N atom is a donor and H^+ is an acceptor.

2. **Formation of Hydronium Ion**

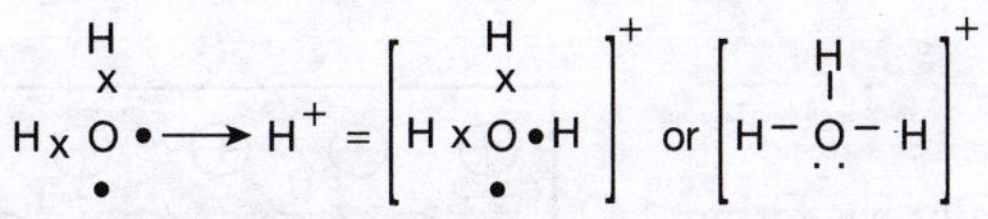

O atom of water molecule is a donor and H^+ is an acceptor.

Info Bytes!

- The famous compound ammonia (NH_3) can form a coordinate bond with a hydrogen ion to produce ammonium (NH_4^+).

Forces Acting Between the Covalent Molecules

1. **Van der Waal's forces:** The weak forces which exist between the covalent molecules are known as van der Waal's forces. There is an electrostatic force of attraction between the nucleus of one molecule and the electrons of the other. This is largely, but not completely neutralized by the electrostatic force of repulsion of electrons of one molecule by the electrons of the other or the nucleus of one molecule by the nucleus of the other. The resultant weak forces of attraction between the two molecules are called **van der Waal's forces**.

2. **Dipole–dipole attractions:** In polar covalent molecules, the unequal sharing of bonded electron pair results in partial charge separation within the molecule. The molecule with opposite partial charges is called **dipole**. The opposite charges of adjacent dipoles align with each other and the forces of attraction existing between these oppositely charged ends of the adjacent dipoles are called **dipole–dipole attractions**. These attractions are much stronger than van der Waal's forces of attractions.

   Example:

   In HCl molecule, $H^{\delta+}$ and $Cl^{\delta-}$ charges are formed within the molecule. In a sample of HCl, $Cl^{\delta-}$ of one HCl molecule attracts $H^{\delta+}$ of other molecule and these attractions are known as dipole–dipole attractions.

Hydrogen Bonding

Polar covalent molecules which have a highly electronegative atom bonded to a hydrogen atom become strongly polar. Some examples of such molecules are HF, H_2O, NH_3, etc.

In such types of polar covalent molecules, the H atom of one molecule gets attracted to the strongly electronegative atom of the other molecule due to the formation of the slight positive charge on the hydrogen atom and the slight negative charge on the more electronegative atom.

This force of attraction that holds the hydrogen atom of one molecule to the highly electronegative atom of the other molecule is called **hydrogen bond**.

Konnect

Despite its name, a hydrogen bond isn't a real bond. It's a strong type of dipole-dipole attraction between molecules.
Hydrogen bonds give water its high boiling point, surface tension, and ability to act as a universal solvent.

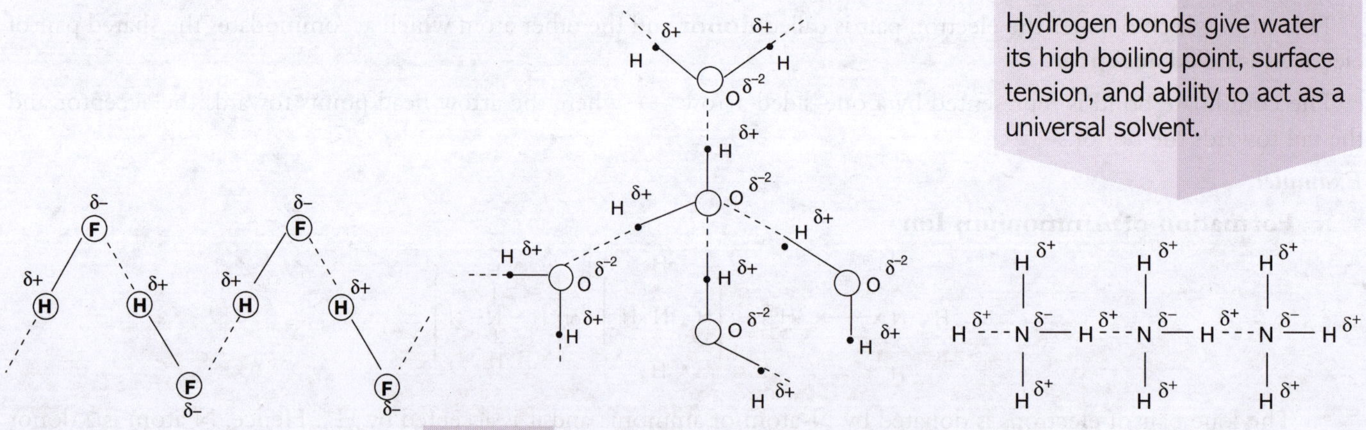

Figure 7.3 H-bonding in some compounds.

Metallic Bond

A metal is a crystalline substance. A metal atom generally has either 1, 2, or 3 electrons in its valence shell. It can easily lose these electrons and gain stability. Metals are, thus, highly electropositive in nature. These electrons lost by the metal are called **free electrons**. The free electrons of all the metal atoms form an electron pool. The resulting positively charged metal ions are believed to be held together by the electron pool.

The force of attraction that exists between the mobile electrons and the metal ions is known as a **metallic bond**.

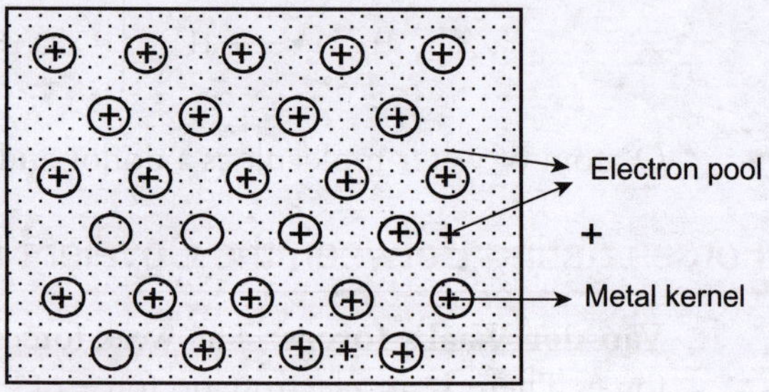

Figure 7.4 Schematic illustration of the metallic bond in an 'electron sea model'

EXAMPLE 7.5 Explain the factor which affects the strength of hydrogen bond.

SOLUTION

The strength of the hydrogen bond depends on the electronegativity of the highly electronegative atom to which hydrogen is bonded. The greater is the electronegativity, the higher will be the magnitude of charges on the bonded atoms, and therefore, the greater will be the strength of hydrogen bond.

EXAMPLE 7.6 Why is water called universal solvent?

SOLUTION

Water (H_2O) is a polar covalent compound. Hence, it can dissolve many compounds, such as, polar covalent compounds. Due to the high charge separation, it can dissolve even ionic compounds. Owing to its ability to form hydrogen bond, it can dissolve number of polar covalent compounds. As such it dissolves many types of substances in it, and hence, is called **universal solvent**.

EXAMPLE 7.7 What type of bond formation takes place in liquor ammonia? Explain.

SOLUTION

In liquor ammonia (NH_4OH), three types of bond formation take place.

(i) Ionic bond between NH_4^+ and OH^-.

(ii) Covalent bonds in NH_3 and OH^-.

(iii) Coordinate bond between NH_3 and H^+

EXAMPLE 7.8 Metals are solids while non-metals are mostly gases. Give reasons.

SOLUTION

Metals are highly electropositive in nature. They lose valence electrons and form positive metal kernels. Thus, there exists strong electrostatic force of attraction called **metallic bond**. These bonds are very strong, and thus, keep the metal atoms close together, and thus, metals are solids. While in case of non-metals, which are mostly covalent compounds, there are only van der Waal's force of attraction between the molecules, which are very weak forces, and thus, non-metals are mostly gases.

Redox Reactions

In a chemical reaction, if loss and gain of electron(s) take place by the atoms or the ions, then the phenomenon can be defined in terms of oxidation and reduction. A chemical reaction in which loss and gain of electrons take place simultaneously is called **redox reaction**.

> **Info Bytes!**
> The rusting of iron is a redox reaction. Iron gets oxidized to form rust, while oxygen gets reduced.

Oxidation

During a chemical reaction, if an atom or an ion loses one or more electrons, then the atom or the ion is said to be oxidized and this process is called **oxidation**.

Reduction

During a chemical reaction, if an atom or an ion gains one or more electrons, then the atom or the ion is said to be reduced and this process is called **reduction**.

Oxidizing agent: In the redox reaction, the atom or the ion that gains electron(s) is called **oxidizing agent**.

Reducing agent: In the redox reaction, the atom or the ion that loses electron(s) is called **reducing agent**.

1. When zinc granules are dipped in dilute H_2SO_4, H_2 gas is liberated with the formation of $ZnSO_4$:

$$Zn + H_2SO_4 \rightarrow ZnSO_4 + H_2\ (g)$$

In the above chemical reaction, the zinc atom loses two electrons and forms Zn^{2+} ion and each of the two hydrogen atoms gains an electron each.

$$Zn - 2e^- \rightarrow Zn^{2+}$$

$$2H^+ + 2e^- \rightarrow H_2$$

In this reaction, zinc is oxidized and acts as a reducing agent. H^+ is reduced and acts as an oxidizing agent.

Konnect

The Earth's atmosphere was oxygenated around 2.4 billion years ago due to redox reactions driven by cyanobacteria, changing the course of life on our planet.

2. When iron powder and sulphur are mixed and heated, they form ferrous sulphide (FeS):

$$Fe + S \rightarrow FeS$$

In this reaction, Fe loses two electrons and forms Fe^{2+}, whereas S forms to S^{2-} by gaining two electrons. Hence, Fe is oxidized and S is reduced. Sulphur is an oxidizing agent, whereas iron is a reducing agent.

POINTS TO REMEMBER

- ✔ In order to attain stability, atoms unite to form molecules, their electrons get re-arranged and a bond is said to be formed.
- ✔ A chemical bond is formed between two atoms by complete transfer of one or more electrons from one atom to the other as a result of which the atoms attain their nearest inert gas configuration.
- ✔ The electrostatic force of attraction which holds the two oppositely charged ions together is called ionic bond.
- ✔ During the formation of an ionic bond, one atom loses electron(s) forming positively charged ion called cation while the other atom gains electron(s) forming negatively charged ion called anion.
- ✔ The cation and anion are held together by strong electrostatic forces of attraction. The resulting compounds formed are called ionic compounds.
- ✔ Covalent bond is a bond formed when two atoms share one or more electron pairs.
- ✔ The bond formation takes place at this distance which corresponds to minimum possible energy state and the system becomes stable. This distance between the two nuclei is called bond length.
- ✔ Coordinate bonds are those covalent bonds where the electron pair is provided by only one of the bonded atoms but shared by both the atoms.
- ✔ This atom which donates the electron pair is called donor and the other atom which accommodates the shared pair of electrons is called acceptor.
- ✔ The force of attraction that holds the hydrogen atom of one molecule to the highly electronegative atom of the other molecule is called hydrogen bond.
- ✔ A chemical reaction in which loss and gain of electrons take place simultaneously is called redox reaction.
- ✔ During a chemical reaction, if an atom or an ion loses one or more electrons, then the atom or the ion is said to be oxidized and this process is called oxidation.
- ✔ During a chemical reaction, if an atom or an ion gains one or more electrons, then the atom or the ion is said to be reduced and this process is called reduction.
- ✔ In the redox reaction, the atom or the ion that gains electron(s) is called oxidizing agent.
- ✔ In the redox reaction, the atom or the ion that loses electron(s) is called reducing agent.

PRACTICE QUESTIONS CLASSROOM WING

Very Short Answer Type Questions

Directions for questions from 1 to 10:
Fill in the blanks

1. The atoms of an element with electronic configuration 2, 8 are held by __________ forces of attraction.
2. __________ compounds conduct electricity in a fused state or in an aqueous solution.
3. The nature of bond in H_2S is __________.
4. The electrical conductivity of ionic compounds in molten state is due to the presence of __________.
5. Metallic lustre is due to the presence of __________.
6. In the __________ bond, the contribution of an electron pair is one sided, but the sharing is equitable.
7. In a covalent bond, __________ of electrons takes place between the two atoms.
8. The chemical reaction in which loss and gain of electrons takes place is called __________ reaction.
9. In ammonium ion, the lone pair of electrons is donated by __________ and it is accepted by __________. Hence, __________ is called donor and __________ is called acceptor.
10. In the reaction $2Mg + CO_2 \rightarrow 2MgO + C$, oxidizing and reducing agents are, respectively, __________ and __________.

Directions for questions from 11 to 25:
Answer the following questions

11. Which of the following: NaCl, $MgCl_2$, $AlCl_3$, $CaCl_2$ is not associated with an ionic bond?
12. Is a significant difference in ionization energy suitable for ionic bond formation or not?
13. Is the co-existence of water and water vapour in nature the effect of intermolecular H-bonding?
14. In which state do ionic compounds conduct electricity?
15. Which of the following compounds: NH_4Cl, H_2O, KCl, CCl_4, is associated with only ionic bond?
16. What are the two opposing forces that start acting between two hydrogen atoms when they are brought together?
17. Why are the fractional positive and negative charge developed within a polar covalent molecule?
18. What is a coordinate covalent bond?
19. What are van der Waal's forces of attraction?
20. Define
    (a) polar covalent compound and
    (b) non-polar covalent compound
21. Give some examples in which coordinate covalent bond formation takes place.
22. Write two effects of van der Waal's forces of attraction.
23. Give some examples of the compounds where hydrogen bond exists.
24. Draw the Lewis dot formulae for the bond formations in the following compounds:
    (a) NaCl (b) CaF_2 (c) H_2 (d) O_2
    (e) N_2 (f) H_2O (g) NH_3 (i) CH_4
25. Define the following terms on the basis of electron transfer:
    (a) oxidation
    (b) reduction
    (c) redox reaction
    (d) oxidizing agent
    (e) reducing agent

Short Answer Type Questions

26. Which force of attraction acts among the atoms in a molecule of type B – A – B, where A and B belong to group 16 and group 17, respectively?
27. Find the odd one out of Ammonia, Water, Methane, and Hydrochloric acid, based on the presence of a dative bond.

28. Does the atom, which is underlined, in the molecule: BCl_3, attain octet configuration?

29. $A^+ \rightarrow A^{++}$ signifies oxidation or reduction?

30. Identify the bond present in CH_2Cl_2.

31. What is the role of ionization potential and electron affinity of the elements in the formation of ionic and covalent bonds?

32. Why is the density of the ionic compounds high and that of covalent compounds low?

33. Why are the melting and boiling points of the ionic compounds high and those of covalent compounds low?

34. Why do the pure covalent compounds not conduct electricity?

35. Why are the ionic compounds soluble in water?

36. Explain the hydrogen bond formation with the help of a diagram in the following compounds:
   (a) hydrogen fluoride (b) ammonia
   (c) water

37. What types of bonds exist in the following ions?
   (a) ammonium ion
   (b) hydronium ion

38. (a) Write in short about van der Waal's forces.
   (b) Does the electrical conductivity of metals depend on temperature? Justify with respect to metallic bonding.

39. Mention the oxidizing agent and the reducing agent in the following redox reactions and give a reason in support of your answer.
   (i) $Mg + 2HCl \rightarrow MgCl_2 + H_2$
   (ii) $2ZnS + 3O_2 \rightarrow 2ZnO + 2SO_2$
   (iii) $2KMnO_4 + 16HCl \rightarrow 2KCl + 2MnCl_2 + 8H_2O + 5Cl_2$
   (iv) $2H_2S + SO_2 \rightarrow 2H_2O + 3S$
   (v) $4HCl + O_2 \rightarrow 2H_2O + Cl_2$

Essay Answer Type Questions

40. Write in detail about metallic bond.

41. Complete the following table:

Molecules	No. of valence electrons of the constituent atoms	Structure of the molecule (present diagrammatically the sharing of electrons for covalent bond formation)
Chlorine		
Methane		
Water		
Nitrogen		

42. Differentiate between ionic and covalent bonding on the basis of the following parameters:
   (a) formation
   (b) physical state
   (c) melting and boiling points
   (d) solubility
   (e) electrical conductivity

43. Describe hydrogen bonding with the help of examples.

44. Describe the formation of a coordinate bond and present diagrammatically the formation of the coordinate bond in ammonium and hydronium ions.

45. Potential energy diagram for the formation of hydrogen molecule is given below. Explain the portions A to B, B to C; C to D in terms of force operating between the atoms.

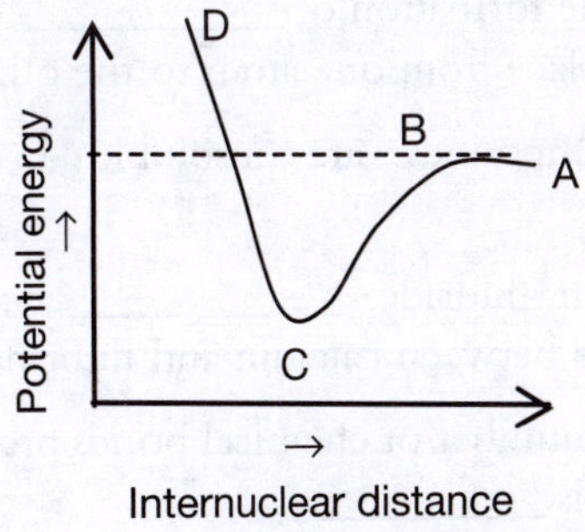

PRACTICE QUESTIONS COMPETITION WING

Level 1: Apply your Concepts

Direction for questions from 1 to 8:

State whether the following statements are true or false.

1. Atoms are less stable than molecules.
2. Sharing of electrons takes place in calcium fluoride.
3. In a nitrogen molecule, only one pair of electrons is shared between the two nitrogen atoms.
4. Metallic bond is unidirectional.
5. Covalent compounds conduct electricity since they have free electrons.
6. In a redox reaction, the oxidizing agent itself gets reduced.
7. In HF, unsymmetrical distribution of shared pair of electrons takes place.
8. Non-polar covalent compounds do not conduct electricity because of the absence of charged species.

Direction for questions from 9 to 18:

Fill in the blanks.

9. __________ can dissovle most of the ionic compounds.
10. During the formation of __________ electron transfer takes place from one atom to the other.
11. Ionic compounds are insoluble in __________ solvents.
12. In calcium fluoride, __________ bond formation takes place between calcium and fluorine.
13. The total number of chemical bonds present in hydronium ion is __________.
14. The distance where the energy of the atoms taking part in the bond formation is minimum, is called __________.
15. If the shared pair of electrons is present nearer to one of the bonded atoms, then the nature of the bond is __________.
16. Covalent compounds having giant molecules are virtually __________ in all solvents.
17. In a water molecule __________ bond formation takes place between hydrogen and oxygen.
18. The nature of bonds formed between atoms of elements X and Y with higher ionization potential is __________.

Direction for question 19:

Match the entries given in Column A with appropriate ones in Column B.

19.

Column A	Column B
A. Ionic bond	a. Weak forces existing between molecules
B. Polar covalent bond	b. 2 shared pairs of electrons
C. Coordinate covalent bond	c. Electron transfer takes place from one atom to another
D. Reducing agent	d. Attraction between positive ions and surrounding free mobile electrons
E. Nitrogen	e. 1 shared pair of electrons
F. Oxygen	f. Loses electron in a chemical reaction
G. Chlorine	g. Shared pair of electrons is attracted towards the more electronegative atom. Forces of attraction between bonded
H. Metallic bond	h. hydrogen and a highly electronegative atom.
I. H-bonding	i. 3 shared pairs of electrons
J. van der Waal's force	j. Contribution of a pair of electrons by a single atom

Direction for questions from 20 to 43:

For each of the questions, four choices have been provided. Select the correct alternative.

20. **Assertion (A):** Metallic bond in calcium is stronger than in potassium.

    Reason (R): The radii of alkaline earth metals are smaller than the corresponding alkali metals.

(a) Both A and R are true and R is the correct explanation of A.

(b) Both A and R are true, but R is not the correct explanation of A.

(c) A is true and R is false.

(d) A is false and R is true.

21. Assertion (A): Metals are generally good oxidizing agents.

Reason (R): Metals are electropositive in nature.

(a) Both A and R are true and R is the correct explanation of A.

(b) Both A and R are true, but R is not the correct explanation of A.

(c) A is true and R is false.

(d) A is false and R is true.

22. Assertion (A): Sodium can be cut with a knife.

Reason (R): The bigger the size of the metal kernel, the stronger is the metallic bond.

(a) Both A and R are true and R is the correct explanation of A.

(b) Both A and R are true, but R is not the correct explanation of A.

(c) A is true and R is false.

(d) A is false and R is true.

23. Assertion (A): Non-metals are generally good oxidizing agents.

Reason (R): Electron affinity decreases with an increase in the non-metallic character of the elements.

(a) Both A and R are true and R is the correct explanation of A.

(b) Both A and R are true, but R is not the correct explanation of A.

(c) A is true and R is false.

(d) A is false and R is true.

24. The force of attraction acting between cation and anion of an ionic compound is

(a) electrostatic force of attraction

(b) metallic bond

(c) hydrogen bond

(d) none of these

25. The Lewis dot diagram representing ammonia molecule is

(a)
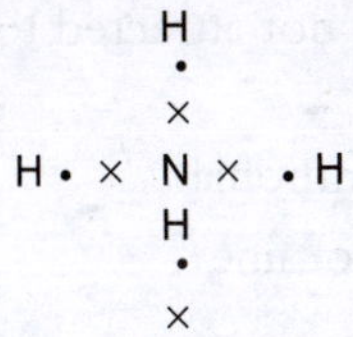

(b)
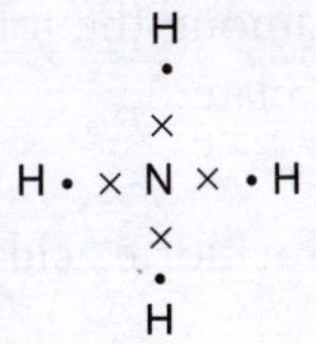

(c)
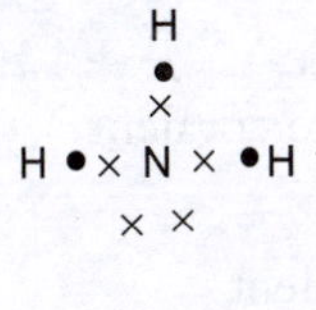

(d)
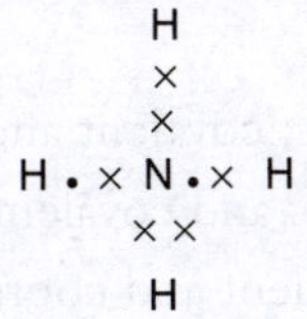

26. Select the correct statement for the following reaction.

$SO_2 + 2H_2S \rightarrow 3S + 2H_2O$

(a) sulphur is oxidized and hydrogen is reduced

(b) hydrogen is oxidized and sulphur is reduced

(c) sulphur is both oxidized and reduced

(d) sulphur is reduced and oxygen is oxidized

27. Though HCl and NH_3 are covalent molecules, their aqueous solutions conduct electricity, and this is due to

(a) the presence of free electrons

(b) the formation of free ions

(c) the formation of hydrated compounds

(d) formation of a dative bond

28. The strength of ionic bond is more when there is

(a) no difference in the atomic radii of the constituent atoms

(b) less difference in the ionization potential of the atoms

(c) less difference in the electronegativity of the atoms

(d) greater difference in the metallic character of constituents atoms

29. Why is the boiling point of ethyl alcohol (C_2H_5OH) higher than that of the corresponding hydrocarbon (C_2H_6)?

(a) Ionic bonds exist in ethyl alcohol molecule.

(b) Hydrogen bonds exist between ethyl alcohol molecules.

(c) Covalent bonds exist between ethyl alcohol molecules.

(d) None of the above

30. Which of the following solutions does not have a hydrogen bond?

(a) H_2S (b) C_2H_5OH

(c) HF (d) NH_3

31. Which among the following is not attracted towards a charged plate?
(a) water (b) ammonia
(c) hydrochloric acid (d) bromine

32. The nature of bonds present in sodium hydroxide include
(a) ionic, covalent and coordinate covalent
(b) ionic and covalent
(c) covalent and coordinate covalent
(d) ionic and coordinate covalent

33. If two atoms A and B of a molecule are brought closer than their minimum internuclear distance, then potential energy of the system:
(a) remains constant at minimum value
(b) starts increasing
(c) remains constant at maximum value
(d) starts decreasing

34. Which among the following liquids shows convex meniscus in a glass tube?
(a) water
(b) hydrochloric acid
(c) alcohol
(d) carbon tetrachloride

35. The electronic configurations of two elements A and B are 2, 8, 8, 2 and 2, 6, respectively. Then the formula of the compound formed between them is _____ and its nature is _____.
(a) AB, covalent
(b) AB, ionic
(c) A_2B, covalent
(d) A_2B, ionic

36. P, Q, R, and S are four substances. P conducts electricity in the solid state, Q conducts electricity only in the solution state, R conducts electricity in the molten state, and S is a bad conductor of electricity either in the molten state or in the solution state. Then P, Q, R, and S may be _____.
(a) P = Aluminium, Q = $MgCl_2$, R = HCl, S = Br_2
(b) P = Aluminium, Q = HCl, R = Na_2O, S = Glucose
(c) P = KCl, Q = HCl, R = Iron, S = Glucose
(d) P = KCl, Q = HF, R = Na_2O, S = Br_2

37. Which among the following can form the strongest hydrogen bond?
(a) HF (b) H_2O
(c) NH_3 (d) CH_4

38. A molecule in which the central atom is associated with contracted octet is:
(a) NH_3 (b) PH_3
(c) $AlCl_3$ (d) CH_4

39. Covalency of N in NH_3, NH_4^+, NH_4Cl are ___, ___ and _____, respectively
(a) 3, 4, 5 (b) 3, 4, 4
(c) 3, 3, 3 (d) 3, 3, 4

40. Which among the following can form the strongest metallic bond?
(a) sodium (b) potassium
(c) magnesium (d) aluminium

41. Arrange the following in sequence for the representation of NH_3 molecule by Lewis dot diagram.
(1) determination of the nature of bond between the constituents
(2) electronic configuration of the constituents
(3) representation of valence electrons as cross or dots
(4) identification of the atomic numbers of the constituent elements
(a) 4 2 3 1 (b) 4 2 1 3
(c) 2 4 1 3 (d) 4 2 3 1

42. 'The strength of ionic bond in $MgCl_2$ is greater than in NaCl.' Arrange the following key points that are essential to explain the above said statement in a correct sequence.
(1) comparison of sizes of respective ions of Na and Mg
(2) factors affecting strength of ionic bond
(3) effect of size and electronegativity difference on the strength
(4) comparison of electronegativity difference of the respective constituents in both the compounds
(a) 4, 3, 2, 1 (b) 2, 3, 1, 4
(c) 2, 1, 4, 3 (d) 4, 1, 3, 2

43. Metals are lustrous in nature, having shiny appearance. Arrange the reasons given below in a sequence.
(1) Emission of radiation or light energy by excited electrons makes a metal shiny in appearance.
(2) The electrostatic forces of attraction between metal ions and the mobile electrons is called metallic bond.

(3) The positive metal ions are surrounded by pool of electrons.

(4) When light falls on the crystal, electrons get excited.

(a) 3, 2, 1, 4

(b) 3, 2, 4, 1

(c) 2, 3, 1, 4

(d) 2, 4, 3, 1

Level 2: Review your Concepts

44. Arrange the following in the increasing order of the strength of ionic bond.

(A) K_2O (B) CaO

(C) MgO (D) KCl

45. Does H-bonding exist in, AH_3, where A is a non-metal with two shells and five valence electrons.?

46. How many electrons does the atom, which is underlined, in the molecule: $SnCl_4$, have in its valence shell?

47. Arrange the following in the decreasing order of the strength of the ionic bond.

(A) CsCl (B) BaO

(C) SrO (D) Cs_2O

48. Why are metals malleable and ductile?

49. Water shows capillary action in a narrow glass tube. Give appropriate reasons.

50. Between NaCl and CsCl, which has greater strength of ionic bond? Justify.

51. On decreasing the temperature, the conductivity of metals gradually increases. However, below a particular temperature, the increase is found to be drastic. How do you account for this?

52. Which one of the two substances should have a higher boiling point—Br_2 or ICl? Give reasons in support of your answer.

53. The electrical conductivity of silicon increases by replacing a fraction of silicon atoms by arsenic atoms. Give appropriate reasons to support the statement.

54. Compound '*x*' conducts electricity in the aqueous solution or molten state. Compound '*y*' conducts electricity in the aqueous solution only. Compound '*z*' does not conduct electricity in the molten state or in the aqueous solution. Predict the nature of bonds in *x*, *y*, and *z*.

55. Diamond, silicon carbide, and silica can be used as abrasives. How do you account for the above said property?

56. 'Though nitrogen and chlorine have almost equal electronegativity values, nitrogen forms hydrogen bonding, chlorine does not.' Justify.

57. (a) The leaves of aquatic plants do not decay though these are completely submerged. Explain.

(b) Identify the oxidizing and reducing agents in the following reactions and state the reason.

(A) $H_2S + O_2 \rightarrow S + H_2O$.

(B) $Zn + S \rightarrow ZnS$

(C) $Cu + H_2SO_4 \rightarrow CuSO_4 + H_2O + SO_2$

Directions for questions from 58 to 67:
Application-based Questions

58. HF in the vapor state is associated with covalent molecules while aqueous HF is ionic. Explain.

59. 'Covalent bond is directional, whereas ionic bond is not.' Justify.

60. Compare NaCl and CsCl with respect to ease of formation and also the strength of the ionic bond.

61. Nitrogen and oxygen are the major components in air. However, they do not combine at all to form nitric oxide under normal conditions. Give reasons.

62. Intermolecular forces do not exist in ionic compounds. Justify the statement.

63. Compare and contrast the metallic character and hardness of sodium and iron. Justify.

64. Although the molecular mass of H_2S is more than that of H_2O, H_2O is a liquid, whereas H_2S is a gas. Justify the statement.

65. Explain why when equal volumes of both ethyl alcohol and water are mixed, the volume of the resulting solution is less than the sum of the volumes of water and alcohol.

66. The leaves of aquatic plants do not decay though these are completely submerged in water. Explain.

67. Identify the redox reaction among the following and give reason.

(a) acid–base neutralization

(b) precipitation reaction

(c) metal displacement reaction

(d) all of these

Level 3: Assess Your Concepts

68. Why are ionic compounds hard and brittle?

69. (a) Density of water is maximum at 4°C. Explain.

(b) Do ease of formation of ionic bond and strength of ionic bond depend on the same factors? Give justification by taking alkaline earth metal fluorides of 3rd period and 5th period and fluoride and iodide of any one alkaline earth metal.

70. Graphite is used as a solid lubricant. Why?

71. $SnCl_4$ is liquid while $SnCl_2$ is solid. Explain.

Directions for questions from 72 to 77:
Application-Based Questions

72. Pure iron is relatively soft, ductile, and malleable. But its hardness increases by diffusing carbon atoms in it. Explain with appropriate reasons.

73. Both zinc and mercury belong to the same group in which differentiating electron enters into d-subshell of the penultimate shell. But zinc is a solid while mercury is a liquid. How do you justify this?

74. Three gases, methane, ammonia, and water vapor which have comparable molecular masses are liquefied at the same temperature. However, the pressure required to be applied is different for the three gases. Justify.

75. Among the various inorganic acids, like, HNO_3, $HClO_4$, and H_2SO_4, sulphuric acid is highly syrupy in nature. Explain.

76. Molten $AlCl_3$ is a poor conductor of electricity while hydrated $AlCl_3$ is a very good conductor. How do you account for this? Also explain the nature of bonding in the product.

77. On the basis of the data given in the table, answer the following questions:

(a) Analyse the intermolecular forces of attraction among the hydrides of the given elements.

(b) Arrange the hydrides in the decreasing order of strength of intermolecular forces of attractions.

(c) Draw a comparison between boiling points of hydrides of first two elements by giving proper justification.

Element	Electronegativity	Atomic radius
Fluorine	3.98	0.57 A°
Oxygen	3.44	0.65 A°
Chlorine	3.16	0.97 A°
Nitrogen	3.04	0.75 A°

AT

PRACTICE QUESTIONS JEE-NEET SPECIAL WING

Multiple-Answer Type Questions

Directions for questions 1 to 5:

Select one or more correct alternative(s) from the given choices.

1. Two liquids X and Y are taken in glass capillary tubes. X shows concave meniscus while Y shows convex meniscus as shown in the figure below. Identify the characteristics of X and Y which comply with the given observation.

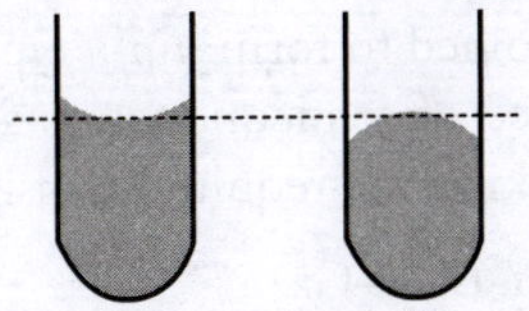

(a) X would be a polar covalent compound
(b) X could be having stronger intermolecular forces of attraction than Y
(c) Y is likely to be associated with weak metallic bond
(d) Molecules of Y should be held together by van der Waal's forces of attraction

2. Observe the following potential energy diagram for the formation of hydrogen molecule.

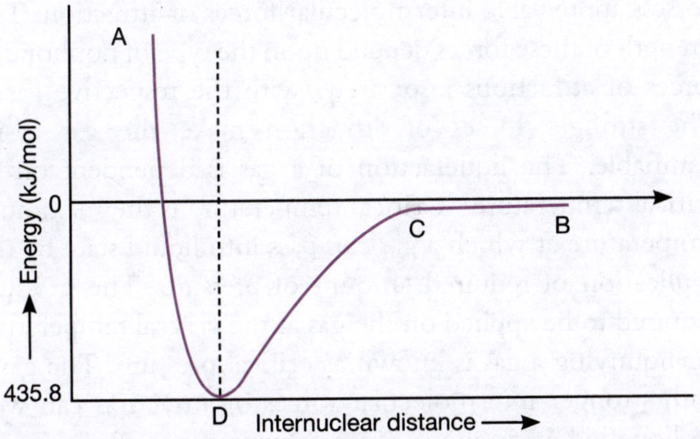

(a) 'B' indicates the hydrogen atoms at infinite distance
(b) 'D' indicates the intermolecular distance equal to the bond length of hydrogen molecule
(c) D to A represents the increase in repulsive forces between hydrogen atoms.
(d) B to C represents the increase in attractive forces between hydrogen atoms as they come closer.

3. Identify the sets of elements which when bonded to hydrogen result in establishing hydrogen bonding.

		Group	Period
(a)	A	17	3
(b)	B	16	3
(c)	C	15	2
(d)	D	17	2

4. Identify the processes of conversion which are considered to be reduction reactions.
(a) Hydrogen chloride to chlorine
(b) Sulphur dioxide to sulphur
(c) Phosphorus pentachloride to phosphorus trichloride
(d) Nitrogen to ammonia

5. In which among the following compounds, nitrogen has the covalency equal to 4?
(a) Ammonia (b) Ammonium chloride
(c) Nitrogen trioxide (d) Nitrogen pentoxide

Comprehension-Based Questions

Directions for questions 6 to 10:

Read the content given in the paragraph and answer the questions given below the paragraph.

Metals act as conductors due to the presence of free electrons. On the other hand, most of the nonmetals and other materials like glass act as insulators. In between these two categories, there is another special and more significant class of materials called semiconductors. These substances act as insulators under certain conditions and as conductors under different conditions.

Band theory of solids clearly explains the differential behaviour of semiconductors and the conductors. This theory visualises the presence of energy bands in all the solid materials. The presence of electrons in the conduction band renders a material conduct electricity. The energy gap between the conduction band and the valence band is known as forbidden gap. The flow of electrons from the valence band into the conduction band can impart conductivity to that particular material.

The pure substances like silicon and germanium are known as intrinsic semiconductors. These substances when doped with other elements act as extrinsic semiconductors. If the doping of impurity results in excess free electrons, it is called n type semiconductor. If the doping of impurity results in the formation of vacant spaces or holes, it is called *p* type semiconductor.

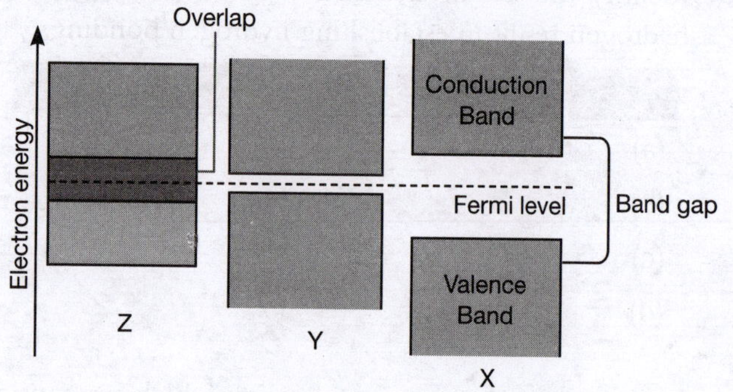

6. Identify the material which by thermal agitation can conduct electricity.
   (a) X because of the presence of conduction band filled with electrons
   (b) Y because of small forbidden gap
   (c) Z because of overlapping valence band and conduction band
   (d) Both a and b
7. Doping of silicon with which of the following elements results in *n* type semiconductor?
   (a) Arsenic (b) Antimony
   (c) Gallium (d) Both a and b
8. Which among the following is a p type semiconductor?
   (a) Silicon doped with germanium
   (b) Germanium doped with phosphorus
   (c) Pure silicon or germanium
   (d) Germanium doped with gallium
9. Under certain specific conditions, 'Y' is likely to act as an insulator. Predict the conditions.
   (a) 10 K (b) 273 K
   (c) STP (d) All of these
10. Doping silicon with other elements alters the crystal structure of silicon. X and Y given below represent the crystal structures of the samples of silicon doped with other elements.

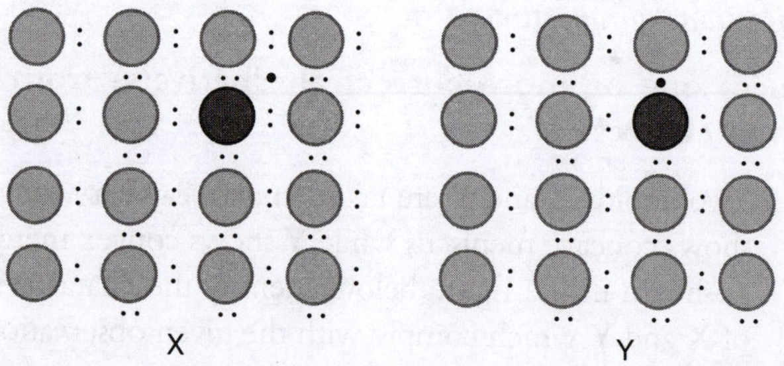

These are joined to form *n-p-n* type transistor. Identify the sequence of semiconductors along with the dopants for making the required transistor.
   (a) X-Sb; Y-B; X-Ga
   (b) X-As; Y-Ga; X-Sb
   (c) Y-B; X-As; Y-Ga
   (d) Y-Sb; X-Ga; Y-As

Directions for questions 11 to 15:

Read the content given in the paragraph and answer the questions given below the paragraph.

Though an ideal gas is supposed to have negligible intermolecular forces of attraction, real gases are known to possess appreciable intermolecular forces of attraction. The strength of these forces depend upon the type of nonbonded forces of attractions associated with the respective gases. The stronger forces of attraction make the gas easily liquifiable. The liquefaction of a gas is dependent on its critical temperature. Critical temperature is the maximum temperature at which a gas can pass into liquid state by the application of required amount of pressure. The pressure required to be applied on the gas at the critical temperature for liquifying a gas is known as critical pressure. The gases with stronger intermolecular forces of attraction can well be liquefied at or above room temperature and are hence called vapours. The other gases need to be cooled to or below their critical temperatures before applying pressure in order to liquify them.

The liquids which are vapourisable under normal conditions are listed below along with their critical temperatures and critical pressures.

Liquid in vapour state	Critical temperature (°C)	Critical pressure (atm)
A	240	79
B	243	60
C	374	218
D	235	46
E	132	112

11. Which among the above substances is most likely to exist in gaseous state under atmospheric conditions (room temperature)?

(a) C (b) E

(c) B (d) D

12. Identify the substance with the strongest intermolecular forces of attraction.

(a) E (b) C

(c) D (d) A

13. A, B and C are miscible liquids and their mixture is subjected to fractional distillation. Identify the statement which complies with the process.

(a) 'A' is left behind in the distillation flask

(b) 'B' is left behind in the distillation flask

(c) 'C' is left behind in the distillation flask

(d) 'C' is collected first in the receiver flask

14. Identify the correct order of volatility among the following.

(a) C > A (b) A >D

(c) B < C (d) D > B

15. Which among the following conclusions is incorrect with respect to the substances given in the table?

(a) The liquid and vapour states of all substances coexist at room temperature.

(b) The substance 'E' is associated with the least vapour pressure among all

(c) The order of boiling points would be A > B > D

(d) The substance 'C' requires minimum pressure to go into liquid state at room temperature.

Directions for question 16

Read the content given in the paragraph and based on that, match the entries of column I with those in column II

Ionic bond is the strong electrostatic force of attraction between the oppositely charged ions formed by the transfer of electrons. The number of electrons lost or gained during the formation of the respective ions is known electro valency. Therefore, ionic bond is also known as electrovalent bond. The electro valency of metal and nonmental can be same or different.

16. Match the entries in column-I with those in column-II

	Column I Ionic compound		Column II Electrovalency of metal and nonmetal
(a)	Potassium sulphide	(i)	2 ; 2
(b)	Magnesium nitride	(ii)	3 ; 2
(c)	Aluminium fluoride	(iii)	1 ; 1
(d)	Calcium bromide	(iv)	3 ; 3
(e)	Barium oxide	(v)	3 ; 1
		(vi)	2 ; 3
		(vii)	1 ; 2

ANSWER KEYS

Crossword

Across

5. Dative bond
6. Double covalent bond
8. Ionic bond
11. Contracted octet
12. Electrovalence
13. Bond length
14. One
15. Hydrogen bond
19. High electron affinity
21. Metal kernel

Down

1. Single covalent bond
2. Metallic bond
3. Low ionization potential
4. Expanded octet
7. Covalency
9. Lattice energy
10. Five
16. Octet
17. Three
18. Neon
20. Two

Classroom Wing

Very Short Answer Type Questions

1. van der Waal's
2. Ionic
3. polar covalent bond
4. mobile ions
5. free electrons
6. coordinate covalent
7. sharing
8. Redox
9. N-atom of ammonia, H^+, N-atom, H^+
10. CO_2 and Mg

Competition Wing

Level 1: Apply your Concepts

1. True
2. False
3. False
4. False
5. False
6. True
7. True
8. True
9. Water (Polar solvent)
10. Ionic bond
11. non-polar
12. ionic
13. three
14. bond length
15. polar covalent
16. insoluble
17. polar covalent bond
18. covalent
19. A : c, B : g, C : j, D : f, E : i, F : b, G : e, H : d, I : h, J : a
20. (a)
21. (d)
22. (c)
23. (c)
24. (a)
25. (c)
26. (c)
27. (b)
28. (d)
29. (b)
30. (a)
31. (d)
32. (b)
33. (b)
34. (d)
35. (b)
36. (b)
37. (a)
38. (c)
39. (b)
40. (d)
41. (b)
42. (b)
43. (b)

JEE-NEET Special Wing

Multiple-Answer Type Questions

1. (a; c)
2. (a; b; c)
3. (c; d)
4. (b; c; d)
5. (b; c; d)

Comprehension-Based Questions

6. (b)
7. (d)
8. (d)
9. (a)
10. (d)
11. (b)
12. (b)
13. (c)
14. (d)
15. (b)
16. (a) ↔ (vii); (b) ↔ (vi); (c) ↔ (v); (d) ↔ (ii) ; (e) ↔ (i)

Hints and Explanations

Classroom Wing

Very Short Answer Type Question

1. van der Waal's
2. Ionic
3. polar covalent bond
4. mobile ions
5. free electrons
6. co-ordinate covalent
7. sharing
8. Redox
9. N-atom of ammonia, H^+, N-atom, H^+
10. CO_2 and Mg
11. $AlCl_3$ is a polar covalent compound.
12. Yes, a significant difference in ionization energy is suitable for the formation of an ionic bond.
13. No, the co-existence of water and water vapour in nature is not the effect of H-bond.
14. Ionic compounds conduct electricity in a molten state.
15. KCl is an electrovalent compound.
16. Attractive and repulsive forces
17. Difference in electronegativity
18. Coordinate bonds are those covalent bonds where the electron pair is provided by only one of the bonded atoms but shared by both the atoms.
19. The weak forces which exist between the covalent molecules are known as van der Waal's forces.
20. (a) Polar compounds: Electron pairs contributed by both the bonded atoms of the molecule are unequally shared.

    (b) Non-polar compounds: Electron pairs contributed by both the bonded atoms forming the covalent molecule are equally shared.
21. NH_4^+, H_3O^+
22. (1) Boiling point (2) physical state
23. H_2O, HF
24. Representation of

    (i) valence electrons

    (ii) sharing and transfer of electrons
25. (i) Loss of electrons

    (ii) Gain of electrons

    (iii) Mutual transfer of electrons

    (iv) The substance that gains electrons

    (v) The substance that loses electrons

Short Answer Type Questions

26. Since A and B belong to the 16th and 17th groups, the molecule is a polar covalent molecule. Hence, the force of attraction among them is dipole–dipole interaction.
27. In hydrochloric acid, H_3O^+ ions are present. In H_3O^+, the dative bond is present between H_2O and H^+.
28. No, it does not. In BCl_3, boron (B) has six electrons in its valence shell.
29. Oxidation is the loss of electrons. Therefore, A^+ to A^{++} is oxidation.
30. The bond present in CH_2Cl_2 is a polar covalent bond because all four bonds belong to non-identical atoms.
31.

	Ionic bond	Covalent bond
(a) I.P.	Large difference	High for both atoms
(b) E.A.	Large difference	Small difference

32. Because ionic compounds have strong electrostatic forces of attraction.
33. Ionic compounds have strong electrostatic forces of attraction, hence they have high melting and boiling points.
34. Pure covalent compounds do not ionize.
35. They exist in the form of ions.

36. (i) partial charge separation takes place on constituent atoms.
(ii) electrostatic force of attraction exist between H^+ and more electronegative element.

37. (i) Nitrogen donates its pair of electrons to H^+
(ii) Oxygen donates its pair of electrons to H^+

38. (a) The weak forces which exist between the covalent molecules are known as van der Waal's forces.
There is an electrostatic force of attraction between the nucleus of one molecule and the electrons of the other. This is largely, but not completely, neutralized by the electrostatic force of repulsion of electrons of one molecule by the electrons of the other or the nucleus of one molecule by the nucleus of the other. The resultant weak forces of attraction between the two molecules are called van der Waal's forces.
(b) Electrical conductivity of metals is due to the presence of free or mobile electrons in metallic crystal.
At low temperatures, the vibratory motion of metal ions, that is metal kernels, decreases and hence it allows the easy movement of the mobile electrons between the positive metal ions and thus the metal the mobile electrons move towards the positive pole and conduct electricity. Hence, electrical conductivity increases with a decrease in temperature. However, at very very low temperature (close to 0 K) the vibratory motion of metal ions totally cease and hence the electrons move very freely and conductivity increases drastically and they become superconductors. With the increase in temperature, vibrations of metal kenels increases. Hence, the movement of elections gets restricted and thus the conductivity decreases.

39.

	Oxidizing agent	Reducing agent
(i)	Mg	HCl
(ii)	O_2	ZnS
(iii)	$KMnO_4$	HCl
(iv)	SO_2	H_2S
(v)	O_2	HCl

Essay Answer Type Questions

40. A metal is a crystalline substance. A metal atom generally has either 1, 2, or 3 electrons in its valence shell. It can easily lose these electrons and gain stability. Metals are, thus, highly electropositive in nature. These electrons lost by the metal are called free electrons. The free electrons of all the metal atoms form an electron pool. The resulting positively charged metal ions are believed to be held together by the electron pool.

41.

Molecules	No. of valence electrons
Chlorine	7
Methane	C (4), H (1)
Water	H (1), O (6)
Nitrogen	5

42. (a) Ionic bond is formed between two atoms by complete transfer of one or more electrons from one atom to the other as a result of which the atoms attain their nearest inert gas configuration. Covalent bond is a bond formed when two atoms share one or more electron pairs
(b) Most of the ionic compounds are crystalline solids. Covalent compounds are generally liquids or gases
(c) Ionic compounds have high melting and boiling points. Covalent compounds have low melting and boiling points.
(d) Ionic compounds are generally soluble in polar solvents. Polar covalent compounds are soluble in polar solvents and non-polar covalent compounds are soluble in non-polar covalent liquids.
(e) Ionic compounds conduct electricity. Polar covalent compounds conduct electricity and non-polar covalent compounds do not conduct electricity.

43. Polar covalent molecules which have a highly electronegative atom bonded to a hydrogen atom become strongly polar. Some examples of such molecules are HF, H_2O, NH_3, etc.
In such types of polar covalent molecules, the H atom of one molecule gets attracted to the strongly electronegative atom of the other molecule due to the formation of the slight positive charge on the hydrogen atom and the slight negative charge on the more electronegative atom.
This force of attraction that holds the hydrogen atom of one molecule to the highly electronegative atom of the other molecule is called hydrogen bond.

44. Coordinate bonds are those covalent bonds where the electron pair is provided by only one of the bonded atoms but shared by both the atoms.

The atom which donates the electron pair is called donor and the other atom which accommodates the shared pair of electrons is called acceptor.

The coordinate bond is represented by a one-sided arrow '$\rightarrow$' where the arrow head points towards the acceptor and the tail towards the donor.

45. When the two hydrogen atom are at infinite distance, they do not experience any attractive or repulsive forces. Therefore, there is almost no change in potential energy. When two hydrogen atoms approach each other, attractive forces develop between the electrons of one atom and the nucleus of the other atom. At the same time, repulsive forces also exist between the nuclei of the two atoms and the electrons of the two atoms. However, initially the attractive forces being greater than the repulsive forces, the approach of atoms results in gradual decrease in potential energy. The portion B-C in the curve corresponds to this state. As the two atoms are brought closer to each other, at some distance, the proton-electron attraction just balances the electron-electron repulsion and proton-proton repulsion. The bond formation takes place at this distance which corresponds to minimum possible energy state and the system becomes stable. The point 'C' indicates this state. If the two hydrogen atoms approach closer than the internuclear distance, repulsive force increases drastically without any corresponding increase in attractive force. The portion C to D represents this condition.

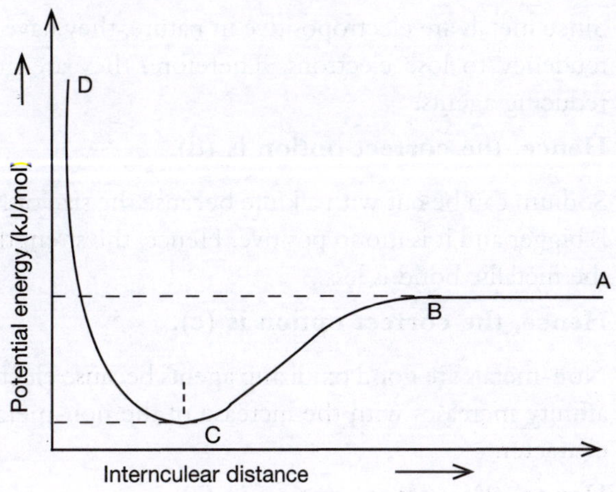

Competition Wing

Level 1: Apply your Concepts

20 Metallic bonds in calcium are stronger than in potassium because the charge possessed by Ca^{+2} ion is more than K^+ and the radius of Ca^{+2} is smaller than K^+.

Hence, the correct option is (a).

21. Since metals are electropositive in nature, they have the tendency to lose electrons. Therefore, they are good reducing agents.

Hence, the correct option is (d).

22 Sodium can be cut with a knife because the size of Na^+ is bigger and it is mono positive. Hence, the strength of the metallic bond is less.

Hence, the correct option is (c).

23. Non-metals are good oxidizing agents because electron affinity increases with the increase of the non-metallic character.

Hence, the correct option is (c).

34. Glass is made up of silicates which are ionic in nature. CCl_4 is covalent in nature, as a result, CCl_4 shows convex meniscus in a glass tube.

Hence, the correct answer is (d).

35. Element B gains two electrons to attain an octet configuration forming B^{-2}. However, element A loses two electrons to attain the octet configuration and forms A^{+2}. Between A^{+2} and B^{-2}, there exists strong electrostatic forces of attraction (ionic bond), and hence, they form AB.

Hence, the correct answer is (b).

36. Generally, metals conduct electricity in a solid state. Ionic compounds conduct electricity in the molten state as well as in the solution state. Polar covalent compounds conduct electricity in the solution state.

Non-polar covalent compounds conduct electricity neither in the molten state nor in the solution state, and hence, P = Al, Q = HCl, R = Na_2O, S = Glucose.

Hence, the correct answer is (b).

37. The strength of hydrogen bond depends on size and electronegativity of an atom. The more the electronegativity and lesser the atomic size, the more is the strength of hydrogen bond. Hence, HF can form the strongest hydrogen bond.

Hence, the correct answer is (a).

38. In $AlCl_3$ the central atom Al possesses six electrons in its valence shell. Hence, $AlCl_3$ is a molecule with contracted octet.

Hence, the correct answer is (c).

39. Number of electron pairs involved in sharing will give the covalency of an atom of an element. Hence, covalency of 'N' in NH_3, NH_4^+ and NH_4Cl are 3, 4, and 4, respectively.

Hence, the correct answer is (b).

40. The strength of metallic bond depends on the number of valence electrons and size of metal kernel. The more the number of valence electrons and less the size of metal kernel, the more is the strength of metallic bond. Hence, Al can form the strongest metallic bond.

Hence, the correct answer is (d).

41. 4. identification of atomic numbers of the constituents
2. electronic configuration of the constituents
1. determination of the nature of bond between the constituents
3. representation of the valence electrons as crosses or dots

Hence, the correct answer is (b).

42. 2. factors affecting strength of ionic bond
3. effect of size and electronegativity difference on the strength
1. comparison of sizes of respective ions of Na and Mg
4. comparison of electronegativity difference of the constituents in both the compounds

Hence, the correct answer is (b).

43. 3. The positive metal ions are surrounded by a pool of electrons.
2. The electrostatic forces of attraction between metal ions and the mobile electrons is called metallic bond.
4. When light falls on the crystal, electrons get excited.
1. Emission of radiation or light energy by excited electrons makes a metal shiny in appearance.

Hence, the correct answer is (b).

Level 2: Review your Concepts

44. The strength of an ionic bond is directly proportional to the charge possessed by the ions and inversely proportional to the distance between them. Hence, the order is D < A < B < C.

45. H-bonding exists in AH_3 where A is nitrogen according to the description given.

46. In $SnCl_4$, Sn has 8 electrons in its valence shell, whereas the other given atoms have 10 electrons.

47. The strength of the ionic bond is directly proportional to the charge possessed by the ions and inversely proportional to the distance between them. The order is $SrO > BaO > Cs_2O > CsCl$.

48. (i) presence of free electrons
(ii) movement of free electrons
(iii) directionality of metallic bond
(iv) effect of directionality on malleability and ductility

49. The forces of cohesion and adhesion in water causes capillary action.
Adhesion of water to the walls of a vessel will cause an upward force on the liquid at the edges and result in a meniscus which turns upward.
As the tube is narrow the effect of cohesion and adhesion is increased.

50. (i) factors affecting ionic bond strength
(ii) comparison of radius of cation
(iii) effect of radius on electrostatic force of attraction

51. (i) particles responsible for electrical conductivity in metals
(ii) factors that affect conductivity
(iii) relation between temperature and vibration of metal atoms
(iv) relation between vibration of metal atoms and conductivity

52. Boiling points are a measure of intermolecular forces. The intermolecular forces in ICl is higher as it has a dipole-dipole bond and Br_2 is london bond and hence is weak in nature

53. (i) No. of valance electron in arsenic = 5
(ii) comparison of number of valence electrons in silicon and arsenic
(iii) bonding in presence and absence of arsenic
(iv) dependence of electrical conductivity on free electrons

54. Compound 'X' is ionic compound and the bond is ionic bond.
Compound 'Y' is polar covalent compound and the bond is polar covalent bond.
Compound 'Z' is nonpolar covalent compound.

55. (i) nature of bonding in diamond, SiC, and SiO_2
(ii) strength of the bond
(iii) requisite for abrasive nature

56. Chlorine is a little more electronegative than Nitrogen but it has a bigger atomic size than Nitrogen and hence fails to keep the hydrogen electron attracted and stabilized and do not form hydrogen bonding.

57. (a) (i) Aquatic plants have the different epidermal layer of cells and the cuticle is more thick.
(ii) forces between water and aquatic plants

(b) (A) $\overset{+1}{H_2}\overset{-2}{S} + \overset{0}{O_2} \rightarrow \overset{0}{S} + \overset{+1}{H_2}\overset{-2}{O}$

Since the negative valency of oxygen increases, it undergoes reduction and acts as an oxidizing agent. The valency of sulphur changes from –2 to 0. Hence, it gets oxidized and acts as a reducing agent.

(B) $\overset{0}{Zn} + \overset{0}{S} \rightarrow \overset{+2}{Zn}\overset{-2}{S}$

Since the valency of Zn increases, it acts as a reducing agent and the valency of S decreases it acts as an oxidizing agent

(C) 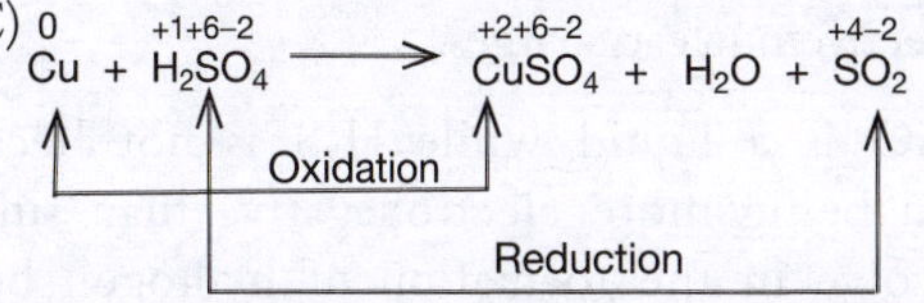

$\therefore Cu \rightarrow$ Reducing agent, $H_2SO_4 \rightarrow$ Oxidising agent

58. Due to the greater difference in the electronegativity between F and H in HF, the strength of H bonding is strong even in the vapor state as it exists in the associated form. (of 2 to 6 HF molecules).
But HF in water exists in the form of ions because of high dielectric constant of H_2O, i.e., due to the high charge separation between O and H in H_2O, it breaks the polar covalent forces between H and F in HF, and thus, aqueous HF is an ionic compound.

59. Strong electrostatic forces of attraction exist between ions in all directions in the ionic bond. Hence, it is non-directional in nature, whereas electron pair is localized between the atoms in covalent bond which gives proper shape to the molecule and is directional in nature.

60. Ionic compounds are formed easily between larger cation and smaller anion. This is because an atom whose atomic radius is large can form a cation easily and an atom which has a small atomic radius can form an anion easily. Cs^+ ion can be formed more easily than Na^+ ion. Formation of CsCl is easier than the formation of NaCl. Among NaCl and CsCl, as the anion is the same, i.e., Cl^-, the cations are compared. Cs has a larger atomic radius than sodium. Thus, the strength of ionic bond is more in NaCl than CsCl.

61. N_2 is formed by sharing of three electron pairs, i.e., a triple covalent bond is present between two nitrogen atoms in N_2. The bond strength is very high since under normal conditions N_2 cannot react with any of the components present in air. Thus, N_2 does not react with O_2 to form NO. High temperature favors the formation of NO.

62. Ionic compounds exist in the form of oppositely charged ions even in solid state. Therefore, in ionic compounds, intermolecular forces do not exist, only interionic forces exist. These forces are so strong that the ions come together to form the crystal lattice.

63. Sodium belongs to IA group and has lower IP value than iron. Therefore, it can lose electrons more easily than iron. Hence, it is more electropositive and more metallic than iron. Strength of the metallic bond increases with an increase in the number of valence electrons and effective nuclear charge. Thus, iron is harder than sodium which contains only one valence electron and has less effective nuclear charges.

64. H_2O is a liquid while H_2S is not because oxygen being more electronegative than sulphur, can involve in the formation of hydrogen bonding in water. Thus, water is a liquid while in H_2S there is no hydrogen bonding due to less electronegativity of sulphur and the molecules are far apart, and hence, H_2S is a gas.

65. The extent of intermolecular H bonding between water and ethyl alcohol is greater compared to the extent of intermolecular H bonding between ethyl alcohol molecules, i.e., aqueous or diluted ethyl alcohol has H bonding to a greater extent compared to pure ethyl alcohol. Since each water molecule can form 4H bonds, many ethyl alcohol molecules get surrounded by it, and thus, more number of ethyl alcohol molecules is associated with water molecules, thus, decreasing the intermolecular spaces. Hence, when equal volumes of both are mixed, the net volume is less than the sum of the two volumes taken. Thus, the ethyl alcohol molecules are brought closer in water due to greater extent of H bonding.

66. The texture of aquatic plants (leaves, hydrocarbons stem, etc.) is soft and waxy as they are made up of organic compounds, which are non-polar in nature. Since water molecules are highly polar, they hardly come in contact with the waxy surface of the leaves.

67. Only metal displacement reactions are redox reactions.

Level 3: Assess Your Concepts

68. (i) forces of attraction in ionic compounds

(ii) type of constituents

(iii) arrangement of constituents

(iv) effect of this arrangement on directionality

69. (a) At 4 °C two opposing effects are in balance

In ice, the water molecules are in a crystal lattice that has a lot of empty space. When the ice melts to liquid water, the structure collapses and the density of the liquid increases

(b) Ease of formation of ionic bond is nothing but the ease of formation of cations and anions. Cation formation depends upon the atomic size and IP value of the respective metals. Similarly, anion formation depends up on the atomic size and electron affinity of the respective non-metal. However, the strength of ionic bond depends up on the extent of electrostatic force of attraction between the oppositely charged ions. The lesser is the distance between the nucleus of cation and anion, the greater is the force of attraction between them. That means the smaller size of cation and anion leads to a stronger ionic bond.

If the alkaline earth metal fluorides of 3rd period and 6th period are considered that is magnesium fluoride and barium fluoride. The former has a stronger ionic bond than the latter due to the smaller size of Mg^{2+} ion than Ba^{2+} ion. But ease of formation of BaF_2 is more than that of MgF_2 due to lesser I.P. value of Ba than that of Mg. When barium fluoride and barium iodide are compared, barium fluoride has a stronger ionic bond than barium iodide due to the smaller size of fluoride ion than iodide ion. Ease of formation of BaF_2 is more than BaI_2. This is because of higher E.A. of fluorine than that of iodine.

70. (i) Graphite has a giant covalent structure. the carbon atoms form layers with a hexagonal arrangement of atoms

(ii) In graphite every atom is covalently bonded to 3 other carbon atoms and 1 electron that is free and conducts electricity.

(iii) Graphite has layers of carbon atoms, with weak forces, residing in between its layers because of which it is quite slippery.

71. (i) comparison of charges on positive radial of $SnCl_2$ and $SnCl_4$

(ii) comparison of nuclear charge

(iii) effect of charge and nuclear charge on size

(iv) relation between size and intermolecular force of attraction

72. Pure iron has metallic bond which is omnidirectional. When pressure is applied layers of metal kernels slide over the other layers, and hence, the metal can be made into thin sheets and wires. Therefore, pure iron is malleable and ductile. When some amount of carbon is added, a covalent compound Fe_3C (cementite) between iron and carbon is formed. Since covalent bonds are directional, layers of metal kernels cannot slide easily. Hence, the hardness of metal increases by the addition of carbon due to the formation of these bonds.

73. Zinc belongs to the 4th period and '3d' series of transition metals. The electronic configuration of zinc is 2, 8, 18, 2. It can contribute 2 electrons for metallic bond. Thus, strong metallic bond in zinc imparts hardness to the metal which makes its physical state to be solid. Mercury belongs to 6th period and '5d' series of transition metals. The electronic configuration of Hg is 2, 8, 18, 32, 18, 2. Due to the poor screening effect of 14 'f' electrons, the effective nuclear force of attraction on the outermost shell increases. Therefore, the electrons contributing for metallic bond are less which results in the formation of a thinner electron pool, and hence, a weaker metallic bond. As a result of this, mercury is a liquid.

74. In H_2O and NH_3, there is hydrogen bonding, and hence, the intermolecular forces of attraction are stronger. Between NH_3 and H_2O, H_2O has stronger intermolecular forces of attraction than NH_3 due to stronger hydrogen bonding with oxygen. CH_4, being a non-polar molecule, has only van der Waal's forces of attraction, which are weak.

Therefore, the order of critical temperatures is

$CH_4 < NH_3 < H_2O$.

The pressure required to be applied is in the order:

$H_2O < NH_3 < CH_4$.

The greater the intermolecular force of attraction, the lower is the pressure required to liquefy it.

75. 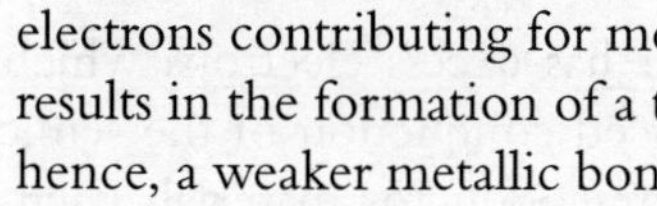

Since the electronegativity difference between S and O is more compared with N and O in HNO_3, Cl and O in $HClO_4$, the intensity of negative charge is more on oxygen, and thus, the hydrogen bonded to such oxygen can form hydrogen bonds more effectively. Thus, H_2SO_4 molecules are associated with stronger bonding and form a syrupy liquid, i.e., a liquid with high viscosity.

76. $AlCl_3$ is covalent in nature because of small size and high nuclear charge of Al^{+3}.

But when $AlCl_3$ is dissolved in water, Al^{+3} ions get surrounded by water molecules by means of coordinate covalent bonds in which a lot of energy is liberated.

$$AlCl_3 + 6H_2O \rightarrow [Al(H_2O)_6]^{3+}$$

Thus, $AlCl_3$ gets dissolved in aqueous medium in which mobile hydrated aluminium and chloride ions are present, and hence, it conducts electricity due to the mobility of these ions in an electrical field. However, molten $AlCl_3$ exists as a molecule, and thus, is a bad conductor of electricity.

77. (a) The hydrides of the given elements are HF, H_2O, HCl and NH_3. Except HCl, the other three compounds are associated with hydrogen bonding. Hydrogen chloride has dipole forces of attraction which is weaker than hydrogen bonding.

(b) Strength of a hydrogen bond is proportional to the electronegativity of the element bonded to hydrogen. The decreasing order of strength of intermolecular forces of attraction is

$HF > H_2O > NH_3 > HCl$.

(c) The hydrides of first two elements are HF and H_2O. Since HF has a stronger hydrogen bond than H_2O, HF is expected to have a higher boiling point than H_2O. However, contrary to the expectation, H_2O has a higher boiling point than HF in spite of presence of weaker hydrogen bond in H_2O than in HF. Each HF molecule can form two hydrogen bonds while each H_2O molecule can form four hydrogen bonds. The number of hydrogen bonds in water is more than those in HF. Secondly, HF exists as associated molecules even in vapour state whereas water exists as isolated molecules in vapour state. That means vapourisation of H_2O requires the breakage of all the hydrogen bonds while vapourisation of HF requires the breakage of some of the hydrogen bonds. As a result, HF boils at a lower temperature than H_2O.

JEE-NEET Special Wing

Multiple-Answer Type Questions

1. The shape of the meniscus depends on the extent of cohesive and adhesive forces. The liquids which possess stronger forces of attraction with the molecules of container (adhesive forces) show concave meniscus as in X. The liquids which possess stronger intermolecular forces of attraction among its molecules (cohesive forces) show convex meniscus as in Y. Glass being a polar compound, the liquid X also would be a polar compound. Y is likely to possess metallic bond which is much stronger than the other intermolecular forces of attraction.

2. From B to C, there is no change in potential energy while the atoms are approaching each other. That means, they would be at an infinite distance where there is no attractive forces operating between the atoms. Therefore, 'B' indicates the hydrogen atoms at infinite distance. At the point 'D' the potential energy is minimum which indicates the maximum intermolecular forces and hence the bond length (the distance at which bond is formed). D to A shows a steep increase in the potential energy of the system. This implies the increase in repulsive forces between the atoms.

3. Fluorine, nitrogen and oxygen when bonded to hydrogen show hydrogen bonding due to their high electronegativity and small size.

		Group	Period	Element
(a)	A	17	3	Chlorine
(b)	B	16	3	Sulphur
(c)	C	15	2	Nitrogen
(d)	D	17	2	Fluorine

4. Reduction is the process associated to the addition of hydrogen or removal of oxygen or addition of electropositive element or removal of electronegative element. Sulphur dioxide to sulphur ; phosphorus pentachloride to phosphorus trichloride; nitrogen to ammonia-these are the conversions which are considered to involve reduction.

5. The number of electrons shared by an atom of an element during the formation of a covalent molecule is known as covalency.

Compound	Covalency of nitrogen
Ammonia	3
Ammonium chloride	4
Nitrogen trioxide	4
Nitrogen pentoxide	4

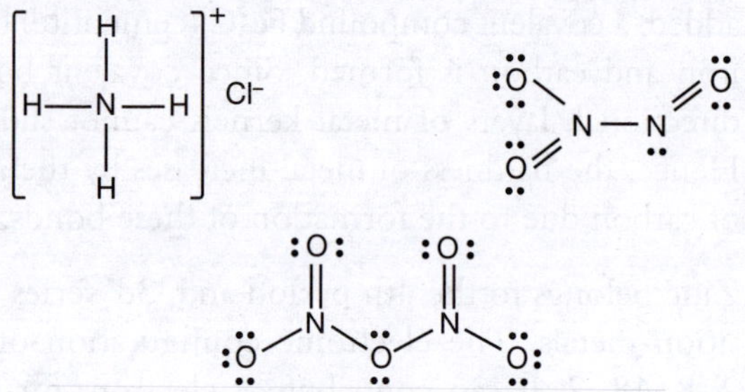

Comprehension-Based Questions

6. The materials with small forbidden gap can conduct electricity by thermal agitation as electrons take up energy and pass into the conduction band from the valence band.

7. *n* type semiconductor has excess electrons which are responsible for enhanced conduction of the semiconductor. Silicon is a semiconductor material. Each silicon atom has 4 electrons. When it is doped by a pentavalent element such as arsenic or antimony, the excess electrons introduced into the crystal lattice makes the material a good semiconductor.

8. When the tetravalent semiconducting element is doped with a trivalent element, the semiconductor shows conductivity due to the holes formed and hence is known as a *p* type semiconductor. Germanium is tetravalent and doping it with gallium makes it act as a *p* type semiconductor.

9. At very low temperatures close to 0K, semiconducting materials act as insulators because of the lack of motion of electrons in the conduction band of the crystal lattice.

10. As per the figures, X is *p* type semiconductor while Y is *n* type semiconductor. Y should have been doped by a pentavalent element such as Sb or As. X would have been doped by a trivalent element such as gallium. *n-p-n* transistor would consist of *p* type semiconductor between two *n* type semiconductors.

11. 'E' has the least critical temperature and hence least intermolecular forces of attraction. Hence, it has the least tendency to pass into liquid state and therefore is most likely to exist in gaseous state.

12. The higher is the critical temperature, the higher will be the intermolecular forces of attraction. Among the substances given, 'C' has the highest critical temperature and hence has the strongest intermolecular forces of attraction.

13. The liquid which has the least boiling point will be vapourised and collected first in the receiver flask. The one with the highest boiling point will be left behind in the distillation flask. Among the liquids in the mixture, 'C' has the highest critical temperature and hence the highest boiling point. Therefore it is left behind in the distillation flask. Both A nd B possess equal critical temperatures.

14. Though A, B and D have almost equal critical temperatures, D is associated with the least critical pressure value which implies that it can be the most volatile lquid among A, B, C and D.

15. Since the critical temperatures of all the substances are much above room temperature, the liquid and vapour states of all the substances coexist at the room temperature. Since E has the least critical temperature and hence boiling point, it would be having the highest vapour pressure among all the given substances. A > B > D would be the correct order of boiling points based on their critical pressures. At room temperature, the substance 'C' being in the liquid state has only little vapour above it. It requires minimum pressure to go into liquid state.

16.

Ionic compound		Electrovalency of metal and nonmetal
(a) Potassium sulphide	(vii)	1;2
(b) Magnesium nitride	(vi)	2;3
(c) Aluminium fluoride	(v)	3;1
(d) Aluminium sulphide	(ii)	3;2
(e) Barium oxide	(i)	2;2

CHAPTER

8

Water

Remember

Before beginning this chapter, you should be able to:

- understand different states of matter.
- have knowledge of layers of atmosphere and hydrosphere.

Key Ideas

After completing this chapter, you should be able to:

- understand the importance and different sources of water.
- know the causes of hardness of water, types of hardness, and various processes to remove the hardness.
- describe water pollution, its causes, effects, and ways for preventing the water pollution and maintaining the water cycle.
- study the classification of solutions based on the physical states of solute and solvent and know about solubility, factors affecting solubility and importance of solubility curves.
- define crystals, their shapes, physical properties, and different processes of crystallization.
- explain different types of salts, hydrated, efflorescent, deliquescent, hygroscopic salts and know about water of crystallization.
- describe electrolytes, non-electrolytes, process of electrolysis, Faraday's laws of electrolysis and applications of electrolysis, like, electroplating, electrorefining, and electrometallurgy

Scientific Crypt

A Tribute to Michael Faraday (1791–1867)

Michael Faraday was an English chemist and physicist who gained a worldwide reputation for his commendable contributions to the fields of electromagnetism and electrochemistry. It is largely due to his effort that electricity became viable for use in day-to-day life and technology.

Michael Faraday's major and most significant contribution to Chemistry was a study of electrolysis and his laws of electrolysis. His other contributions include the discovery of benzene, a system of oxidation numbers, the liquefaction of gases, alloys of steel, various kinds of optical glass, etc. Invention of an early form of the Bunsen burner which is universally used in science laboratories is another feather in his cap. Throughout his career, Faraday secured very high positions. He was the first Fullerian professor of Chemistry at the Royal Institution of Great Britain, a position to which he was appointed for a lifetime. There Faraday gave a series of lectures entitled 'Chemical History of a Candle'. Faraday rejected a knighthood and twice refused to become President of the Royal Society. He was elected as a foreign member of the Royal Swedish Academy of Sciences and the French Academy of Sciences.

Faraday took his last breath at Hampton Court in 1867 and has a memorial near Issac Newton's tomb. SI unit of capacitance, Farad and Faraday constant were named in honour of him. He became the source of inspiration for the later scientists which is evident from the fact that the eminent Nobel laureate, Albert Einstein kept Faraday's photograph on his study wall alongside pictures of Isaac Newton and Clark Maxwell.

FUN TIME

CROSSWORD

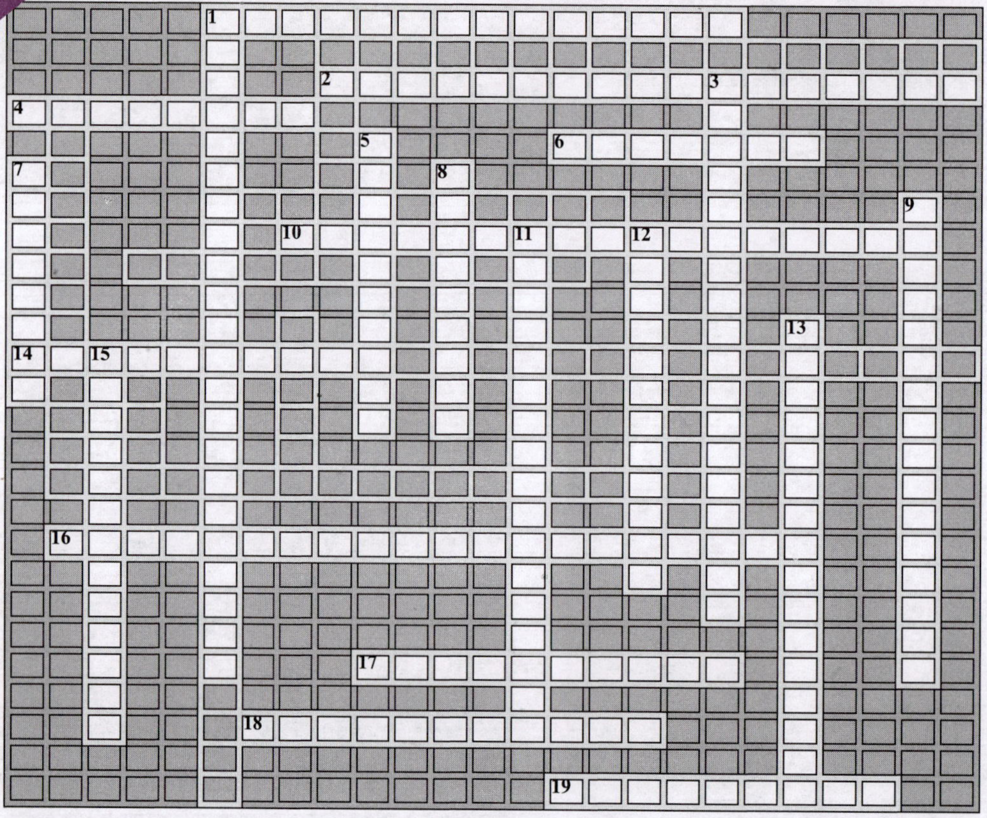

Across

1. Purest form of water which is used in the medical field for preparing soluble injectables
2. Hardness imparted to water due to chlorides and sulphates of calcium and magnesium
4. Homogeneous mixture of two or more components
6. Heterogeneous mixture of two or more components.
10. Solution containing the maximum amount of solute in the solvent at a given temperature
14. Amount of heat energy required to convert the unit mass of solid or liquid to liquid or gas respectively without any change in temperature
16. Radiation that decomposes the dissolved oxygen present in water and used in aqua purifiers
17. A heterogeneous mixture in which the suspended particles settle down and can be filtered easily
18. Law that establishes the quantitative relationship between the mass of substance deposited at the electrode to the amount of electricity passed
19. Water that forms a lather with soap readily

Down

1. Substances that absorb moisture and dissolve in it forming a saturated solution
3. Phenomenon of unusual expansion of water between 0°C to 4°C
5. The cell in which the process of electrolysis is carried out
7. Smallest unit of a crystalline solid
8. Water that does not produce lather with soap readily
9. Water available beneath the earth's surface
11. Bicarbonates of calcium and magnesium impart ______ to water
12. Amount of heat required to raise the temperature of a unit mass of substance through 1°C / 1K
13. Random movement of colloidal particles in the dispersion medium
15. Scattering of light by colloidal particles

INTRODUCTION

Our planet Earth is inhabited by a wide variety of flora and fauna and this makes it a unique planet. Water is one of the vital natural resources which impart this uniqueness to the planet. The significant role played by water in the sustenance of life owes not only to its abundance but also to its characteristic properties, such as, its state of existence, its ability to undergo interconversion to other states and above all to its universal solvent property.

The universal solvent property of water which means the ability to form solutions with a wide range of substances contributes for all life processes occurring in nature. At the same time, the most prevalent hazard of water pollution can also be attributed to the same property. In short, either way water or solution is considered as an invariable part of chemistry.

Sources of Water

Water in the liquid state is found in oceans and seas. Apart from this, liquid water is also found in rivers, lakes, streams, and other water bodies. Water available in the above sources is called **surface water**. Water present in oceans and seas contains appreciable proportions of dissolved salts, predominantly sodium chloride. The presence of these salts imparts salty taste to water and this water is, hence, called **saline water**.

In addition to surface water, water is also available under the earth's surface. This is called **underground water**. This water is stored due to the seepage of rain water through the soil. The underground water may come out in the form of springs. This can be drawn out artificially by digging wells or with the help of tube wells.

Info Bytes!

Groundwater, derived from aquifers, is a critical source of drinking water in many parts of the world. It gets replenished by rain but can get depleted if not managed sustainably.

Hard Water and Soft Water

Water obtained from different sources contains different salts in dissolved state. The physical properties of water are by and large attributed to the salts dissolved in it.

Water that dissolves soap and readily produces lather is known as **soft water**. Rainwater and distilled water are the examples of soft water.

Water that produces a curdy substance on treatment with soap and cannot lather easily is known as **hard water**. This happens due to the presence of dissolved salts, like, chlorides, sulphates, and bicarbonates of calcium and magnesium. The constituents of soap are soluble sodium salts of higher fatty acids, like, palmitic acid, stearic acid, or oleic acid. When hard water is treated with soap, reactions take place among the soluble salts of calcium and magnesium present in hard water and the constituent salts of soap producing insoluble palmitate, stearate, or oleate of calcium and magnesium in the form of curdy precipitate which prevents the formation of lather.

Info Bytes!

Dissolution of soap and formation of lather in water also depends on the presence of the dissolved salts.

Hardness of Water

Hardness of water can be classified into two types depending on the ease of removal of it. These are **temporary hardness** which can be removed by boiling and **permanent hardness** which cannot be removed by simple boiling.

Removal of Hardness

Table 8.1 Different methods of removal of hardness of water

Types of hardness	Processes of removal of hardness
Temporary hardness	**By boiling:** $Ca(HCO_3)_2 \rightarrow CaCO_3 + CO_2 + H_2O$ $Mg(HCO_3)_2 \rightarrow MgCO_3 + CO_2 + H_2O$ Precipitates of insoluble $CaCO_3$ and $MgCO_3$ can be filtered off
Temporary and permanent hardness	**By passing through ion exchange resins:** • Removal of cation: $2RCOO^-H^+ + Ca^{2+} \rightarrow (RCOO)_2Ca + 2H^+$ Acid resin $2RCOO^-H^+ + Mg^{2+} \rightarrow (RCOO)_2Mg + 2H^+$ Acid resin • Removal of anion: $RNH_3^+OH^- + Cl^- \rightarrow RNH_3Cl + OH^-$ Basic resin $2RNH_3^+OH^- + SO_4^{2-} \rightarrow (RNH_3)_2SO_4 + 2OH^-$ Basic resin (acid and basic resins are giant organic molecules where R represents the alkyl group)

After prolonged use, resins lose their activity and are, hence, required to be reactivated. Acid resin can be regenerated by using a strong acid like H_2SO_4, whereas regeneration of a basic resin is carried out by treating it with a strong base like NaOH.

$$(RCOO)_2Ca + H_2SO_4 \rightarrow 2RCOOH + Ca^{2+} + SO_4^{2-}$$

Acid resin after use — Regenerated Acid resin

$$RNH_3Cl + NaOH \rightarrow RNH_3OH + Na^+ + Cl^-$$

Basic resin after use — Regenerated Basic resin

Info Bytes!

The process of removing hardness from water is termed as softening. There are various methods, including ion exchange, lime-soda, and distillation.

Important Properties of Water

The significance of 'solutions' in chemistry originates from the universal solvent property of water. Water can dissolve many substances in it due to its high dielectric constant. Dielectric constant is the property of a solvent to reduce the force of attraction between the ions (cations and anions) of inorganic compounds. It can also dissolve a large number of organic compounds, like, glucose, sugar, alcohol, etc. Due to its ability to dissolve a wide range of substances in it, water is called **universal solvent**.

Day-to-day human activities, like, washing, cooking, cleaning, etc., and all life processes occurring in nature involve the usage of water. Therefore, the ability of water to form solutions is responsible for sustenance of life. On the other hand, the same characteristic forms the basic cause for adding pollutants to water. In whichever way it is considered, the ability of water to form solutions influences the survival of humanity on earth.

Solutions

A **solution** is a homogeneous mixture of two or more substances. The proportion of the constituents of the solution can be varied within certain limits. The solutions comprising two components are called **binary solutions**.

That component of a solution which is in the same physical state (i.e., solid, liquid, or gas) as the solution is called **solvent**, whereas the other component is called **solute**.

If both the components are in the same state, the component which is present in larger proportions is called **solvent** and the one which is present in minor proportions is called **solute**.

EXAMPLE 8.1 How are the cation-exchange resins regenerated after they are saturated?

SOLUTION

With continuous use, cation-exchange resins become saturated with unwanted cations, diminishing their ion-exchange capacity. To regain their effectiveness, the saturated resins are treated with an acid.

$$RCa + 2HCl \rightarrow R_2H + CaCl_2$$

where R represents the resin matrix.

Classification of Solutions

Depending on the physical states of the solute and the solvent, solutions can be classified into various types.

Table 8.2 Classification of solutions with examples

Solvents	Solutes	Examples
Solid	Solid	Alloys of metals
	Liquid	Hydrated crystalline salts
	Gas	Hydrogen gas adsorbed on platinum or palladium
Liquid	Solid	Common salt in water
	Liquid	Petrol in kerosene
	Gas	Aerated water or soft drinks
Gas	Gas	Air

When the solvent is a gas and the solute is a solid or a liquid, the resultant mixture becomes heterogeneous. All other solutions being homogeneous are called **true solutions**. The other two types of mixtures being heterogeneous are called **suspensions**. Examples of suspension are fog, mist and dust particles in air.

Solubility

The process of dissolving a substance in the given solvent is called **dissolution**.

The maximum amount of a particular solute in grams which can dissolve in 100 g of the solvent at a given temperature is called **solubility**.

$$\text{Solubility} = \frac{\text{Mass of solute}}{\text{Mass of solvent}} \times 100$$

Example: Solubility of copper sulphate in water at 20°C is 20.7 and solubility of potassium chloride in water at 20°C is 34.

Konnect

The amount of a solute dissolved in a definite quantity of a solvent depends upon the nature of the solute as well as nature of the solvent.

A given solution may or may not contain the maximum amount of solute in it. The further dissolving capacity of a given solution depends on the amount of solute already present in the solution. On the basis of the capacity of the solution to dissolve certain amount of solute further, the solutions are classified into three types as discussed here under.

Saturated Solution

A solution which contains maximum amount of a solute that can be dissolved in a solvent at a given temperature is called **saturated solution** at that particular temperature. This solution can no longer dissolve any more solute under the given conditions.

Unsaturated Solution

The solution containing lesser amount of the solute than the saturated solution at a given temperature is called an **unsaturated solution**. In the unsaturated solution, the solvent has the capacity of dissolving more amount of the solute at that particular temperature.

Supersaturated Solution

If the solution holds more solute than the saturated solution at a given temperature, it is called **supersaturated solution**.

When more solute is made to dissolve in the saturated solution by raising its temperature, and then, cooling it slowly without causing any disturbances (like shaking), then, the resultant solution holds more solute than the saturated solution.

Supersaturated solution is metastable and slight disturbances, like, shaking, stirring, scratching the wall of the container or adding a solute crystal to the solution make the additional amount of the solute to precipitate out, thereby resulting in the formation of the saturated solution again.

Factor effecting solubility

Temperature

For most of the substances, solubility increases with the increase in temperature. However, the solubility of some substances decreases with increase in temperature. In case of some substances, the temperature has no or little effect on the solubility. The solubility of sodium sulphate and calcium sulphate increases with the increase in temperature up to a certain extent and then decreases, whereas solubility of sodium chloride does not show much variation with the increase of temperature.

The solubilities of gases in liquids show a different trend with regard to the effect of temperature. With the increase in temperature, the solubility of a gas in a particular liquid decreases. In these solutions, the solubility is also influenced by the pressure.

Pressure

The effect of pressure on the solubility of a gas in a liquid is given by Henry's law, which states that at constant temperature, the increase in pressure on the surface of the liquid increases the solubility of the gas in the liquid.

Nature of Solute and Solvent: Polar solutes dissolve in polar solvents; nonpolar solutes prefer nonpolar solvents.

Presence of Other Solutes: Can reduce solubility due to the common ion effect or salting out.

Particle Size: Finer particles dissolve faster due to increased surface area.

Agitation: Increases dissolution rate but doesn't impact maximum solubility.

pH: Affects solubility for certain salts.

Polarity: Polar solvents dissolve polar and ionic compounds.

[*Remember:* "Like dissolves like," and external conditions (temperature, pressure) often play significant roles in solubility.]

Concentration of Solution

Many chemical reactions take place in the solution state. In order to calculate the volume or mass of the solution required to be taken for the reaction, the concentration of the solution should be known. There are different methods for measuring the concentration of the solution. Among these, molarity and weight percentage are the two methods which are commonly used.

Molarity

Molarity is the most convenient and commonly used method for expressing the concentration of a solution. **Molarity** can be defined as the number of moles of a solute present in 1 L of a solution. It is denoted by 'M.'

If n = number of moles of the solute present in the solution

W = Weight of the solute in grams

GMW = Gram molecular weight (mass) of the solute

V = Volume of the solution, then

$$M = \frac{n}{V} = \frac{W}{\text{GMW}} \times \frac{1}{V \text{ in L}} \text{ or } M = \frac{W}{\text{GMW}} \times \frac{1000}{V \text{ in mL}}$$

Example: 0.4 M sodium carbonate solution means 0.4 moles of sodium carbonate present in 1000 mL of the solution.

Weight Percentage (w/w)

The mass of a solute expressed in grams present in 100 g of a solution is called **weight percentage of the solute in the solution.**

$$\text{Weight percentage of the solute} = \frac{\text{Weight of the solute}}{\text{Weight of the solution}} \times 100$$

Example:

10% (w/w) sodium hydroxide solution

10 g of sodium hydroxide is present in 100 g of the solution.

Crystallisation

When a saturated solid–liquid solution is cooled slowly, solid solute settles down with a highly regular arrangement of its constituent particles (atoms, molecules, or ions).This regular arrangement of component particles in a three-dimensional system is uniform throughout the entire solid. This type of solid is called **crystalline solid**. The smallest unit of this arrangement of particles which gets repeated throughout the crystalline solid is called **unit cell**. The unit cell of each substance has a definite geometric shape.

Hence, **crystals** can be defined as solids in which the constituent atoms, molecules or ions are packed in a regularly ordered and repeating pattern extending in all three spatial dimensions.

Crystallization is the process of formation of a crystalline solid from the corresponding solution.

Different Processes of Crystallization

1. Slow cooling of a hot saturated solution of a solid solute from a higher temperature to a lower temperature.
2. Evaporation of an unsaturated solution at moderate temperature.
3. Slow cooling of a molten solid.
4. Sublimation of the solid followed by condensation of the resultant vapors.

Water of Crystallization

When a solid gets crystallized from its respective hot concentrated aqueous solution, a certain fixed number of water molecules also get attached to the solid crystals to form unit cells of the crystals.

The fixed number of water molecules which combine with a crystal are necessary for the maintenance of crystalline properties, but capable of being lost either at normal temperature or at a higher temperature is called **water of crystallization**.

Examples: green vitriol ($FeSO_4.7H_2O$), blue vitriol ($CuSO_4.5H_2O$), washing soda ($Na_2CO_3.10H_2O$), etc. The salts which contain water of crystallization are called **hydrated salts**.

When the hydrated salt completely loses its water molecules, it is called **anhydrous salt**. When a hydrated salt gets dehydrated and forms the anhydrous salt, the color of the salt changes. For example, $CuSO_4$. $5H_2O$ is blue in color. It changes to white color due to the loss of water molecules on heating.

Efflorescence and Deliquescence

There are some hydrated crystals which lose some of the water of crystallization or all the water of crystallization on exposure to air at normal temperature. This phenomenon is known as **efflorescence** and the hydrated crystals which lose water molecules are called **efflorescent substances**.

After the release of the water molecules, efflorescent substances lose their crystalline property and get transformed into a powdery mass, which is called the anhydrous salt.

Example: Glauber's salt, $Na_2SO_4.10H_2O$ loses all of its water molecules on exposure to air at ordinary temperature.

Some crystalline salts absorb moisture on exposure to air and ultimately dissolve in it to form an aqueous solution. This phenomenon is called **deliquescence** and these crystalline salts are called **deliquescent substances**. These salts may or may not contain water of crystallization.

Examples: hydrated magnesium chloride ($MgCl_2.6H_2O$), hydrated calcium chloride ($CaCl_2$. $6H_2O$), etc.

Hygroscopic Substances and Desiccating Agents

There are certain substances which absorb moisture from air without changing their physical state. These substances are called **hygroscopic substances**. They may exist in solid or liquid state under normal temperature and pressure.

Examples: calcium oxide (solid), concentrated sulphuric acid (liquid), etc.

After absorbing moisture, solid hygroscopic substances remain as solids and liquid substances remain as liquids.

Unlike deliquescent substances, these hygroscopic substances retain their physical states (solids or liquid) on the absorption of moisture.

Hygroscopic substances which are used to remove water from the surroundings are called **desiccating agents**.
Examples: calcium oxide and anhydrous calcium chloride.

Study of solutions is an important and vital part of chemistry because of its various applications. Besides solutions, there are some other mixtures known as colloids and suspensions which also have equal importance in chemistry because of their unique properties. The basic difference in the properties of solution, colloid, and suspension is attributed to the variation in size of their constituent particles.

In solution, the size of the solute particles is less than 10 nm and they do not settle down on long standing. However, in a suspension, the size of the suspended particles is more than 1 μm. Hence, the suspended particles settle down slowly. The mud particle present in muddy water is an example of suspension.

Colloids

A **colloid** is a mixture where one of the constituents is dispersed evenly throughout another. The size of the constituent particles which is dispersed is in between 10 nm to 1 μm and is called **dispersed phase**. The medium in which these particles are dispersed is called **dispersion medium**.

Like solutions, colloids can also be classified based on the physical state of the dispersed phase and dispersion medium.

Table 8.3 Classification of colloids

Dispersion media	Dispersed phases	Examples
Solid	Solid	Solid sol: colored glass
	Liquid	Gel: jelly, cheese, butter
	Gas	Solid foam: pumice
Liquid	Solid	Sol-paint, blood
	Liquid	Emulsion: milk, face cream, etc.
	Gas	Foam: moisture in air, whipped cream, etc.
Gas	Solid	Solid aerosol: smoke
	Liquid	Liquid aerosol: fog, mist, clouds, etc.

Properties of Colloid

Colloids have some unique properties due to the specific size of the particles of the dispersed phase. Some important properties of colloids are discussed below.

Konnect

The smallest size of a colloidal particle is around 1 nanometer, which is roughly 10 times the size of a hydrogen atom.

Tyndall Effect

When a beam of light rays is passed through a colloid, particles of the dispersed phase scatter the light rays and the path of the light becomes visible. The scattering of light by the colloid particles is known as **Tyndall effect**.

Brownian Movement

The random movement exhibited by the colloid particles throughout the dispersion medium is known as **Brownian movement**. This type of movement resists the colloid particles to settle down.

Coagulation of Colloid Particles

Colloid particles can be coagulated by the addition of salt because these particles are charged. Coagulation takes place due to the neutralization of the charge associated with the colloid particles, and thus, the colloid particles can settle down.

Action of Water on Some Metals

1. **Potassium and Sodium:** These two metals react with cold water. They even react with moisture (water vapour):

   $2K + 2H_2O \rightarrow 2KOH + H_2$

   $2Na + 2H_2O \rightarrow 2NaOH + H_2$

2. **Calcium:** The following reaction takes place in cold water:

   $Ca + 2H_2O \rightarrow Ca(OH)_2 + H_2$

Info Bytes!

Gallium is a metal that can melt in your hand and can be supercooled below its melting point and still remain liquid, but it reacts vigorously with water.

EXAMPLE 8.2

What happens when red litmus paper is dipped in water in which a piece of magnesium metal is dropped?

SOLUTION

Red litmus paper turns blue as magnesium reacts with water to form $Mg(OH)_2$ which is basic in nature.

EXAMPLE 8.3

Decompression bubbles form when a diver ascends too quickly from deep waters. What is the reason behind it?

SOLUTION

Due to the release of dissolved gases, like nitrogen, from the blood and body tissues, decompression bubbles form. The solubility of a gas in a liquid decreases with the decrease in pressure.

EXAMPLE 8.4

How many grams of potassium chloride is present in 250 g of saturated solution? The solubility of KCl is 35.8 at 25°C?

SOLUTION

$$\text{Solubility} = \frac{\text{Mass of solute}}{\text{Mass of solvent}} \times 100$$

$$35.8 = \frac{x}{250 - x} \times 100$$

$(250 - x)35.8 = 100x \Rightarrow 8950 - 35.8x = 100x \Rightarrow x = 65.9$ g

EXAMPLE 8.5

Complete the following table:

Weight %	Mass of solute (g)	Mass of solution (g)	Mass of solvent (g)
–	20	80	–
30	–	–	80
20	–	–	75

SOLUTION

Weight %	Mass of solute (g)	Mass of solution (g)	Mass of solvent (g)
25	20	80	60
30	34.3	114.3	80
20	18.75	93.75	75

Electrolysis of Water

Water conducts electricity when a few drops of an acid are added to it. On electrolysis, water gives two volumes of H_2 and one volume of O_2. Hoffman's voltameter is an apparatus in which acidulated water is electrolyzed by using platinum electrodes.

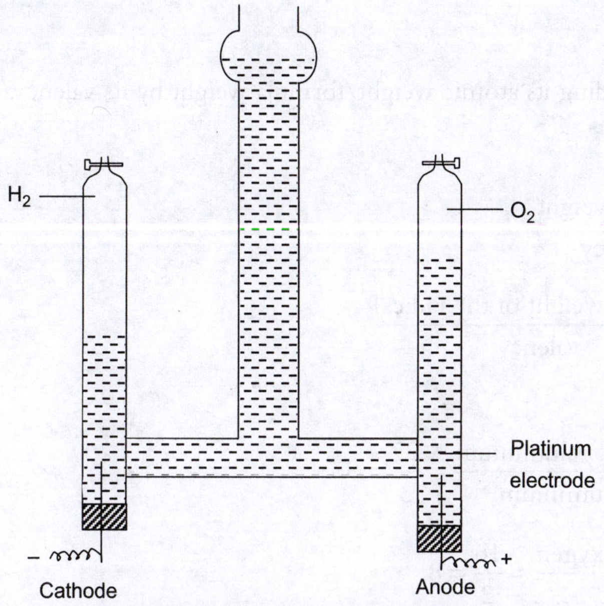

Figure 8.1 Hoffman's voltameter

Konnect

Electrolysis of water was discovered in 1800 by two scientists, Anthony Carlisle and William Nicholson.

Mechanism of Electrolysis

The process of electrolysis results in the decomposition of an electrolyte and subsequent deposition or liberation of the constituent products at the respective electrodes. However, the quantities of the electrolytic products at the respective electrodes are not same for all the electrolytes.

For the establishment of quantitative relationship between the electricity passed through the electrolyte and the products obtained at the electrodes, Michael Faraday conducted some experiments. The results were given out as Faraday's laws of electrolysis.

Faraday's Laws of Electrolysis

First Law of Faraday

The amount of substance deposited or liberated or dissolved at an electrode is directly proportional to the quantity of electricity passing through the electrolyte.

Mathematical Representation

$m \propto Q$ (m = mass of substance deposited at the electrode)

(Q = quantity of electricity passing through the electrolyte)

$Q = c \times t$ (c = current strength in amperes)

(t = time of flow of current in seconds)

$m \propto ct$ or $m = ect$ (e = constant called **electrochemical equivalent)**

If $c = 1$ amp; $t = 1$ s (or Q = 1 coulomb), then $m = e$

Therefore, electrochemical equivalent can be defined as the mass of a substance which undergoes an electrode reaction at an electrode by the passage of one coulomb of electricity through the electrolyte.

Info Bytes!

Faraday's first law of electrolysis states that the amount of any substance deposited or liberated during electrolysis is directly proportional to the quantity of electricity passed through the solution.

Since the charge of an electron is equal to 1.602×10^{-19} coulombs, passage of one mole of electrons through an electrolyte corresponds to passage of $(6.023 \times 10^{23} \times 1.602 \times 10^{-19})$ coulombs of electricity.

Charge of 1 mole of electrons $= 6.023 \times 10^{23} \times 1.602 \times 10^{-19} = 96{,}496$ coulombs

$\approx 96{,}500$ coulombs is called **one Faraday**.

The amount of the substance which undergoes electrode reaction by the passage of one Faraday (96,500 coulombs) of electricity is equal to the **equivalent weight** of the substance.

Calculation of Equivalent Weight

The equivalent weight of an element or radical is calculated by dividing its atomic weight/formula weight by its valency. The unit of equivalent weight is **atomic mass unit**.

$$\text{Equivalent weight of an element} = \frac{\text{Atomic weight}}{\text{valency}}$$

$$\text{Equivalent weight of a radical} = \frac{\text{Formula weight of the radical}}{\text{valency}}$$

Example:

$$\text{Equivalent weight of aluminium} = \frac{\text{Atomic weight of aluminium}}{\text{valency of aluminium}} = \frac{27}{3} = 9$$

$$\text{Equivalent weight of oxygen} = \frac{\text{Atomic weight of oxygen}}{\text{valency}} = \frac{16}{2} = 8$$

$$\text{Equivalent weight of sulphate radical} = \frac{\text{Formula weight of sulphate radical}}{\text{valency}} = \frac{96}{2} = 48$$

Therefore, the number of equivalents of the substance deposited or liberated or dissolved at an electrode is equal to the number of faradays of electricity passed through the electrolyte.

Relation Between Equivalent Weight and Electrochemical Equivalent

$$\text{Electrochemical equivalent} = \frac{\text{Equivalent weight}}{96{,}500} = \frac{\text{Atomic weight}}{z \times 96{,}500} \quad (\text{where } z = \text{valency element})$$

Second Law of Faraday

For the passage of same quantity of electricity through different electrolytes, the amounts of respective substances deposited at the electrodes are in the ratio of the equivalent weights of the substances.

If m_1, m_2 and m_3 are masses of different substances and E_1, E_2, and E_3 are the equivalent weights of the substances, respectively

$m_1 : m_2 : m_3 = E_1 : E_2 : E_3$ (when quantity of electricity is constant)

EXAMPLE 8.6

(i) Calculate the weight of aluminium deposited during the electrolysis of molten aluminium chloride by passing 193 A of current for 500 min.

(ii) A current of 9.65 amperes is passed through three different electrolytes, i.e., $NaNO_3$, KCl and $ZnSO_4$ for 30 min separately. Calculate the mass ratio of the metals deposited at the respective electrodes. Also find out the weights of various metals deposited at the respective electrodes.

SOLUTION

(i) $Al^{3+} + 3e^- \rightarrow Al$

$$\text{Mass of Al deposited (W)} = \frac{Mct}{ZF}$$

M = molecular weight = 27

c = 193 amp

$t = 500 \times 60$ s

Z = 3

F = 96,500 C

$$W = \frac{27 \times 193 \times 500 \times 60}{3 \times 96500} = 540\,g$$

(ii) Quantity of electricity passed through the electrolyte = current strength × time of flow = 9.65 × 30 × 60 coulombs

$$m_{Na} : m_K : m_{Zn} = E_{Na} : E_K : E_{Zn}$$

$$E_{Na} = \frac{23}{1} = 23 \qquad (Na^+ + e^- \rightarrow Na)$$

$$E_K = \frac{39}{1} = 39 \qquad (K^+ + e^- \rightarrow K)$$

$$E_{Zn} = \frac{65}{2} = 32.5 \qquad (Zn^{2+} + 2e^- \rightarrow Zn)$$

$$m_{Na} : m_K : m_{Zn} = 23 : 39 : 32.5$$

$$\text{Weight of sodium deposited} = \frac{23 \times 9.65 \times 30 \times 60}{96500} = 4.14\,g$$

$$\text{Weight of potassium deposited} = \frac{39 \times 9.65 \times 30 \times 60}{96500} = 7.02\,g$$

$$\text{Weight of zinc deposited} = \frac{32.5 \times 9.65 \times 30 \times 60}{96500} = 5.85\,g$$

EXAMPLE 8.7 What is ratio by mass of magnesium and calcium obtained when the electrolysis of their respective chlorides are carried out in the molten state, if the number of moles of both the chlorides taken are same?

SOLUTION

$MgCl_2 \rightarrow Mg^{2+} + Cl^-$; $CaCl_2 \rightarrow Ca^{2+} + Cl^-$

$Mg^{2+} + 2e^- \rightarrow Mg$; $Ca^{2+} + 2e^- \rightarrow Ca$

Ratio of mass = 24 : 40 = 3 : 5

EXAMPLE 8.8

Calculate the mass of magnesium deposited during the electrolysis of molten magnesium chloride by passing 193 amperes of current for 600 minutes.

SOLUTION

$$\text{Mass} = \frac{Mct}{ZF}, \; Mg^{2+} + 2e^- \rightarrow Mg$$

$$\text{Mass} = \frac{24 \times 193 \times 600 \times 60}{2 \times 96500} = 864 \text{ g}$$

EXAMPLE 8.9

Complete the following table

Mass of metal deposited (g)	Atomic mass	Current (amp)	Time (min)	Valency
23	23	–	500	–
–	24	386	600	–
–	27	193	965	–

SOLUTION

(i) Atomic mass of 23 corresponds to sodium, valency = 1

$$W = \frac{Mct}{ZF} = \frac{23 \times c \times 500 \times 60}{1 \times 96500} = 23$$

$$c = \frac{23 \times 96500}{23 \times 500 \times 60} = 3.21 \text{ amp}$$

(ii) Atomic mass of 24 corresponds to magnesium, valency = 2

$$W = \frac{24 \times 386 \times 600 \times 60}{2 \times 96500} = 1728 \text{ g}$$

(iii) Atomic mass of 27 corresponds to aluminium, valency = 3

$$W = \frac{27 \times 193 \times 965 \times 60}{3 \times 96500} = 1042.2 \text{ g}$$

Mass of metal deposited (g)	Atomic mass	Current (amp)	Time (min)	Valency
23	23	3.21	500	1
1728	24	326	600	2
1042.2	27	193	965	3

POINTS TO REMEMBER

- ✔ Water available in the above sources is called surface water.
- ✔ The presence of these salts imparts salty taste to water and this water is, hence, called saline water.
- ✔ In addition to surface water, water is also available under the earth's surface. This is called underground water.
- ✔ Water that dissolves soap and readily produces lather is known as soft water.
- ✔ Water that produces a curdy substance on treatment with soap and cannot lather easily is known as hard water.
- ✔ Hardness of water can be classified into two types depending on the ease of removal of it. These are temporary hardness which can be removed by boiling and permanent hardness which cannot be removed by simple boiling.
- ✔ Due to its ability to dissolve a wide range of substances in it, water is called universal solvent.
- ✔ A solution is a homogeneous mixture of two or more substances.
- ✔ The solutions comprising two components are called binary solutions.
- ✔ That component of a solution which is in the same physical state (i.e., solid, liquid or gas) as the solution is called solvent, whereas the other component is called solute.
- ✔ When the solvent is a gas and the solute is a solid or a liquid, the resultant mixture becomes heterogeneous. All other solutions being homogeneous are called true solutions. The other two types of mixtures being heterogeneous are called suspensions.
- ✔ The process of dissolving a substance in the given solvent is called dissolution.
- ✔ The maximum amount of a particular solute in grams which can dissolve in 100 g of the solvent at a given temperature is called solubility.
- ✔ A solution which contains maximum amount of a solute that can be dissolved in a solvent at a given temperature is called saturated solution at that particular temperature.
- ✔ The solution containing lesser amount of the solute than the saturated solution at a given temperature is called an unsaturated solution.
- ✔ If the solution holds more solute than the saturated solution at a given temperature, it is called supersaturated solution.
- ✔ Molarity can be defined as the number of moles of a solute present in 1 L of a solution. It is denoted by 'M.'
- ✔ The mass of a solute expressed in grams present in 100 g of a solution is called weight percentage of the solute in the solution.
- ✔ This regular arrangement of component particles in a three-dimensional system is uniform throughout the entire solid. This type of solid is called crystalline solid.
- ✔ The smallest unit of this arrangement of particles which gets repeated throughout the crystalline solid is called unit cell.
- ✔ Crystallization is the process of formation of a crystalline solid from the corresponding solution.
- ✔ The fixed number of water molecules which combine with a crystal are necessary for

the maintenance of crystalline properties, but capable of being lost either at normal temperature or at a higher temperature is called water of crystallization.

- ✔ There are certain substances which absorb moisture from air without changing their physical state. These substances are called hygroscopic substances.
- ✔ Hygroscopic substances which are used to remove water from the surroundings are called desiccating agents.
- ✔ A colloid is a mixture where one of the constituents is dispersed evenly throughout another.
- ✔ The size of the constituent particles which is dispersed is in between 10 nm to 1 μm and is called dispersed phase. The medium in which these particles are dispersed is called dispersion medium.
- ✔ The scattering of light by the colloid particles is known as Tyndall effect.
- ✔ The random movement exhibited by the colloid particles throughout the dispersion medium is known as Brownian movement.
- ✔ The equivalent weight of an element or radical is calculated by dividing its atomic weight/formula weight by its valency. The unit of equivalent weight is atomic mass unit.

DW

PRACTICE QUESTIONS CLASSROOM WING

Very Short Answer Type Questions

Directions for questions from 1 to 8:
Fill in the blanks.

1. A pale blue tinge in milk is due to ______.
2. Butter is a(an) ______.
3. Addition of potash alum results in the purification of water. The phenomenon associated with this reaction is ______.
4. In foam, the dispersion medium is _____ and the dispersed phase is _____, respectively.
5. Equivalent weight of phosphate radical is equal to ________
6. Total charge of Avogadro number of electrons = ________.
7. Hydrated copper sulphate on heating turns to ________.
8. The number of water molecules present in Glauber's salt is ________.

Directions for questions from 9 to 24:
Answer the following questions.

9. Bleeding from a wound stops by the application of $FeCl_3$ solution and the addition of alum hastens the process of purification of water are examples of which phenomenon.
10. Mention the specific property of water due to which it acts as a universal solvent.
11. Define solubility.
12. Give examples of the following solutions:
    (i) solid in solid (ii) gas in liquid
    (iii) liquid in solid
13. Why do we get a fizzing sound when a cool drink bottle is opened?
14. Effervescence is observed when water is warmed. What is the reason behind it?
15. Solubility of salt 'A' in water at 25°C is 15. What is the meaning this statement?
16. Name one hygroscopic substance whose physical state does not change by absorbing water.
17. How is an unsaturated solution made from a saturated one?
18. What is meant by an unit cell of a crystalline solid?
19. Why does the colour of the solid blue copper sulphate becomes white on heating?
20. What is the relation between coulomb and faraday?
21. What is dispersed phase and dispersion medium?
22. In what ratio by mass, hydrogen and oxygen are produced by the electrolysis of water?
23. What is the total charge of 2 moles of electrons in faraday?
24. What are the equivalent weights of cuprous ion and cupric ion?

Short Answer Type Questions

25. Arrange the following saturated solutions in the increasing order of solubilities of the respective solutes.
    (A) 125 g of solute is present in 625 g of solution 'A'.
    (B) 20 g of solute is present in 180 g of solution 'B'.
    (C) 30 g of solute is present in 210 g of solution 'C'.
    (D) 15 g of solute is present in 120 g of solution 'D'.
26. The atomic weight of a trivalent metal is x. Calculate its electrochemical equivalent.
27. The electrochemical equivalent of a divalent metal is x. Calculate the mass of the metal obtained at the cathode by the passage of 0.5 Faraday of electric charge, in terms of x.

28. How are resins regenerated after long use?

29. (a) What is the mass of the solute present in 1 L of 0.2 M sodium carbonate solution?

(b) 386 ampere current is passed through molten alumina under suitable conditions for about 30 minutes.

(A) Calculate amount of aluminium obtained.

(B) Find out the volume of the gaseous product obtained at STP.

30. How many grams of potassium chloride are present in 250 g of saturated solution if the solubility of KCl is 35.8 at 25°C?

31. What is the effect of temperature and pressure on the solubility of solids and gases in liquids?

32. Establish the relationship between equivalent weight and electrochemical equivalent.

33. Correlate the bond present in water with its solvent property.

34. If small pieces of sodium and potassium are dropped separately in two beakers containing water, golden and lilac flames are observed on the surface of water in the respective beakers. Justify these observations.

35. What are the different processes of crystallization?

36. Explain molarity and weight percentage.

37. How many moles of electrons are required to liberate 112 L of oxygen at STP when acidulated water is electrolyzed?

38. Differentiate deliquescence and efflorescence.

39. What is ratio by mass of magnesium and calcium obtained when the electrolysis of their respective chlorides are carried out in the molten state, if the number of moles of both the chlorides taken are same?

Essay Answer Type Questions

40. The molarity of NaOH solution is 5 M. Calculate the amount of solute required to be added to 1 L of the solution to saturate it at 25°C. The solubility of the solute is 20 at 25°C and the density of 5 M NaOH solution is 1.5 g/mL.

41. If '*a*' g of a divalent metal gets deposited at the cathode by passing 10 A of current for 30 min, calculate its atomic weight.

42. Calculate the molarity of *a* g of *b*% (w/w) $Ca(OH)_2$ solution. Density of the solution is *x* g/mL.

43. Explain the different processes of removal of temporary and permanent hardness of water.

44. What are the different properties of colloids? Explain.

45. Five different substances are considered—blue vitriol, glauber's salt, washing soda, anhydrous calcium chloride and calcium oxide. What observations do you find when they are exposed to atmosphere? Justify the observations with respect to their vapour pressures.

PRACTICE QUESTIONS COMPETITION WING

Level 1: Apply your Concepts

Direction for questions from 1 to 10:
State whether the following statements are true or false.

1. Temporary hardness of water can be removed by boiling.
2. The molarity of 4 g of NaOH in 100 mL solution is 0.5 M.
3. Calcium oxide retains its physical state on exposure to air.
4. During electrolysis of water hydrogen and oxygen are liberated at cathode and anode, respectively.
5. The solvent is in a solid state in hydrated salts.
6. 27 g of aluminium is deposited by passing one faraday of electric charge.
7. 144750 C is equal to two faradays.
8. Soft water dissolves soap and produces lather.
9. Calcium chloride does not impart hardness to water.
10. Boiling decomposes sodium bicarbonates to soften water.

Direction for questions from 11 to 19:
Fill in the blanks.

11. Colloidal particles show ________ movement.
12. The molarity of a 250 mL solution is 0.5 M. The amount of solute present in it is_____ g. (molecular weight of the solute = 58).
13. In a face cream, the dispersion medium and dispersed phase are in ________ and ________ states, respectively.
14. Formula of green vitriol is ________.
15. Salts with water of crystallization are known as _____
16. To deposit 216 g of silver _____ faradays of charge is required.
17. Washing soda on exposure to air loses ________ water molecules.
18. Presence of _____ and _____ of _____ and _____ imparts permanent hardness of water.
19. Anhydrous calcium chloride is a _____ agent.

Direction for question 20:
Match the entries in Column A with the appropriate ones in Column B.

20.

	Column A		Column B
A.	RNH_3OH	(a)	Particles settle down on long standing
B.	RCOOH	(b)	Hygroscopic substance
C.	Washing soda	(c)	Coagulation takes place on addition of salt
D.	Sulphuric acid	(d)	Acid resin
E.	Suspension	(e)	Water of crystallization
F.	Colloid	(f)	Basic resin

Direction for questions from 21 to 44:
For each of the questions, four choices have been provided. Select the correct alternative.

21. Which of the following electrolyte will deopist maximum amount of metal deposited at the cathode by passing the same quantity of electricity.
(A) NaCl (B) Al_2O_3
(C) $Fe_2(SO_4)_3$ (D) $ZnCl_2$

22. In which of the following condition minimum amount of magnesium obtained during the electrolysis of molten $MgCl_2$.
(A) $i = 5$ A, $t = 15$ min
(B) $i = 12$ A, $t = 6$ min
(C) $i = 8$ A, $t = 570$ s
(D) $i = 14$ A, $t = 330$ s

23. **Assertion (A):** Temporary hardness of water can be removed by boiling.

Reason (R): Bicarbonates of calcium and magnesium undergo thermal decomposition.

(a) Both A and R are true and R is the correct explanation of A.

(b) Both A and R are true, but R is not the correct explanation of A.

(c) A is true and R is false.

(d) A is false and R is true.

24. Assertion (A): Permanent hardness can be removed by adding zeolite to hard water.

Reason (R): Zeolite decomposes and forms insoluble sodium zeolite.

(a) Both A and R are true and R is the correct explanation of A.

(b) Both A and R are true, but R is not the correct explanation of A.

(c) A is true and R is false.

(d) A is false and R is true.

25. Assertion (A): Water is used in car radiators as a coolant.

Reason (R): Water has a high specific heat capacity.

(a) Both A and R are true and R is the correct explanation of A.

(b) Both A and R are true, but R is not the correct explanation of A.

(c) A is true and R is false.

(d) A is false and R is true.

26. Which of the following does not show much variation of solubility with the change of temperature?

(a) sodium chloride

(b) sodium sulphate

(c) potassium chloride

(d) potassium sulphate

27. Time required for the deposition of 40 g of calcium by passing 965 amp current through molten calcium chloride is:

(a) 100 s (b) 200 s

(c) 50 s (d) 150 s

28. The w/w % of 25 g of calcium hydroxide in 50 g of solvent is ________ %.

(a) 40 (b) 33.33

(c) 36.3 (d) 30

29. What is the molarity of 24.5% (w/w) sulphuric acid solution? [density of the solution is 1.8 g/cc]

(a) 6 M (b) 3 M

(c) 4 M (d) 4.5 M

30. Which of the following changes take place due to the addition of aluminium sulphate to muddy water?

(a) Muddy water becomes free from germs and bacteria.

(b) Coagulation of mud particles takes place.

(c) Adsorption of mud on aluminium sulphate crystals results in isolation of mud from water.

(d) A part of the mud becomes soluble in water.

31. When a small crystal of a solute is added to a supersaturated solution,

(a) unsaturated solution is formed

(b) supersaturated solution is formed

(c) some amount of solute is precipitated

(d) both (b) and (c)

32. Which among the following is used as a desiccating agent?

(a) calcium hydroxide

(b) magnesium chloride

(c) calcium oxide

(d) calcium nitrate

33. Which of the following statements is true?

(a) Solubility of the gases in water decreases with decrease in pressure.

(b) Solubility of the gases in water decreases with increase in temperature.

(c) Solubility of the gases at depth of the sea is more than that at it surface.

(d) All of the above

34. An aqueous solution of a metal salt on electrolysis with 1930 A current for 20 s produces 8 g of the metal. The valency of the metal is ______ (atomic weight = 40).

(a) three (b) two

(c) four (d) one

35. In which of the following colloids, both dispersed phase and dispersion medium are liquids?

(a) blood (b) smoke

(c) mist (d) paint

36. The solubility of a solute A in four solvents P, Q, R, and S is 20 g, 30 g, 15 g, 40 g, respectively, at a given temperature. Arrange the four solvents in the increasing order of their dielectric constant.

(a) $P < Q < R < S$ (b) $R < P < Q < S$

(c) $R < Q < P < S$ (d) $P < Q < S < R$

37. The weight of a china dish with a saturated solution of sodium nitrate at 40°C is 80 g. After evaporating the whole solution the dish's weight along with the crystals is 40 g and the solubility of $NaNO_3$ at 40°C is 20 g. What is the weight of the empty china dish?

(a) 30 g (b) 32 g
(c) 34 g (d) 28 g

38. What is the weight percentage of 4 M calcium hydroxide solution?
[Density of solution = 1.3 g/mL]

(a) 11.6% (b) 48.3%
(c) 38.5% (d) 22.8%

39. Which of the following statements is true?

(a) Solubility of the gases in water decreases with decrease in pressure.
(b) Solubility of the gases in water decreases with increase in temperature.
(c) Solubility of the gases at deep sea is more than that at its surface.
(d) all the above

40. Arrange the solutes, A, B, C, and D in decreasing order of amount of solute precipitated when their respective hot saturated solutions are cooled from 100°C to 30°C:

		30°C	60°C	100°C
(1)	A	120	140	160
(2)	B	130	120	150
(3)	C	125	130	140
(4)	D	140	135	130

(a) 3 2 4 1 (b) 1 3 2 4
(c) 2 4 3 1 (d) 1 2 3 4

41. Write the steps in sequence for electroplating of brass spoon with silver.

(1) K^+ and H^+ ions are not discharged at cathode due to higher discharge potential than Ag^+.
(2) Silver gets deposited on brass spoon.
(3) A highly cleaned brass spoon which has to be electroplated is taken.
(4) Due to electrolytic dissociation, Ag^+, K^+, H^+, OH^- and CN^- ions are formed.

(a) 3 4 1 2 (b) 1 4 3 2
(c) 4 1 3 2 (d) 1 4 2 3

42. Which among the following has minimum molarity?

(a) 20 g of NaOH in 100 mL solution
(b) 24.5 g of H_2SO_4 in 500 mL solution
(c) 14 g of HCl in 100 mL solution
(d) 37 g of $Ca(OH)_2$ in 2000 mL solution

43. Which among the following is a true solution?

(a) vinegar in water
(b) sulphur in water
(c) aluminium paint
(d) starch solution

44. Arrange the statements in sequence for the calculation of weight of aluminium deposited during the electrolysis of molten aluminium chloride by passing *c* amperes of current for *t* minutes.

(1) Find the product of current (c) and time (t).
(2) Convert time in minutes to seconds.
(3) Write reduction equation of the metal ion.
(4) Conversion of charge into Faradays.
(5) Relation between mass of metal and number of Faradays passed through

(a) 2 1 4 3 5 (b) 1 2 3 4 5
(c) 4 2 1 5 3 (d) 2 1 4 5 3

Level 2: Review your Concepts

45. The solubility of salt 'A' is 20 at a given temperature. How much of salt A is present in 600 g of saturated solution at that temperature?

46. 1 kg of a saturated solution contains 200 g of solute at a given temperature. Calculate its solubility at that temperature.

47. (a) Why are carbonated beverages kept in sealed containers?

(b) Calculate the amount of heat energy required to convert 15 g of ice at –5°C to 15 g of steam at 150°C. Consider specific heat of ice, water and steam as 0.5, 1 and 0.5 cal/g respectively.

48. Some amount of Glauber's salt, hydrated magnesium chloride and hydrated calcium chloride are separately is kept in three containers. What will you observe, if blue colored cobalt chloride is introduced in the three containers? Explain with a reason.

49. 100 g of 25 % (w/w) sodium hydroxide is prepared in a laboratory. If the density of water is 0.9 g/cc at room temperature, calculate the volume of water taken

50. 200 mL of pure water contains 60 g of a solute at 60°C. The salt solution is cooled slowly up to 30°C. Based on the data given below calculate the mass of the solute precipitated from the solution:

Temperatures (°C)	Solubilities of the given solute
60	55
45	30
30	40

51. The amount of solute (H_2SO_4) and solvent present in a solution are 49 g and 90 g, respectively. If the specific gravities of the solute and solvent are 1.96 and 0.9, respectively, then calculate the molarity of the solution.

52. 5.4 g of a trivalent metal is deposited by passing 5 amp current during the electrolysis of its molten chloride. If the atomic weight of the metal is 27, calculate the time taken for the deposition.

53. The density of the particles of the dispersed phase is more than that of the dispersion medium in a colloid. But the colloid particles do not settle down. Give a reason.

54. Calculate the molarity of 30 % (w/w) NaOH solution, if the density of the solution is 1.05 g/cc.

55. If 6 g of a metal gets deposited by passing 2 amp of current for 2 h 30 min, calculate the equivalent weight of the metal.

56. Why does smoke produced by a cigarette appear blue in colour?

57. Why is ferric chloride solution used to stop bleeding from a wound?

58. Common salt increases in weight on long standing. Justify with an appropriate reason.

59. Compare the conductivity of a solution of NaOH in water and in alcohol.

Directions for questions from 60 to 69:
Application-Based Questions

60. Why does the color of the solid blue copper sulphate becomes white on heating?

61. When equal number of moles of CO_2, SO_3, and nitrogen gases are passed through water under pressure and then heated, which gas is evolved in maximum percentage? Justify.

62. Amount of solutes A, B and C in 400 g of water at 20°C, 40°C, and 80°C in their saturated solutions are given below.

	20°C	40°C	80°C
A	120 g	100 g	115 g
B	150 g	180 g	190 g
C	140 g	160 g	150 g

When the hot saturated solutions A, B and C are cooled slowly from 80°C to 20°C, analyse the changes that take place gradually in the given solutions with an appropriate reason.

63. A sample X loses its water of crystallization when exposed to dry air, a sample Y absorbs moisture from the atmospheric air. Justify the above action on the basis of vapor pressures of respective substances.

64. 8 g of bivalent metal is deposited by passing 10 amp current during the electrolysis of its molten chloride. If the atomic weight of the metal is 40, calculate the time taken for the deposition.

65. The time taken for the deposition of same number of moles of silver and copper, by the electrolysis of molten silver salt and copper salt, respectively, is in the ratio 1 : 2 carried out in two electrolytic cells connected in series. Find out the ratio of valences of two metals.

66. What will be the volume of oxygen gas liberated at STP when 15 amp current is passed through acidulated water for 4 h?

67. Though distilled water is pure water, people prefer potable water for drinking. Justify.

68. (a) Why is ethylene glycol used as anti-freeze?
(b) (A) Commercial sample of phosphoric acid is usually available as 84.0% (w/w) phosphoric acid solution. If it is 12.0 M, what is the density of the solution?
(B) In an aqueous solution of sulphuric acid, the acid concentration is 5 mole percent and the density of solution is 1.1 g/mL. (mole percent is no. of moles of solute in 100 moles of solution) Calculate:
(i) weight percent of the acid
(ii) molarity of the solution

69. 50 g of 15% (w/w) sodium hydroxide is prepared in a laboratory. Calculate the volume of water utilized if the density of water is 0.9 g/cc at the experimental conditions.

Level 3: Assess Your Concepts

70. The weight percentage of a solution is 10. Calculate the amount of solute to be added to 1 kg of the solution in order to saturate it. The solubility of the solute at that temperature is 25.

71. If '*m*' g of metal gets deposited by passing 1 A current for 1 s and the atomic weight of the metal is *n*, then calculate its valency in terms of *m*, *n* and *p* (assuming 1 Faraday = *p* Coulomb).

72. The amounts of solutes 'A', 'B' and 'C' in 300 g of water at 25°C, 40°C and 60°C in their saturated solutions are given below. Is the statement below true or false?

	25°C	40°C	60°C
A	110 g	90 g	105 g
B	140 g	170 g	180 g
C	130 g	150 g	140 g

Statement: 'A' can form a precipitate on cooling its saturated solution at 60°C – 40°C, whereas C forms a precipitate on cooling its saturated solution at 40°C – 25°C.

73. Examine the constituents of the containers given below and identify the container in which a change in colour is observed.

Container 'A': Glauber's salt + anhydrous copper sulphate

Container 'B': Hydrated $MgCl_2$ + anhydrous copper sulphate

Container 'C': Calcium oxide + anhydrous cobalt chloride

Container 'D': Anhydrous $CaCl_2$ + anhydrous cobalt chloride

74. Acidulated water is taken in Hoffman voltmeter to carry out the electrolysis process. If a piece of litmus paper is dipped in both the compartments of Hoffman voltmeter, what change will be observed in the color of the litmus during the electrolysis process?

Directions for questions from 75 to 80:
Application-Based Questions

75. A little amount of $CaCO_3$ is added to two test tubes, containing dil sulphuric acid and dil hydrochloric acid, respectively, and the resultant mixture is cooled slowly. What observation we can make? Justify the same.

76. Anhydrous cobalt chloride is used as a dehumidifying agent for absorbing moisture from highly humid air and again it is made reusable by low humid air. Justify the action of cobalt chloride with respect to its vapor pressure.

77. Find the ratio of time taken for the deposition of the same number of moles of zinc and silver, by the electrolysis of zinc sulphate and silver nitrate, respectively, carried out in two electrolytic cells connected in series.

78. If small pieces of sodium and potassium are dropped separately in two beakers containing water, golden yellow and lilac flames are observed, respectively, on the surface of water in the respective beakers. Justify the above observations.

79. Though sodium chloride is not deliquescent, table salt shows deliquescent nature. Justify.

80. The amounts of solutes P, Q and R in 300 g of their saturated solutions at three different temperatures are given below. The order of temperatures is X < Y < Z.

Solute	X°C	Y°C	Z°C
P	110 g	130 g	115 g
Q	90 g	105 g	120 g
R	80 g	60 g	70 g

(a) Predict the changes observed when the hot saturated solutions are cooled slowly from higher temperature to lower temperature.

(b) Caculate the solubilities of P, Q, R at X°C temperature.

AT

PRACTICE QUESTIONS JEE-NEET SPECIAL WING

Multiple-Answer Type Questions

Directions for questions 1 to 4:

Select one or more correct alternative(s) from the given choices.

1. Identify the correctly matched pairs among the following.

	Example of mixture	Dispersed phase	Dispersion medium
(a)	Whipped cream	Gas	Liquid
(b)	Fruit jam	Solid	Liquid
(c)	Coloured glass	Solid	Solid
(d)	Mist	Liquid	Gas

2. Identify the substances which act as desiccants among the following.

(a) Glauber salt (b) P_4O_{10}

(c) $CaCl_2$ (d) NaOH

3. The solubility of a salt is 52 at 80°C. Sufficient quantity of this salt with molecular mass equal to 100 is dissolved in 500 g water to form a saturated solution at that temperature. Now, when this solution is cooled to 30°C, 80 g of the salt gets precipitated out. Identify the correct statements pertaining to this activity. [Consider density of water as 1g/cc]

(a) The solubility of the salt decreases by 16 units on cooling from 80°C to 30°C

(b) The weight percent of the solution is increased by 1.8 units.

(c) The molarity of the solution is reduced by 0.78 units on cooling.

(d) The molarity of the solution does not change on cooling

4. The A certain quantity of electricity is passed through the aqueous solution of zinc sulphate.

The oxygen released at the anode occupied 3.92 l volume at STP. Another electrolytic cell containing dilute aqueous solution of cupric chloride is connected to this cell in series. Which among the following results comply with this activity as per the laws pertaining to electrolysis?

(a) Nearly 23 g of zinc is deposited at the cathode

(b) The gaseous product released at cathode possesses 2.1×10^{23} molecules

(c) 0.175 mole copper is expected to be deposited in the second vessel

(d) The quantity of electricity passed through the electrolysis vessels could be 67550 Coulomb.

Directions for questions 5 and 6

Observe the following diagram and answer the questions given below.

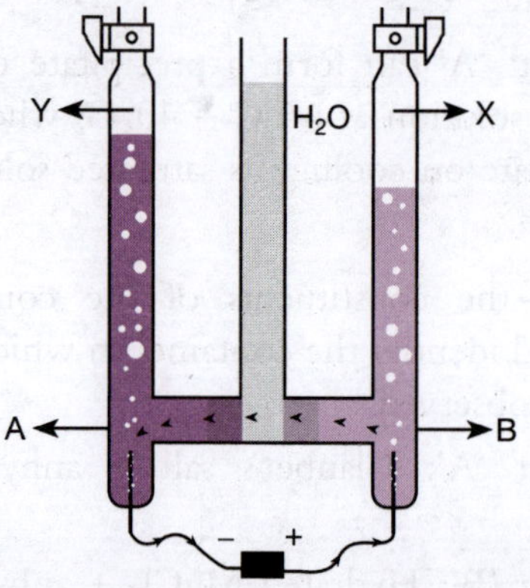

5. Identify the correct observation in the experiment of electrolysis of water by using Hofmann voltameter.

(a) The volume of oxygen is double to the volume of hydrogen.

(b) When a glowing splinter is introduced into B, it burns with a pop sound

(c) The water in B turns red litmus blue

(d) The water in A turns phenolphthalein pink

6. Identify the mistake in the diagram.

(a) The volume of X and Y should be equal.

(b) The terminals of the battery should be marked in reverse sign.

(c) Pure water should be taken in the vessel.

(d) Iron plate should be taken in the place of platinum plate.

Comprehension-Based Questions

Directions for questions 7 to 11

Read the information given in the following passage and answer the questions given below.

Water occupies the most significant position in the field of science and has innumerable applications from simple day to day activities to the most advanced scientific research. The significance of water and its wide range of applications is attributed to the unique properties of water. One of the properties is its high specific heat which is defined as the amount of heat required to rise the temperature of one gram of a substance through 1⁰ Celsius. The value of specific heat is unity for water. Another property is latent heat. Latent heat of vaporisation(L_v) is the amount of heat required to convert 1 gram of water into steam at its boiling point. Similarly, latent heat of fusion(L_f) is the amount of heat required to convert 1 gram of water into ice at its boiling point. The values are L_v= 540 cal/g ; L_f = 80 cal/g. Apart from this, water has the ability to form hydrogen bonds and it also has high value of dielectric constant. These two properties are responsible for making water a universal solvent.

7. Identify the application(s) of high specific heat of water.
   (a) Usage of water as a coolant in car radiators
   (b) Usage of water for cleaning and washing purpose
   (c) Removal of ice piled on roads by using brine solution
   (d) Usage of boiled water to extinguish fire

8. The following diagram illustrate the drinking bird toy which appears like showing perpetual motion as no force is seen to be applied. This is made by taking water in the beaker and a volatile liquid in the bulb at the bottom of the toy. Identify the principle exploited in the working of this.

   (a) Higher specific heat of the liquid taken in the bulb
   (b) Higher latent heat of vaporisation of liquid taken in the bulb
   (c) Higher latent heat of vaporisation of water taken in the beaker
   (d) Higher density of the liquid taken in the bulb

9. 1.5 kg of pure water at 0°C is converted to ice. The heat released is utilised to heat half the initial quantity of another sample of pure water at room temperature(30°C). What would be the quantity of water left over without getting converted to steam?
   (a) 550 g (b) 125 g
   (c) 370 g (d) 625 g

10. Observe the graphical representation of the changes taking place with time for two substances when heat is supplied to two substances.

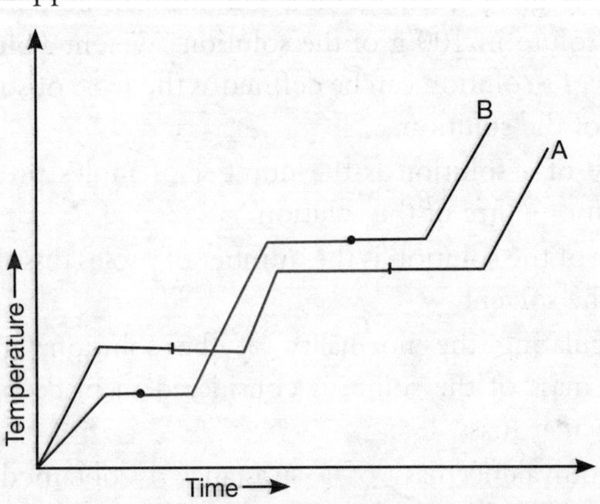

Identify the statement(s) which draw a correct comparison between the substances A and B.
   (a) Liquid A has a higher specific heat than liquid B.
   (b) Latent heat of fusion is greater for liquid A than for liquid B.
   (c) Both the liquids possess same boiling points.
   (d) The latent heat of fusion and vaporisation are equal in case of liquid B.

11. Observe the phase diagrams of the substances A,B,C,D given in the following graph and choose the incorrect conclusion. [One of these is associated with hydrogen bonding in liquid state.]

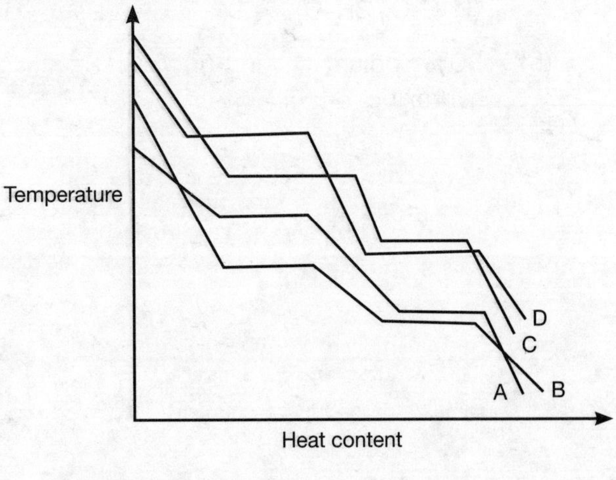

(a) Order of melting points → B<A<D<C
(b) D has greater latent heat of fusion that C
(c) C is the liquid associated with hydrogen bonding
(d) B has the least specific heat in liquid state.

Directions for questions 12 to 17:

Read the information given in the following passage and answer the questions given below.

The concentrations of solutions are expressed in various methods. The various methods include weight-weight percentage, weight-volume percentage, molarity, normality, molality, mole fraction etc.,

Weight-weight percentage of a solution can be defined as mass of solute in 100 g of the solution. Weight-volume percentage of a solution can be defined as the mass of solute in 100 ml of the solution.

Molarity of a solution is the number of moles present dissolved in one litre of the solution

Molality of the solution is the number of moles dissolved per kg of the solvent.

For calculating the normality of the solution, gram equivalent mass of the solute is considered in place of its gram molecular mass.

Gram equivalent mass of a substance is obtained by dividing the GMM by the basicity of an acid or acidity of a base or the charge on the ion in case of a salt.

Mole fraction of a component in a solution can be defined as the ratio of number of moles of that component to the total number of moles of all the components in the solution. The sum of the mole fractions of both the components of the solution should be equal to unity.

12. Match the entries in column-I with those in column II

	Column I w/W% of solution		Column II Mole fraction of solute
(a)	60% Oxalic acid ($H_2C_2O_4.2H_2O$)	(i)	0.62
(b)	90% Sodium hydroxide	(ii)	0.18
(c)	90% sulphuric acid	(iii)	0.14
(d)	70% sodium bicarbonate	(iv)	0.8
(e)	50% sodium carbonate	(v)	0.32

Consider a 98% (w/V) solution of sulphuric acid with density as 1.84 g/ml.

13. If 100 ml this solution is taken and diluted to give 1.6M solution, what would be the volume of water added for the purpose of dilution?
(a) 160 ml (b) 625 ml
(c) 600 ml (d) 525 ml

14. If the density of the diluted solution is 0.6 times that of the concentrated solution, find the no. of times of change in molality of the solution on dilution.
(a) 5.43 (b) 0.54
(c) 0.26 (d) 1.42

15. If this is the saturated solution, identify the w/W% of the solution.
(a) 53.2% (b) 90.4%
(c) 36% (d) 78%

16. What would be the normality of the solution?
(a) 11.9 (b) 10
(c) 20 (d) 1.08

17. If this solution is diluted by 200 times and the resultant solution is used to neutralise 20 ml of 0.5 N solution of sodium hydroxide, what volume of the diluted sulphuric acid would have been used?
(a) 20 ml (b) 40 ml
(c) 50 ml (d) 100 ml

Match the Column

18. Observe the solubility curve and the information given in the table below and match the entries in column I with those in column II.

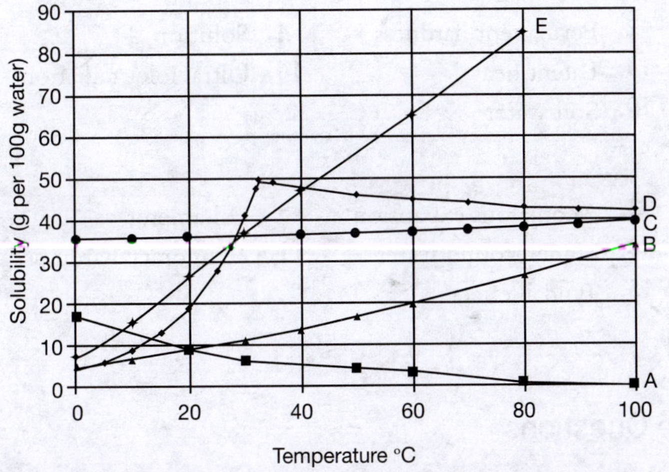

Salt	Characteristic wrt solubility
NaCl	Solubility is not much affected by the change in temperature
$NaHSO_4$	Sharp rise in solubility with temperature
$Ce_2(SO_4)_3$	Solubility decreases with temperature
Na_2SO_4	Solubility increases and then decreases with temperature
$Ba(NO_3)_2$	Solubility rises moderately with temperature

	Column I		Column II		Column III
(a)	A	(1)	The amount of solute in saturated solution is almost same at 30°C and 90°C	(i)	$Ba(NO_3)_2$
(b)	B	(2)	420 g is precipitated till the temperature where it contains same amount of solute as D	(ii)	$NaHSO_4$
(c)	C	(3)	Cooling the solution makes the solution unsaturated	(iii)	NaCl
(d)	D	(4)	When cooled to 20°- C, 115 g of the substance is precipitated	(iv)	$Ce_2(SO_4)_3$
(e)	E	(5)	Cooling of saturated solution shows negligible precipitation	(v)	Na_2SO_4

ANSWER KEYS

Crossword

Across

1. Distilled water
2. Permanent hardness
4. Solution
6. Colloid
10. Saturated solution
14. Latent heat
16. Ultraviolet radiation
17. Suspension
18. Faraday's law
19. Soft water

Down

1. Deliquescent substances
3. Anomalous expansion
5. Voltameter
7. Unit cell
8. Hard water
9. Underground water
11. Temporary hardness
12. Specific heat
13. Brownian movement
15. Tyndall effect

Classroom Wing

Very Short Answer Type Questions

1. Tyndall effect
2. Emulsion
3. Coagulation
4. Liquid; gas
5. 32
6. 96,500
7. colourless
8. 10

Competition Wing

Level 1: Apply your Concepts

1. True
2. False
3. True
4. True
5. True
6. False
7. False
8. True
9. False
10. False
11. Brownian
12. 7.25 g
13. liquid, liquid
14. $FeSO_4.7H_2O$
15. hydrated salts
16. 2
17. 9
18. sulphates, chlorides, calcium, magnesium
19. drying
20. A. : f, B. : d, C. : e, D. : b, E. : a, F. : c
21. (b)
22. (b)
23. (a)
24. (c)
25. (a)
26. (a)
27. (b)
28. (b)
29. (d)
30. (b)
31. (d)
32. (c)
33. (d)
34. (b)
35. (d)
36. (b)
37. (b)
38. (d)
39. (d)
40. (d)
41. (a)
42. (d)
43. (a)
44. (a)

JEE-NEET Special Wing

Multiple-Answer Type Questions

1. (c; d)
2. (b; c)
3. (a; c)
4. (b; d)
5. (b; c)
6. (b)

Comprehension-Based Questions

7. (a)
8. (c)
9. (d)
10. (b)
11. (c)
12. (a) ↔ (ii); (b) ↔ (iv); (c) ↔ (i); (d) ↔ (v) ; (e) ↔ (iii)
13. (d)
14. (c)
15. (a)
16. (c)
17. (d)

Match the Column

18. (a) ↔ (3) ↔ (iii), (b) ↔ (4) ↔ (v), (c) ↔ (5) ↔ (iv), (d) ↔ (1) ↔ (i), (e) ↔ (2) ↔ (ii)

Hints and Explanations

Classroom Wing

Very Short Answer Type Question

1. A pale blue tinge in milk occurs due to the Tyndall effect because milk is a colloid.
2. Since pig iron is brittle in nature, it cannot be used for making any article.
3. Addition of potash alum makes the clay particles, which are present in water, settle down. This refers to the coagulation of clay particles by alum.
4. In foam, the dispersion medium is liquid and the dispersed phase is gas.
5. 32
6. 96,500
7. colourless
8. 10
9. Coagulation. Bleeding from the wound stops because of coagulation of blood due to the addition of $FeCl_3$ solution. Similarly, fine clay particles which are present in tap water can be coagulated by adding alum to water.
10. High dielectric constant.
11. The maximum amount of a particular solute in grams, which can dissolve in 100 grams of solvent at a given temperature.
12. (i) Alloy (ii) Soft drink (iii) Glauber salt
13. Due to escaping of gases.
14. Due to the evolution of dissolved gases like oxygen, carbon dioxide etc, effervescence is observed.

    Solubility of a gas in liquid decreases with the increase in temperature.
15. 15 g of salt A is dissolved in 100 g of solvent.
16. Calcium oxide
17. By adding solvent.
18. The smallest repeating pattern of crystalline solid.
19. Loss of water of crystallization.
20. One faraday = 96,500 coulombs.
21. Constituent particle in a solution which is dispersed is in between 10 nm to 1 μm is called dispersed phase and the medium in which dispersed phase is dispersed is called dispersion medium.
22. 1 : 4
23. Two faraday.
24. 63.5 and 31.75

Short Answer Type Questions

25. (A) 20 g of solute is present in 180 g of solution B.

    $$\text{Solubility} = \frac{20}{160} \times 100 = 12.5.$$

    (B) 15 g of solute is present in 120 g of solution D.

    $$\text{Solubility} = \frac{15}{105} \times 100 = 14.29.$$

    (C) 30 g of solute is present in 210 g of solution C.

    $$\text{Solubility} = \frac{30}{180} \times 100 = 16.66.$$

    (D) 125 g of solute is present in 625 g of solution A.

    $$\text{Solubility} = \frac{125}{500} \times 100 = 25.$$

    Hence, the correct order is BDCA.

26. $$\text{Electrochemical equivalent} = \frac{\text{atomic weight}}{\text{valency} \times 96500}$$

    ∴ Electrochemical equivalent of the metal

    $$= \frac{x}{3 \times 96500}$$

27. Electrochemical equivalent = x

    ∴ Mass of the metal obtained at the cathode

    $= x \times 96{,}500 \times 0.5 = 48{,}250\ x$ g

28. (i) By using strong acids.

    (ii) By using strong bases.

29. (a) $$\text{Molarity} = \frac{\text{No. of moles}}{\text{Volume of solution (in L)}}$$

    Molecular mass of sodium carbonate = 106g

    Molarity = 0.2M

    Volume = 1L

    No of moles od sodium carbonate = $\frac{w}{106}$

    $$\text{Molarity} = 0.2 = \frac{w}{(106 \times 100)}$$

w = 0.2 × 106

w = 21.2g

(b) (A) $Al_2O_3 \rightleftharpoons Al^{3+} + O^{2-}$

$Q = c \times t = 386 \times 30 \times 60 = 694800$ C

$$\text{No. of Faradays} = \frac{694800}{96500} = 7.2 \text{ F}$$

At cathode:

$$4Al^{3+} + 12\bar{e} \rightarrow 4Al$$

$$\Rightarrow 12F \rightarrow 4 \times 27\,g$$

$$\therefore 7.2F \rightarrow \frac{4 \times 27 \times 7.2}{12} = 64.8 \text{ g of Al}$$

(B) At anode: $6O^{2-} - 12\bar{e} \rightarrow 3O_2$

$\Rightarrow 12$ F $\rightarrow 3. \times 22.4$ L of O_2 at STP

$$\therefore 7.2F \rightarrow \frac{3 \times 22.4 \times 7.2}{12}$$

$= 40.32$ L of O_2 at STP.

30. $$\text{Solubility} = \frac{\text{Mass of solute}}{\text{Mass of solvent}} \times 100$$

$$35.8 = \frac{x}{250 - x} \times 100$$

$(250-x)35.8 = 100\,x$

$\Rightarrow 8950-35.8\,x = 100\,x$

$\Rightarrow x = 65.9\,g\,x$

31. For most of the substances, solubility increases with the increase in temperature. However, the solubility of some substances decreases with increase in temperature.

The effect of pressure on the solubility of a gas in a liquid is given by Henry's law, which states that at constant temperature, the increase in pressure on the surface of the liquid increases the solubility of the gas in the liquid.

32. (i) Electrochemical equivalent is the mass of ions deposited or liberated on an electrode during electrolysis.

(ii) Equivalent weight is molecular weight of the solute.

(iii) Relation between electrochemical equivalent and equivalent weight.

$$\text{Electrochemical equivalent} = \frac{\text{Equivalent weight}}{96,500}$$

$$= \frac{\text{Atomic weight}}{z \times 96,500}$$

(where z = valency element)

33. Water molecules have a polar arrangement of the oxygen and hydrogen atoms-one side (hydrogen) has a positive electrical charge and the other side (oxygen) had a negative charge. This allows the water molecule to become attracted to many other different types of molecules. Hence, it has a good solvent property.

34. Reaction with sodium:

$$2Na(s) + 2H_2O \rightarrow 2NaOH(aq) + H_2(g)$$

The reaction is exothermic. The sodium metal may well become so hot that it catches fire and burns with a characteristic orange color.

Reaction with potassium:

$$2K(s) + 2H_2O \rightarrow 2KOH(aq) + H_2(g)$$

The reaction is exothermic. The potassium metal becomes so hot that it catches fire and burns with a characteristic pale lilac color.

35. (i) Slow cooling of hot saturated solution.

(ii) Evaporation of an unsaturated solution.

(iii) Slow cooling of a molten solid.

36. Molarity(M) indicates the number of moles of solute per liter of solution (moles/Litre).

$$M = \frac{\text{moles of solute}}{\text{liters of solution}}$$

Weight Percentage of a solution is mass of solute by mass of the solution.

$$\left(\frac{\text{Weight of the solute}}{\text{Weight of the solution}}\right) \times 100$$

$$M = \frac{n}{v} = \frac{W}{\text{GMW}} \times \frac{1}{v \text{ in L}} \text{ or } M = \frac{W}{\text{GMW}} \times \frac{1000}{v \text{ in mL}}$$

37. 20 moles

38. **Efflorescence and Deliquescence:** There are some hydrated crystals which lose some of the water of crystallization or all the water of crystallization on exposure to air at normal temperature. This phenomenon is known as **efflorescence**.

Some crystalline salts absorb moisture on exposure to air and ultimately dissolve in it to form an aqueous solution. This phenomenon is called **deliquescence**.

39. 3 : 5

Essay Answer Type Questions

40. Molarity of NaOH solution is 5 M.

Mass of 1l of solution = density × volume

= (1.5 × 1000) g

= 1500 g

Mol. wt. of NaOH = 40

∴ (40 × 5) g = 200 g of NaOH is present in 1500 g of solution.

∴ 200 g of NaOH is dissolved in (1500 − 200) = 1300 g of solvent.

Since the solubility of the solute is 20,

1300 g of solvent can dissolve (20 × 13) = 260 g of solute.

Hence, (260 − 200)g = 60 g solute (NaOH) has to be added.

41. 10 amp × (30 × 60) s = 18,000 C electrical charges deposit *a* g of metal

∴ 96,500 C electric charges deposits

$\frac{a \times 96{,}500}{1800}$ g of metal

Since the metal is divalent, the atomic weight of the metal

$= \frac{a \times 96500}{1800} \times 2$

$= \frac{a \times 965}{9} = 107.2\, a$

42. $b = \frac{W_{\text{solute}}}{a} \cdot 100$

$\therefore W_{\text{solute}} = \frac{ab}{100} \text{g}$

$\therefore V_{\text{solution}} = \frac{a}{x} \text{mL}$

$M = \frac{W_{\text{solute}}}{\text{GMM}} \times \frac{1000}{V}$, GMM of $Ca(OH)_2 = 74$

$M = \frac{ab}{100 \times 74} \times \frac{1000x}{a}$

$M = 0.135\, b\, x$ M

43. (i) Boiling

(ii) Ion exchange resins.

(iii) Regeneration of resins.

44. (i) Tyndall effect

(ii) Brownian movement

(iii) Coagulation

45. Blue Vitriol—Vapour pressure of blue vitriol is equal to the pressure of water vapour in the atmosphere. So, it retains its state and colour when exposed to the atmosphere.

Glauber's Salt—Vapour pressure of this salt is greater than that of the pressure of water vapour. So, when exposed to the atmosphere, loses its water of crystallization, and become an anhydrous salt. Hence is known as efflorescent salt

Washing Soda—Vapour pressure of this salt is also greater than that of the pressure of water vapour. So, when exposed to the atmosphere, loses nine water molecules, and retain one water molecule (it loses this on heating). This is also an efflorescent salt but as it is not losing all its water of crystallization, it does not become anhydrous.

Anhydrous calcium chloride and calcium oxide-vapour pressure of both the salts being less than that of the pressure of water vapour in the atmosphere, both the salts absorb moisture. Calcium chloride absorbs moisture till it gets converted into a saturated solution and calcium oxide absorbs moisture without change in its state. Hence, calcium chloride is known as a deliquescent salt while calcium oxide is known as hygroscopic salt and is used as a desiccating agent.

Competition Wing

Level 1: Apply your Concepts

21. According to Faraday II law, mass ∝ Equivalent weight

$NaCl \Rightarrow E_{Na} = \frac{23}{1} = 23$

$Al_2O_3 \Rightarrow E_{Al} = \frac{27}{3} = 9$

$Fe_2(SO_4)_3 \Rightarrow E_{Fe} = \frac{56}{3} = 18.66$

$ZnCl_2 \Rightarrow E_{Zn} = \frac{65.3}{2} = 32.65.$

Hence, the correct option is (b).

22. According to Faraday's I law, $m \propto Q$

$i = 5$ amp, $t = 15$ min $\Rightarrow Q = 5 \times 15 \times 60 = 4500$ C

$i = 12$ amp, $t = 6$ min $\Rightarrow Q = 12 \times 6 \times 60 = 4320$ C

$i = 8$ amp, $t = 570$ s $\Rightarrow Q = 8 \times 570 = 4560$ C

$i = 14$ amp, $t = 330$ s $\Rightarrow Q = 14 \times 330 = 4620$ C

Hence, the correct option is (b).

23 Temporary hardness is imparted to water due to the presence of bicarbonates of calcium and magnesium. Bicarbonates of calcium and magnesium undergo thermal decomposition to form respective carbonates which are insoluble.

Hence, the correct option is (a).

24 Permanent hardness can be removed by adding zeolite. Zeolite replaces Ca^{+2} and Mg^{+2} present in water with Na^+.

Hence, the correct option is (c).

25. Since the specific heat capacity of water is high, it is used as a coolant in car radiators.

Hence, the correct option is (a).

36. The higher the dielectric constant of a solvent, the more is the solubility of a solute in that particular solvent. Hence, increasing order of dielectric constants is R < P < Q < S.

Hence, the correct answer is (b).

37. Let the weight of an empty china dish x g.

Weight of saturated solution = $(80 - x)$g

Weight of $NaNO_3$ crystals = $(40 - x)$ g

Weight of H_2O in saturated solution

$= 80 - x - 40 + x = 40$

$\therefore \text{Solubility} = \frac{\text{weight of } NaNO_3}{\text{weight of water}}$

$$20 = \frac{40 - x}{40} \times 100$$

$$800 = 4000 - 100x$$

$$x = 32\ g$$

Hence, the correct answer is (b).

38. $M = \frac{w}{Mwt} \times \frac{1000}{V \text{ in mL}}$

4 M $Ca(OH)_2$ solution means 296 g of $Ca(OH)_2$ is dissolved in 1000 mL of the solution.

Mass of the solution = $d \times v$

$= 1.3 \times 1000$

$= 1300$ g

$\text{Weight percentage} = \frac{\text{weight of solute}}{\text{weight of solution}} \times 100$

$= \frac{296}{1300} \times 100 = 22.8\%$

Hence, the correct answer is (d).

39. Solubility of gases in water decreases with the decrease of pressure and increase of temperature.

Hence, the correct answer is (d).

40. A = 160 – 120 = 40 g

B = 20 g

C = 15 g

D = No ppt

Hence, the correct answer is (d).

41. 3. A highly cleared brass spoon which has to be electroplated is taken.

4. Due to electrolytic dissociation, Ag^+, K^+, H^+, OH^- and CN^- ions are formed.

1. K^+ and H^+ ions are not discharged at cathode due to higher discharge potential than Ag.

2. Silver gets deposited on brass spoon.

Hence, the correct answer is (a).

42. Molarity $= \frac{37}{74} \times \frac{1000}{2000} = 0.25$

37 g of $Ca(OH)_2$ in 2000 mL solution has minimum molarity.

Hence, the correct answer is (d).

43. Vinegar in water is a true solution since it is highly soluble in water.

Hence, the correct answer is (a).

44. 2. convert time in minutes to seconds
1. Find the product of y current (c) and time (t).
4. conversion of charge into Faradays.
3. Write reduction equation of metal ion.
5. relation between mass of metal and Faradays passed through

Hence, the correct answer is (a).

Level 2: Review your Concepts

45. 100 g of solvent can dissolve 20 g of solute.

∴ 120 g saturated solution has 20 g of solute.

∴ 600 g saturated solution contains $\frac{20}{120} \times 600$ g.

= 100 g solute

46. 1 kg saturated solution contains 200 g of solute.

∴ (1000 − 200) g = 800 g solvent dissolves 200 g of solute.

∴ 100 g solvent dissolves $\frac{200 \times 100}{800}$ g.

= 25 g of solute

47. (a) CO_2 molecules naturally try to leave liquid by rising through the surface to escape as a gas.

(b) 15g of ice→15g of ice→15g of water→15g of water
at −5°C at 0°C at 0°C at 100°C
↓
15 g of steam ←15 g of steam
at 150°C at 100°C

Heat energy required Q

$= Q_1 + Q_2 + Q_3 + Q_4 + Q_5$

$= m.s.\Delta t + m.L_f + ms\Delta t + m.L_v + m.s.\Delta t$

$= (15 \times 0.5 \times 5) + (15 \times 80) + (15 \times 1 \times 100) + (15 \times 540) + (15 \times 0.5 \times 50)$

$= 37.5 + 1200 + 1500 + 8100 + 375 = 11212.5$ cal

Q = <u>11.2 kcal</u>

48. Cobalt chloride is a compound that changes colour in presence of water. It changes its color from blue to pink. Hence it is used to detect water in the system. All other compounds are hygroscopic in nature.

49. 25%(w/w) sodium hydroxide solution means 25 grams of sodium hydroxide present in 100 grams of solution.

50. (i) determination of the nature of the solution at 60°C from the given data
(ii) determination of nature of solution at 45°C
(iii) determination of nature of solution at 30°C
(iv) relation between the nature of the solution and the amount of precipitation

51. (i) determination of the volumes of the solute and solvent
(ii) calculation of total volume of the solution
(iii) calculation of number of moles of H_2SO_4
(iv) calculation of molarity of solution

52. (i) calculation of number of moles of the metal deposited
(ii) calculation of amount of charge required
(iii) calculation of the time taken for the deposition
(iv) 3.22 h

53. (i) properties of colloid particles
(ii) charge possessed by colloid particles
(iii) forces acting between colloid particles
(iv) effect of these forces against coagulation of colloid particles

54. (i) calculation of the volume of 100 g of the solution
(ii) calculation of number of moles of NaOH present in the calculated volume of the solution
(iii) 7.88 M

55. (i) calculation of the amount of charge required to deposit the given amount of metal
(ii) calculation of equivalent weight of the metal, based on the amount of charge passed through the electrolyte
(iii) 32.2

56. (i) constituents of smoke
(ii) The smoke changes color because the size of the smoke particles changes. The smoke particles rising from the cigarette tip are very small, smaller than the wavelengths of visible light

57. (i) Blood is a colloidal solution

(ii) Ferric chloride ($FeCl_3$) is a chemical agent and a strong coagulant

(iii) Blood contains colloidal impurities and $FeCl_3$ neutralizes the charge on these colloidal impurities and precipitation occurs.

58. (i) impurities present in common salt

(ii) nature of the impurities present in common salt

(iii) effect of nature of the impurities on the increase in weight

59. (i) The polar characteristic of water molecules causes them to attract each other well whereas less polar alcohol molecules do not attract one another as strongly.

(ii) type of bonds present in sodium hydroxide

(iii) relation between polarity and dielectric constant

(iv) effect of dielectric constant on solubility

(v) comparison of dielectric constants of water and alcohol

60. Due to the loss of water molecules from $CuSO_4.5H_2O$.

61. As solubility of nitrogen is very less in water, it is expelled in maximum percentage. CO_2 and SO_3 are soluble in water. Hence, they will be expelled in lesser percentage.

62. **Sample A:** When the solution is cooled from 80 to 40°C, the solute forms a precipitate of 15 g and when cooled from 40°C to 20°C solubility increases from 100 g to 120 g and the solution becomes unsaturated.

Sample B: When the solution is cooled from 80°C to 40°C, solute forms a precipitate of 10 g and when cooled from 40 to 20°C solubility decreased from 180 to 150 g forming 30 g of precipitate.

Sample C: When solution is cooled from 80 to 40°C, solubility increase from 150 to 160 g forming unsaturated solution and while cooling from 40 to 20°C solubility decreases from 160 to 140 g forming 10 g of precipitate.

63. Sample X shows efflorescence and sample Y shows deliquescence nature.

In sample X vapor pressure of hydrated crystal is lesser than pressure of moisture present in the atmosphere.

In sample Y vapor pressure of hydrated crystal is greater than pressure of moisture present in the atmosphere.

64. Formula $w = \dfrac{M C.t}{2 96{,}500} \Rightarrow t = \dfrac{W \times 96{,}500 \times 2}{M.C}$

$W = 8g, C = 10$ amp

$M = 40, Z = 2$

$$\therefore t = \frac{8 \times 2 \times 96500}{40 \times 10} = 3860\,s$$

65. According to Faraday's first law

$$W = \frac{Z.C.t}{n \times 96{,}500} \Rightarrow \frac{n \times 96{,}500}{C.t} = \frac{Z}{W}$$

$$\Rightarrow \frac{C.t}{n \times 96{,}500} = \frac{W}{Z} = \text{no. of moles}$$

$$\therefore n_{Ag} = \frac{C_{Ag}.t_{Ag}}{n_{Ag} \times 96{,}500} \qquad n_{Cu} = \frac{C_{Cu}.t_{Cu}}{n_{Cu} \times 96{,}500}$$

Given that $n_{Ag} = n_{Cu}$ and two electrolytic cells are connected in series, i.e., $C_{Ag} = C_{Cu}$

$$\therefore \frac{t_{Ag}}{n_{Ag}} = \frac{t_{Cu}}{n_{Cu}} \Rightarrow \frac{n_{Ag}}{n_{Cu}} = \frac{t_{Ag}}{t_{Cu}}$$

$$\therefore \frac{n_{Ag}}{n_{Cu}} = \frac{1}{2} = 1:2$$

66. $H_2O \rightarrow H^+ + OH^-$

$$4OH^- \rightarrow 2H_2O + O_2 + 4e^-$$

4F of electricity $\rightarrow$ 22.4 L of O_2 at STP

$4 \times 96{,}500$ C $\rightarrow$ 22.4 L of O_2 at STP

$15 \times 4 \times 60 \times 60$ C $\rightarrow$?

$$= \frac{15 \times 4 \times 3600 \times 22.4}{4 \times 96{,}500} = 12.53\,L \text{ of } O_2 \text{ at STP}$$

67. Potable water has a pleasant taste and odour and has dissolved matter, like, air, CO_2 and minerals which are absent in distilled water. The salts present in our body dissolves in distilled water causing health problems.

68. (a) The melting point of water decreases by addition of ethylene glycol. Hence, within a wide range of temperature it remains in the liquid state. Thus, ethylene glycol can conveniently work as anti-freeze for the water used as a coolant in automobiles especially in cold countries.

(b) (A) (w/w)% = 84%

$\Rightarrow$ 84 g of H_3PO_4 is present in 100 g of solution.

Volume of solution is $V = \dfrac{100}{d}$

Molarity = 12.0 M

$$\therefore \text{Molarity M} = \frac{W_{H_3PO_4}}{GMM_{H_3PO_4}} \times \frac{1000}{V}$$

$$\Rightarrow 12 = \frac{84}{98} \times \frac{100 \times d}{100}$$

$$\Rightarrow d = \frac{12 \times 98 \times 100}{84 \times 1000} = 1.4 \text{ g/mL}$$

(B) 5 mole percent of sulphuric acid solution ⇒ 5 moles of H_2SO_4 in 95 moles of water.

⇒ 490 g of H_2SO_4 in 1710 g of water

∴ Weight of solution $W_{sol} = 2200$ g

$$\text{Volume of solution } V_{sol} = \frac{2200}{1.1} = 2000 \text{ mL}$$

$$\text{(i) Weight percentage (W/W)} = \frac{W_{H_2SO_4}}{W_{Solution}} \times 100$$

$$= \frac{490}{2200} \times 100$$

$$= 22.3\%$$

$$\text{(ii) Molarity} = \frac{490}{98} \times \frac{1000}{2000} = 2.5\text{M}$$

69. 50 g of 15% $\left(\frac{W}{W}\right)$ sodium hydroxide

⇒ 7.5 g of NaOH is present in 50 g of solution

⇒ 42.5 g of water is present in 50 g of solution

$$\text{Volume of water} = \frac{\text{mass}}{\text{density}}$$

$$\text{Volume of water} = \frac{425}{0.9} = 47.22 \text{ cm}^3$$

Level 3: Assess Your Concepts

70. 100 g of solution has 10 g of solute.

∴ 1 kg of the solution has 100 g of solute.

∴ (1000 – 100) g = 900 g solvent has 100 g of solute dissolved in it. The solubility of the solute is 25.

∴ 900 g of solvent can dissolve $\left(\frac{25}{100} \times 900\right)$ g = 225 g of solute.

∴ (225 – 100) g = 125 g of solute has to be added to saturate the solution.

71. 1 amp × 1 s = 1 Coulomb

1 Coulomb charge deposits *m* g of metal.

P Coulombs charge deposits (*P* × *m*) g of metal.

Atomic wt. of the metal is *n*.

$$\Rightarrow \text{Valency} = \frac{\text{atomic weight}}{\text{equivalent weight}} = \frac{n}{m \times p}$$

72. Yes, it is true.

	25°C	40°C	60°C	
A	110 g	90 g	105 g	⇒ 105 – 90 = 15 g of precipitate
C	130 g	150 g	140 g	⇒150 – 130 = 20 g of precipitate

73. Since Glauber's salt is an efflorescent substance, it loses water of crystallization. These water molecules combine with anhydrous copper sulphate, to form hydrated copper sulphate which is blue in colour.

$$CuSO_4 + 5H_2O \rightarrow CuSO_4.\ 5H_2O$$

Colourless Blue

Hence, the colour change is observed in container A.

74. (i) product obtained at the electrodes in Hoffman voltmeter

(ii) reaction at the cathode

(iii) reaction at the anode

(iv) comparison of change in number of ions at the respective electrodes

(v) effect of the above change on the colour of litmus paper

75. In the first test tube crystallization takes place, and in the second test tube no crystallization is observed. In the second test tube, calcium chloride is formed which is deliquescent in nature, and therefore, it does not crystallize.

76. Cobalt chloride is a desiccating material, and hence, it absorbs water molecules from moisture and turns pink. When cobalt chloride is kept in low humid air, it loses its water molecules and it becomes blue in colour. Vapor pressure of anhydrous cobalt chloride is less than that of water vapor pressure. In low humid air the vapor pressure of hydrated cobalt chloride is comparatively higher than water vapor pressure, and hence, it loses water of crystallization.

77. I cell

$ZnSO_4$ dissociates into Zn^{2+} and SO_4^{2-}

II cell

$AgNO_3$ dissociates into Ag^+ and NO_3^-

As per Faraday's II law of electrolysis, $\frac{m_1}{E_1} = \frac{m_2}{E_2}$

$$W = \frac{MCt}{ZF} \Rightarrow \frac{W_1}{M_1} = \frac{Ct}{ZF}$$

In case of $ZnSO_4$ $\frac{W_1}{M_1} = \frac{C_1t_1}{Z_1F}$ (1)

In case of $AgNO_3$ $\frac{W_2}{M_2} = \frac{C_2t_2}{Z_2F}$ (2)

As same number of moles. i.e. $n_1 = n_2$

$$\Rightarrow \frac{W_1}{M_1} = \frac{W_2}{M_2}$$

As the cells are connected in series, same amount of current flows.

$C_1 = C_2$

From equations (1) and (2),

$$\frac{C_1t_1}{Z_1F} = \frac{C_2t_2}{Z_2F} \Rightarrow \frac{t_1}{z_1} = \frac{t_2}{z_2} \Rightarrow \frac{t_1}{t_2} = \frac{z_1}{z_2}$$

$$\frac{t_1}{t_2} = \frac{2}{1} = 2:1$$

78. Potassium and sodium are two metals which react with cold water producing heat. They can even react with moisture. As they float on water, they burn in oxygen producing flames. Potassium burns with lilac flame and sodium burns with golden yellow flame.

$2K + 2H_2O \rightarrow 2KOH + H_2$

$2Na + 2H_2O \rightarrow 2NaOH + H_2$

79. Table salt contains impurities, like, $CaCl_2$ and $MgCl_2$ in small percentages which absorb moisture from air on account of their deliquescent nature, therefore, table salt shows deliquescent nature.

80. (a) Solute P $\rightarrow$ When the solution is cooled from Z°C to Y°C, the solubility increases. The amount of solute to be present is increased from 115g to 130g.

So, the solution remains unsaturated at Y°C. Further cooling of the solution from Y°C to X°C resulted in decrease in solubility. The amount of solute in the solution decreases to 110g. As the original solution contained 115g of solute, 5g of precipitate is formed.

Solute Q $\rightarrow$ When the solution is cooled from Z°C to Y°C, 15g of precipitate is formed. Further cooling to X°C resulted in the precipitation of 15g of solute. On the whole, 30g of solute is precipitated.

Solute R $\rightarrow$ When the solution is cooled from Z°C to Y°C, 10g of precipitation is formed. Further cooling to X°C has not resulted in the precipitation of any amount of solute as the solubility is increased making the solution unsaturated at X°C.

(b) At X°C

Solubility of P = $\frac{110}{190} \times 100 = 57.89$

Solubility of Q = $\frac{90}{210} \times 100 = 42.85$

Solubility of R = $\frac{80}{220} \times 100 = 36.36$

JEE-NEET Special Wing

Multiple-Answer Type Questions

1. Identify the correctly matched pairs among the following.

Coloured glass	Solid	Solid
Mist	Liquid	Gas

2. P_4O_{10} and $CaCl_2$ are hygroscopic in nature. They absorb moisture from the air without undergoing any change in physical state. Therefore, these two substances act as desiccants or drying agents.

3. Amount of salt in saturated solution at 80°C
= 52 × 5 = 260 g
Amount of salt precipitated on cooling to 30°C = 80 g
Amount of salt left behind in the solution
= 260 – 80 = 180 g
Solubility of salt at 30°C = $\frac{180}{5}$ = 36
Difference in solubility = 52 – 36 = 16
Weight percent of the solution at 800C
= 260 × $\frac{100}{760}$ = 34.2 %
Weight percent of the solution at 30°C
= 180 × $\frac{100}{680}$ = 26.5 %
Difference in weight percentage = 34.2 – 26.5 = 7.7
Molarity of solution at 80°C
= 260 × $\frac{1000}{100}$ × 760 = 3.42
Molarity of solution at 30°C
= 180 × $\frac{1000}{100}$ × 680 = 2.64
Difference in Molarity = 3.42 – 2.64 = 0.78

4. No. of moles of oxygen released at anode
= $\frac{3.92}{22.4}$ = 0.175
Electrolysis of aqueous solution of zinc sulphate produces hydrogen gas at cathode and not zinc.
No. of faradays of electricity used
= 0.175 × 4 = 0.7
No. of moles of hydrogen gas released = $\frac{0.7}{2}$
= 0.35 mole = 2.1×10^{23} molecules
No. of moles of copper deposited = 0.35 mole

5. Cathodic reaction
$2H^+ + 2e^- \rightarrow H_2$
Anode reaction
$4OH^- \rightarrow O_2 + 2H_2O + 4e^-$
Passing 4 Faraday of electricity results in the discharge of 2 mole hydrogen and 1 mole oxygen. Therefore, the volume of hydrogen produced is double to the volume of oxygen produced. The gas in the compartment A is identified as oxygen and that in the compartment B is identified as hydrogen. Hydrogen burns with a pop sound. The water in B has free OH^- ions as H^+ ions are consumed. Therefore, the water turns red litmus blue. The water in the anodic compartment that is A remains acidic due to the left over H^+ ions. Phenolphthalein is colourless in acidic medium.

6. The marking of the terminals of the battery is wrong. The positive terminal should be towards compartment A and the negative terminal should be towards the compartment B.

Comprehension-Based Questions

7. Water is used as a coolant in car radiators as it can absorb huge amount of heat without increasing its temperature to a great extent and reaching the boiling point. This is an important application in which high specific heat of water is exploited.

8. Since the fluid taken in the bulb at the bottom of the toy is volatile that means has low boiling point, the upper portion of the toy is occupied by the vapours of the liquid. When the bird dips in the water taken in the beaker, the water occupies the beak portion of the bird. This water undergoes evaporation by taking the latent heat of vaporisation from the vapours. Thus, the temperature of the vapours decreases, and the vapours condense into the liquid. This results in creation of low-pressure region or partial vacuum in the upper head portion of the toy. This pressure difference forces the liquid from the bulb to rise into the head portion. As the head now becomes heavier, the bird tips over and dips into the beaker. Now, the vapours rise to the head portion and the same process is repeated again.

9. The amount of heat released during the conversion of water to ice = 1.5 × 1000 × 80
= 120000 cal
The amount of heat required to heat 750 g of water to boiling point = 750 × 70 × 1 = 52500 cal

The amount of heat left over = 120000 – 52500
= 67500 cal

The amount of water that can be converted to steam

$= \frac{67500}{540} = 125$ g

The amount of water left over in the sample
= 750 – 125 = 625 g

10.. Liquid A has a higher specific heat than liquid B as liquid A takes same amount of heat to rise its temperature to lesser extent than liquid B. The first horizontal portion indicates the process of melting. Liquid A has a greater value of latent heat of fusion than liquid B. Liquid B boils at a higher temperature than liquid A. The latent heat of vaporisation for liquid B is greater than the latent heat of fusion. This can be known by observing the horizontal portions for the respective substance.

11. Hydrogen bonding is relatively stronger intermolecular forces of attraction. The liquids which possess hydrogen bonding are associated with higher boiling points. The substance D has the highest boiling point and hence can be predicted to possess hydrogen bonding. All others are correct observations.

12.

Column I w/W% of solution	Column II Mole fraction of solute
(a) 60% Oxalic acid ($H_2C_2O_4.2H_2O$)	(ii) 0.18
(b) 90% Sodium hydroxide	(iv) 0.8
(c) 90% sulphuric acid	(i) 0.62
(d) 70% sodium bicarbonate	(v) 0.32
(e) 50% sodium carbonate	(iii) 0.14

13. $V_{\text{before dilution}} \times M_{\text{before dilution}} = V_{\text{after dilution}} \times M_{\text{after dilution}}$

$100 \times 10 = 1.6 \times V_{\text{after dilution}}$

$V_{\text{after dilution}} = \frac{100 \times 10}{1.6} = \frac{100}{1.6} = 625$

Volume of water added = 625 – 100 = 525 mL

14. Molality of the solution $= \left(\frac{W_{solute}}{GMW}\right) \times \left(\frac{1000}{Mass\,of\,water}\right)$

Molality of original solution

$= \left(\frac{98}{98}\right) \times \left(\frac{1000}{184}\right) = 5.43$

Density of diluted solution = 0.6 × 1.84 = 1.12 g/mL

Mass of diluted solution = 1.12 × 625 = 700 g

Molality of diluted solution $= \left(\frac{98}{98}\right) \times \frac{1000}{700} = 1.42$

No. of times of change in molality $= \frac{1.42}{5.43} = 0.26$

15. (w/W%) of solution $= \left(\frac{98}{184}\right) \times 100 = 53.2$

16. Normality of solution $= \left(\frac{98}{49}\right) \times \left(\frac{1000}{100}\right) = 20$

17. According to the law of neutralisation,

$V_aN_a = V_bN_b$

Normality of acid after diluting by 200 times $= \frac{20}{200}$ = 0.1N

$V_a \times 0.1 = 20 \times 0.5$

$V_a = 100$ mL

Match the Column

18.

	Column I		Column II		Column III
(a)	A	(3)	Cooling the solution makes the solution unsaturated	(i)	$Ce_2(SO_4)_3$
(b)	B	(4)	When cooled to 20° C, 115 g of the substance is precipitated	(ii)	$Ba(NO_3)_2$
(c)	C	(5)	Cooling of saturated solution shows negligible precipitation	(iii)	NaCl
(d)	D	(1)	The amount of solute in saturated solution is almost same at 30°C and 90°C	(iv)	Na_2SO_4
(e)	E	(2)	420 g is precipitated till the temperature where it contains same amount of solute as D	(v)	$NaHSO_4$

CHAPTER

9

Metals and Non-Metals

Remember

Before beginning this chapter, you should be able to:

- classify matter into elements, compounds and mixtures.
- illustrate physical and chemical properties of met

Key Ideas

After completing this chapter, you should be able to:

- compare properties of metals and non-metals.
- know the general processes of extraction of metals.
- describe the extraction of iron and manufacture of steel.
- understand the preparation, properties and uses of elements like hydrogen, carbon, nitrogen, and their compounds.
- describe the preparation, properties and uses of elements like phosphorus, oxygen, sulphur, chlorine, and their compounds.

Scientific Crypt

A Tribute to Fritz Haber (1868–1934)

Fritz Haber, a German chemist received the Nobel Prize in Chemistry in the year 1918 for his contribution to the preparation of ammonia, an important component of fertilizers and explosives.

Fritz Haber was born on 9th December 1868 in Breslau, Germany. He worked in his father's chemical business after being educated in Berlin, Heidelberg and Zurich. In 1894, he became assistant to Hans Bunte at the University of Karlsruhe.

Haber and his brother-in-law Carl Bosch, also a chemist, have developed the method of catalytic synthesis of ammonia from hydrogen and atmospheric nitrogen under high temperature and pressure. This process of synthesis of ammonia is well-known as Haber-Bosch process or Haber's process was a milestone in Industrial Chemistry as it ended the dependence on the fast-disappearing natural sources of ammonia located along the coast of Chile.

In 1918, Fritz Haber received the most prestigious award, the Nobel Prize, for his work on the preparation of ammonia. Apart from the most prestigious honour, Haber also received many honours during his lifetime. He was regarded as the "Father of chemical warfare" for being associated with the usage of chlorine gas and other deadly poisonous gases during World War I.

After a grave illness, Haber passed away on 29th January 1934 in Basel, Switzerland. The Institute for Physical Chemistry and Electrochemistry at Berlin was renamed as Fritz Haber Institute in his honour.

FUN TIME

CROSSWORD

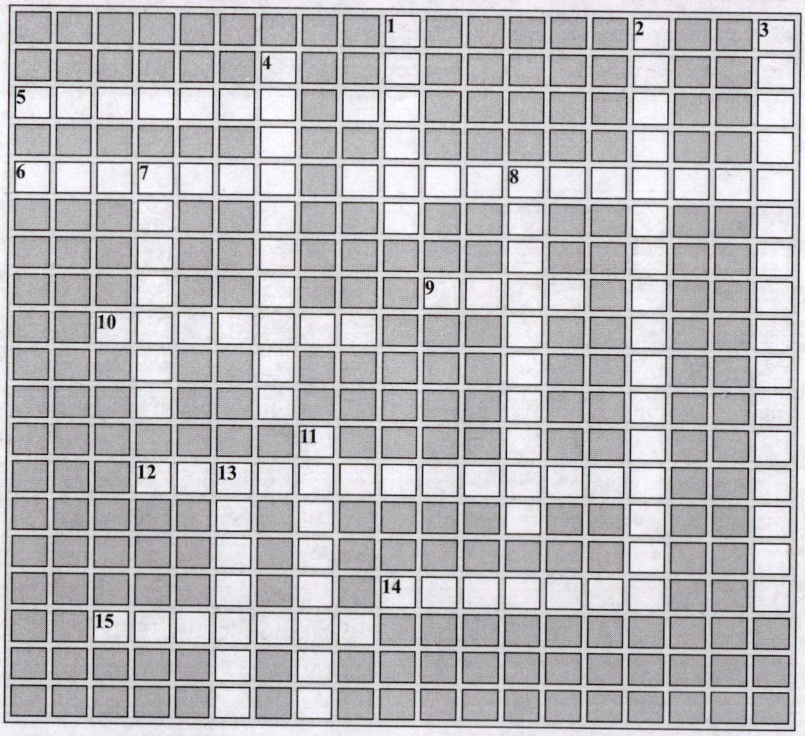

Across

5. Mixture of 95% oxygen and 5% carbon dioxide
6. Bacteria which help in the conversion of nitrites to nitrates
9. Noble gas used in advertisement sign boards
10. The variety of iron obtained from smelting
12. Allotrope of phosphorus used in making safety matches
14. Element extracted by Frasch process
15. Gas manufactured by Haber's process

Down

1. The activity of this gas gets diluted because of the presence of nitrogen in the air, thereby allowing natural processes to take place at a moderate rate.
2. Device used for putting off fires
3. Rubber used for the manufacture of automobile tyres
4. The process of extraction of metals from their respective ores
7. Corrosion of iron
8. The accumulation of molecules of one compound over the surface of another compound
11. Elemental raw material used in the manufacture of bleaching powder
13. Crystalline allotrope of carbon that has a regular tetrahedral arrangement

INTRODUCTION

In nature, metals exists in the form of compounds. The extraction of metals from their respective compounds involves various processes from simple mechanical crushing or grinding to complicated chemical reactions under specific conditions for a better yield. These processes are carried out in well-designed furnaces. Finally, these metals are purified to different extents based on their end use. All these processes come under the purview of **metallurgy**. The properties of metals can be improvized by doping a small amount of another metal or non-metal which makes the same metal usable for a variety of purposes and this area comes under the study of alloy.

Certain useful non-metals like sulphur and carbon are available in the elemental state under the earth's crust. These non-metals are excavated and refined before using them in various fields. Apart from this, different compounds which consist of various metals and non-metals in different proportions are manufactured in industries at a large scale and prepared in the laboratories at a small scale depending on their application. The study of these metals, non-metals and their compounds is necessary because of their wide range of applications.

Metallurgy

Some metals like silver, gold and platinum are less reactive and are found in their free states. The other metals being highly reactive are found in their combined states like oxides, carbonates, or sulphides. These solid inorganic compounds found in the earth's crust are called **minerals**.

In certain minerals, the percentage of a particular metal is high and these metals can be extracted from them profitably, and such minerals are called **ores**. The impurity associated with the ore is called **gangue**. The process of extraction of metals from their respective ores is called **metallurgy**.

Example of some ore are:

Iron Ores

Hematite (Fe_2O_3): A reddish-brown mineral and a primary source of iron.

Magnetite (Fe_3O_4): A black, magnetic mineral that also serves as a significant source of iron.

Copper Ores

Chalcopyrite ($CuFeS_2$): The most abundant ore used for extracting copper.

Malachite ($Cu_2CO_3(OH)_2$): A green mineral used as a secondary source of copper.

Aluminum Ore

Bauxite: Contains various aluminum minerals like gibbsite, boehmite, and diaspore. It's the principal ore for aluminum extraction. The primary constituent of bauxite is aluminum oxide (Al_2O_3).

Lead Ore

Galena (PbS): The primary source of lead.

Zinc Ore

Sphalerite (ZnS): The most common ore for obtaining zinc.

Silver Ore:

Argentite (Ag_2S): A primary source for silver extraction.

Gold Ore

Most gold is extracted from native gold ores, but it can also be found combined with tellurium in the mineral calaverite ($AuTe_2$).

Tin Ore

Cassiterite (SnO_2): The main ore from which tin is derived.

Nickel Ores

Pentlandite ($(Fe,Ni)_9S_8$): A significant source of nickel.

Garnierite (a general term for a green nickel ore): Contains a mixture of various nickel and magnesium silicates.

Uranium Ore

Uraninite (UO_2 or U_3O_8): The primary ore for uranium extraction.

Metals are extracted from suitable ores through certain general metallurgical processes like:

1. **Dressing of Ore:** The ores are in the form of huge rocks. In this process, the rocks are broken down into small pieces and ground to powder. This powdered form of ore is used for further metallurgical processes.

2. **Concentration of Ore:** The ore is associated with huge amounts of impurities like sand, other metal compounds and certain non-metals. The impurities that are associated with the ore are called **gangue**. In this process, certain amount of gangue is removed from the ore, thus increasing the concentration of a metal in the ore. The process by which the gangue is removed depends on the type of ore and gangue.

   (a) **Magnetic Separation:** This process is carried out for those ores in which either the ore or the gangue is magnetic in nature. The powdered ore is made to fall on a rubber belt which moves horizontally over two pulleys of which one is a strong magnet. Magnetic components are retained on the belt and are collected as a separate heap after coming out of the magnetic influence.

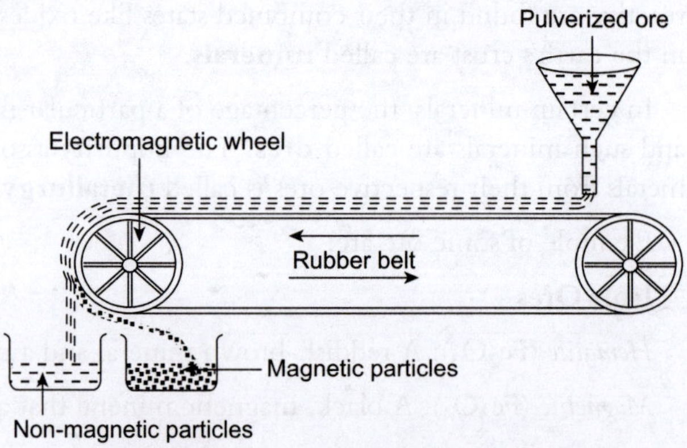

Figure 9.1 Electromagnetic separation

   (b) **Gravity Separation:** The ores in which the specific gravity difference between the ore and gangue is high are concentrated by gravity separation. This is generally applicable for iron ore. The ore is taken on a sloping table with ridges and washed with water. The water washes away the lighter gangue particles leaving behind the concentrated ore.

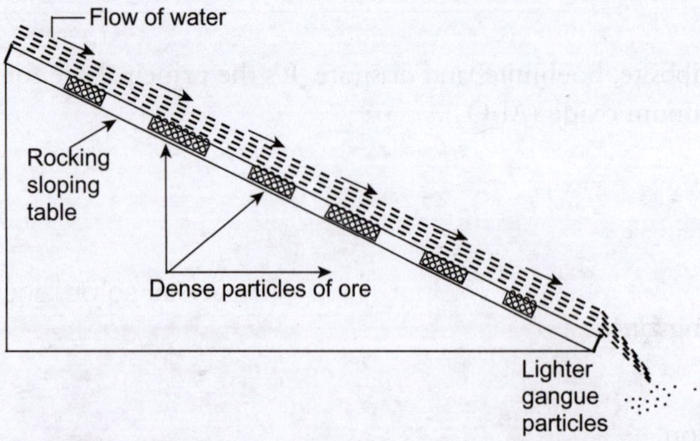

Figure 9.2 Concentration of ore by gravity process

Konnect

The word 'metallurgy' comes from the Greek words 'metallon' meaning metal and 'ergon' meaning work. This ancient art is all about extracting metals from their ores and refining them for use.

(c) Froth Floatation: This process is generally followed for sulphide ores. The ore is taken in a tank with oil and water, and mixed thoroughly by blowing air. Bubbles of oil are formed. The ore sticks to these bubbles and rises up while the gangue sticks to the water and settles at the bottom. The froth along with the ore is separated.

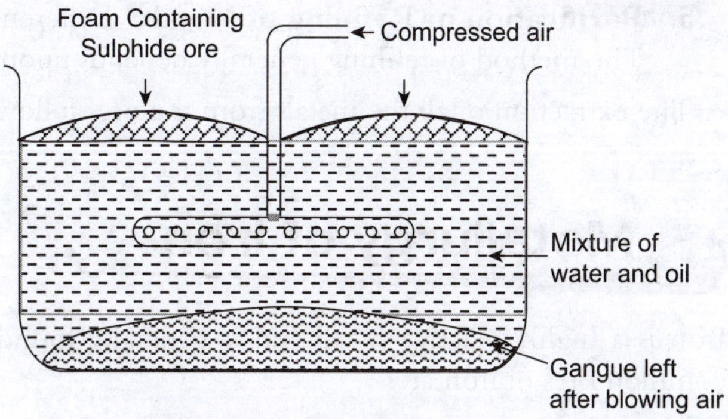

Figure 9.3 Froth floatation process

3. **Conversion of Ore to Oxide:** The conversion of ore to oxide is carried out by two methods.

(a) Roasting: This is generally carried out for sulphide ores. The ore is heated to a temperature below the fusion point of the ore where the ore reacts with the oxygen present in air and forms metal oxide and sulphur dioxide.

$$MS + O_2 \rightarrow MO + SO_2$$

Volatile impurities present in the ore are removed during this process.

Table 9.1 General process of purification

Processes of purification	Metals to be refined	Steps involved
Distillation	Iron, mercury	The metal is strongly heated above its boiling point in the absence of air. The metal vaporizes, leaving behind the impurities. The vapors are cooled in earthen retorts, to get the metal in the solid or in the liquid form.
Liquation	Lead, tin (metals with low melting point)	The metal is taken on the upper part of the sloping hearth and heated above its melting point. The metal melts, flows down the hearth and is collected at the bottom.
Polling	Copper with cuprous oxide as impurity	Molten copper is stirred with wooden poles. These poles emit wood gas which reduces copper oxide to copper.
Oxidation	Iron with oxidizable impurities	Oxygen is blown through molten metal where the impurities get converted to gaseous oxides and are removed. $C + O_2 \rightarrow CO_2 \uparrow$ $S + O_2 \rightarrow SO_2 \uparrow$
Electrolytic refining	Aluminium	A block of the impure metal is taken as anode and a thin strip of pure metal as cathode. The electrolyte is the soluble salt of the metal. On passing the current, the metal ions from the anode dissolve in the electrolyte, go towards the cathode and get discharged there. Electrolysis continues and the cathode becomes a thick block of pure metal.

(b) Calcination: This process is carried out specifically for carbonate ores. The main purpose of this process, is the removal of CO_2 from the ore. Hence, the ore is heated to its decomposition temperature and gets converted to the oxide form. Along with CO_2, volatile impurities are also removed in this process. Apart from carbonate ores, hydrated ores are also subjected to calcination for the removal of water of crystallization.

$$MCO_3 \rightarrow MO + CO_2$$

4. **Extraction of Metal:** The oxide ores obtained from the above process are reduced to metals by smelting. During this process flux (a material which combines with gangue) is added. This converts the gangue into slag (the fusible material gangue forms when flux reacts with it), which is separated from the ore.

Konnect

The metal so obtained in extraction is not 100 per cent pure and needs to be further purified.

5. **Purification or Refining of Metals:** Different methods of the refining of metals are followed for different metals. The method of refining generally depends upon the type of impurities present within the metal.

The extraction of all the metals from the ores follows one of the above processes.

Metallurgy of Iron

Iron is a highly reactive metal and is generally found in the oxide state. The most common ores of iron are:

Haematite	Fe_2O_3	Siderite	$FeCO_3$
Limonite	$Fe_2O_3 . H_2O$	Iron pyrites	FeS_2
Magnetite	Fe_3O_4	Magnetite	Fe_3O_4

Iron is generally extracted from hematite, limonite, and siderite. Among these hematite and limonite are the most preferred ores.

Info Bytes!

The use of iron revolutionized human civilization. In fact, the period after the Bronze Age is often called the Iron Age due to the widespread use of this metal.

The manufacturing of pig iron is the first step in the metallurgy of iron. This pig iron is further converted to cast iron which is used for the manufacture of steel and wrought iron.

1. **Dressing and Concentration of Ore:** The ore is crushed to make smaller pieces from large chunks. The crushed ore is concentrated by the process of magnetic separation and further concentration is done by gravity separation process.
2. **Conversion to Oxide:** The concentrated ore is converted to oxide form by the process of roasting which involves heating the ore in the presence of excess of air.
   On roasting, the carbonate ore decomposes to oxide giving out carbon dioxide. This process is also associated with other advantages like:
   (a) the removal of moisture and other volatile impurities;
   (b) the removal of impurities like sulphur, phosphorous, arsenic and antimony in the form of gaseous oxides;
   (c) the conversion of ferrous oxide to ferric oxide
   (d) inducing porosity in the mass, thus rendering the metal to easy reduction.
3. **Reduction of Oxide to Metal:** The reduction of oxide to metal is carried out with carbon in a blast furnace by the process called **smelting**.

Smelting in Blast Furnace

Blast furnace is a huge chimney-like structure about 30-m high and 8 m in diameter. It is made of iron plates and lined internally with refractory bricks. On top, it has a double cup and cone arrangement. Below this, there is an outlet for waste gases. A hearth is present at the bottom to collect cast iron and slag, and has separate outlets for each. Hot compressed air is blown into the furnace through pipes called tuyeres which are placed above the hearth.

The ore is mixed with coke and limestone approximately in the ratio of 8 : 4 : 1.This mixture is called **charge**.

The charge is lowered into the furnace from the top through the cup and cone arrangement, and various reactions take place in the furnace at different levels.

(a) **Lower Region (1500–2000°C)**

Coke combines with the heated air coming from the tuyeres and burns to form carbon dioxide. The reaction, being highly exothermic, increases the temperature in this zone to 2000°C.

$$C + O_2 \rightarrow CO_2 + 97 \text{ kcal}$$

Info Bytes!

Lower region of blast furnace is also called the **combustion zone.**

(b) Middle Region or Fusion Zone (1500–1000°C)

The carbon dioxide formed in the lower layer moves to the middle layer where it is reduced to carbon monoxide:

$$CO_2 + C \rightarrow 2CO - 39 \text{ kcal}$$

At such a high temperature, the limestone added decomposes into calcium oxide and carbon dioxide:

$$CaCO_3 \rightarrow CaO + CO_2 - 43 \text{ kcal}$$

The calcium oxide (quick lime) formed reacts with impurities like sand in the ore and converts them to slag:

$$CaO + SiO_2 \rightarrow CaSiO_3$$

The slag, calcium silicate goes towards the hearth present at the bottom of the furnace. As the reactions in the middle region are endothermic, the temperature of this zone decreases.

(c) Upper Region or Reduction Zone (1000–500°C)

The carbon monoxide formed in the middle region moves to the upper region where it reduces the iron oxide to iron:

$$FeO + CO \xrightarrow{750\text{–}600°C} Fe + CO_2$$

$$Fe_3O_3 + 3CO \xrightarrow{600\text{–}400°C} 2Fe + 3CO_2$$

The iron formed here melts due to high temperature and then, due to its high density, settles down. Both the slag (calcium silicate) and iron settle down in the hearth. Iron being heavier forms the bottom layer with slag on top. From here, iron and slag are tapped through separate outlets.

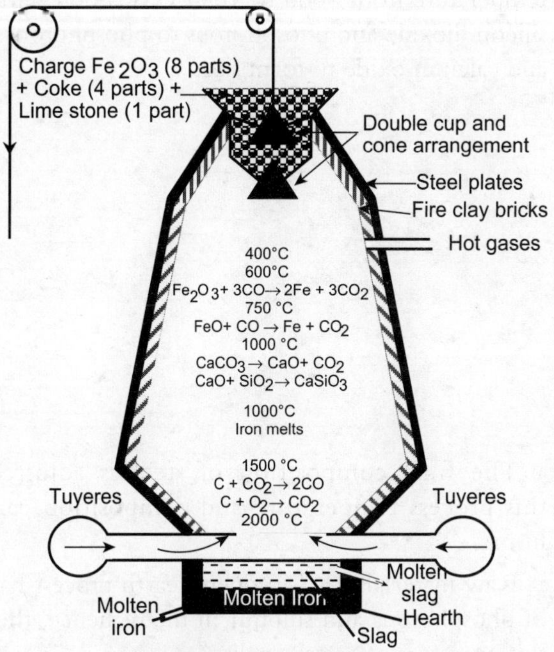

Figure 9.4 Blast furnance

Pig Iron

The iron obtained from this process is called the **pig iron**. This is not 100 per cent pure and acts as the basic raw material for cast iron and steel.

Cast Iron

This is obtained by re-melting pig iron in a vertical furnace called **cupola** and thereby gets refined. It is then poured into suitable moulds where it solidifies. This re-melted pig iron is called **cast iron**.

Wrought Iron

This is a comparatively purer form of iron. Cast iron is taken in a reverberatory furnace and stirred at high temperature. This process is called **puddling**. Most of the impurities are lost during this process due to the high temperature. Iron at this stage is in a semi-solid state. This, on cooling, gives wrought iron.

Steel

Steel is an **alloy of iron** with some amount of carbon in it. The carbon added increases the hardness of iron. Thus steel is harder than iron and the hardness increases with increase in the carbon content. The manufacture of steel is carried out by many processes. The best quality is, however obtained by the **open-hearth process**.

Open-hearth Process for Making Special Type of Steel

As the name suggests, the shape of the furnace is like a hearth, the top of which is open. The charge is pig iron and steel scrap. The process can be carried out in two ways depending on the impurities present in the raw material.

Konnect

Basic process is adopted if phosphorus is present as an impurity.

Acid Process: In this process, the furnace is lined with acidic refractories, i.e., silica brick.

Basic Process: In this process, the furnace is lined with magnesite or dolomite.

Along with pig iron, steel scrap is added as a raw material in this process. To promote oxidation of the impurities, small amount of iron ore is added to provide additional oxygen.

The temperature on the top of the hearth is generated by a hot fuel gas which burns on the hearth and produces a temperature from 1600 to 1650°C. Carbon starts getting oxidized. Sulphur gets oxidized to sulphur dioxide, silicon to silicon dioxide and phosphorous to phosphorous pentoxide. The silica and phosphorous pentoxide react with manganese and calcium oxide to form slag.

$$C + O_2 \rightarrow CO_2$$

$$2CO_2 + C \rightarrow 2CO$$

$$P + O_2 \rightarrow P_2O_5$$

$$Si + O_2 \rightarrow SiO_2$$

$$MnO + SiO_2 \rightarrow MnSiO_3$$

$$CaO + P_2O_5 \rightarrow 2Ca_3\ (PO_4)_2$$

The final composition of steel is adjusted by adding ferrosilicon and/or ferromanganese alloy. Thus, in this process temperature and composition can be controlled. It is a very lengthy process and takes about 5–15 hours.

Raw materials used in open-hearth process have low content of phosphorous and sulphur in them; hence, the steel made by this process is of better quality.

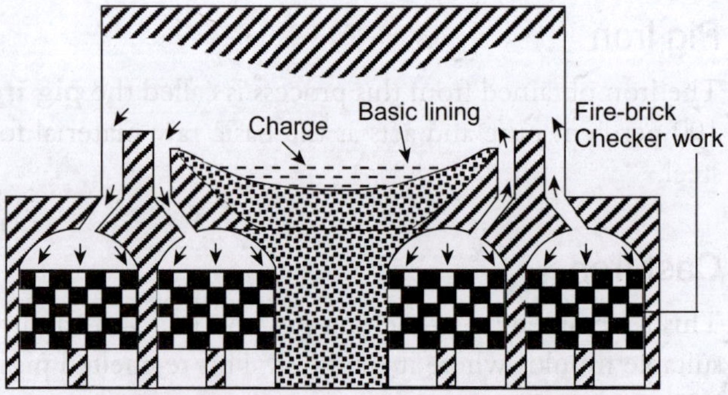

Figure 9.5 An open-hearth furnace

Alloying

Alloying of a metal changes its physical properties and thus makes it useful for a variety of purposes depending on the composition of the alloy.

Another important aspect of the alloy is prevention of corrosion. Stainless steel, a unique alloy of iron does not get corroded at all.

Corrosion of iron can be prevented in many other ways.The most common ones are listed hereunder:

1. **Galvanization:** The process of coating a layer of zinc on the metal is called galvanization.
2. **Electroplating:** In this process, one metal is deposited over the other metal through anelectrolytic process. The metal to be coated is taken as the cathode and the metal with which it is coated is taken as the anode. On passing electricity, the anode dissolves in the electrolyte which is generally a salt solution of the anodic metal. The metal ions move towards the cathode where they are discharged and get deposited on the cathode, thus forming a coating over it.

EXAMPLE 9.1 Compare metals and non-metals based on the following properties

(i) Electrical conductivity (ii) Tensile strength
(iii) Formation of ions (iv) Reaction with acids

SOLUTION

S. No.	Parameters	Metals	Non-metals
(i)	Electrical conductivity	Good conductors of electricity **Exceptions**: Bi and W are poor conductors of electricity	Bad conductors of electricity **Exceptions**: Graphite and gas carbon are good conductors of electricity
(ii)	Tensile strength	Metals have high tensile strength. **Exceptions**: Zn, Hg, and Ga have low tensile strength	Do not have tensile strength. **Exceptions**: Carbon fibre has high tensile strength
(iii)	Formation of ions	Metals form cations	Non-metals form anions
(iv)	Reaction with acid	Metals which are more reactive than hydrogen replace hydrogen from the acids	Generally non-metals do not react with acids

EXAMPLE 9.2 Explain the gravity separation method for concentrating metallic ores.

SOLUTION

Gravity separation is commonly utilized for concentrating metallic ores. In this method, the powdered ore is placed on a sloping table with water. Due to the difference in densities, the heavier ore particles settle at the bottom, while the lighter gangue particles are washed away with the flowing water. The concentrated ore remains on the table and is then collected.

EXAMPLE 9.3 Why isn't the primary iron from the blast furnace directly utilized for construction purposes?

SOLUTION

In the high-temperature environment of the blast furnace, carbon from coke reacts with oxygen to produce carbon monoxide. This carbon monoxide, in the presence of iron and its oxides, can further decompose into carbon dioxide and elemental carbon. As a result, the iron produced accumulates a high amount of carbon. This excess carbon content gives the iron from the blast furnace a brittle and hard nature, making it inappropriate for construction applications.

Metals thus have various applications in the form of elements, compounds, alloys, etc. Similarly, non-metals also play a very important role in various fields due to their specific properties. Consequently, this makes the study of non-metals also equally significant as that of metals.

Non-Metals

Hydrogen

Hydrogen is the lightest among all elements. Atmospheric air is found to contain only trace amounts of hydrogen. Hydrogen gas was first prepared by the action of dil H_2SO_4 on iron. In 1762, Henry Cavendish for the first time established the elemental nature of hydrogen. He prepared this gas by the action of dil H_2SO_4 on zinc. Lavoisier named it hydrogen which means water former (*Hydro*–water, *gen*–producing).

Occurrence

Availability of hydrogen gas in free state is very rare. Though it is present in trace amounts in the atmosphere, hydrogen is present in sun's atmosphere upto 1.1%. Very minute quantities of hydrogen is present in volcanic gases.

Most of the hydrogen is present in combined state in nature. Hydrogen is present in various carbon compounds in the form of proteins, nucleic acids, vitamins, hormones, enzymes etc., in plants and animals. Most of the naturally occurring substances such as wood, cotton, paper pulp, rubber etc., contain hydrogen. Water is the most important source of hydrogen as hydrogen is present upto 11.1% by weight in water.

Info Bytes!

Hydrogen, the lightest element, is abundant and powers stars through nuclear fusion. Carbon, in the form of graphite, is one of the few materials that can disrupt a magnetic field, leading to its use in many technological applications.

Preparation of Hydrogen

(i) General Methods of Preparation

Following table illustrates some methods to prepare hydrogen:

Table 9.2 General methods to prepare hydrogen

Method	Equation	Observation
Action of active metals with cold water.	$2M + 2H_2O \rightarrow 2MOH + H_2$ (M = Na, K, Ca)	Na and K → Reaction is violent. They float on the surface of water. Ca → Brisk reaction and metal sinks in water.
Action of steam on hot metals	$M + H_2O \rightarrow MO + H_2$ (steam) (M = Mg, Al, Zn, Fe)	Reaction is fast for Mg and slow for Al, Zn, and Fe. In the case of Mg, Al, Zn the reaction stops after some time because the oxides of these metals stick to the surface of the metal and therefore, the steam does not come into contact with metal and hence the reaction stops.
Action of dilute acids on metals	$M + 2HCl \rightarrow MCl_2 + H_2$ (M = Zn, Mg) $M + H_2SO_4 \rightarrow MSO_4 + H_2$ (M = Fe) **Note:** Aluminium also gives this reaction in which the formula of the salt could be $M_2(SO_4)_3$	The hydrogen gas liberated burns with pop sound when lighted wooden stick is brought nearer to it.
Action of concentrated alkali on metals	$2NaOH + 2M + 2H_2O \rightarrow 2NaMO_2 + 3H_2$ (M = Al, Zn, Pb) $2M + 2KOH + 2H_2O \rightarrow 2KMO_2 + 3H_2$ (M = Al, Zn)	Reaction takes place only on boiling.

(ii) Laboratory Method of Preparation

Principle: All metals, present above hydrogen in the reactivity series on reaction with dilute HCl or dilute H_2SO_4, liberate hydrogen gas. Zinc metal is preferred for this reaction.

$$Zn + 2HCl \rightarrow ZnCl_2 + H_2\uparrow$$

$$Zn + H_2SO_4 \rightarrow ZnSO_4 + H_2\uparrow$$

Experiment: Some granulated zinc pieces which provides large surface area are taken in a flat bottomed flask, fitted with a two holed air tight cork. In one hole, a thistle funnel is inserted and in another hole, a long delivery tube is inserted. Dilute H_2SO_4 is allowed to drop into the flask dropwise through the thistle funnel.

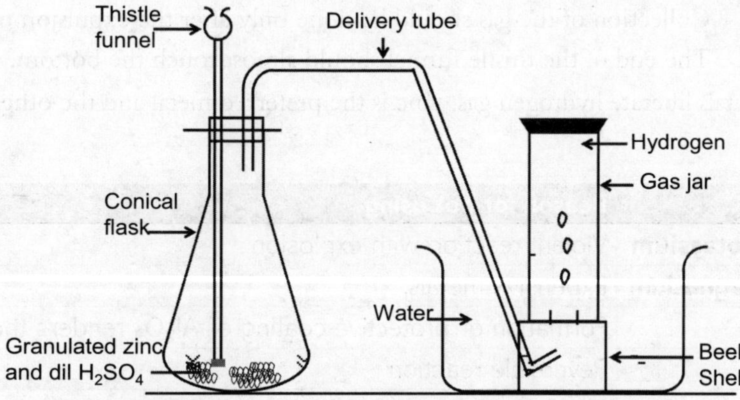

Figure 9.6 Laboratory preparation of hydrogen

Observation:
Effervescence is observed in the initial stages of the reaction. Then a colorless and odorless gas is evolved.

Collection of Gas: Hydrogen is collected by the downward displacement of water.

Table 9.3 Some impurities and their process of removal

Impurities	Process of removal
AsH_3, PH_3	Silver nitrate solution
H_2S	Lead nitrate solution
CO_2, SO_2, NO_2	Caustic potash
H_2O (water Vapour)	$CaCl_2$ or P_2O_5 (drying agent)

Purification of Hydrogen Gas: Since impure zinc is used for hydrogen gas preparation, the hydrogen gas collected is found to contain some impurities such as H_2S, SO_2, PH_3, AsH_3, and CO_2. These impurities are removed in stages.

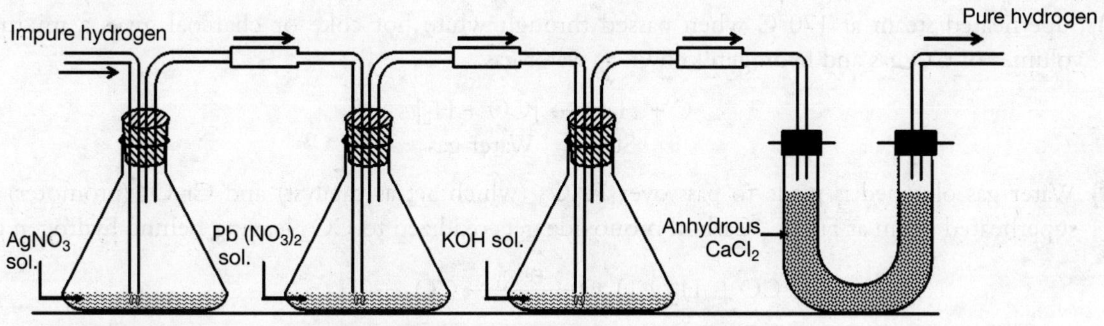

Figure 9.7 Purification of hydrogen gas

Collection of Purified Hydrogen Gas: To obtain pure and dry hydrogen, pure hydrogen gas is collected over mercury.

Precautions:

1. Entire apparatus should be kept air-tight.
2. Contact with flame should be avoided.
3. Collection of the gas should be done only after the expulsion of air.
4. The end of the thistle funnel should almost touch the bottom.

Though all active metals liberate hydrogen gas, zinc is the preferred metal and the other metals are not used for this preparation method.

Metals	Reason for not using
Sodium and potassium	Violent reaction with explosion
Calcium and magnesium	Expensive metals
Aluminium	Formation of protective coating of Al_2O_3 renders the metal passive
Iron	Reversible reaction
Lead	Formation of insoluble $PbCl_2$ or $PbSO_4$ stops the further reaction

(iii) Industrial Methods of Preparation

1. Electrolysis of Water: Electrolysis of acidulated water liberates oxygen at the anode and hydrogen at the cathode. In fact, this method is employed for the preparation of oxygen gas where hydrogen is obtained as a bi-product.

$$2H_2O \rightarrow 2H_2 + O_2$$

2. Bosch Process

Principle: This method involves two stages

- Preparation of water gas
- Removal of carbon monoxide from water gas.

Water gas is a mixture of carbon monoxide and hydrogen. Catalytic oxidation of carbon monoxide gives hydrogen gas. Water gas can be prepared by passing steam over red hot coke.

$$C + \underset{\text{Steam}}{H_2O} \rightarrow \underset{\text{Water gas}}{[CO + H_2]}$$

$$[CO + H_2] + H_2O \xrightarrow{Fe_2O_3} CO_2 + 2H_2$$

Process:

(i) Superheated steam at 170°C when passed through white hot coke or charcoal gives a mixture of equal volumes of CO gas and hydrogen known as water gas.

$$C + \underset{\text{Steam}}{H_2O} \rightarrow \underset{\text{Water gas}}{[CO + H_2]}$$

(ii) Water gas obtained is made to pass over Fe_2O_3 (which act as catalyst) and Cr_2O_3 (promoter) along with superheated steam at 500°C. Carbon monoxide gets oxidized to CO_2 leaving behind hydrogen gas.

$$CO + H_2 + H_2O \xrightarrow{Fe_2O_3} CO_2 + 2H_2$$

(iii) The CO_2 gas is removed by compressing the gas at 30 atm pressure and passing through water. Hydrogen being insoluble remains as such.

$$H_2O(\ell) + CO_2(g) \xrightarrow{300\text{ atm}} H_2CO_3$$

(iv) The water vapor present in the gas can be removed by cooling the gas to −20°C.

(v) The traces of carbon monoxide remaining unoxidised can be removed by passing the gas through ammonical cuprous chloride solution.

$$CuCl + CO + 2H_2O \rightarrow \underset{\text{Addition compound}}{CuCl.CO.2H_2O}$$

Bosch process can also be carried out for the preparation of hydrogen from natural gas. Natural gas contains methane as the major constituent. Methane on mixing with superheated steam at high temperature followed by compression to 30 atm pressure also gives water gas. This is subjected to Bosch process for getting pure hydrogen gas.

Physical Properties

Some of the physical properties are tabulated below:

Table 9.4 Physical properties of hydrogen

Property	Characteristic
Color	Colorless
Odor	No characteristic odor for pure hydrogen. But fishy odor of hydrogen gas is attributed to the presence of impurities.
Solubility	Negligible
Density	Least density
Action on litmus	Neutral
Liquefaction	Difficult due to very low critical temperature and not possible at room temperature
Diffusion	High rate of diffusion

Adsorption or Occlusion: In addition to the normal physical properties, hydrogen shows a specific property called adsorption or occlusion. The accumulation of molecules of one compound over the surface of another compound is called **adsorption**. Hydrogen gas gets adsorbed on the surface of some metals like palladium, platinum, nickel etc.

Chemical Properties

(i) Reaction with Air: Hydrogen burns in air or oxygen with a blue flame and forms water.

$$2H_2 + O_2 \rightarrow 2H_2O$$

(ii) Reaction with Nonmetals: Hydrogen reacts with most of the nonmetals forming corresponding hydrides.

(a) Reaction with Chlorine: Hydrogen reacts with chlorine in the presence of sunlight to give hydrogen chloride. This is a photochemical reaction.

$$H_2 + Cl_2 \xrightarrow{\text{light}} 2HCl$$

(b) Reaction with Nitrogen: Nitrogen and hydrogen react in 1 : 3 ratio at a high temperature and a high pressure to form ammonia.

$$N_2 + 3H_2 \rightleftharpoons 2NH_3$$

(c) Reaction with Sulphur: On reaction with molten sulphur, hydrogen forms hydrogen sulphide.

$$H_2 + S \rightarrow H_2S$$

(iii) Reactions with Metals: Hydrogen reacts with highly electropositive metals to form metallic hydrides.

Examples:

$$2K + H_2 \xrightarrow{\Delta} 2KH$$

$$2Na + H_2 \xrightarrow{\Delta} 2NaH$$

$$Ca + H_2 \xrightarrow{\Delta} CaH_2$$

(iv) Reactions with Metal Oxides: Oxides of less reactive metals react with hydrogen to form the corresponding metal and water. This is due to the reduction of metallic oxide.

Examples: $\underset{\text{White}}{ZnO} + H_2 \rightarrow \underset{\text{Bluish white}}{Zn} + H_2O$; $\underset{\text{Brown}}{2Fe_2O_3} + 6H_2 \rightarrow \underset{\text{Grey}}{4Fe} + 6H_2O$

$\underset{\text{Yellow}}{PbO} + H_2 \rightarrow \underset{\text{Grey}}{Pb} + H_2O$; $\underset{\text{Black}}{CuO} + H_2 \rightarrow \underset{\text{Red}}{Cu} + H_2O$

(v) Hydrogenation: Catalytic addition of hydrogen to some carbon compounds is called hydrogenation.

$$\underset{\text{Ethylene}}{H_2C=CH_2} + H_2 \xrightarrow{Pt} \underset{\text{Ethane}}{H_3C-CH_3}$$

This principle is made use of in the process of hydrogenation of oils or hardening of oils.

Hydrogenation of Oils: Vegetable oils which contain carbon and oxygen in greater percentage, cannot be solidified easily, due to less percentage of hydrogen.

Examples: Ground nut oil, coconut oil.

Animal oils such as ghee which contain hydrogen in greater percentage get solidified easily under normal conditions. Vegetables oils also get solidified when hydrogen gas is passed through them at high pressure and high temperature in the presence of nickel catalyst.

Examples: Palm oil, linseed oil

Uses of Hydrogen

1. In the synthesis of industrial chemicals.

(i) Manufacture of ammonia (Haber's process)

$$N_2 + 3H_2 \xrightarrow{Fe} 2NH_3$$

(ii) Manufacture of HCl

$$H_2 + Cl_2 \xrightarrow{\text{sunlight}} 2HCl$$

(iii) Manufacture of methyl alcohol

$$\underset{\text{Water Gas}}{[CO + H_2]} + H_2 \xrightarrow[\text{Catalyst}]{\Delta} CH_3OH$$

(iv) Manufacture of dalda/vanaspathi by hydrogenation of oils.

(v) Manufacture of petrol/gasoline from coal.

2. As a source of fuel

(i) Many fuels contain hydrogen as a major constituent. This is because of high heat of combustion of hydrogen.
Examples: Water gas, coal gas, semi-water gas etc.

(ii) Electrical cells called fuel cells are also designed which use hydrogen gas.

(iii) **Oxyhydrogen Blow Torch:** A mixture of hydrogen and oxygen is burnt to give high temperature of 2800°C. This is used for welding of metals and for melting platinum and quartz.

(iv) Liquid hydrogen is used as rocket fuel.

(v) **Atomic hydrogen torch:** When an electric arc is generated in a stream of hydrogen between tungsten electrodes, the hydrogen molecules dissociate to give hydrogen atoms by absorbing large amount of energy. The atoms recombine to form hydrogen molecules by evolving the absorbed heat energy. As a result, high temperature is generated. This can be made use of in welding alloys.

3. Metallurgy: Hydrogen is used as a good reducing agent in the extraction of some metals from their oxides.
Examples: Tungsten, molybdenum.

$$WO_3 + 3H_2 \rightarrow W + 3H_2O$$

Carbon

It is one of the most important non-metallic elements. It is invariably present in all the living organisms in the form of biomolecules.

Occurrence

Carbon occurs both in the free and in the combined states.

Free State: Carbon exists as the native element in the form of coal in the earth's crust. It occurs in a very small amount in the form of its allotropic forms such as diamond and graphite.

Combined State: In the combined state, carbon exists in the form of oxides, (carbon dioxide, carbon monoxide), carbonates (metal carbonates) and many organic compounds (proteins, carbohydrates, etc.).

Allotropy

Allotropy is the phenomenon in which an element exhibits different physical forms with similar chemical properties. The different physical forms exhibited by the element are called allotropes. Carbon exhibits various allotropic forms which have a wide variety of applications. The allotropic forms are broadly classified into **crystalline and amorphous forms**.

1. **Crystalline Forms:** In these allotropic forms, the carbon atoms have a well-defined regular geometrical arrangement.
   Examples: Diamond and Graphite

Table 9.5 Comparative study of diamond and graphite

Parameters	Diamond	Graphite
Structure	Diamond has a regular tetrahedral arrangement. This is due to the bonding of each atom of carbon with four other carbon atoms covalently, forming a single unit of crystal. These crystal units lie in different planes accounting for a rigid three-dimensional structure. Carbon has a valency of four and each carbon is bonded to four other carbon atoms forming a tetrahedral unit. These tetrahedral units lie in different planes, thus forming a rigid three-dimensional structure. 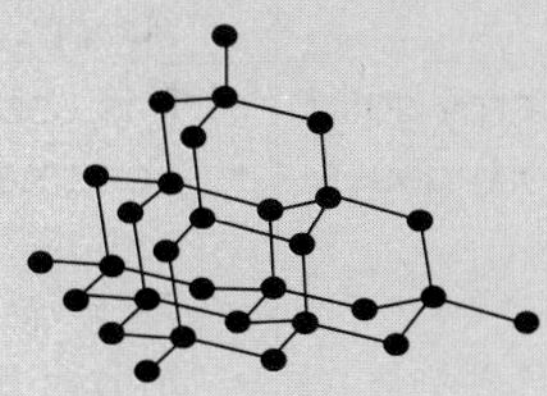	In graphite, each carbon atom is bonded covalently to three other carbon atoms resulting in the arrangement of hexagonal rings in a single plane. The forces of attraction between the atoms of two single crystals, in the parallel planes are weak. Each carbon is bonded to three carbon atoms only leaving behind one free valency. A three-dimensional arrangement of hexagonal rings is resulted. These rings lie on a single plane. The entire structure is such that the layers of the hexagonal rings are arranged parallel to each other. 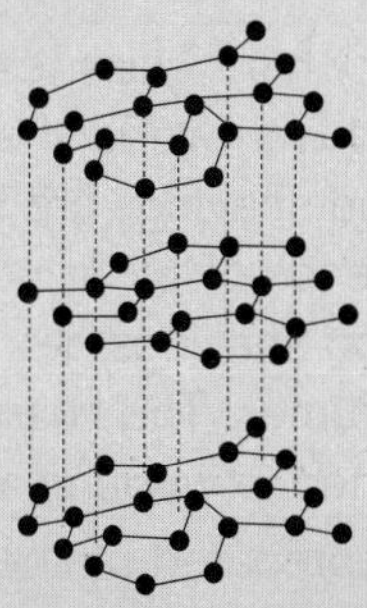
Appearance	A pure diamond is a Colorless, transparent, crystal. It is the hardest among naturally occuring solids.	Graphite is a dark grey, very soft solid with metallic lustre.
Conduction	It is a good conductor of heat and bad conductor of electricity.	It is a bad conductor of heat and good conductor of electricity.
Refractive index	It has a high refractive index of 2.5.	It is opaque.

Continued

Table 9.5 Contd.

Parameters	Diamond	Graphite
Solubility	It is insoluble in common solvents.	It is insoluble in common solvents.
Density	Density of diamond is 3.5 g/cm^3, which is the densest form of carbon.	Density is 2.25 g/cm^3.
Melting Point	The melting point of diamond is about 3700°C.	It has a melting point of about 3600°C.

2. **Amorphous Allotropes of Carbon:** In these forms of carbon, the carbon atoms are not arranged in an orderly manner.
   Examples: Coke, wood, charcoal, sugar, lamp black, animal charcoal, etc.

Table 9.6 Comparative study of amorphous allotropes

Allotropes	Preparation	Properties	Uses
Coke	Coke is prepared by heating coal in the absence of air up to a temperature of 1300°C in huge iron retorts.	It is a greyish black porous solid.	• It is used as a household fuel. • It is used extensively in the extraction of metals like copper and lead, from their oxides and sulphide ores as it is an excellent reducing agent. • It is used in the manufacture of graphite and calcium carbide. • It is used in the manufacture of water gas and producer gas.
Lamp black	Lamp black is prepared by burning mustard oil, turpentine oil, and petroleum in the absence of oxygen. A clean dry glass slide is placed over the flame of mustard oil lamp. After some time a deep black powdery substance is coated on the slide, which is known as lamp black.	Lamp black is a light, powdery black substance, having a velvet touch. It has an oily feel due to the presence of Vapors of some amounts of oil.	• Lamp black is used as a stabilizing filler for rubber in making tyres and plastics. • It is used as a black pigment in inks and paints. • It is used for making black shoe polishes. • It is used in the manufacture of black carbon papers and carbon ribbons for type-writers.
Wood charcoal	A dry hard glass test tube is half filled with wood shavings. The wood shavings are heated in the absence of air using Bunsen burner. Wood shavings get charred, giving off fumes. The charred product formed is wood charcoal.	It is a brittle grey solid and can adsorb gases and liquids.	• It is used as a house hold fuel. • For small scale extraction of metals. • As a deodorant. • In gas masks.
Sugar charcoal	It is prepared by the destructive distillation of sugar.	It is a thick, black residue.	• It is used for extracting metals from their oxides. • It is used as an adsorbent material in place of activated charcoal.
Animal charcoal	Animal bones contain organic matter and calcium phosphate. The crushed fine powder of the animal bones if subjected to destructive distillation produces residue. This residue is called bone charcoal.	It has less percentage of carbon and has the property of adsorption. It has high adsorptive capacity for mercury, arsenic, etc.	• Bone charcoal is used to remove Color from sugar cane juice by adsorbing impurities. • It is used in the extraction of yellow phosphorous.

Compounds of Carbon

Carbon, in nature, exists largely in the form of compounds. These compounds exist invariably in the form of organic and inorganic compounds. Some of the important inorganic compounds of carbon are the following:

Oxides of Carbon

Carbon reacts with oxygen to form two types of oxides, namely carbon monoxide and carbon dioxide.

(a) Carbon Monoxide: It is prepared by passing carbon dioxide over heated coke:

$$CO_2(g) + \underset{\text{(red hot)}}{C} \rightarrow 2CO(g) - Q$$

Carbon monoxide is a very harmful gas. On breathing, it combines with blood, reacts with haemoglobin forming carboxyhaemoglobin thus decreasing the oxygen-carrying capacity of the blood.

Uses of Carbon Monoxide:

(i) It is used in the preparation of fuel gases.

(ii) It is used as a reducing agent.

(iii) It is used in the preparation of metal carbonyls.

(b) Carbon Dioxide: This is prepared by treating hydrochloric acid with limestone:

$$CaCO_3 + 2HCl \rightarrow CaCl_2 + CO_2 + H_2O$$

Uses of Carbon Dioxide:

(i) It is used in the photosynthesis of plants.

(ii) It also traps the heat radiation and keeps the earth warm.

The characteristic feature of carbon dioxide gas is seen when it is passed through lime. A milky white precipitate of calcium carbonate is formed, which dissolves on excess passage of carbon dioxide due to the formation of soluble calcium bicarbonate:

$$Ca(OH)_2 + CO_2 \rightarrow CaCO_3 + H_2O$$
$$CaCO_3 + H_2O + CO_2 \rightarrow Ca(HCO_3)_2$$

Info Bytes!

Carbon dioxide gas plays a very important role in the atmosphere.

Carbonates and Bicarbonates

Carbonates and bicarbonates form another important class of compounds of carbon.

All carbonates except sodium and potassium carbonates on thermal decomposition give carbon dioxide. All bicarbonates on heating undergo decomposition to give carbon dioxide. Thus carbonates and bicarbonates act as sources, for the preparation of carbon dioxide.

Nitrogen

Nitrogen is an inactive element and is present in maximum proportion in air. The significance of nitrogen in air is to dilute the activity of oxygen thereby allowing natural processes like respiration and combustion to take place at a moderate rate.

Occurrence

Free State: Nitrogen exists in the free state in the atmospheric air. It is the major constituent of air comprising 78 per cent by volume and 75 per cent by weight.

Combined State: Nitrogen occurs in the combined state in various forms. It is present in the form of minerals like nitre (KNO_3) and Chile saltpeter ($NaNO_3$). Nitrogen is present in major amounts in organic matter such as proteins, nucleic acids, enzymes and various compounds of biological importance.

Preparation

In the industries, nitrogen is manufactured by isolation from the atmospheric air as it contains nitrogen in abundance. This is done by fractional distillation of liquid air.

Laboratory Method of Preparation of Nitrogen Gas

Principle: Ammonium chloride reacts with sodium nitrite to give ammonium nitrite which decomposes thermally to give nitrogen gas:

$$NH_4Cl + NaNO_2 \rightarrow NH_4NO_2 + NaCl$$

$$NH_4NO_2 \rightarrow N_2 + 2H_2O$$

Procedure: Equimolar solutions of ammonium chloride and sodium nitrite are taken in a round bottom flask and heated gently. Ammonium nitrite is formed which decomposes to give nitrogen which is collected by the downward displacement of water.

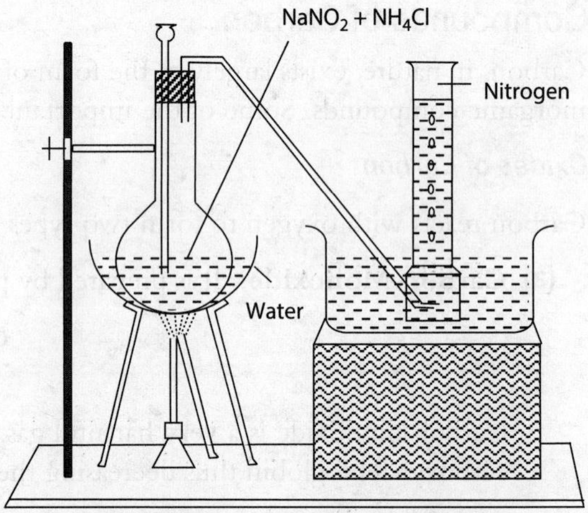

Figure 9.8 Preparation of nitrogen

Physical Properties

Some physical properties of nitrogen are tabulated below:

Table 9.7 Physical properties of nitrogen

Parameters	Features
Solubility	Slightly soluble in water (2.3 vol in 100 vol)
Density	Slightly lighter than air. Vapor density of air = 14.4 Vapor density of N_2 = 14.0
Liquefaction	It can be liquefied to a colorless liquid which boils at –195.8°C
Solidification	It can be solidified under high pressure to a white snow-like mass which melts at –209.8°C
Nature	It is a chemically a non-reactive gas. Due to this non-reactive nature, it is used in: (i) the filling of electric bulbs to prevent the oxidation of the filament present in it (ii) the preservation of food stuffs

Chemical Properties

Some chemical properties of nitrogen are tabulated below:

Table 9.8 Chemical properties of nitrogen

Parameters	Reactions
Reaction with non-metals	Nitrogen reacts with hydrogen at high temperature and pressure to give ammonia gas (i) *Reaction with hydrogen* $N_2 + 3H_2 \rightarrow 2NH_3$ (ii) *Reaction with oxygen* Nitrogen and oxygen react in equal volumes to form nitric oxide: $N_2 + O_2 \rightarrow 2NO$

Continued

Table 9.8 Contd.

Parameters	Reactions
Reaction with metals	(i) *Reaction with magnesium* Magnesium reacts with nitrogen to form magnesium nitride $3Mg + N_2 \rightarrow Mg_3N_2$ (ii) *Reaction with calcium* $3Ca + N_2 \rightarrow Ca_3N_2$ (iii) *Reaction with aluminium* $2Al + N_2 \rightarrow 2AlN$
Reaction with compounds	*Reaction with calcium carbide* Heating calcium carbide with nitrogen at 800°C–1000°C forms a mixture of calcium cyanamide and graphite $CaC_2 + N_2\downarrow$ 800°C$CaCN_2 + C$ $\rightarrow$ 800°C

Uses of Nitrogen

1. It is used in filling of electric bulbs
2. It is used in manufacture of fertilizers
3. It is used for storage of canned food

Compounds of Nitrogen - Ammonia

Since nitrogen is the most essential element for the growth of plants and most of the plants are incapable of absorbing nitrogen directly from the atmosphere, the manufacture of useful compounds from nitrogen has lot of industrial significance. The most important compounds are ammonia and nitric acid which form the basic raw materials for the manufacture of a number of fertilizers.

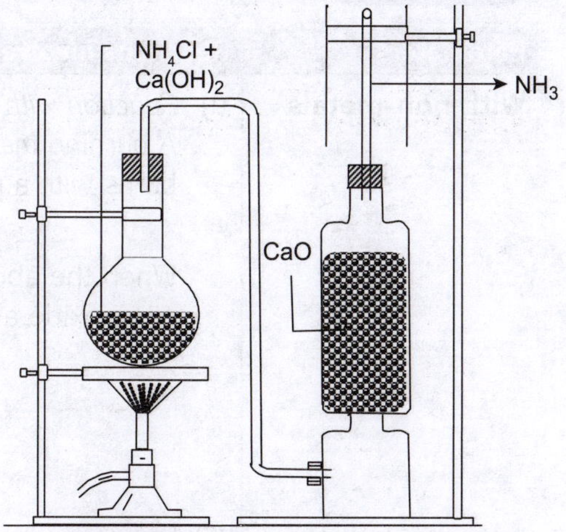

Figure 9.9 Preparation of ammonia

Laboratory Preparation of Ammonia

Ammonium chloride on reaction with an alkali like calcium hydroxide liberates ammonia gas.

$$NH_4Cl + Ca(OH)_2 \rightarrow CaCl_2 + 2H_2O + 2NH_3\uparrow$$

Procedure: Ammonium chloride and calcium hydroxide are taken in 1 : 3 ratio by weight in a round bottom flask and heated gently. The gas evolved is passed through a delivery tube which is connected to the bottom of a tower packed with quick lime. The gas passes through this tower and is collected in an inverted gas jar by downward displacement of air.

Physical Properties

Some physical properties of ammonia are tabulated below:

Table 9.9 Physical properties of ammonia

Parameters	Features
Color	Colorless
Odor	Pungent smell, causes burning sensation in the upper part of nasal track and brings tears to eyes
Taste	Bitter in taste
Physiological nature	Poisonous, damages respiratory system

(Continued)

Table 9.9 Contd.

Parameters	Features
Density	It is lighter than air (Vapor density 8.5)
Solubility	Highly soluble in water, so it cannot be collected by the downward displacement of water. However, 1300 vol. of NH_3 can be dissolved in 1 vol. of H_2O at STP
Boiling point	–33.4°C
Freezing point	–78°C

Chemical Properties

Some chemical properties of ammonia are tabulated below:

Table 9.10 Chemical properties of ammonia

Parameters	Reactions involved
With non-metals	(i) *Reaction with oxygen* A burning match stick when introduced into a jar containing ammonia and oxygen burns with a pale blue flame $4NH_3 + 3O_2 \rightarrow 2N_2 + 6H_2O$ When the above mixture of ammonia and oxygen is passed over heated platinum, nitric oxide and water vapor are formed with the evolution of heat $4NH_3 + 5O_2 \xrightarrow[900°C]{Pt} 4NO + 6H_2O$ $2NO + O_2 \rightarrow 2NO_2$ $2NO_2 + H_2O \rightarrow HNO_2 + HNO_3$ (ii) *Reaction with chlorine* 1) Limited amount of Cl_2 White, dense fumes of ammonium chloride are formed along with nitrogen $8NH_3 + 3Cl_2 \rightarrow 6NH_4Cl + N_2$ 2) Excess amount of Cl_2 Nitrogen trichloride and HCl are formed $NH_3 + 3Cl_2 \rightarrow NCl_3 + 3HCl$
With metals	On reaction with active metals, corresponding amides are formed $2NH_3 + 2Na \rightarrow 2NaNH_2 + H_2$ $2NH_3 + 2K \rightarrow 2KNH_2 + H_2$
With acids	Ammonia being slightly basic, reacts with acids to form salts $NH_3 + HCl \rightarrow NH_4Cl$ $NH_3 + HNO_3 \rightarrow NH_4NO_2$ $2NH_3 + H_2SO_4 \rightarrow (NH_4)_2SO_4$
Reducing Property	When ammonia is passed over hot cupric oxide, it gets reduced to copper $CuO + 2NH_3 \rightarrow N_2 + 3Cu + 3H_2O$

Uses of Ammonia

1. It is used in the manufacture of fertilizers
2. It is used as a laboratory reagent
3. It is used in the manufacture of rayon, plastic, rubber, etc.
4. It is used in the preparation of explosives like ammonal (NH_4NO_3 + Al powder) and amatol (NH_4NO_3 + 20 per cent TNT)

EXAMPLE 9.4

Silica gel is commonly found in packets inside new shoes or handbags. Justify.

SOLUTION

Silica gel is frequently used in these packets because of its excellent desiccant properties. It is synthesized from silicon dioxide, which allows it to absorb moisture from its surroundings. New shoes or handbags might retain moisture due to their manufacturing process or during storage, which can lead to fungal growth or foul smell.

Silica gel helps in removing this moisture, thus ensuring the product remains dry and in good condition.

EXAMPLE 9.5

Complete the following table:

Reactants	Colour of oxide	Colour of metal obtained	Metals
$ZnO + H_2$	–	–	–
– + H_2	Brown	Grey	–
$PbO + H_2$	–	Grey	–
– + H_2	–	–	Cu

SOLUTION

$ZnO + H_2 \rightarrow Zn + H_2O$
White Bluish white

$PbO + H_2 \rightarrow Pb + H_2O$
Yellow Grey

$2Fe_2O_3 + 6H_2 \rightarrow 4Fe + 6H_2O$
Brown Grey

$CuO + H_2 \rightarrow Cu + H_2O$
Black Red

EXAMPLE 9.6

(i) Diamond is a better conductor of heat than copper and silver. Give appropriate reasons.
(ii) Graphite is a good conductor of electricity. Justify the statement.

SOLUTION

(i) Diamond crystals have a very regular arrangement. The forces binding the atoms together are strong and the atoms are close to each other. Hence, they can easily transfer vibratory motion from one atom to the next. In metals, free electrons are there which hinder the tranfer of vibration of the metal atoms to some extent. But in diamond there are no free electrons. Hence, it is a very good conductor of heat.

(ii) Each carbon atom in graphite is inturn attached to other three carbon atoms forming a planar structure. Many such planar rings attach themselves to from hexagonal, layered structure. Since every carbon is attached to three other carbon atoms, one electron is left behind which is responsible for the conductivity. Thus, due to the presence of free electrons, graphite is a good conductor of electricity.

Phosphorous

Phosphorous is an important element and is used in the elemental state and in the compound form. It is one of the essential nutrients required in larger amounts (macronutrient) for plants. It plays an important role in photosynthesis.

Occurrence

Phosphorous, being highly reactive, does not exist in the free state. In the combined state, it exists in the form of phosphates in inorganic as well as organic matter.

Inorganic Compounds

Chlorapatite $3Ca_3(PO_4)_2.CaCl_2$
Fluorapatite $3Ca_3(PO_4)_2.CaF_2$
Phosphorite $Ca_3(PO_4)_2$

Organic Matter: It is found in phosphoproteins of yolk, bone marrow, brain, nervous system, bones, teeth, etc.

Preparation

Phosphorous is prepared by the electrolytic reduction of mineral phosphate.

Procedure: The mineral phosphate (calcium phosphate) is mixed with sand and coke. This mixture is taken in an electric furnace with carbon electrodes. The mixture is electrically heated up to 1775K.

The following reactions take place:

$$2Ca_3(PO_4)_2 + \underset{\text{(sand)}}{6SiO_2} \rightarrow \underset{\text{(slag)}}{6CaSiO_3} + P_4O_{10}$$

$$P_4O_{10} + 10C \rightarrow P_4 + 10CO$$

The slag formed settles at the bottom and is removed. Phosphorous vapors and carbon monoxide gas formed are let out of the furnace from the top. The subsequent cooling of these vapors under water results in the condensation of phosphorous into solid phosphorous.

Purification: The phosphorous obtained is purified using potassium dichromate in an acidic medium. The impurities are oxidized and removed as vapors or slag. Pure liquid phosphorous settles at the bottom where it is collected, filtered through chamois leather, and sent through water-cooled pipes for solidification.

Allotropy

The phenomenon of the existence of an element in more than one form is called allotropy and the different forms of the element are called **allotropes**. Allotropes have almost same chemical properties but different physical properties.

Phosphorous exists in two important allotropic forms.

1. White phosphorous
2. Red phosphorous

Physical Properties

Some physical properties of white and red phosphorus are tabulated below:

Table 9.11 Comparative study of white phosphorous and red phosphorous

Parameters	White phosphorous	Red phosphorous
State	Soft solid	Brittle powder
Color	White initially, gradually changes to yellow	Dark red
Odor	Garlic smell	Odourless

(Continued)

Table 9.11 Contd.

Parameters	White phosphorous	Red phosphorous
Density	1.82 g/cm^3	2.1 g/cm^3
Melting point	317 K	–
Boiling point	553.5 K	Sublimes at 565 K
Ignition temperature	308 K	533 K
Physiological nature	Poisonous	Non-poisonous
Atomicity	Four	Exists as chains
Structure	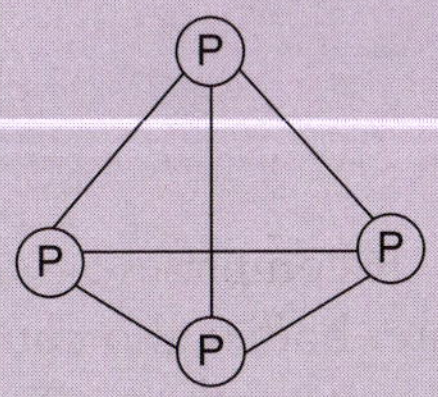 Isolated tetrahedral P_4 units	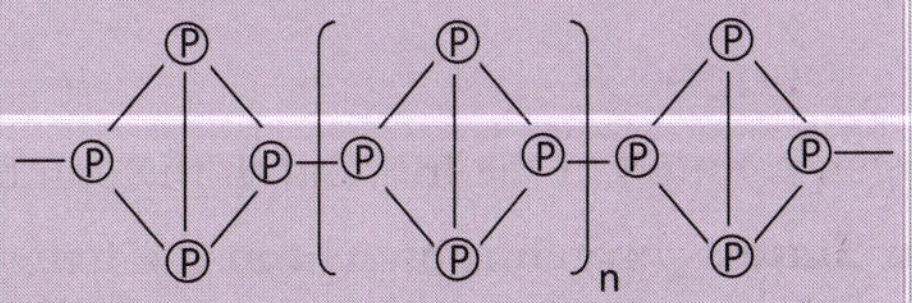 Chains of tetrahedral P_4 units linked to each other by P–P bonds

Chemical Properties

Some chemical properties of phosphorus are tabulated below:

Table 9.12 Chemical properties of phosphorous

Property	Reactions
With air/oxygen	Phosphorous reacts with oxygen to form two types of oxides P_2O_3 and P_2O_5 $P_4 + 3O_2 \xrightarrow[\text{Limited supply}]{} 2P_2O_3$ $P_4 + 5O_2 \xrightarrow[\text{excess}]{} 2P_2O_5$ These oxides with (excess) water produce oxyacids like HPO_3, H_3PO_4, H_3PO_3, and $H_4P_2O_7$
With chlorine	Phosphorous reacts with chlorine to form PCl_3 and PCl_5 $P_4 + \underset{\text{Limited supply}}{6Cl_2} \rightarrow 4PCl_3$ $P_4 + \underset{\text{Excess}}{10Cl_2} \rightarrow 4PCl_5$
With NaOH	Phosphorous when boiled with NaOH produces a colorless, poisonous gas phosphine $P_4 + 3NaOH + 3H_2O \rightarrow PH_3 + 3NaH_2PO_2$

Uses of Phosphorous

1. Red phosphorous is used in making safety matches.
2. Used in making phosphor bronze, an alloy of phosphorous, copper, and tin.
3. Used in making rat poison (zinc phosphide).
4. Used in making fertilizers.

Phosphorous plays a vital role in the growth of plants. It is available to plants in the form of phosphate. One of the important constituents of fertilizers is phosphorous. It is given to plants in the form of calcium phosphate, superphosphate of lime and lime nitrogenous phosphate.

Superphosphate of lime is a widely used as phosphatic fertilizer which is prepared by treating calcium phosphate with concentrated sulphuric acid:

$$Ca_3(PO_4)_2 + H_2SO_4 \rightarrow 2CaSO_4 + \underbrace{Ca(H_2PO_4)_2}_{\text{Superphosphate of lime}}$$

Oxygen

Oxygen is one of the most important non-metals. It plays a very important role in the life of most of the living organisms.

Occurrence

Oxygen is found in the free and in the combined states.

Free State: Oxygen is present in the free state in the atmospheric air. It comprises about 21 per cent by volume and about 23 per cent by mass of the total air. Water in oceans and other water bodies also contains some amount of oxygen in the dissolved state. Due to the presence of this dissolved oxygen in water, all aquatic species are able to survive in water.

Combined State: Water is the most important compound which contains oxygen in the combined state. Plants and animals also contain 50−70 per cent of oxygen in the combined state. However, 50 per cent of oxygen is present in the form of silicates, carbonates, limestone, and other ores.

Laboratory Preparation of Oxygen

In the laboratory, oxygen is prepared by the thermal decomposition of potassium chlorate or lead nitrate or potassium permanganate. The oxygen gas released is collected by the downward displacement of water.

$$2\,KClO_3 \xrightarrow[MnO_2]{\Delta} 2KCl + 3O_2 \uparrow$$

$$2\,Pb(NO_3)_2 \xrightarrow{\Delta} 2PbO + 4NO_2 + O_2 \uparrow$$

$$2KMnO_4 \xrightarrow{\Delta} K_2MnO_4 + MnO_2 + O_2 \uparrow$$

Konnect

Oxygen is the third most abundant element in the universe, and it's the breath of life for many organisms on Earth.

Physical Properties

Some physical properties of oxygen are tabulated below:

Table 9.13 Physical properties of oxygen

Parameters	Description
Color	Colorless
Taste	No characteristic taste
Odour	No characteristic odour
Physiological nature	Non-poisonous
Density	Vapor density = 16
Solubility	Slightly soluble in water
Liquefaction	−183°C at atmospheric pressure.
Boiling and freezing points	Boiling point is −183°C Freezing point is −218.4°C
Action on litmus	Neutral

Chemical Properties

Some chemical properties of oxygen are tabulated below:

Table 9.14 Chemical properties of oxygen

Parameters	Reactions involved
With metals	Metals react with oxygen to form basic or amphoteric oxides $2Ca + O_2 \rightarrow 2CaO$ } basic $2Mg + O_2 \rightarrow 2MgO$ } basic $4Al + 3O_2 \rightarrow 2Al_2O_3$ (amphoteric)
With non-metals	Non-metals react with oxygen to form basic or neutral oxides $S + O_2 \rightarrow SO_2$ $C + O_2 \rightarrow CO_2$ $2H_2 + O_2 \rightarrow 2H_2O$

If few drops of acid are added to water, it can be decomposed into its components, i.e., hydrogen and oxygen by passing electricity through it. This process is called **electrolysis of water** and is used for the industrial preparation of hydrogen and oxygen.

Electrolysis of Water

If a little amount of sulphuric acid is added to water, the water is called **acidulated water**. When this is subjected to electrolysis, water decomposes to give hydrogen and oxygen. Hydrogen is liberated at the cathode and oxygen is liberated at the anode.

$$2H_2O \xrightarrow{\text{Electric current}} 2H_2(g) + O_2(g)$$

Experiment I

Acidulated water is taken in a rectangular tank. Platinum plates are inserted into the tank which are connected to the opposite terminals of the battery. When high voltage is passed through the tank, water electrolyses to give hydrogen gas at the cathode and oxygen gas at the anode.

Advantages:

1. The process is comparatively economical and can be used especially in places where the electricity is available at cheaper rates.
2. Hydrogen gas is obtained as a by-product.

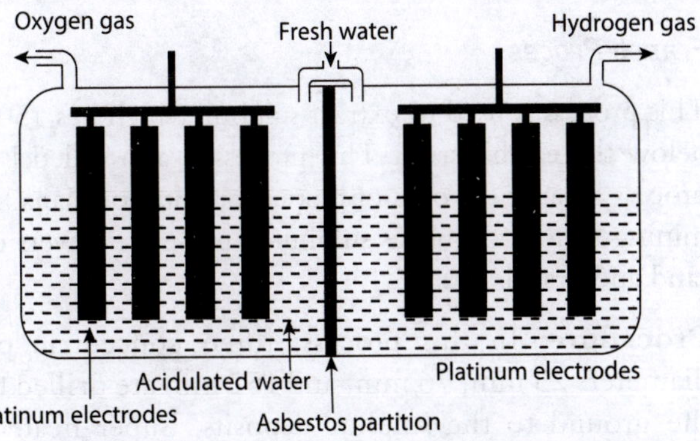

Figure 9.10 Industrial electrolysis of water

Uses of Oxygen

1. Respiration of living organisms.
2. Combustion or burning of fuels.
3. Manufacture of H_2SO_4 and HNO_3 in industry.
4. **As an explosive:** for blasting big rocks in mines, a mixture of coal, petroleum jelly and liquid oxygen is used in the form of cartridge.

5. **Metal extraction:** used in blast furnace for the extraction of iron.
6. **Welding:** a mixture of oxygen and hydrogen on burning gives an oxyhydrogen flame which is at a temperature of 2800°C. In place of hydrogen, when acetylene is used, it becomes oxyacetylene flame which gives a still higher temperature of 3300°C. Both are used for welding purposes.
7. **Stimulant for breathing:** a mixture of 95 per cent oxygen and 5 per cent CO_2 is called **carbogen**. It is used for aiding breathing in patients with breathing problems.
8. **As an anaesthetic:** a mixture of N_2O and oxygen is used as an anaesthetic during surgical operations.
9. **Rocket fuel:** Liquid oxygen is used.
10. **Artificial respiration:** Oxygen cylinders are carried by mountaineers, astronauts, miners, divers, submariners, aviators, firemen, etc.

Sulphur

Sulphur is an important non-metallic element. It reacts with metals thus destroying their metallic properties. Hence, its name is derived from the Sanskrit word *'sulvari'* which means enemy of copper.

Occurrence

In nature, sulphur occurs in both free and combined states.

Free State: Sulphur in the free state is found in the earth's crust in the volcanic regions.

Combined State: Sulphur in the combined state is found in organic matter in the form of many biomolecules (insulin, glucosinolates of plants and animals, natural gas, etc.) and in inorganic matter in the form of sulphides (cinnabar—HgS, galena—PbS, Iron pyrites—FeS) and sulphate (gypsum—$CaSO_4.2H_2O$, Epsom salt—$MgSO_4.7H_2O$).

Extraction

Sulphur is extracted from the earth's crust by the following process:

Frasch Process

This process is used to extract sulphur which lies 150–400 m below the earth's crust. This process is also called Louisiana process as large deposits of it are found in Louisiana. A direct mining is not possible as sulphur is present in layers of quick sand and gravel.

Procedure: In this process, three concentric pipes of diameters 25 mm, 76 mm, and 152 mm are drilled through the ground to the sulphur deposits. Super heated steam (170°C) under pressure is sent through the outermost pipe. This melts the sulphur below (mp of sulphur = 112°C). Hot compressed air (up to 35 atm) is sent through the innermost pipe, which froths up the molten sulphur below. The sulphur foam formed rises up the middle pipe and is collected.

Advantage: The sulphur extracted in this process is 99.5 per cent pure and does not need further purification.

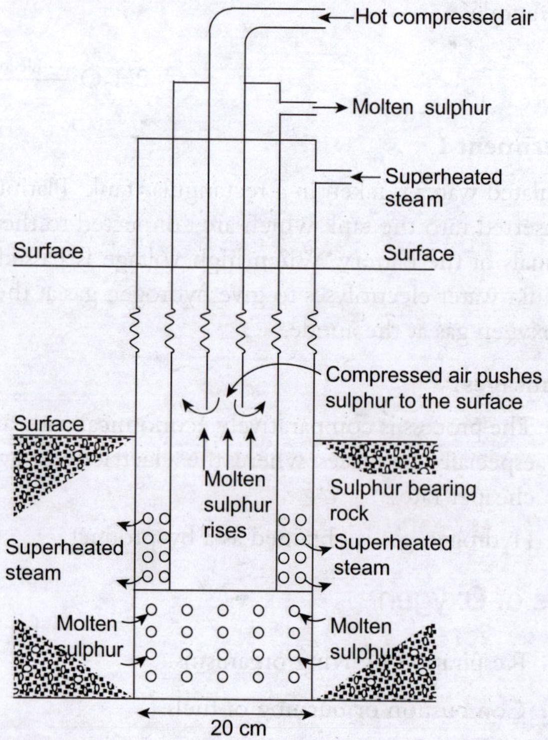

Figure 9.11 The Frasch process for extracting sulphur

Allotropes of Sulphur

Sulphur exists in different allotropic forms. Allotropes have same chemical properties but different physical properties.

The three main allotropic forms of sulphur are the following:

1. Rhombic sulphur
2. Monoclinic sulphur
3. Plastic sulphur

Konnect

Rhombic sulphur and monoclinic sulphur are crystalline, whereas plastic sulphur is amorphous.

Table 9.15 Comparative study of the allotropic forms of sulphur

Parameters	Rhombic sulphur	Monoclinic sulphur	Plastic sulphur
Other names	Octahedral sulphur, alpha-sulphur	Prismatic sulphur, Beta-sulphur	Gamma-sulphur
Preparation	Roll sulphur is dissolved in carbon disulphide. This is allowed to evaporate slowly by slight heating. Rhombic sulphur crystals are left behind	Roll sulphur is heated on an evaporating dish till it melts to pale yellow liquid. This on cooling forms a crust on the surface. Holes are pierced on the crust and the molten sulphur is drained out. Needle shaped sulphur (monoclinic sulphur) crystals are left behind	Roll sulphur is heated to above 300°C till it turns to dark brown, this is poured into cold water and the sulphur formed is plastic sulphur
Color	Pale yellow	Amber	Dark brown
Shape/ structure	Octahedral 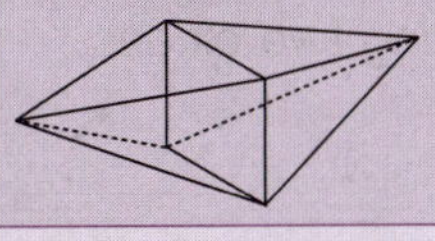	Needle-shaped 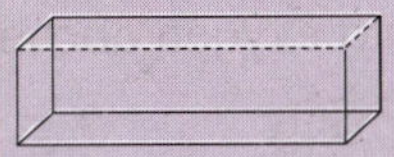	Amorphous
Density	2.08 g/cm^3	1.98 g/cm^3	1.92 g/cm^3
Solubility	Soluble in carbon disulphide	Soluble in carbon disulphide	Insoluble in carbon disulphide
Melting point	112.8°C	119°C	No sharp melting point
Boiling point	Sulphur boils at 444°C		
Conductivity	Sulphur is a bad conductor of heat and electricity		

Rhombic sulphur is the most stable form at normal temperature. Monoclinic sulphur and plastic sulphur change to rhombic form on long standing.

Transition Between Rhombic Sulphur and Monoclinic Sulphur

Rhombic sulphur is stable below 95.6°C and above this temperature, it changes to monoclinic sulphur. Conversely, monoclinic sulphur is stable above 95.6°C, but changes to the rhombic variety below this temperature. Hence, 95.6°C is called transition temperature of these two allotropes of sulphur.

Puckered Ring Structure of Sulphur

Both rhombic and monoclinic sulphur exist in the form of S_8 molecules. These S_8 molecules are in the form of a ring. It forms a crown-shaped molecule with four atoms on the top and four atoms at the bottom (Fig 9.12).

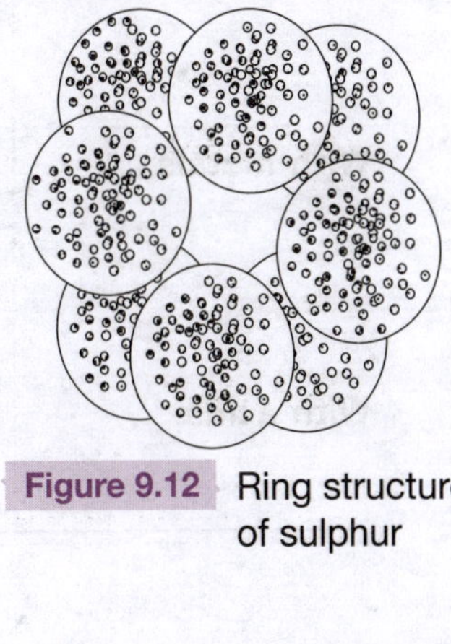

Figure 9.12 Ring structure of sulphur

The rhombic and the monoclinic forms differ in the arrangement of these S_8 puckered rings. In rhombic sulphur, these rings fit snugly into each other while in monoclinic sulphur the rings are stacked one on top of the other.

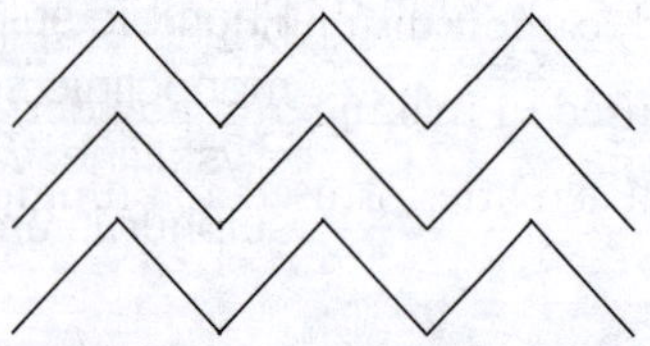

Figure 9.13 Rhombic sulphur

Figure 9.14 Monoclinic sulphur

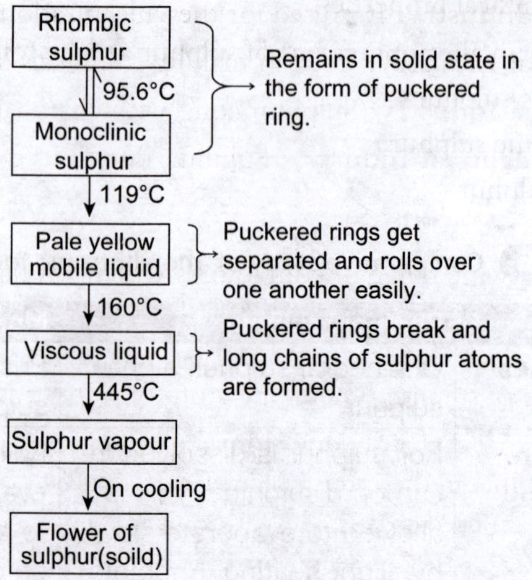

Figure 9.15 Action of heat on sulphur

Chemical Properties

Some chemical properties of sulphur are tabulated below:

Table 9.16 Chemical properties of sulphur

Parameters	Diamond
With non-metals	(i) *Reaction with oxygen* Sulphur reacts with oxygen above 300°C giving two oxides $S + O_2 \xrightarrow{800°C} \underset{\text{(Sulphur dioxide)}}{SO_2}$ $S + O_2 \rightarrow \underset{\text{(Sulphur trioxide)}}{2SO_3}$ (trace amounts) (ii) *Reaction with hydrogen* Boiling sulphur with hydrogen gas evolves a gas with a bad smell $H_2 + S \rightarrow \underset{\text{(Hydrogen sulphide)}}{H_2S}$ (iii) *Reaction with carbon* Sulphur vapors when passed over red hot coke and form carbon disulphide $\underset{\text{(red hot)}}{C} + S \rightarrow \underset{\text{(carbon disulphide)}}{CS_2}\ (l)$
With metals	Sulphur vapors when passed over the heated surface of the metals, give the corresponding metal sulphides: $Zn + S \rightarrow ZnS$ $Fe + S \rightarrow FeS$
With acids	Sulphur is oxidized to sulphuric acid and reduces nitric acid to nitrogen dioxide: $S + HNO_3 \rightarrow H_2SO_4 + 6NO_2 + 2H_2O$

Uses of Sulphur

Sulphur has a wide variety of uses in various industries.

- **Rubber Industry:** It is used for the vulcanization of rubber to make it hard and elastic.
- **Chemical Industry:** Used in making chemicals like sulphuric acid, carbon disulphide, etc.
- **Explosive Industry:** Sulphur along with charcoal and nitrogen is used in making gun powder.
- **Pharmaceutical Industry:** Sulphur, due to its excellent fungicidal activities, is used as a fungicide.

Compounds of Sulphur

Sulphur forms a wide range of compounds which have applications in various fields.

Sulphur Dioxide

This is an oxide of sulphur where one atom of sulphur is associated with two atoms of oxygen.

It is found in exhaust emissions of internal combustion engine, in the industrial areas where coal and petroleum are used as fuels. In nature, it is found in volcanic gases.

Laboratory Preparation of Sulphur Dioxide

Sulphur dioxide is prepared in the laboratory by heating copper turnings with concentrated sulphuric acid:

$$Cu + 2H_2SO_4 \rightarrow CuSO_4 + 2H_2O + SO_2 \uparrow$$

Table 9.17 Physical properties of SO_2

Parameters	Characteristics
Odour	Pungent and suffocating
Taste	Sour
Vapor density	32 (2.2-times heavier than air)
Solubility in water	Fairly soluble
Boiling point	−10°C
Freezing point	−76°C
Physiological nature	Poisonous

Table 9.18 Chemical properties of SO_2

Parameters	Reactions involved
Acidic nature	(i) *Reaction with litmus* Sulphur dioxide is acidic in nature and can change blue litmus to red (ii) *Reaction with water* Sulphur dioxide with water forms unstable sulphurous acid $H_2O + SO_2 \rightarrow H_2SO_3$
Reducing property	Sulphur dioxide when passed through chlorine water reduces the chlorine to hydrogen chloride $SO_2 + Cl_2 + H_2O \rightarrow HCl + H_2SO_4$
Bleaching property	Sulphur dioxide is a good bleaching agent. This on reaction with moisture or water, produces nascent hydrogen which helps in the bleaching action $SO_2 - +H_2O \rightarrow H_2SO_4 + 2[H]$ (reducing agent) The nascent hydrogen produced on being exposed to moisture acts as the bleaching agent. It reduces the colored matter to colorless. This reaction is reversible. The colorless product on exposure to atmospheric oxygen can get oxidized and thus regains its color Colored vegetable + [H] → Colorless product + Water (bleached product)

Hydrogen Sulphide

Hydrogen sulphide gas is well known for its rotten egg smell. In free state, it is present in volcanic gases, water of springs, in the air near and around industrial area.

Although the gas has bad smell and pollutes atmosphere, it is still prepared in the laboratory due to its certain unique properties and uses.

Laboratory Preparation of Hydrogen Sulphide

Principle: Ferrous sulphide on reaction with hydrochloric acid gives ferrous chloride, liberating hydrogen sulphide gas.

$$FeS + 2HCl \rightarrow FeCl_2 + H_2S\uparrow$$

Table 9.19 Physical properties of H_2S

Parameters	Characteristics
Color	Colorless
Odor	Smell of rotten eggs
Taste	Sour taste
Solubility	Fairly soluble in water
Vapor density	17 (1.2-times heavier than air)

Table 9.20 Chemical Properties of H_2S

Parameters	Diamond
Acidic nature	It can change blue litmus to red It reacts with a base to form salt and water $NaOH + H_2S \rightarrow NaHS + H_2O$ (sodium hydrogen) sulphide) $NaOH + NaHS \rightarrow Na_2S + H_2O$ (sodium sulphide)
Reducing Property	(i) *Reaction with oxygen* Hydrogen sulphide undergoes combustion during which it reduces oxygen to water $2H_2S + O_2 \rightarrow 2S + 2H_2O$ It however does not support combustion (ii) *Reaction with chlorine* Chlorine on reaction with hydrogen sulphide is reduced to hydrogen chloride $H_2S + Cl_2 \rightarrow 2HCl\uparrow + S$ (iii) *Reaction with $FeCl_2$* H_2S reduces ferric chloride to ferrous chloride $FeCl_3 + H_2S \rightarrow FeCl_2 + HCl + S$ (iv) *Reaction with acids* H_2S on reaction with conc. H_2SO_4 and HNO_3 reduces these to their respective oxides $H_2SO_4 + H_2S \rightarrow SO_2 + S + 2H_2O$ (conc.) $2HNO_3 + H_2S \rightarrow 2NO_2 + S + 2H_2O$

Uses of Hydrogen Sulphide

The most important application of hydrogen sulphide gas is in analytical chemistry.

Hydrogen sulphide on reaction with aqueous solutions of metal salts converts them to metal sulphides. These metal sulphides are in the form of precipitates. The Color of the precipitate depends upon the nature of metal ion. Therefore, hydrogen sulphide is mainly used for the detection of metal cations present in the metal salts:

$$Pb(NO_3)_2 + H_2S \rightarrow \underset{\text{(Black precipitate)}}{PbS} + 2HNO_3$$

$$CuSO_4 + H_2S \rightarrow \underset{\text{(Black precipitate)}}{CuS} + H_2SO_4$$

$$ZnSO_4 + H_2S \rightarrow \underset{\text{(White precipitate)}}{ZnS} + H_2SO_4$$

$$MnSO_4 + H_2S \rightarrow \underset{\text{(Flesh coloured)}}{MnS} + H_2SO_4$$

Chlorine

Chlorine is not only a member of the halogen family but also considered as the typical halogen. It is diatomic and highly reactive gas. Chlorine generally exists in a combined state rather than in a free state.

Info Bytes!

Chlorine was first synthesized by Scheele and the elemental nature was established by Davy.

Laboratory Method of Preparation

Oxidation of hydrochloric acid: hydrochloric acid on oxidation with MnO_2 or $KMnO_4$ or $K_2Cr_2O_7$ gives chlorine gas. Oxidation of HCl by MnO_2 is the most common method employed for the preparation of chlorine gas in the laboratory.

When manganese dioxide is heated with concentrated HCl. HCl gets oxidized to chlorine gas.

$$MnO_2 + 4HCl \rightarrow MnCl_2 + 2H_2O + Cl_2$$

Physical Properties

Following are the physical properties of chlorine.

Table 9.21 Physical properties of chlorine

Parameters	Characteristics
Color	Greenish Yellow
Odor	pungent smell
Solubility	Sparingly soluble in water
Density	Heavier than air. Vapor density 35.5
Atomicity	2

Chemical Properties

Following are the chemical properties of chlorine.

Table 9.22 Chemical properties of Chlorine

Parameters	Reactions involved
With non-metals	(i) Reaction with phosphorus Chlorine reacts with phosphorous to form phosphorous trichloride which further reacts with chlorine to produce phosphorous pentachloride: $2P + 3Cl_2 \rightarrow 2PCl_3$ $PCl_3 + Cl_2 \rightarrow PCl_5$

(Continued)

Table 9.22 Contd.

Parameters	Reactions involved
	(ii) Reaction with hydrogen Chlorine has a very high affinity towards hydrogen. It reacts with hydrogen to form hydrogen chloride: $H_2 + Cl_2 \rightarrow 2HCl$ Chlorine reacts with hydrogen in hydrocarbon to form carbon and hydrogen chloride: $C_{10}H_{16} + 8Cl_2 \rightarrow 10C + 16HCl$
With metals	Chlorine reacts with most of the metals. $2Na + Cl_2 \rightarrow 2NaCl$ E.g.: burning magnesium ribbon reacts with chlorine gas to form. $MgCl_2$ with the evolution of light energy. $Mg + Cl_2 \rightarrow MgCl_2$
With water	Chlorine dissolves in water forming a mixture of hydrochloric acid and hypochlorous acid. This reaction is responsible for the bleaching action of chlorine since HOCl dissociates giving nascent oxygen: $Cl_2 + H_2O \rightarrow HCl + HOCl$ $HOCl \rightarrow HCl + [O]$

Uses of Chlorine

1. Used in the manufacture of bleaching powder. Bleaching powder is one of the most important compounds of chlorine which is widely used for the purification of drinking water owing to its disinfectant action. It is prepared by treating slaked lime with chlorine gas:

$$Ca(OH)_2 + Cl_2 \rightarrow CaOCl_2 + H_2O$$

2. For bleaching wood pulp, cotton, paper, silk, rayon, etc.
3. For preparing poisonous gas like mustard gas ($ClC_2H_4–S–C_2H_4Cl$), phosgene ($COCl_2$) and tear gas (CCl_3NO_2).
4. In the preparation of hydrochloric acid.
5. In the extraction of metals like platinum, gold, titanium, etc.
6. In the manufacture of chloroform ($CHCl_3$), carbon tetrachloride (CCl_4), dichloro diphenyl trichloroethane (DDT), etc. and also in rubber, plastic and paint industries.
7. In the purification of drinking water.

EXAMPLE 9.7 Bleaching action of SO_2 is reversible. Justify

SOLUTION

Sulphur dioxide on reaction with moisture or water produces nascent hydrogen which helps in the bleaching action.

$$SO_2 + 2H_2O \rightarrow H_2SO_4 + 2[H]$$

The nascent hydrogen produced on being exposed to moisture act as a bleaching agent. It reduces the colored matter to colorless. This reaction is reversible. The Colorless product on exposure to atmospheric oxygen, gets oxidized and thus regains its color. Hence, the bleaching action is reversible in nature.

POINTS TO REMEMBER

- ✔ The solid inorganic compounds found in the earth's crust are called minerals.
- ✔ In certain minerals, the percentage of a particular metal is high and these metals can be extracted from them profitably, and such minerals are called ores.
- ✔ The impurity associated with the ore is called gangue.
- ✔ The process of extraction of metals from their respective ores is called metallurgy.
- ✔ Iron is generally extracted from haematite, limonite and siderite. Among these haematite and limonite are the most preferred ores.
- ✔ The reduction of oxide to metal is carried out with carbon in a blast furnace by the process called smelting.
- ✔ The ore is mixed with coke and limestone approximately in the ratio of 8 : 4 : 1. This mixture is called charge.
- ✔ The iron obtained from this process is called the pig iron. This is not 100 per cent pure and acts as the basic raw material for cast iron and steel.
- ✔ Cast iron is obtained by re-melting pig iron in a vertical furnace called cupola and thereby gets refined.
- ✔ Steel is an alloy of iron with some amount of carbon in it.
- ✔ The process of coating a layer of zinc on the metal is called galvanization.
- ✔ A mixture of 95 per cent oxygen and 5 per cent CO2 is called carbogen.
- ✔ Rhombic sulphur is the most stable form at normal temperature. Monoclinic sulphur and plastic sulphur change to rhombic form on long standing.

OXYGEN

- ✔ Oxygen is the most abundant element in the Earth's crust and the second most abundant gas in the Earth's atmosphere (about 21% by volume).
- ✔ Oxygen is a strong oxidizing agent and is involved in combustion reactions.
- ✔ It exists as a diatomic molecule (O_2) in its elemental form under standard conditions.
- ✔ A triatomic form of oxygen (O_3) that forms a protective layer in the Earth's stratosphere, shielding the planet from harmful ultraviolet (UV) radiation.

NITROGEN

- ✔ Nitrogen is the most abundant gas in the Earth's atmosphere, making up about 78% by volume.
- ✔ It exists as a diatomic molecule (N_2) in its elemental form under standard conditions.
- ✔ Nitrogen is relatively inert under standard conditions due to the strong triple bond between the N atoms in N_2.

PHOSPHOROUS

- ✔ Not found free in nature due to its high reactivity, but is commonly found in the form of phosphate rocks.
- ✔ Phosphorus exists in several allotropes, with the most common being white phosphorus, red phosphorus, and black phosphorus.
- ✔ White phosphorus is highly reactive, especially with oxygen, and can self-ignite at room temperature in air.
- ✔ Phosphorus is a crucial element for life. It's a key component of ATP (adenosine triphosphate), DNA, and bones.

PRACTICE QUESTIONS CLASSROOM WING

Very Short Answer Type Questions

Direction for questions from 1 to 8:
Fill in the blanks.

1. The property exploited in the usage of argon in incandescent light bulbs along with mercury is ______.
2. The impurities that are associated with the ore are called ____________.
3. Non-metals react with oxygen to form __________ or __________ oxides.
4. ________ is the chemical name of bleaching powder.
5. When carbon dioxide is passed through lime water, a milky white precipitate of __________ is formed.
6. Geometry of α-sulphur is __________.
7. During the manufacture of wrought iron, cast iron is taken in a reverberatory furnace and stirred at high temperature and this process is called ________.
8. _________ is an alloy of phosphorous, copper, and tin.

Direction for questions from 9 to 25:
Answer the following questions:

9. Which hydrogen halide gives a scarlet red precipitate with mercuric chloride solution?
10. Which inert gas is used in advertisement signboards?
11. Name a sulphide ore which can be separated by froth floatation.
12. The structure if which phosphorus is given below? Is it used in strike anywhere matches?

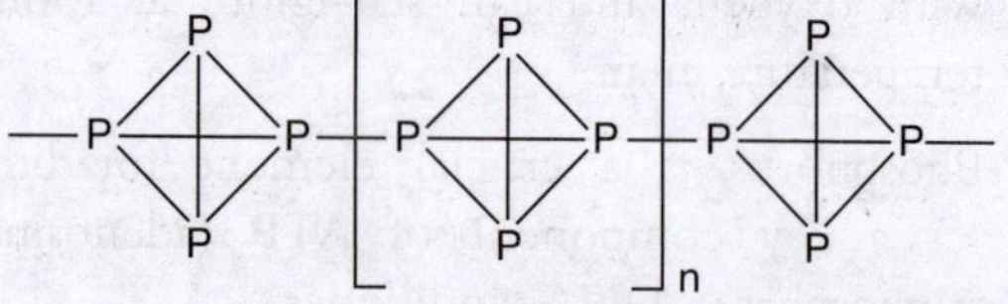

13. Which type of iron is not used for making any article?
14. Which is the purest form of iron? How is it useful?
15. What are the catalysts and promoters used in the manufacture of ammonia during Haber's process?
16. What are the various explosives that can be prepared from ammonia?
17. Discuss three important uses of graphite.
18. How nitric acid reacts with sulphur?
19. What is the color of the precipitate formed when H_2S is made to react with lead nitrate?
20. Write the reaction of sulphuric acid with sodium chloride and potassium nitrate.
21. Explain the acidic nature of sulphur dioxide based on its reactivity with water.
22. Explain the chemical reaction of chlorine with hydrogen sulphide.
23. List the allotropes of phosphorous.
24. What is superphosphate of lime?
25. Write the reaction of phosphorous with chlorine.

Short Answer Type Questions

26. Complete the following table giving a comparison between metals and non-metals.

	Parameters	Metals	Non-metals
1.	Melting point and boiling point		
2.	Conductivity		
3.	Tensile strength		
4.	Density		
5.	Formation of ions		
6.	Formation of oxides		

27. Examine the following reaction: $Cu + H_2SO_4 \rightarrow A + H_2O + SO_2$

Aqueous solution of 'A' on treatment with H_2S forms 'B'. Identify A and B.

28. Which pair of compounds gives pale yellow precipitates with silver nitrate solution?

29. A burning match stick, when introduced into a jar containing NH_3 and O_2, burns with a pale blue flame. Identify one of the products of the reaction.

30. Which method of concentration is inappropriate for an oxide ore?

31. Write the balanced equations for the following preparations:
(i) ammonium sulphate from ammonia
(ii) ammonium phosphate from ammonia

32. Give any two general methods of preparation of hydrogen.

33. During the laboratory method of preparation of hydrogen gas how are the following impurities removed?
(a) PH_3 (b) H_2S
(c) CO_2 (d) H_2O (water vapor)

34. Explain with equations the reaction of sulphur with metals and non-metals.

35. What are the different processes involved in the dressing of ore? Explain.

36. Differentiate between rhombic sulphur and monoclinic sulphur.

37. In industries, chlorine is used in the manufacture of hydrogen chloride. Explain.

38. How is H_2S used as an analytical reagent?

39. Explain the reaction of ammonia with chlorine.

40. How is ore concentrated in the gravity separation process? Explain.

41. How is chlorine gas prepared?

42. State the reactions that take place at the cathode and anode during the process of electrolytic reduction of alumina.

Essay Answer Type Questions

43. Explain how iron is extracted from its various ores, emphasising the differences between haematite, magnetite, and siderite ores. Write down all of the reactions that occur during the extraction process for each type of ore.

44. Once extracted, iron can be alloyed with other elements to improve its properties. Stainless steel is one such alloy, which is created primarily by adding chromium and nickel to iron. Explain the advantages of making this alloy and how the added elements affect the steel's properties and applications.

45. Describe the structure of diamond.

46. Differentiate between white phosphorous and red phosphorous.

47. Compare cast iron, steel, and wrought iron.

48. (a) Extraction of zinc from its ores involves the heating of zinc oxide with wood charcoal which results in the reaction $ZnO + C \rightarrow Zn + CO$. Can wood charcoal be replaced by animal charcoal? Justify.

(b) Which is the most suitable form of charcoal for use as a reducing agent for the extraction of metals? Justify.

PRACTICE QUESTIONS COMPETITION WING

Level 1: Apply your Concepts

Direction for questions from 1 to 9:
State whether the following statements are true or false.

1. Wrought iron is the purest form of iron and is less malleable.
2. Red phosphorus is constituted of chains of tetrahedral units, whereas white phosphorus contains isolated tetrahedral units.
3. Metals react with oxygen only to form basic oxides.
4. Phosphorous reacts with air and forms P_2O_5.
5. Metallic oxides are produced in calcination and roasting.
6. Colorless gas formed by treating phosphorus with NaOH is phosphine.
7. Burning magnesium ribbon continuously burns in nitrogen atmosphere.
8. Process of the extraction of metals from their respective ores is called metallurgy.
9. Non-metals form basic oxides or amphoteric oxides.

Direction for questions from 10 to 20:
Fill in the blanks.

10. During calcination, carbonate ores are converted to ________.
11. In electroplating process the metal to be coated is taken as ________.
12. ________ is used for making shoe polishes.
13. During the purification of hydrogen gas, CO_2 and SO_2 are removed by passing through ______ solution.
14. When carbon dioxide is passed through lime water, a milky white precipitate of ________ is formed.
15. The reduction of metallic oxide in presence of carbon or carbon monoxide in blast furnace is called ________.
16. Silica acts as ________ in the process of extraction of iron from its oxides.
17. In open hearth process for making steel, the final composition of steel is adjusted by adding ________ alloy.
18. Hydrogen sulphide on reacting with aqueous solution of metal salts converts them to ________.
19. Reaction taking place in lower region of blast furnace is associated with ________ of energy.
20. Hardness of steel increases with the increase of ________.

Direction for question 21:
Match the entries in Column A with the appropriate ones in Column B.

21. Match the statements of Column A with those of Column B.

Column A (Substances)	Column B (Uses)
(i) Wood charcoal	(A) Black shoe polishes
(ii) Activated charcoal	(B) Extraction of metal
(iii) Lamp black	(C) Gas masks
(iv) Coke	(D) Removal of colour from sugar cane juice
(v) Animal charcoal	(E) Adsorbent material

Direction for questions from 22 to 46:
For each of the questions, four choices have been provided. Select the correct alternative.

22. **Assertion (A):** Diamond is a better conductor of heat than metals.

    Reason (R): Diamond has no free electrons.

    (a) Both A and R are true and R is the correct explanation of A.
    (b) Both A and R are true, but R is not the correct explanation of A.
    (c) A is true and R is false.
    (d) A is false and R is true.

23. **Assertion (A):** Diamond is a good conductor of heat.
Reason (R): Carbon atoms are very closely packed in diamond.
(a) Both A and R are true and R is the correct explanation of A.
(b) Both A and R are true, but R is not the correct explanation of A.
(c) A is true and R is false.
(d) A is false and R is true.

24. **Assertion (A):** Graphite is a good conductor of electricity.
Reason (R): Graphite has free electrons.
(a) Both A and R are true and R is the correct explanation of A.
(b) Both A and R are true, but R is not the correct explanation of A.
(c) A is true and R is false.
(d) A is false and R is true.

25. Pig iron obtained from blast furnace cannot be used for making tools because
(a) high percentage of impurities decrease malleability
(b) high percentage of impurities increase malleability
(c) low carbon content increases hardness
(d) low carbon content decreases hardness

26. Which of the following is the gaseous product obtained in roasting?
(a) SO_2 (b) O_2
(c) SO_3 (d) H_2S

27. Which of the following reactions does not take place in the smelting process?
(a) $FeO + CO \rightarrow Fe + CO_2$
(b) $CaO + SiO_2 \rightarrow CaSiO_3$
(c) $C + CO_2 \rightarrow 2CO$
(d) $Fe_2O_3.H_2O \rightarrow Fe_2O_3 + H_2O$

28. Which of the following helps in the bleaching action of sulphur dioxide?
(a) H_2 (b) O_2
(c) [H] (d) O

29. Graphite is generally used as a refractory material in electric furnaces because
(a) of its high melting point
(b) it has a layered structure
(c) both (a) and (b)
(d) it is lustrous

30. Reaction: $FeCl_3 + H_2S \rightarrow FeCl_2 + HCl + S$
In the above reaction,
(a) H_2S is the reducing agent
(b) $FeCl_3$ undergo oxidation
(c) H_2S acts as an oxidizing agent
(d) $FeCl_3$ acts as a reducing agent

31. Which would quickly absorb oxygen?
(a) alkaline solution of pyrogallol
(b) lime water
(c) Conc. H_2SO_4
(d) alkaline solution of $CuSO_4$

32. Which of the following changes takes place during the process of calcination of ore?
(a) thermal decomposition of ore takes place
(b) the mass become porous
(c) moisture is removed
(d) all the above

33. Which of the following substance is used as lining in Bessemer converter in case of acidic process?
(a) quick lime (b) silica
(c) slacked lime (d) caustic potash

34. The sulphide ores which involve roasting as one of the steps of extraction are concentrated by certain method. Identify the main principle involved.
(a) adsorption of ore particles to pine oil
(b) specific gravity difference between ore and gangue
(c) attraction of ore or gangue particles towards the magnet
(d) coagulation of gangue particles by the addition of pine oil

35. Which of the following properties of diamond is not attributed to its rigid giant polymeric tetrahedral structure?
(a) good thermal conductivity
(b) good abrasive nature
(c) poor electrical conductivity
(d) both (a) and (b)

36. Which of the following oxides react to form slag in open hearth process?
(a) CaO, CO (b) P_2O_5, CaO
(c) P_2O_5, SiO_2 (d) CaO, CO_2

37. Which of the following negative radical is present in bleaching powder?
(a) hypochlorite (b) chlorate
(c) chloride (d) both (a) and (c)

38. Which of the following compositions is used as a fertilizer?

(a) $CaCN_2 + C$ (b) $CaC_2 + C$
(3) $Ca_3N_2 + C$ (d) $AlN + C$

39. Which of the following salt of calcium is used in the preparation of superphosphate of lime?

(a) $Ca_3(PO_3)_2$ (b) $Ca_3(PO_4)_2$
(c) $Ca(HPO_4)_2$ (d) $CaSO_4$

40. General metallurgical processes are given below. Arrange them in correct sequence.

(1) conversion of ore to oxide
(2) refining
(3) dressing of ore
(4) extraction of metal
(5) concentration of ore

(a) 51423 (b) 35142
(c) 45321 (d) 25341

41. Reactions involved in the smelting of iron in the blast furnace are given below. Arrange them in the correct sequence.

(1) $CaCO_3 \rightarrow CaO + CO_2 + 43$ kcal
(2) $CaO + SiO_2 \rightarrow CaSiO_3$
(3) $C + O_2 \rightarrow CO_2 + 97$ kcal
(4) $CO_2 + C \rightarrow 2CO - 39$ kcal
(5) $FeO/Fe_2O_3 + CO \rightarrow Fe + CO_2$

(a) 34125 (b) 31452
(c) 54321 (d) 23541

42. Different stages involved in the manufacture of hydrogen gas by Bosch process are given below. Arrange them in the correct sequence.

(1) removal of unoxidized CO
(2) preparation of water gas
(3) removal of CO_2
(4) removal of water vapor
(5) removal of CO

(a) 35421 (b) 34215
(c) 25341 (d) 24153

43. Different stages involved in the nitrogen cycle are given below. Arrange them in correct sequence starting from nitrates.

(1) conversion of animal protein to excretory product
(2) conversion of ammonia to nitrites
(3) conversion of plant protein to animal protein
(4) conversion of nitrites to nitrates
(5) conversion of nitrates to plant protein
(6) conversion of excretory product to ammonia

(a) 425163 (b) 324165
(c) 562431 (d) 531624

44. Epsom salt is

(a) $MgSO_4.7H_2O$
(b) $KCl.MgCl_2.6H_2O$
(c) Na_3AlF_6
(d) $CaSO_4.2H_2O$

45. Which of the following reactions takes place in the lower region of a blast furnace?

(a) $CO_2 + C \rightarrow 2CO - 39$ kcal
(b) $C + O_2 \rightarrow CO_2 + 97$ kcal
(c) $FeO + CO \xrightarrow{750\text{–}600°C} Fe + CO_2$
(d) $CaO + SiO_2 \rightarrow CaSiO_3$

46. When ammonia reacts with excess chlorine it forms

(a) $NH_4Cl + N_2$ (b) $N_2 + HCl$
(c) $NOCl + HCl$ (d) $NCl_3 + HCl$

Level 2: Review your Concepts

47. Arrange the following metals in the order of the ores given below.

Epsom salt, anglesite, limonite, cryolite and pitchblende

(A) U (B) Al (C) Pb (D Mg (E) Fe

48. Arrange the following ores in the order of the metals given below.

Metals: Calcium, iron, lead, manganese and thorium

(A) Haematite (B) Pyrolusite
(C) Monazite (D) Gypsum
(E) Galena

49. Certain metallurgical processes for the extraction of a particular metal are mentioned below. Arrange them in proper order.

(A) Gravity separation (B) Smelting
(C) Pulverization (D) Distillation
(E) Roasting

50. Why are diamonds found in coal mines?

51. H_3PO_4 serves as very important intermediate in fertilizer industry. Justify.

52. Why are the metals sodium and potassium not extracted by the electrolysis of their respective salt solutions?

53. In two containers A and B, NH_3 is allowed to react with Cl_2 under suitable conditions. If the gaseous products formed in A responds to litmus test compare the molar ratio of reactants in both the containers and identify the products formed.

54. Among white phosphorous and red phosphorous which is more preferable for use in match sticks? Give reasons in support of your answer.

55. Turpentine oil when exposed to an atmosphere of chlorine ignites with a black sooty flame. Justify.

56. Two solid non-metals X and Y are taken which are used for the purpose of vulcanization of rubber and for use in sugar industry, respectively. A mixture of X, Y, and 'Z,' which is a salt of an alkali metal of corresponding 'ic' acid of nitrogen can explode on heating even in the absence of oxygen. Justify.

57. (a) 'Graphite cannot be used as a lubricant in space.' Give reasons.

(b) During metallurgy of iron, ore, coke and limestone are added to the blast furnace.

(A) What is the role of limestone?

(B) Identify the reducing agent in the extraction of iron during the above process.

(C) Identify the slag formed during the above process.

(D) What are the different gases liberated in this process?

58. X and Y are the elements which belong to VI A, VII A group or 3rd period. Oxide of an element 'X' and element 'Y' act as a bleaching agents in the presence of water. Explain bleaching action of which one is permanent.

59. What are the different reactions taking place in fusion zone of blast furnace and explain how these reactions affect the temperature of the zone.

60. Phosphor bronze is an alloy of copper with 3.5 per cent to 10 per cent of tin and up to 1 per cent of phosphorous. What is the reason for the addition of phosphorous?

61. Iron exposed to moist air for a long time does not liberate hydrogen gas from dilute acids like HCl and H_2SO_4. Explain.

62. Wrought iron is more malleable than cast iron. Give reasons.

63. Metals like platinum, palladium find application in the process of purification of hydrogen. Justify.

64. Mr. John is working in IICT as a scientist. During the synthesis of a drug in the laboratory by his assistant he found that some impurities were associated with the drug. Mr. John dissolved the drug obtained in the solvent and added charcoal to it. This was then filtered off which on evaporation gave back the pure drug. Then the assistant asked Mr. John the following question 'what is the role of charcoal'? What was Mr. John's answer?

65. A group of students in a school were supposed to demonstrate some experiments in a science exhibition to be conducted on the National Science Day. As a part of planning for the above activity, they gathered in the science laboratory and were discussing their ideas. Smith took a beaker of water and a piece of charcoal. He asked his friends to predict whether it will float or sink in the water. Most of them said that it would float and it actually did. He then asked them whether anybody could make it sink in the water. After a few seconds of silence, Andy came forward and said he could do it by boiling the beaker containing water and charcoal. Then all of them were astonished to see the charcoal slowly sinking in the water. Predict the principle involved in the above experiment.

66. An oxide of a non-metal 'X' is the mixed anhydride of two oxy acids. Identify 'X' and the other two oxyacids. Also mention how the oxide is formed from the stable hydride of the same element.

67. (a) Explains the disadvantage of P_2O_5 as a drying agent though it is known to be a good desiccant.

(b) How can P_2O_5 be used in the preparation of SO_3?

68. Carbon dioxide and water vapor present in air moderates the temperature of the earth. Explain.

69. Anhydrides of sulphurous acid and carbonic acid produce milkiness when passed through a solution of the same substance 'X.' When chlorine gas is made to react with the same solution 'X,' it gives a compound 'Y' having disinfectant action. Identify 'Y' and justify its use for the above purpose.

70. (a) Account for the changes observed in the surroundings when carbon dioxide gas comes out of a fire extinguisher.

(b) Although CO_2 is generally used as a material in fire extinguisher it cannot be used to put out fires caused by metals like Na, Mg and K.

71. A practical examination was being conducted for the students. The examiner, in the viva voice, asked Julie the question 'Two salts X and Y are given to you. Salt 'X' is obtained by treating potassium with oxyacid of a non-metal with suffix 'ic' which has seven electrons in the 'M' shell which is the valence shell. Salt 'Y' is formed between lead and oxyacid of a non-metal with five electrons in its valence 'L' shell. Both the salts can give oxygen on thermal decomposition. Which salt do you prefer for the preparation of pure oxygen and why? When she answered the question correctly, examiner was very much impressed and awarded her full marks. What was the answer that Julie gave?

Level 3: Assess Your Concepts

72. With the advances in technology, there have been discussions about 'green steel' produced using hydrogen instead of carbon. How might this impact the traditional blast furnace method, and what are the potential benefits and challenges?

73. If the primary advantage of stainless steel is its resistance to corrosion due to the presence of chromium, how might other elements be incorporated into iron to achieve specific desirable properties, such as greater conductivity or magnetic properties?

74. Rusted iron is washed with phosphoric acid before soldering. Justify.

75. Given the vast amount of steel and iron products in our modern world, how might recycling and repurposing practices play a role in reducing the need for new iron extraction? What challenges and opportunities exist in creating a more circular economy for iron and steel?

76. Burning of coal leads to increase in the acidity of soil. Comment on this statement.

77. Graphite and iodine are the only non-metals possessing lustre which is actually an important attribute of metals. Comment on the statement with proper justification.

78. How does soda water help in digestion of food after overeating?

79. Metals like platinum and palladium find application in the process of purification of hydrogen. Justify.

80. Mr. Paul, who is working for Asian paints, while constructing a house coated the building with white paint. After a few months his friend Mr. Richard who is working in a chemical laboratory visited the house and noticed a few dark patches on the white paint here and there due to which the building lost its original lustre. He advised his friend to try for restoration of lustre by washing with hydrogen peroxide. Justify the role of hydrogen peroxide.

81. 'Metals are good thermal conductors and electrical conductors.' How the above said properties vary in case of diamond and graphite, which are allotropes of the non-metallic element carbon?

82. The electronic configuration of five metals are given below:

A → 2, 8, 18, 2
B → 2, 8, 14, 2
C → 2, 8, 18, 32, 18, 4
D → 2, 8, 18, 1
E → 2, 8, 13, 2

How is it possible to identify the bivalent and trivalent (if existing) ions of the given metals using the following reagent?

(a) NH_4OH (b) H_2S

AT

PRACTICE QUESTIONS JEE-NEET SPECIAL WING

Multiple-Answer Type Questions

Directions for questions 1 to 5:
Select one or more correct alternative(s) from the given choices.

1. A compound X on thermal decomposition produces 2 solid products A and B along with a gaseous component, oxygen. 'A' on the addition of concentrated hydrochloric acid results in the release of a greenish yellow coloured gas with pungent odour. Identify the statements which comply with the reactions in this activity.
   (a) The gram molecular mass of 'X' would be 158.
   (b) 'B' is constituted of the ions or radicals which are monovalent
   (c) 2.5 mol X taken initially required 5 mol concentrated HCl for the second reaction
   (d) 1 mole 'X' on complete reaction produces greenish yellow gas which occupies 11.2L volume at STP.

2. If the iron coming out of blast furnace nearly weighs 0.56 ton, which among the following would be the predictable quantities of various components of charge are correct?
   (a) Ore containing 0.8 tone Ferric oxide.
   (b) 400 kg coke.
   (c) 100 kg limestone.
   (d) 0.8 ton coke and limestone mixture

3. The preparation methods and uses of the amorphous allotropes of carbon are given below. Choose the correctly matched sets among those.

	Preparation method	Important use
(a)	Heating coal in the absence of air	Decolourisation of sugarcane juice in manufacture of sugar
(b)	Heating of wood shavings in the absence of air	Gas masks
(c)	Destructive distillation of bone powder	Extraction of yellow phosphorus
(d)	Burning of turpentine oil	Tyre manufacture

4. Two reactions X and Y are considered.
   Reaction X: One mole sample of pure ammonia is subjected to combustion with 1 mole oxygen in the absence of any catalyst.
   Reaction Y: One mole ammonia of the same sample is subjected to heating with 1 mole of chlorine gas.
   The common product obtained in these two reaction vessels is collected separately. Identify the statements which comply with the above activity.
   (a) The amount of the common product in reaction X is 4 times that in reaction Y
   (b) The common product burns with a blue flame
   (c) The other product obtained are in equimolar proportions in the reactions X and Y
   (d) Same number of moles of the reactant is left behind in both the reaction vessels.

5. A sample of ammonia is subjected to burning with oxygen under suitable conditions in the presence of platinum catalyst. The product obtained (P) is subjected to oxidation to give a substance 'Q'. Identify the statements which comply with this reaction.
   (a) 'Q' is a mixed anhydride of the oxyacids of nitrogen
   (b) 'Q' is also obtained as the product of thermal decomposition of potassium nitrate
   (c) 'Q' usually exists as a dimer.
   (d) 'P' is colourless while 'Q' has characteristic colour and odour

Comprehension-Based Questions

Directions for questions 6 to 9:

Based on the information given in the following table, answer the questions given.

A list of ores and their names/formulae is given in the following table.

Metal	Ore	Formula
Magnesium	Dolomite	$CaCO_3.MgCO_3$
Lead	Galena	PbS
Zinc	Calamine	$ZnCO_3$
Mercury	Cinnabar	HgS
Iron	Siderite	$FeCO_3$
Calcium	Fluorspar	CaF_2
Aluminium	Bauxite	$Al_2O_3.2H_2O$

6. Identify the ores which are concentrated by froth flotation method.

(a) Galena (b) Calamine
(c) Bauxite (d) Cinnabar

7. The metal obtained from which ore is purified by heating the impure metal strongly at its boiling point?

(a) Fluorspar (b) Cinnabar
(c) Dolomite (d) Both (a) and (b)

8. Electrolysis is employed for extraction of metals from some ores. Identify the ores.

(a) Cinnabar (b) Fluorspar
(c) Bauxite (d) Galena

9. Calcination and roasting are the methods employed for the conversion of ore to oxide form which is subjected to reduction with the suitable reducing agents to obtain the metals. Which among the following ores are subjected to calcination?

(a) Siderite (b) Dolomite
(c) Calamine (d) Galena

Directions for questions 10 to 14:

Based on the information given below, answer the following questions.

Important reactions of some elements are given below. Answer the questions given below based on the given reactions.

(i) The metal 'M' reacts with steam to form the oxide of the formula M_xO_y.

$M + H_2O \text{ (steam)} \rightarrow M_xO_y + H_2$

(ii) The metal 'N' reacts with potassium hydroxide solution to liberate hydrogen gas

$N + KOH + 2H_2O \rightarrow KNO_2 + 3H_2O$

(iii) A nonmetal X undergoes the following reaction.

$X + NaOH + H_2O \rightarrow XH_3 + NaH_2XO_2$

(iv) The oxide of the metal 'P' reacts with the higher oxide of the nonmetal 'X' of the above reaction forming a compound 'Y'.

10. The metal M shows a fast reaction with steam and the reaction takes place to completion.

Identify the electronic configuration of the metal M.

(a) 2, 8, 18, 2 (b) 2, 8, 8, 2
(c) 2, 8, 2 (d) 2, 8, 14, 2

11. If the metal 'N' belongs to 4th period in the periodic table, what would be the name of the product formed in the reaction (ii)?

(a) Potassium plumbite
(b) Potassium meta-aluminate
(c) Potassium stannate
(d) Potassium zincate

12. If the nonmetal 'X' of the reaction (iii) forms a compound with the metal mentioned in reaction (ii), identify the true statements regarding the compound.

(a) It is used for testing the presence of nitrogen.
(b) It is used as rat poison.
(c) It is used as a bleaching agent.
(d) It is the component of human body.

13. If the metal 'M' mentioned in reaction (i) reacts with wateralso but not violently, the oxide formed in that reaction is made to react with the higher oxide of the nonmetal X given in reaction(iv), what would be the number of atoms present in 1 mole of the product 'Y' formed at the end of the reaction?

(a) 13 (b) 6
(c) 17 (d) 8

14. If the metal 'M' is a non-transition metal and the product formed contains around 53% metal, identify the statement which does not comply with the product of the reaction.

(a) One mole of the compound contains 48 g oxygen.
(b) The compound undergoes thermal decomposition to form the metal.
(c) The compound can react with acid and alkali.
(d) The compound is almost insoluble in water.

Match the Column

15. Observe the metal reactivity series given below. Match the entries in column I with those in column II.

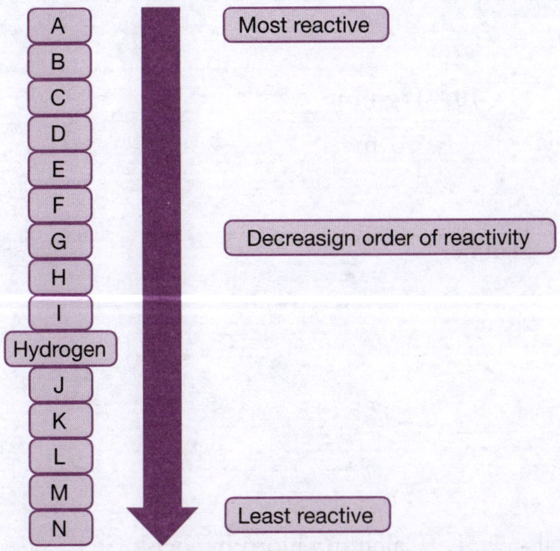

Column I Metal		Column II Characteristic feature	
(a)	I	(i)	Hydride of formula MH
(b)	K	(ii)	Forms a binary compound of the formula M_2N_3 with nitrogen
(c)	J	(iii)	Reacts with sodium hydroxide to form $NaMO_2$
(d)	B	(iv)	Metal oxide reduced by strong heating for the extraction of metal
(e)	D	(v)	Oxide reduced by ammonia to form a colourless gas which burns with blue flame

Directions for question 16:

The percentage composition of a compound gives the percentage of each element present in the compound. This can be calculated by using the concept of molecular mass. Since the molecular mass is the sum of the atomic weights of all the elements in the molecule, the amount of an element in 100 g of the substance can be calculated.

Percentage of an element =

$$\frac{\text{Gram atomic mass} \times \text{No. of atoms of the element in a molecule} \times 100}{\text{Gram molecular mass of the compound}}$$

16. Match the entries in column I with those in column II. Consider only higher oxides of the given metals.

Column I Oxide of Metal		Column II Percentage of oxygen	
(a)	Iron	(i)	26
(b)	Magnesium	(ii)	47
(c)	Sodium	(iii)	20
(d)	Aluminium	(iv)	30
(e)	Copper	(v)	40

ANSWER KEYS

Crossword

Across

5. Carbogen
6. Nitrobacter bacteria
9. Neon
10. Pig iron
12. Red phosphorus
14. Sulphur
15. Ammonia

Down

1. Oxygen
2. Fire extinguisher
3. Vulcanized rubber
4. Metallurgy
7. Rusting
8. Adsorption
11. Chlorine
13. Diamond

Classroom Wing

Very Short Answer Type Questions

1. Tungsten
2. Gangue
3. Acidic, neutral
4. Calcium chloro hypochlorite
5. Calcium carbonate
6. octahedral
7. puddling
8. Phosphobronze

Competition Wing

Level 1: Apply your Concepts

1. False
2. True
3. False
4. True
5. True
6. True
7. True
8. True
9. False
10. Oxide
11. Cathode
12. Lampblack
13. KOH
14. calcium carbonate
15. smelting
16. flux
17. ferrosilicon and/or ferromanganese
18. metallic sulphides
19. release
20. carbon content
21. (i) → (C); (ii) → (E); (iii) → (A); (iv) → (B); (v) → (D)
22. (b)
23. (a)
24. (a)
25. (a)
26. (a)
27. (d)
28. (c)
29. (a)
30. (a)
31. (a)
32. (d)
33. (b)
34. (a)
35. (c)
36. (b)
37. (d)
38. (a)
39. (b)
40. (b)
41. (a)
42. (c)
43. (d)
44. (a)
45. (b)
46. (d)

JEE Special Wing

Multiple-Answer Type Questions

1. (a; c)
2. (a; b, c)
3. (b; c; d)
4. (a; b)
5. (a; c; d)

Comprehension-Based Question

6. (a; d)
7. (b)
8. (b; c)
9. (a; b; c)
10. (c)
11. (d)
12. (b)
13. (a)
14. (b)

Match the Column

15. (a) ↔ (iii); (b) ↔ (iv); (c) ↔ (v); (d) ↔ (i); (e) ↔ (ii)
16. (a) ↔ (iv); (b) ↔ (v); (c) ↔ (i); (d) ↔ (ii); (e) ↔ (iii)

Hints and Explanations

Classroom Wing

Very Short Answer Type Question

1. The property exploited is the prevention of oxidation of tungsten.
2. Gangue
3. Acidic, neutral
4. Calcium chlorohypochlorite
5. Calcium carbonate
6. octahedral
7. puddling
8. Phosphobronze
9. $2HI + HgCl_2 \rightarrow 2HCl + \underset{\text{Scarlet red}}{HgI_2\downarrow}$
10. Neon is used in advertisement signboards.
11. Cinnabar is a sulphide ore and can be concentrated by froth floatation.
12. The given structure indicates red phosphorus. Red phosphorus is not used in strike anywhere matches.
13. Since pig iron is brittle in nature, it cannot be used for making any article.
14. Wrought iron, chains, bolts etc
15. Fe, Mo
16. Ammonal (NH_4NO_3 + Al powder), Amatol (NH_4NO_3 + 20% T.N.T)
17. Leads of pencils, moderator in nuclear reactors, making refractory crucibles
18. $S + HNO_3 \rightarrow H_2SO_4 + 6NO_2 + 2H_2O$
19. Black precipitate
20. $H_2SO_4 + 2NaCl \rightarrow Na_2SO_4 + 2HCl$
    $H_2SO_4 + 2KNO_3 \rightarrow K_2SO_4 + 2HNO_3$
21. $SO_2 + H_2O \rightarrow H_2SO_3$
22. $H_2S + Cl_2 \rightarrow 2HCl\uparrow + S$
23. White and red phosphorous
24. $Ca(H_2PO_4)_2H_2O + 2CaSO_4 \rightarrow 2H_2O$
25. $2P + 3Cl_2 \rightarrow 2PCl_3$; $PCl_3 + Cl_2 \rightarrow PCl_5$

Short Answer Type Questions

26. (i) High, low
    (ii) Good conductors, Bad conductors
    (iii) High, No tensile strength
    (iv) High, low
    (v) cations, anions
    (vi) basic or amphoteric, acidic or neutral
27. $CuSO_4 + H_2S \rightarrow CuS\downarrow + H_2SO_4$. A is Copper sulphate and B is Black precipitate.
28. $\underset{(aq)}{NaBr} + \underset{(aq)}{AgNO_3} \rightarrow \underset{\text{Pale yellow precipitate}}{AgBr\downarrow} + NaNO_3$.
    $\underset{(aq)}{NaI} + \underset{(aq)}{AgNO_3} \rightarrow \underset{\text{Pale yellow precipitate}}{AgI\downarrow} + NaNO_3$.
29. One of the products is N_2.
30. Froth floatation method of concentration is inappropriate for an oxide ore.
31. (i) $2NH_3 + H_2SO_4 \rightarrow (NH_4)_2SO_4$
    (ii) $NH_3 + H_3PO_4 \rightarrow (NH_4)_3PO_4$
32. General methods of preparation of hydrogen are:
    (a) Action of active metals with cold water
    (b) Action of steam on hot metals
33. (a) PH_3 can be removed by using silver nitrate solution.
    (b) H_2S can be removed by using lead nitrate solution.
    (c) CO_2 can be removed by using caustic potash.
    (d) Water vapor can be removed by $CaCl_2$ or P_2O_5.
34. Boiling sulphur with hydrogen gas evolves a gas with a bad smell.
    Sulphur vapors when passed over red hot coke and forms carbon disulphide.
    Sulphur vapors when passed over the heated surface of the metals, give the corresponding metal sulphides.
35. The ores are in the form of huge rocks. In this process, the rocks are broken down into small pieces and ground to powder. This powdered form of ore is used for further metallurgical processes.

36. Refer table 9.15 on page 9.26
   (i) Preparation
   (ii) Color
   (iii) Structure/shape
   (iv) Melting, boiling points
   (v) Density

37. Hydrogen chloride is widely used in the chemical industry as a reagent in the manufacture of other chemicals.

38. Hydrogen sulphide on reaction with aqueous solutions of metal salts converts them to metal sulphides.

These metal sulphides are in the form of precipitates. The color of the precipitate depends upon the nature of metal ion. Therefore, hydrogen sulphide is mainly used for the detection of metal cations present in the metal salts

39. Color of product (precipitate)

40. The ores in which the specific gravity difference between the ore and gangue is high, are concentrated by gravity separation. This is generally applicable for iron ore. The ore is taken on a sloping table with ridges and washed with water. The water washes away the lighter gangue particles leaving behind the concentrated ore. This method of separation is applicable to all types of ores except sulphide ores.

41. $MnO_2 + 4HCl \rightarrow MnCl_2 + 2H_2O + Cl_2$

Essay Answer Type Questions

43. Iron is primarily extracted from three main types of ores: Haematite (Fe_2O_3), magnetite (Fe_3O_4), and siderite ($FeCO_3$).

Haematite (Fe_2O_3): Haematite is the most commonly used ore for iron extraction due to its high iron content. Reactions during extraction:

At high temperatures	*Using carbon monoxide as a reducing agent*
$Fe_2O_3 + 3C \rightarrow 2Fe + 3CO$	$Fe_2O_3 + 3CO \rightarrow 2Fe + 3CO_2$

Magnetite (Fe_3O_4): Magnetite contains even more iron than haematite and is sometimes used as an ore. Reactions during extraction:

At high temperatures	*Using carbon monoxide as a reducing agent*
$Fe_3O_4 + 4C \rightarrow 3Fe + 4CO$	$Fe_3O_4 + 4CO \rightarrow 3Fe + 4CO_2$

Siderite ($FeCO_3$): Siderite is an iron carbonate which is not as commonly used because of its lower iron content and the presence of impurities. Reactions during extraction:

Calcination to produce FeO	*Reduction of FeO at high temperatures*
$FeCO_3 \rightarrow FeO + CO_2$	$FeO + C \rightarrow Fe + CO$

44. Stainless steel is an alloy created by combining iron with chromium (and sometimes nickel). The incorporation of these elements has the following advantages:

Corrosion Resistance: The main advantage of stainless steel is its resistance to rust or staining. Chromium reacts with oxygen in the air to form a thin layer of chromium oxide, which acts as a protective layer against rusting.

Increased Hardness: The addition of other elements can make the steel harder and more resistant to wear and tear.

Non-reactive: The steel becomes less reactive with foods or products, making it suitable for kitchen utensils, medical instruments, and more.

Improved Aesthetics: Stainless steel has a shiny, mirror-like appearance which is aesthetically pleasing and often used in decorative and architectural applications.

Nickel's Role: When added, nickel can further improve the corrosion resistance, especially against certain chemicals. It also enhances the metal's ductility.

Reaction for formation of the protective layer:

$$2Cr + 3O_2 \rightarrow Cr_2O_3$$

This chromium oxide layer is self-healing, which means that if it is scratched or damaged, a new layer of oxide forms, protecting the iron beneath from corrosion.

Overall, the addition of chromium and nickel to iron to create stainless steel gives it properties that make it a versatile material that can be used in a variety of applications.

45. Diamond has a regular tetrahedral arrangement. This is due to the bonding of each atom of carbon with four other carbon atoms covalently, forming a single unit of crystal. These crystal units lie in different planes accounting for a rigid three-dimensional structure.

46. Refer table 9.11 on page no. 9.22 for detailed answer.
   (i) State
   (ii) Color
   (iii) Odor
   (iv) Melting, boiling points
   (v) Physiological nature
   (vi) Atomicity
   (vii) Structure

47. Wrought iron is the purest form of iron. Its carbon content is least. Hence, it is highly malleable, whereas cast iron has relatively more carbon content along with other impurities. Hence, it is less malleable.

48. (a) Since animal charcoal contains trace amounts of organic matter and large proportion of calcium phosphate, it cannot be used as a reducing agent in the extraction of metals like zinc.

   (b) Sugar charcoal is the most suitable form of charcoal for being used as a reducing agent for the extraction of metals as sugar charcoal is the purest form of amorphous allotrope of carbon. It is prepared by destructive distillation of sugar. During the process, sugar loses water and gets converted to pure carbon that is sugar charcoal.

   It contains only about 10% carbon, the remaining being calcium and magnesium phosphates (80%) and other inorganic material originally present in the bones.

Competition Wing

Level 1: Apply your Concepts

1. False, wrought iron is the purest form of iron and is more malleable.

2.

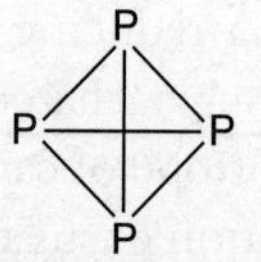

White phosphorus, isolated tetrahedral P_4 units

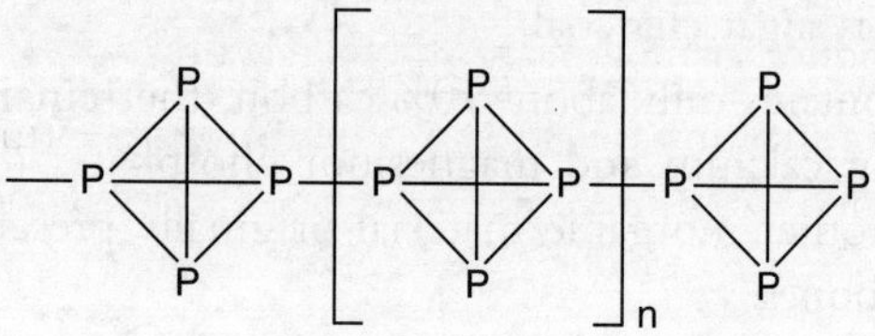

True.

Red phosphorus. Chain of tetrahedral P_4 units linked to each other by P–P bonds.

21 (i) Wood charcoal — (C) Gas masks
(ii) Activated charcoal — (E) Adsorbent material
(iii) Lamp black — (A) Black shoe polishes
(iv) Coke — (B) Extraction of metal
(v) Animal charcoal — (D) Removal of colour from sugarcane juice

Hence, the answer is (i) → (C); (ii) → (E); (iii) → (A); (iv) → (B); (v) → (D).

22. Diamond crystals have a very regular arrangement. The forces binding the atoms together are strong and the atoms are close to each other. Hence, they can easily transfer vibratory motion from one atom to the next.
Hence, the correct option is (b).

23. Since carbon atoms are very closely packed in a diamond, it is a good conductor of heat.
Hence, the correct option is (a).

24. Each carbon atom in graphite is attached to three other carbon atoms, forming a planar structure. Many such planar rings attach themselves to form a hexagonal-layered structure. Each carbon is attached to three other carbon atoms and one electron is left behind, which is responsible for the conductivity.
Hence, the correct option is (a).

40. 3 dressing of ore
5 concentration of ore
1 conversion of ore to oxide
4 extraction of metal
2 refining
Hence, the correct answer is (b).

41. 3 $C + O_2 \rightarrow CO_2 + 97$ kcal
4 $CO_2 + C \rightarrow 2CO - 39$ kcal
1 $CaCO_3 \rightarrow CaO + CO_2 + 43$ kcal
2 $CaO + SiO_2 \rightarrow CaSiO_3$
5 $FeO/Fe_2O_3 + CO \rightarrow Fe + CO_2$
Hence, the correct answer is (a).

42. 2 preparation of water gas
5 removal of CO
3 removal of CO_2
4 removal of water vapor
1 removal of unoxidized CO
Hence, the correct answer is (c).

43. 5 conversion of nitrates to plant protein
3 conversion of plant protein to animal protein
1 conversion of animal protein to excretory product
6 conversion of excretory product to ammonia
2 conversion of ammonia to nitrites
4 conversion of nitrites to nitrates
Hence, the correct answer is (d).

44. Epsom salt is $MgSO_4 . 7H_2O$
Hence, the correct answer is (a).

45. Combustion of carbon takes place in lower region of blast furnace.

$$C + O_2 \rightarrow CO_2 + 97 \text{ kcal}$$

Hence, the correct answer is (b).

46. $NH_3 + 3Cl_2 \rightarrow NCl_3 + 3HCl$
(excess)
Hence, the correct answer is (d).

Level 2: Review your Concepts

47. Ore of Mg is Epsom salt; ore of Pb is anglesite; ore of Fe is limonite; ore of Al is cryolite; and ore of U is pitchblende.

Hence, the correct order is DCEBA.

48.

Metal	Ore
Calcium	Gypsum
Iron	Haematite
Lead	Galena
Manganese	Pyrolusite
Thorium	Monazite

Hence, the correct order is DAEBC.

49. (A) Pulverization (B) Gravity separation
(C) Roasting (D) Smelting
(E) Distillation

Hence, the correct order is CAEBD.

50. (i) composition and conditions in coal mines
(ii) conditions necessary for the formation of diamonds
(iii) Comparison of conditions in coal mines and conditions necessary for diamond formation.

51. (i) reaction of H_3PO_4 with mineral phosphate and ammonia
(ii) composition of phosphate rock
(iii) solubility of the major component of the phosphate rock
(iv) reaction between H_3PO_4 and the above component
(v) solubility of the product formed
(vi) reaction between H_3PO_4 and ammonia
(vii) soluble nature of the product formed

52. (i) electropositivity
(ii) ions formed during electrolysis of aqueous salt solution
(iii) Fate of ions after formation
(iv) discharge of ions at the respective electrodes

53. (i) comparison of products obtained in different conditions
(ii) identification of the products formed in A and B
(iii) comparison of the amount of chlorine reacted with ammonia in A and in B
(iv) balanced chemical equations of the above two reactions
(v) calculation of molar ratio of the reactants in the above reactions

54. (i) comparison of structure of white phosphorous and red phosphorous
(ii) comparison of ignition temperature of white phosphorous and red phosphorous
(iii) relating ignition temperature to usage as match sticks

55. (i) composition of turpentine
(ii) reaction of chlorine with one of the components of turpentine oil
(iii) product formed in the above reaction
(iv) identification of the constituent of turpentine oil which is responsible for the black sooty flame

56. (i) identification of X, Y, and salt Z
(ii) effect of heat on Z
(iii) nature of the products formed
(iv) reaction of the gaseous product with X and Y
(v) change in pressure and heat content due to above reactions

57. (a) (i) layered structure of graphite
(ii) factors that make graphite act as a lubricant
(iii) conditions in space
(iv) relate conditions in space to factors that help graphite to act as a lubricant

(b) (A) Limestone ($CaCO_3$) undergoes thermal decomposition and gives CaO and CO_2. CaO acts as flux.

(B) Carbon monoxide acts as the reducing agent.

$FeO + CO \rightarrow Fe + CO_2$

$Fe_2O_3 + 3CO \rightarrow 2Fe + 3CO_2$

(C) CaO reacts with impurity SiO_2 and forms slag $CaSiO_3$.

$CaO + SiO_2 \rightarrow CaSiO_3$.

(D) $C + O_2 \rightarrow CO_2(g)$

$CO_2 + C \rightarrow 2CO\ (g)$

$CaCO_3 \rightarrow CaO + CO_2\ (g)$

$FeO + CO \rightarrow Fe + CO_2\ (g)$

$Fe_2O_3 + 3CO \rightarrow 2Fe + 3CO_2\ (g)$

CO_2 gas is liberated. CO gas is formed, but takes part in the process of reduction of Fe_2O_3 and forms CO_2.

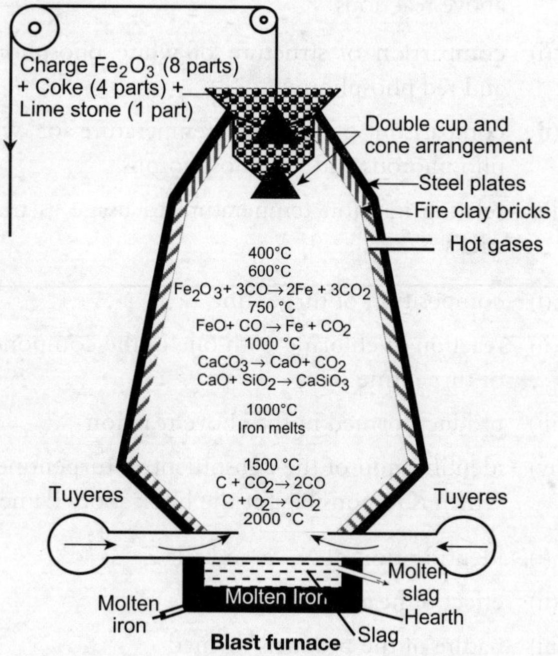

58. (i) identification of X and Y
(ii) identification of oxide of X
(iii) comparison of process of bleaching by Y and that by oxide of X
(iv) comparison of nature of products
(v) effect of atmospheric oxygen on the products

59. (i) reactions associated with energy changes
(ii) change in energy that is involved in the reactions taking place in fusion zone
(iii) effect of this change in energy on the temperature of this zone

60. (i) bonds formed in the alloy
(ii) reactivity of phosphorous with metals
(iii) nature of products formed
(iv) effect of these products on the physical properties of the alloy

61. When iron is exposed to moist air for a long time rust formation takes place, i.e., iron gets converted to $Fe_2O_3.xH_2O$ and hence, iron does not liberate hydrogen gas from dil acids like HCl and H_2SO_4.

62. Wrought iron is the purest form of iron. Its carbon content is least. Hence, it is highly malleable, whereas cast iron has relatively more carbon content along with other impurities. Hence, it is less malleable.

63. Metals like platinum, palladium adsorb hydrogen on their surfaces. When the metal is heated after adsorption, hydrogen gas is expelled. Since other impurities do not get adsorbed, pure hydrogen can be obtained through this process.

64. Charcoal has good adsorbing properties. When charcoal is added, it adsorbs the impurities, and when filtered, the impurities are separated from charcoal.

65. Charcoal is porous in nature and air is present in the pores of charcoal. So in the first case it floats on the water. In the second case, on boiling air escapes from its pores and hence, its density becomes more thus, it sinks in the water.

66. The oxide of nitrogen which is a mixed anhydride of its oxyacids is NO_2. The oxyacids are HNO_2 and HNO_3. NO_2 can be obtained from the stable hydride NH_3 by its reaction with oxygen:

$$4NH_3 + 5O_2 \xrightarrow[900°C]{Pt} 4NO + 6H_2O$$

$$2NO + O_2 \rightarrow 2NO_2$$

67. (a) P_2O_5 is a solid and is a good desiccant since it can absorb moisture from other substances. However, on absorbing moisture, P_2O_5 forms H_3PO_4 which forms a layer on the surface. As a result of this, its desiccating ability decreases and hence, its use for drying is limited.
(b) P_2O_5 is a strong dehydrating agent and hence, removes water molecules from inorganic compounds. H_2SO_4 and HNO_3 are converted into their corresponding anhydrides:

$$2H_2SO_4 + P_4O_{10} \rightarrow 2SO_3 + 4HPO_3$$

68. Air plays a very important role in keeping the temperature of the earth within a certain range. This happens as a result of a phenomenon known as the greenhouse effect. The CO_2 and water Vapor of air are transparent to the visible radiation of the sun that warms the earth's surface during day time. The radiated IR radiation by earth is trapped by water Vapor and CO_2 which maintains the temperature even during night time. The heat is trapped which keeps the earth warm even during the night. Had there been no CO_2 in the air, the night would have been abnormally cold and life would not have existed on earth.

69. Anhydrides of sulphurous acid and carbonic acid are SO_2 and CO_2, respectively. They produce milkiness on passing through a solution of $Ca(OH)_2$. When Cl_2 gas is made to react with $Ca(OH)_2$, $CaOCl_2$ (bleaching powder) is formed. Bleaching power on dissociation in water gives $Ca(OH)_2$, HCl and HOCl. Hypochlorous

acid being unstable decomposes to HCl and nascent oxygen which is responsible for bleaching action:

$$CaOCl_2 + H_2O \rightarrow Ca(OH)_2 + HCl + HOCl$$

$$HOCl \rightarrow HCl + [O]$$

70. (a) Carbon dioxide comes out with great force through a small nozzle from soda acid fire extinguisher. Sudden expansion of CO_2 takes place which leads to reduction in temperature of the carbon dioxide to a great extent and moisture present in air condenses on the carbon dioxide molecules and appears like fog.

(b) Na, Mg and K metals continue to burn in atmosphere of CO_2. It is due to fact that these active metals get oxidized by CO_2 to form respective oxides.

71. Non-metal with seven electrons in its valence shell (M shell) is chlorine. The salt which gives oxygen on thermal decomposition should be an alkali metal chlorate. Non-metal with 5 electrons in its valence shell (L shell) should be nitrogen and the salt which can give oxygen on decomposition should be nitrate. Alkali metal chlorate gives only pure oxygen gas, whereas bivalent, i.e., lead metal nitrate gives a mixture of oxygen and NO_2. Since it is difficult to separate O_2 from this mixture, the first one is a preferred method to get pure O_2 gas.

Level 3: Assess Your Concepts

72. Traditional iron and steel production relies heavily on carbon-based reducing agents, primarily coke. When carbon reacts with iron ore (such as hematite, Fe_2O_3), it converts the ore to iron while also producing carbon dioxide, a greenhouse gas that contributes to global warming.

A novel approach to steel production known as 'green steel' has recently gained popularity. Instead of carbon, hydrogen gas is proposed as a reducing agent. When hydrogen reacts with iron ore, it produces water vapour (rather than carbon dioxide) and iron. From an environmental standpoint, this is extremely promising because the primary emission is only water.

The reactions would look something like this:

$$Fe_2O_3 + 3H_2 \rightarrow 2Fe + 3H_2O$$

However, difficulties do exist. It is very difficult to get pure 'green hydrogen' as the hydrogen used in this process must be produced using renewable energy sources (i.e., from solar energy or wind energy), which is often referred to as 'green hydrogen.' Current hydrogen production relies primarily on natural gas, which emits carbon dioxide. There is also a need to upgrade or build new infrastructure to support this hydrogen-based steel production, which will necessitate significant investments.

73. Alloying is similar to cooking in that different metals can change the taste and texture of iron; just as different ingredients can change the taste and texture of a dish. Pure iron, for example, is soft and rusts easily. However, by adding a small amount of carbon, we obtain steel, which is much harder. When we talk about stainless steel, the main alloying element that is added to iron is chromium. Chromium reacts with air to form a thin layer of chromium oxide on the surface of the steel. This layer protects against rust. That is why stainless steel is used in cutlery; it does not rust and is food-safe. Another example is iron alloying with silicon. Silicon can enhance the magnetic properties of iron, making it more suitable for use in transformers or electric motors. We want the core of a transformer to easily magnetise and demagnetize as the electric current changes, and silicon aids in this.

74. (i) comparison of ignition temperatures
(ii) surface of metals to be soldered
(iii) reactivity of phosphoric acid with rust, impurities
(iv) products formed and nature of products

75. Our planet has limited resources, which are gradually depleting as we continue to extract and use them. A 'circular economy' is a concept in which we strive to reduce waste and make the best use of our resources. Instead of the traditional linear approach of extracting, using, and discarding, it's more like a circle in which products are used, recycled, and then reused. Steel is an ideal material for a circular economy. It is 100 percent recyclable, which means it can be melted down and reused without losing quality. We save energy and resources by recycling steel instead of extracting iron ore, processing it, and refining it into new steel. In fact, recycling steel consumes 75% less energy than producing it from raw materials. Setting up efficient collection, sorting, and recycling processes is the challenge. Contaminants or other metals that have been mixed with steel must be separated, and recycled steel must meet specific quality standards. The environmental benefits, on the other hand, are enormous.

76. (i) composition of coal
(ii) origin of coal
(iii) reactivity of various components of coal when burnt

(iv) product formed by these components

(v) reactivity of these components with water (rain)

77. The reason behind the lustre of metals is the presence of free electrons which undergo excitation and de-excitation in the visible region of spectrum. Iodine being larger atom, electrons can undergo excitation and deexcitation in the visible region, since they experience less nuclear forces of attraction. Graphite in the layer lattice structure has free electrons which can show the same trend. Due to these reasons, these two non-metals exhibit lustre like metals.

78. In soda water, CO_2 dissolves in water to form carbonic acid which creates an acidic medium in the digestive system and helps in digestion of excess food.

79. Metals like platinum and palladium adsorb hydrogen on their surfaces. When the metal is heated after adsorption, hydrogen gas is expelled. Since other impurities do not get adsorbed, pure hydrogen can be obtained through this process.

80. White paint has lead sulphate in it. As the polluted atmosphere has H_2S, it reduces the lead sulphate to lead sulphide which is black in Color. When these walls are washed with hydrogen peroxide, it acts as an oxidizing agent and converts black lead sulphide to white lead sulphate:

$$\underset{\text{White}}{PbSO_4} + H_2S \rightarrow \underset{\text{Black}}{PbS} + H_2SO_4$$

$$\underset{\text{Black}}{PbS} + 4H_2O_2 \rightarrow \underset{\text{White}}{PbSO_4} + 4H_2O$$

81. Thermal conductivity and electrical conductivity of metals are attributed to close packing in metals and the presence of free electrons in the metal lattice respectively. Though diamond and graphite are allotropes of carbon, diamond is a good thermal conductor due to its rigid three-dimensional structure, in which carbon atoms are closely and regularly arranged. Diamond is a not good electrical conductor as there are no free electrons in the structure. Graphite on the other hand has free electrons in the layer lattice structure which makes it a good electrical conductor. Graphite is a bad thermal conductor.

82. A, B, C, D, E are zinc, iron, lead, copper and manganese. All of them form the bivalent ions – Zn^{2+}, Fe^{2+}, Pb^{2+} and Cu^{2+}. Only iron can form Fe^{3+} ion. These ions form precipitates of hydroxides and sulphides when treated with NH_4OH and H_2S respectively.

$Zn(OH)_2 \Rightarrow$ White gelatinous precipitate soluble in excess of NH_4OH

$Fe(OH)_3 \Rightarrow$ Reddish brown precipitate insoluble in excess of NH_4OH

$Pb(OH)_2 \Rightarrow$ White precipitate insoluble in excess of NH_4OH

$Cu(OH)_2 \Rightarrow$ Pale blue precipitate soluble in excess of NH_4OH

$Fe(OH)_2 \Rightarrow$ Dirty green precipitate insoluble in excess of NH_4OH

$ZnS \Rightarrow$ white precipitate

Iron (Fe^{2+} or Fe^{3+}) $\Rightarrow$ Black precipitate

$PbS \Rightarrow$ Black precipitate

$CuS \Rightarrow$ Black precipitate

$MnS \Rightarrow$ Flesh colored precipitate

	Property	Observation
(i)	**Reaction with soluble salts**	All soluble salts except those of sodium and potassium form insoluble precipitates of respective metal hydroxides. These precipitates may differ with respect to colour, texture, solubility, etc. Therefore, this reaction can be used for the identification of cations.
(ii)	**Formation of complex salts**	On addition of limited amount of $CuSO_4$ solution which is blue in colour, a pale blue precipitate of cupric hydroxide is formed. Addition of excess amount of NH_4OH results in the formation of a complex salt, tetraammine copper(II) sulphate which is blue in colour and is soluble in water. Therefore, the precipitate disappears. $CuSO_4 + 2NH_4OH \rightarrow (NH_4)SO_4 + \underset{\text{Pale blue ppt}}{Cu(OH)_2} \downarrow$ $(NH_4)_2SO_4 + Cu(OH)_2 + 2NH_4OH \rightarrow \underset{\text{Deep blue solution}}{[Cu(NH_3)_4]SO_4} + 4H_2O$
(iii)	**Reaction with acids**	Ammonium salts are formed. $NH_4OH + HNO_3 \rightarrow NH_4NO_3 + H_2O$ $2NH_4OH + H_2SO_4 \rightarrow (NH_4)_2SO_4 + 2H_2O$

Metal ion	Formula of precipitate	Colour of precipitate	Soluble in excess of NH_4OH
Zn^{2+}	$Zn(OH)_2$	White gelatinous	Soluble
Fe^{2+}	$Fe(OH)_2$	Dirty green	Insoluble
Pb^{2+}	$Pb(OH)_2$	White	Insoluble
Fe^{3+}	$Fe(OH)_3$	Reddish brown	Insoluble
Cu^{2+}	$Cu(OH)_2$	Pale blue	Soluble

JEE-NEET Special Wing

Multiple-Answer Type Questions

1. The compound X could be potassium permanganate. It decomposes on heating giving potassium manganate, manganous dioxide and oxygen. 'A' should be manganous dioxide as it reacts with concentrated HCl to release greenish yellow coloured pungent gas that is chlorine. The molecular mass of potassium permanganate is 158. 'B' is Potassium manganate which has bivalent negative radical.

$2KMnO_4 \rightarrow K_2MnO_4 + MnO_2 + O_2$

$MnO_2 + 4HCl \rightarrow MnCl_2 + 2H_2O + 2Cl_2$

2 mol $KMnO_4 \rightarrow$ 1 mol MnO_2

2.5 mol $KMnO_4 \rightarrow$ 1.25 mol MnO_2

1 mol $MnO_2 \rightarrow$ 4 mol HCl

1.25 mol $MnO_2 \rightarrow$ 5 mol HCl

2.5 mol $KMnO_4$ taken initially required 5 mol concentrated HCl for the second reaction

2 mol $KMnO_4 \rightarrow$ 1 mol MnO_2

1 mol $KMnO_4 \rightarrow$ 0.5 mol MnO_2

1 mol $MnO_2 \rightarrow$ 2 mol Cl_2

0.5 mol $MnO_2 \rightarrow$ 1 mol Cl_2

1 mol $KMnO_4$ on complete reaction produces greenish yellow gas which occupies 22.4 L volume at STP.

2. The ore, coke and limestone are taken in 8:4:1 ratio in blast furnace and this is called charge.

The final reaction involves the reduction of ferric oxide to iron by carbon monoxide.

$Fe_2O_3 + 3CO \rightarrow 2Fe + 3CO_2$

No. of moles of iron $= 0.56 \times 1000 \times \frac{1000}{56} = 10000$ mol

2 mol iron is obtained from 1 mol ferric oxide

10000 mol iron is obtained from 5000 mol ferric oxide

Mass of 5000 mol ferric oxide $= 160 \times 5000 = 800000$ g $=800$ kg

Mass of coke = 400 kg

Mass of limestone = 100 kg

3. The different allotropic forms of carbon are prepared by different methods and they have different uses.

Heating of wood shavings in the absence of air	Wood charcoal	Gas masks
Destructive distillation of bone powder	Animal charcoal	Extraction of yellow phosphorus
Burning of turpentine oil	Lamp black	Tyre manufacture

4. Reaction X

$4NH_3 + 3O_2 \rightarrow 2N_2 + 6H_2O$

Reaction Y

$8NH_3 + 3Cl_2 \rightarrow N_2 + 6NH_4Cl$

Nitrogen is the common product and it burns with blue flame.

1mol NH_3 gives 0.5 mol nitrogen in reaction X

1 mol NH_3 gives 0.125 mol nitrogen in reaction Y

The amount of nitrogen in reaction X is 4 times that in reaction Y.

The other product in reaction X is water and that in reaction Y is NH_4Cl. 1 mole ammonia gives 1.5 mole water in reaction X. Same 1 mol ammonia gives 0.75 mol ammonium chloride in reaction Y.

4 mole ammonia reacts with 3 mol oxygen

1 mole ammonia reacts with 0.75 mol oxygen.

8 mole ammonia reacts with 3 mol chlorine

1 mole ammonia reacts with 0.375 mol chlorine.

In reaction X, 0.25 mole oxygen is left behind while in reaction Y, 0.63 mole chlorine is left behind.

5. The reaction of ammonia with oxygen in presence of catalyst goes as below.

$4NH_3 + 5O_2 \rightarrow 4NO + 6H_2O$

$2NO + O_2 \rightarrow 2NO_2$

$NO_2 + H_2O \rightarrow HNO_2 + HNO_3$

Nitrogen dioxide(Q) on dissolution in water produces nitrous acid and nitric acid. So, it is a mixed anhydride of these two acids. Thermal decomposition of alkali metal nitrates does not produce nitrogen dioxide at all. Potassium nitrate on decomposition gives potassium nitrite and oxygen. NO_2 generally exists as a dimer that is N_2O_4. NO(P) is colourless while NO_2 is a reddish brown gas with pungent odour.

Comprehension-Based Questions

6. Sulphide ores are concentrated by froth floatation. Galena and cinnabar are the ores which are concentrated by this method.

7. Cinnabar contains mercuric sulphide which is converted to mercuric oxide by roasting. Mercuric oxide on strong heating gives mercury.

8. Fluorspar and bauxite are ores of calcium and aluminium respectively. These are active metals and hence are extracted by the electrolysis of the molten ores.

9. Calcination is heating of ore in the absence of air. Usually carbonate ores or oxide ores are subjected to calcination. Siderite, dolomite, and calamine are subjected to calcination.

10. Magnesium, aluminium, iron and zinc react with steam. Among these magnesium undergoes fas reaction and the reaction goes to completion. The electronic configuration of magnesium is 2, 8, 2.

11. The metal 'N' would be zinc as it is amphoteric metal and reacts with KOH to form $KZnO_2$.

12. 'X' is phosphorus and the reaction of phosphine (PH_3) with zinc gives zinc phosphide which is used as a rat poison.

13. Calcium is the metal which reacts with water but not violently. Calcium oxide reacts with phosphorus pentoxide to form calcium phosphate having the formula $Ca_3(PO_4)_2$. The number of atoms in one molecule of calcium phosphate is 13.

14. The metal 'M' mentioned in the question is aluminium. The oxide of aluminium is thermally stable and hence does not undergo decomposition on heating.

Match the Column

15.

Column I			Column II	
	Metal	Metal		Characteristic feature
(a)	I	Pb	(iii)	Reacts with sodium hydroxide to form $NaMO_2$
(b)	K	Hg	(iv)	Metal oxide reduced by strong heating for the extraction of metal
(c)	J	Cu	(v)	Oxide reduced by ammonia to form a colourless gas which burns with blue flame
(d)	B	Na	(i)	Hydride of formula MH
(e)	D	Mg	(ii)	Forms a binary compound of the formula M_2N_3 with nitrogen

16.

Column I			Column II	
	Metal	Formula of oxide		Percentage of oxygen
(a)	Iron	Fe_2O_3	(iv)	30
(b)	Magnesium	MgO	(v)	40
(c)	Sodium	Na_2O	(i)	26
(d)	Aluminium	Al_2O_3	(ii)	47
(e)	Copper	CuO	(iii)	20

Photo Credits

CHAPTER 1

Page 1.28— Evgeny Karandaev/Shutterstock; Designua/Shutterstock; Pearson Education Ltd; Chaovarut Sthoop/123RF

CHAPTER 4

Page 4.40—Oxford Designers & Illustrators Ltd/Pearson Education Ltd

CHAPTER 8

Page 8.25—Pavel L Photo and Video / Shutterstock